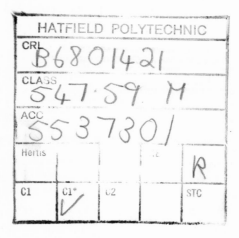

# 1,2-Cycloaddition Reactions

# INTERSCIENCE MONOGRAPHS ON CHEMISTRY

**Organic Chemistry Section**

EDITOR: George A. Olah
    Department of Chemistry
    Case-Western Reserve University
    Cleveland, Ohio

Sulfonation and Related Reactions BY EVERETT E. GILBERT

Peptide Synthesis BY MIKLOS BODANSZKY AND MIGUEL A. ONDETTI

# 1,2-Cycloaddition Reactions

## The Formation of Three- and
## Four-Membered Heterocycles

**BY LINDA LEE MULLER AND JAN HAMER**

DEPARTMENT OF CHEMISTRY
TULANE UNIVERSITY
NEW ORLEANS, LOUISIANA

**INTERSCIENCE PUBLISHERS**  **1967**

a division of John Wiley & Sons, New York · London · Sydney

Library of Congress Catalog Card Number 67-20265
Printed in the United States of America

# Editor's Introduction

The chemical literature in recent years increasingly emphasized multi-author monographs covering broader topics or review articles as part of the numerous "Advances" or "Progress" series. Both fill important needs and became integral parts of our libraries as valuable reference sources. By their nature and price they, however, rarely can reach the desks of individual chemists for their personal use. They also reflect the fact that the ever-growing chemical literature makes it increasingly difficult for individual authors to cover larger fields in a comprehensive and critical way.

To contribute a chapter or to write a review article frequently involves an effort comparable to that of writing a monograph on the topic. There is a genuine and growing need for authentic monographs written by experts actively engaged in research in their respective fields of specialization. These can provide not only a review of the topic, but more importantly, they can critically evaluate the field, point out the major and most important advances achieved, and also possible new avenues of approaches where further future research is most needed. These smaller monographs using improved technical methods can be produced faster and cheaper than multi-author collective volumes, where the "slowest" author or editor inevitably determines the speed of publication. Individual monographs also give full recognition to the author, which is not always possible, if for no other than technical reasons, in edited volumes.

The foregoing were the main reasons which caused the editor and the publishers to initiate a series of monographs in Organic Chemistry. Similar monographs are being published in the field of Inorganic and Physical Chemistry. The Organic Chemistry Section of the Interscience Monographs on Chemistry will be accessible to the average chemist for his own use at reasonable prices and will provide titles of current interest in a wide scope. It is hoped that the high standard and timeliness of these volumes aimed at by the authors, the editors, and the publisher will make them a useful addition to the chemical literature.

GEORGE A. OLAH

# Preface

In the course of our investigations of cycloaddition reactions involving systems not containing solely carbon we were forced to prepare our own survey on the formation of three- and four-membered heterocycles by a cycloaddition reaction, because the information we needed was generally unavailable elsewhere in the form of a review or reviews.

This volume is the result of our survey. In this survey we have chosen to act as historians rather than interpreters of the published data. We have attempted to make this survey an exhaustive one, covering the literature through the middle of 1965 from the major chemical journals and *Chemical Abstracts*. In general, retrograde cycloaddition reactions have not been included in this volume.

For the convenience of the researcher we have included physical data of the cycloaddition products, and details of the reaction conditions whenever possible.

L. L. MULLER
J. HAMER

# Contents

I. Introduction . . . . . . . . . 1
   References . . . . . . . . . 3

II. Synthesis of Heterocyclic Three-Membered Ring Systems . 5

  A. One Heteroatom . . . . . . . . 5
    1. Nitrogen . . . . . . . . . 5
      a. Aziridines, Aziridinium Salts, and Aziridinones . 5
    References . . . . . . . . . 38
    2. Silicon or Germanium . . . . . . 44
      a. Silacyclopropanes . . . . . . 44
    References . . . . . . . . . 48
      b. Silirenes . . . . . . . . 49
    References . . . . . . . . . 53
      c. Germirenes . . . . . . . . 54
    References . . . . . . . . . 56
    3. Sulfur . . . . . . . . . 57
      a. Thiiranes and Thiirane 1,1-Dioxides . . . 57
    References . . . . . . . . . 84

  B. Two Heteroatoms . . . . . . . . 87
    1. Nitrogen Only . . . . . . . . 87
      a. Diaziridines and Diazirines . . . . 87
    References . . . . . . . . . 101
    2. Oxygen and Nitrogen . . . . . . 103
      a. Oxaziranes . . . . . . . . 103
    References . . . . . . . . . 107
    3. Phosphorus and Oxygen or Sulfur . . . 107
      a. Phosphiranes . . . . . . . 107
    References . . . . . . . . . 110

III. Synthesis of Heterocyclic Four-Membered Ring Systems . 111

  A. One Heteroatom . . . . . . . . 111
    1. Oxygen . . . . . . . . . 111
      a. Oxetanes . . . . . . . . 111
    References . . . . . . . . . 136
      b. β-Lactones . . . . . . . . 139
    References . . . . . . . . . 166

2. Nitrogen . . . . . . . . . 168
   a. Azetidines . . . . . . . . 168
References . . . . . . . . . 173
   b. 2-Azetidinones . . . . . . . 173
References . . . . . . . . . 199
   c. 2,4-Azetidinediones . . . . . . 202
References . . . . . . . . . 205
3. Sulfur . . . . . . . . . . 206
   a. Thietanes, Thietane 1,1-Dioxides, Thietanone Di-
      oxides, and Thiete 1,1-Dioxides . . . . 206
References . . . . . . . . . 239

B. Two Heteroatoms . . . . . . . 240
1. Nitrogen Only . . . . . . . . 240
   a. Diazetidines . . . . . . . . 240
References . . . . . . . . . 245
   b. Diazetidinones . . . . . . . 246
References . . . . . . . . . 256
2. Oxygen and Nitrogen . . . . . . 257
   a. Oxazetidines . . . . . . . 257
References . . . . . . . . . 274
3. Oxygen and Sulfur . . . . . . . 276
   a. Oxathietane 1-Oxides and Oxathietane 1,1-Dioxides . 276
References . . . . . . . . . 285
4. Nitrogen and Sulfur . . . . . . . 286
   a. Thiazetidine 1,1-Dioxides and Thiazetidinone 1-Oxides 286
References . . . . . . . . . 290
5. Sulfur Only . . . . . . . . 291
   a. Dithiacyclobutanes, Desaurins, and 1,2-Dithietenes . 291
References . . . . . . . . . 300

C. Miscellaneous . . . . . . . . 301
1. Oxadiazetidine Derivatives . . . . 301
References . . . . . . . . . 304
2. Wittig Type Reactions . . . . . 305
References . . . . . . . . . 329
3. "Quasi-" Wittig Reactions . . . . 332
References . . . . . . . . . 337

Author Index . . . . . . . . . 339
Subject Index . . . . . . . . . 359

# I. Introduction

Cycloaddition reactions may be defined as reactions in which a new ring is formed by the interaction of two reaction partners through a rearrangement of pi bond or nonbonding electrons (in either the ground or excited state) of each partner resulting in sigma bonds responsible for the formation of the new ring system. In some cases suitable reaction partners may be part of the same molecule so that an intramolecular cycloaddition may take place. The photochemical transformation of norbornadiene to

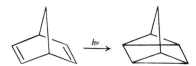

nortricyclene is an example. The vast majority of reported cycloaddition reactions, however, concerns intermolecular reactions.

Since the reaction partners are not necessarily the same, and in fact differ in many cases, a difficulty arises in order to designate the reaction under consideration in a succinct and unambiguous fashion. The classic Diels-Alder reaction is often called a 1,4-cycloaddition reaction. This designation clearly refers to the termini of the conjugated diene involved. In respect to the "dienophile" this reaction should be termed a 1,2-cycloaddition reaction, referring again to the termini of the reaction partner in question. As a rule, however, one refers to the termini of the longer chain involved.

It is also possible to employ a classification system[1] in which the number of ring atoms contributed by each reaction partner and the resulting ring size are indicated. Thus, the cycloaddition reactions leading to the three-membered ring system may be described as $1 + 2 = 3$, to the four-membered ring system as $1 + 3 = 4$, etc. Among the 1,2-cycloaddition reactions listed below the most widely known examples of reaction partner *a* are carbene, $CH_2$, substituted carbenes,[2] and the nitrogen analogs of carbene, $R—\bar{N}|$.* The silicon analogs of carbene have only recently been

* The electron-deficient nitrogen intermediate $R—\bar{N}|$ has been referred to in the literature as nitrene,[3-6] azene,[7-9] azylene,[10] imine radical,[11,12] and azacarbene.[13] In German literature imene[13,14] has been used, while *Chemical Abstracts* and a recent review[15] employ the term imidogen. In this volume $R—\bar{N}|$ will be designated as nitrene.

1

reported, while the electron-deficient phosphorus analog has yet to be detected. Another example is oxygen. The 1,2-cycloaddition reactions of these electron-deficient particles generally lead to three-membered ring systems.

The formation of cyclopropane derivatives[16] and epoxides[17] has been discussed in detail recently, and will not be reviewed further in this volume. The same holds true for the five-membered ring systems.[20] Instead, attention will be focused on the 1,2-cycloaddition of electron-deficient intermediates to imines, azo compounds, carbonyl and thiocarbonyl compounds, and sulfenes, as well as the addition of nitrenes to alkenes, where the resultant three-membered systems are heterocyclic systems.

$$
\begin{matrix} a \\ \| \\ b \end{matrix} + c \longrightarrow \begin{matrix} a \\ | \\ b \end{matrix}\!\!>\!c
$$

$$
\begin{matrix} a \\ \||| \\ b \end{matrix} + c \longrightarrow \begin{matrix} a \\ \| \\ b \end{matrix}\!\!>\!c
$$

$$
\begin{matrix} a \\ \| \\ b \end{matrix} + \begin{matrix} c \\ \| \\ d \end{matrix} \longrightarrow \begin{matrix} a—c \\ | \quad | \\ b—d \end{matrix}
$$

$$
\begin{matrix} a \\ \||| \\ b \end{matrix} + \begin{matrix} c \\ \| \\ d \end{matrix} \longrightarrow \begin{matrix} a—c \\ \| \quad | \\ b—d \end{matrix}
$$

$$
\begin{matrix} a \\ \| \\ b \end{matrix} + \begin{matrix} c \\ \diagdown\!\!\! d \\ e \end{matrix} \longrightarrow \begin{matrix} a\!-\!c \\ | \quad \diagdown d \\ b\!-\!e \end{matrix}
$$

$$
\begin{matrix} a \\ \| \\ b \end{matrix} + \begin{matrix} c \\ \diagdown\!\!\! d \\ | \\ f\!=\!e \end{matrix} \longrightarrow \begin{matrix} a\!-\!c\!\diagdown\! d \\ | \qquad \| \\ b\!-\!f\!-\!e \end{matrix}
$$

Extensive reviews have been published recently concerning the formation of six-[18-20] and five-membered[1] ring systems, e.g., the $2 + 3 = 5$ and the $2 + 4 = 6$ cycloaddition reactions. Attention will be focused on the formation of four-membered heterocyclic systems, since also the formation of cyclobutane derivatives by $2 + 2 \rightarrow 4$ cycloaddition reactions has been recently reviewed.[21]

A wide variety of combinations of a–b and c–d has been reported. If a–b is an alkene, for instance, then c–d may be an imine, an azo compound, a carbonyl or thiocarbonyl compound, a sulfene or sulfine, sulfur trioxide, a ketene or an isocyanate, besides another alkene. If a–b is a ketene or an isocyanate the choice of c–d is even wider and includes, in addition to the compounds listed above, N-sulfinyl and nitroso compounds. Some nitroso compounds will also undergo a 1,2-cycloaddition reaction with perfluoroalkenes, imines, and thiocarbonyl compounds, as will N-sulfinyl compound $R—N{=}SO$, and sulfenes, $R_2C{=}SO_2$. With other combinations reported in the literature so far a whole gamut of four-membered heterocyclic systems may be prepared.

Stereospecificity of cycloaddition reactions has been observed in a large number of cases, including those leading to three- or four-membered systems by either a photochemical or thermal reaction. The question as to whether the two new sigma bounds between the reaction partners are formed simultaneously or in sequence is yet to be resolved conclusively. The process, however, is clearly a concerted one, even if one new sigma bond would be formed at a somewhat faster rate than the other.

An important new development for concerted cycloaddition reactions has been the recent enunciation of selection rules[22,23] based on molecular orbital symmetry relationships. The Hoffmann-Woodward selection rules may enable the discernment of new reactions; they undoubtedly will stimulate further research in cycloaddition reactions, since a theoretical foundation seems now to have been laid.

REFERENCES

1. R. Huisgen, R. Grashey, and J. Sauer, in *The Chemistry of Alkenes*, S. Patai, Ed., Wiley, New York, 1964, pp. 739–929.
2. W. Kirmse, *Carbene Chemistry*, Academic Press, New York, 1964.
3. R. A. Abramovitch, Y. Ahmad, and D. Newman, *Tetrahedron Letters*, 752 (1961).
4. D. H. R. Barton and L. R. Morgan, *J. Chem. Soc.*, **1962**, 622.
5. W. Lwowski and T. W. Mattingly, *Tetrahedron Letters*, **1962**, p. 277.
6. G. Smolinsky, *J. Am. Chem. Soc.*, **82**, 4717 (1960).
7. P. J. Bunyan and J. I. G. Cadogan, *J. Chem. Soc.*, **1963**, 42.
8. P. A. S. Smith and J. H. Hall, *J. Am. Chem. Soc.*, **84**, 480 (1962).
9. G. Smolinsky, *J. Am. Chem. Soc.*, **83**, 2489 (1961).
10. P. A. S. Smith, L. O. Krbechek, and W. Resemann, *Abstr. 144th Natl. Mtg. Am. Chem. Soc.*, Los Angeles, April 1963, p. 35M.
11. J. F. Heacock and M. T. Edmison, *J. Am. Chem. Soc.*, **82**, 3460 (1960).
12. F. O. Rice and T. A. Leickenbach, *J. Am. Chem. Soc.*, **83**, 2681 (1961).
13. A. Lüttringhaus, J. Jander, and R. Schneider, *Chem. Ber.*, **92**, 1756 (1959).
14. L. Horner and A. Christmann, *Angew. Chem.*, **75**, 707 (1963).
15. R. A. Abramovich and B. A. Davis, *Chem. Rev.*, **64**, 149 (1964).
16. W. E. Parham and E. E. Schweizer, *Org. Reactions*, **13**, 55 (1963).
17. A. Roswosky, in *Compounds with Three- and Four-Membered Rings* (*The Chemistry of Heterocyclic Compounds*, Vol. 19, A. Weissberger, Ed.), Wiley, New York, 1964, p. 41.
18. J. Hamer, Ed., *1,4-Cycloaddition Reactions*, Academic Press, New York, 1966.
19. A. Wasserman, *Dields-Alder Reactions*, Elsevier, Amsterdam–London–New York, 1965.
20. J. G. Martin and R. K. Hill, *Chem. Rev.*, **61**, 537 (1961).
21. J. D. Roberts and C. M. Sharts, *Org. Reactions*, **12**, 1 (1962).
22. R. Hoffmann and R. B. Woodward, *J. Am. Chem. Soc.*, **87**, 2046 (1965).
23. R. Hoffmann and R. B. Woodward, *J. Am. Chem. Soc.*, **87**, 4388 (1965).

# II. Synthesis of Heterocyclic Three-Membered Ring Systems

## A. ONE HETEROATOM

### 1. Nitrogen

#### a. Aziridines, Aziridinium Salts, and Aziridinones

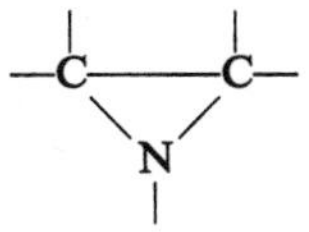

$$-\underset{|}{C}\underset{}{\underset{\diagdown}{\quad}}\underset{N}{\underset{|}{\overset{\diagup}{\quad}}}\underset{|}{C}-$$

The chemistry of aziridines, three-membered rings containing two carbon atoms and one nitrogen atom, has been reviewed extensively[5,29,30,82,90,145,171]; therefore, only syntheses involving a 1,2-cycloaddition reaction will be discussed in this section.

There are two methods of preparing aziridines via a cycloaddition reaction: the addition of a reactive carbene intermediate across a carbon–nitrogen double bond or the addition of a nitrene intermediate across a carbon–carbon double bond. The following discussion will illustrate each type of preparation. However, some discrepancies arise because, depending

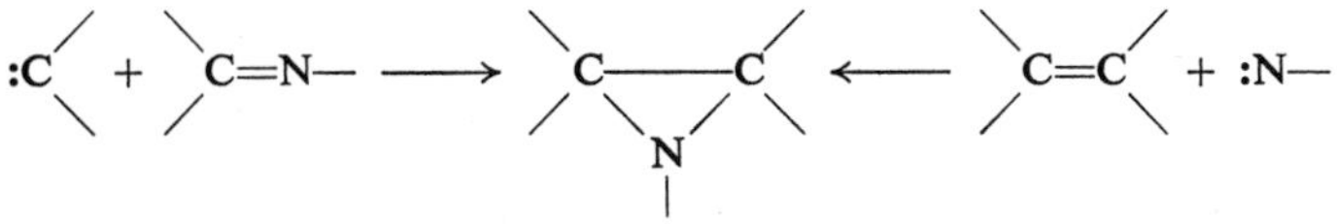

$$:C\diagup + \diagdown C=N- \longrightarrow \diagdown C\diagdown\diagup C\diagup \longleftarrow \diagdown C=C\diagup + :N-$$

on the reaction conditions, carbenes from diazo compounds such as diazomethane and nitrenes from azides are not always generated and therefore may not necessarily be the reactive species. In this case, the diazo compound and the azide molecule react as such, in most instances forming a five-membered triazoline compound which decomposes with evolution of nitrogen into the corresponding aziridine. For example, the rates of unimolecular decomposition of phenylazide (1) in both nitrobenzene and tetralin solutions were found to be the same, indicating that the solvent was not participating in the rate-determining step[185] and that phenylnitrene (2) was formed as an intermediate. When methyl methacrylate was used as the solvent, nitrogen evolution was much more rapid; the

$$C_6H_5N_3 \longrightarrow C_6H_5N: + N_2$$
$$(1) \qquad\qquad (2)$$

5

formation of a triazoline (3), which breaks down in the usual manner, was indicated, and no evidence of a nitrene intermediate was found.[1]

$$\text{C}=\text{C} + \text{C}_6\text{H}_5\text{N}_3 \longrightarrow -\text{C}-\text{C}- \longrightarrow \text{N}_2 + -\text{C}-\text{C}-$$

(1)

(3)

The advent of the formation of dihalocyclopropanes[76,148,196] via the cycloaddition reaction of the dichlorocarbene intermediate, generated by the treatment of chloroform with sodium methoxide,[219] with compounds possessing carbon–carbon double bonds attracted much attention. It was found that dihalocarbenes also added to carbon–nitrogen double bonds of imines, producing 2,2-dihaloethylenimines.[85,86,138] That is, dichloro-carbene (5), generated by treating chloroform (4), hexachloroacetone, or ethyltrichloroacetate with sodium methoxide in a nonprotonic medium, added to N-benzylideneaniline (6) gave the aziridine, 1,3-diphenyl-2,2-dichloroethylenimine (7) in 55% yield. The aziridine (7) slowly evolved

$$\text{CHCl}_3 \xrightarrow{\text{NaOCH}_3} \text{:CCl}_2$$

(4)                    (5)

$$\text{:CCl}_2 + \text{C}_6\text{H}_5\text{CH}=\text{NC}_6\text{H}_5 \longrightarrow \text{C}_6\text{H}_5\text{CH}-\text{NC}_6\text{H}_5$$

(5)                    (6)

(7)

hydrogen chloride when exposed to moist air at room temperature but was stable when stored at $-70°\text{C}$. The infrared absorption spectrum of the imine (6) showed two bands between 1600 and 1650 cm$^{-1}$, one representing the carbon–nitrogen double bond stretching and the other ascribed to the aromatic ring stretching. The spectrum of the product (7), however, showed only the aromatic ring stretching absorption in this region, and a new band appearing at 737 cm$^{-1}$ assigned to the chlorine–carbon–chlorine group.[232] The nuclear magnetic resonance spectrum of the product showed ten aromatic hydrogens and one aliphatic hydrogen, the aliphatic hydrogen band being shifted due to its position on a three-membered ring and adjacent to the chlorine–carbon–chlorine group. Analogously, the reaction of benzylidine p-chloroaniline (8) with dichlorocarbene (5) gene-rating in situ from potassium t-butoxide and chloroform (4) resulted in a

**Table 1**

Aziridines

A. From Dichlorocarbene and Imines

| Imine | Aziridine | MP (°C) | Yield (%) | Ref. |
|---|---|---|---|---|
| $C_6H_5CH=NC_6H_5$ | 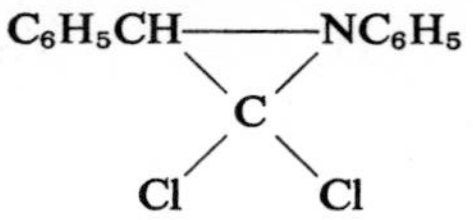 | 98–99 | 55 | 85, 86 |
| $H_6C_5CH=NC_6H_4Cl$ | | 98–99 | 61 | 138 |
| | 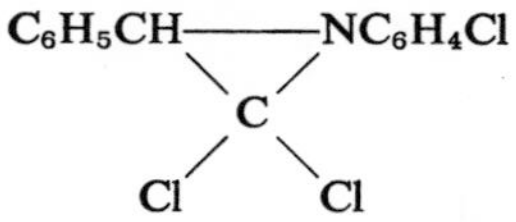 | 71–72 | 68 | 54 |
| $C_6H_5CH=NC_6H_4OC_2H_5$ | 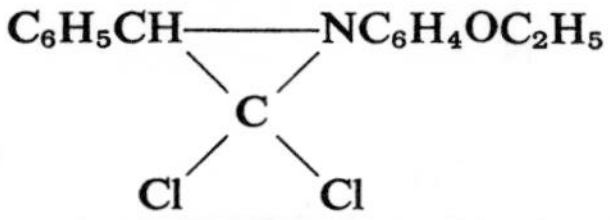 | 76.5.77.5 | 91 | 54 |
| $(C_6H_5)_2C=NC_6H_5$ | 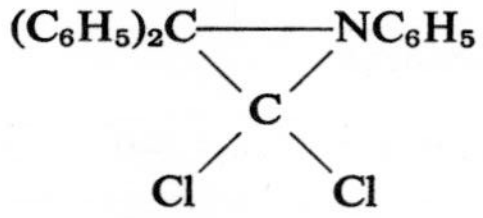 | 95.5–96 | — | 71 |

(continued)

**Table 1** (*continued*)

**B. From Nitrenes and Olefins**

| Olefin | Nitrene | Aziridine | MP, °C (BP[°/mm]) | Yield (%) | Ref. |
|---|---|---|---|---|---|
| $CH_2{=}CH_2$ | :NH | 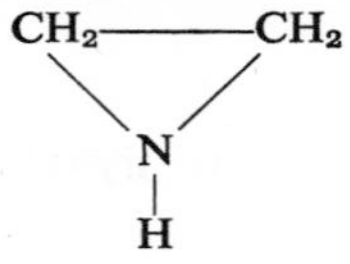 | — | — | 136 |
| 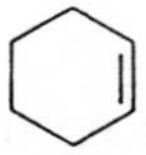 | $C_2H_5O_2CN$: |  | 67–68 | 50 | 166 |
| 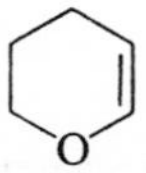 | $C_2H_5O_2CN$: | 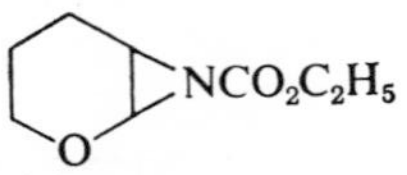 | — | 30 | 1 |
| 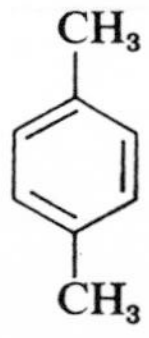 | :NH | 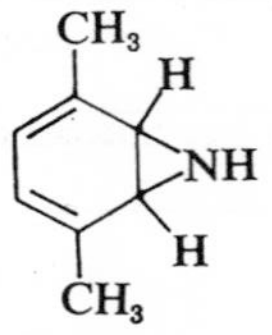 | 112 | — | 65 |

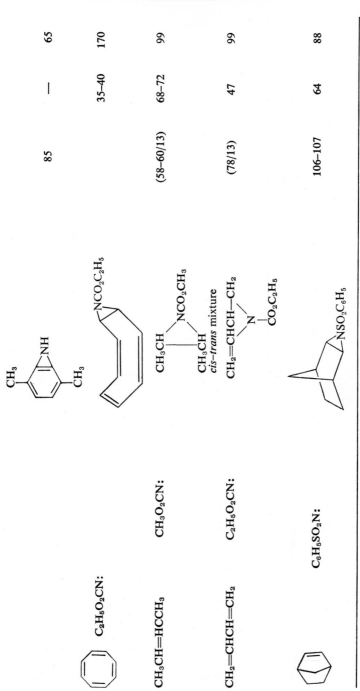

| Reagent | Product | bp/mp | | |
|---|---|---|---|---|
| C₂H₅O₂CN: <br> (cyclooctatetraene) | 2,6-dimethyl-NCO₂C₂H₅ azaannulene | 85 | — | 65 |
| CH₃O₂CN: <br> CH₃CH=HCCH₃ | CH₃CH–NCO₂CH₃, CH₃CH (cis–trans mixture) | | 35–40 | 170 |
| C₂H₅O₂CN: <br> CH₂=CHCH=CH₂ | CH₂=CHCH–CH₂, N–CO₂C₂H₅ | (58–60/13) | 68–72 | 99 |
| | | (78/13) | 47 | 99 |
| C₆H₅SO₂N: <br> (bicycloheptadiene) | NSO₂C₆H₅ bicyclic | 106–107 | 64 | 88 |

(continued)

## Table 1 (*continued*)

### B. From Nitrenes and Olefins

| Olefin | Nitrene | Aziridine | MP, °C (BP[°/mm]) | Yield (%) | Ref. |
|---|---|---|---|---|---|
| 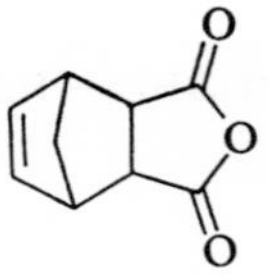 (olefin structure) | 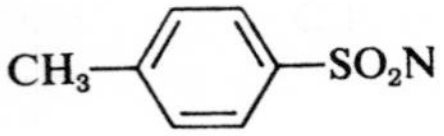 4-CH$_3$C$_6$H$_4$SO$_2$N | 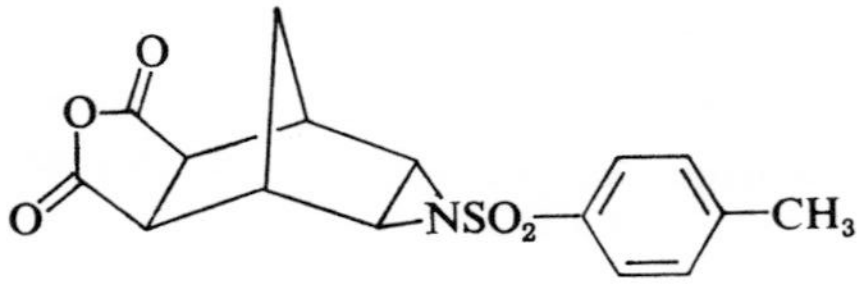 (aziridine structure, NSO$_2$–C$_6$H$_4$CH$_3$) | 242(*d*) | 64.6 | 88 |
| 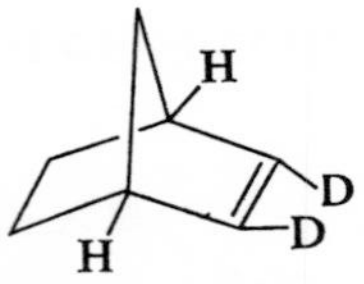 (olefin structure, D, D, H, H) | C$_6$H$_5$SO$_2$N: | 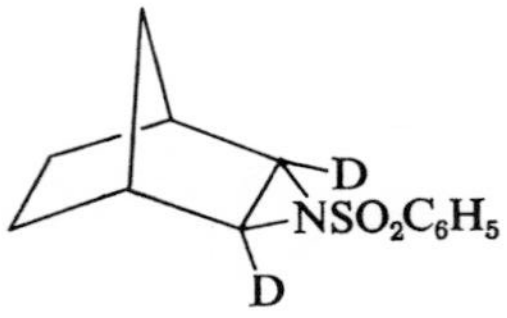 (aziridine structure, D, NSO$_2$C$_6$H$_5$, D) | 105.5–107 | 53.3 | 89 |
| (olefin structure) | C$_6$H$_5$SO$_2$N: | (aziridine structure, NSO$_2$C$_6$H$_5$) | 138 | — | 237 |

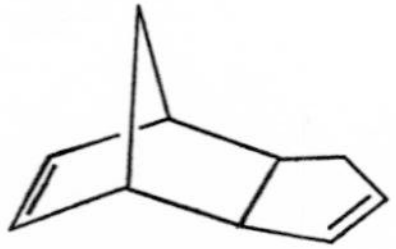

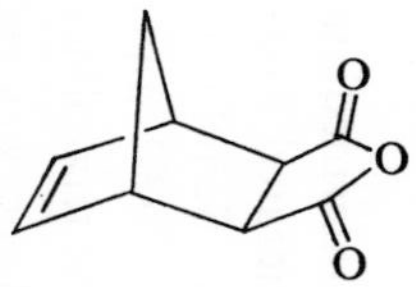

C$_6$H$_5$SO$_2$N:      NSO$_2$C$_6$H$_5$      168–168.5    —    236

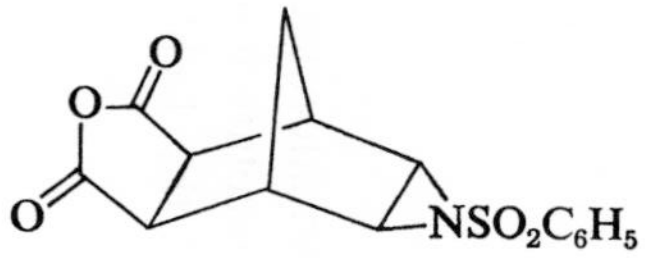

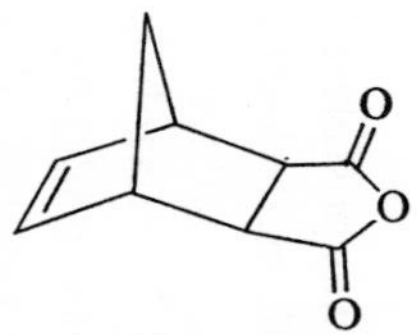

C$_6$H$_5$SO$_2$N:      NSO$_2$C$_6$H$_5$      215–216.5    —    236

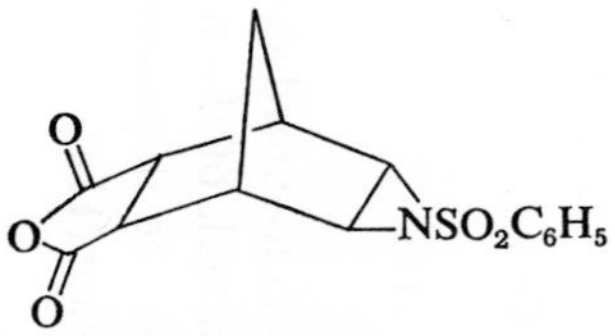

68% yield of the aziridine **(9)**, 1-*p*-chlorophenyl-3-phenyl-2,2-dichloro-ethylenimine.[54] Similarly, 1-*p*-ethoxyphenyl-3-phenyl-2,2-dichloroethyleni-

$$C_6H_5CH = NC_6H_4Cl\text{-}p + :CCl_2 \longrightarrow C_6H_5CH \underbrace{\quad\quad}_{} NC_6H_4Cl\text{-}p$$

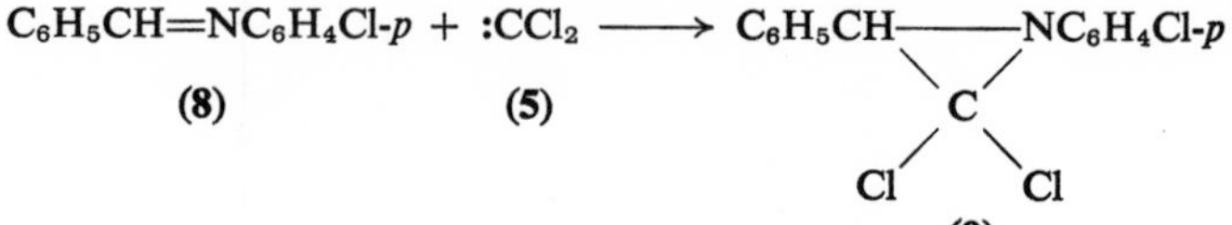

**(8)**                **(5)**

**(9)**

mine was produced by the cycloaddition of dichlorocarbene to benzylidene-*p*-phenetidine **(9)** (Table 1).

Treatment of an iminium salt, *N*-cyclohexylidene pyrrolidinium perchlorate **(10)**, with dichlorocarbene **(5)**, generated by refluxing sodium trichloroacetate in ethylene dichloride,[228] gave *N*-(1-trichloroacetoxy-1-carboxycyclohexyl)pyrrolidine **(11)** in 29% yield.[54] Since it was unexpected to find the trichloroacetoxy group in place of the chlorine atom at the 1-

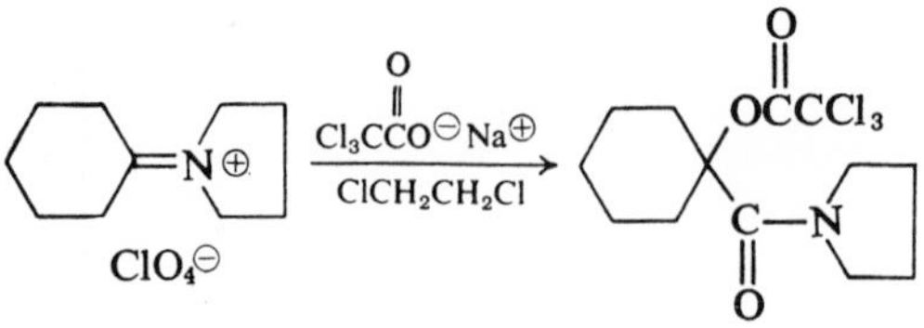

**(10)**                **(11)**

position in **(11)**, it was assumed that the trichloroacetoxy compound **(11)** was formed by the attack of the trichloroacetate ion on the intermediate imine rather than by the displacement of the 1-chlorine atom from the alternative intermediate **(11a)**.

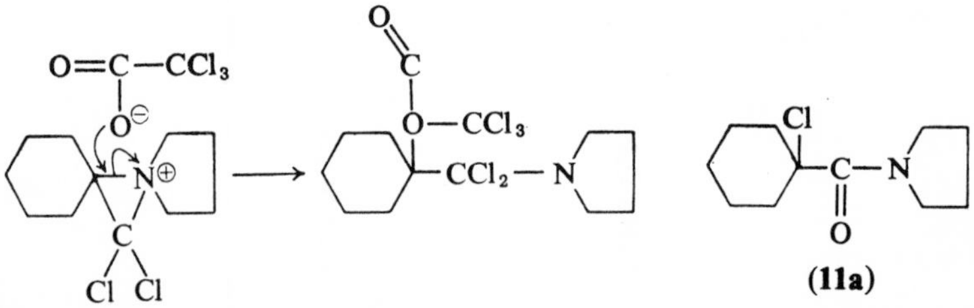

**(11a)**

The aziridine **(14)** was postulated as an intermediate in the reaction of the diazoketone **(12)** with methylcarbene generated from diazoethane **(13)**.[235]

The addition of diazomethane to various Schiff bases, however, has been reported to form 1,2,3-triazolines,[12, 40, 172, 234] and attempts to obtain aziridines by pyrolysis or photolysis of the triazolines resulted in degradation products.[139] In contrast, diazomethane was reported to react with

$$O_2N—C_6H_4\overset{\overset{O}{\|}}{C}—CH{=}N—N{=}CHCH_3 + CH_3CHN_2 \xrightarrow{-N_2}$$

$$\textbf{(12)} \qquad\qquad\qquad\qquad \textbf{(13)}$$

$$\left[ O_2N—C_2H_4\overset{\overset{O}{\|}}{C}{=}\overset{\displaystyle}{CH}—\underset{\underset{\underset{CH_3}{|}}{CH}}{N}—\ddot{N}{=}CHCH_3 \right] \longrightarrow$$

$$\textbf{(14)}$$

$$O_2N—C_6H_4\overset{\overset{O^{\ominus}}{|}}{C}{=}CH\overset{\overset{CH_3}{|}}{C}HN{=}\overset{\oplus}{N}CHCH_3 \longrightarrow O_2N—C_6H_4\overset{\overset{O}{\|}}{C}CH{=}\overset{\overset{CH_3}{|}}{C}HN{=}NCHCH_3$$

negatively substituted imines having electronegative substituents to give the corresponding aziridines directly; for example, the reaction of diazo-

$$CH_2N_2 + R—CH{=}N—R' \longrightarrow R—\underset{\underset{N\diagdown_{N}\diagup N—R'}{|}}{CH}\!\!—\!\!\underset{}{CH_2}$$

methane **(15)** with perfluoro-2-azapropene **(16)** in xylene at 0° gave the aziridine **(17)**.[161] Analogous reactions were repeated with the imines (1-chloro-2,2,2-trifluoroethylideneamino)pentafluorosulfur **(18a)** and (1-

$$CF_3N{=}CF_2 + CH_2N_2 \xrightarrow{-N_2} CF_3N\underset{\underset{CH_2}{\diagdown\diagup}}{\!\!—\!\!}CF_2$$
$$\textbf{(16)} \qquad \textbf{(15)}$$
$$\textbf{(17)}$$

azido-2,2,2-trifluoroethylideneamino)pentasulfur **(18b)**, yielding the aziridines, **19a, 19b, 20a,** and **20b.**

$$SF_5N{=}\overset{\overset{X}{|}}{C}—CF_3 + CH_2N_2 \xrightarrow{-N_2} SF_5N\underset{\underset{CH_2\quad CF_3}{\diagdown\quad\diagup}}{\!\!—\!\!}\overset{\overset{X}{|}}{C} + SF_5N\underset{\underset{CF_3\quad CH_2X}{\diagdown\quad\diagup}}{\!\!—\!\!}\underset{C}{\overset{CH_2}{\diagdown}}$$
$$\textbf{(18a)}, X = Cl \quad \textbf{(15)}$$
$$\textbf{(18b)}, X = N_3 \qquad\qquad\qquad \textbf{(19)} \qquad\qquad\qquad \textbf{(20)}$$

The postulated mechanism assumed that diazomethane as such (the carbene was not generated) added to the fluorine-substituted imines via a nucleophilic attack forming the intermediate **(21)**, which did not cyclize to the triazoline (triazoline formation was deemed unfavorable due to the electron-attracting substituents on the nitrogen atom of the imine—a situation similarly observed with tetrazoles).[80] The intermediate (21), similar to an aliphatic diazonium compound, loses nitrogen followed either by a ring closure to obtain 19a and b (process A) or, by a shift of X (X = Cl, $N_3$), to yield 22a and b (process B). The latter reacts further with excess diazomethane, resulting in the final product (20a and b). When

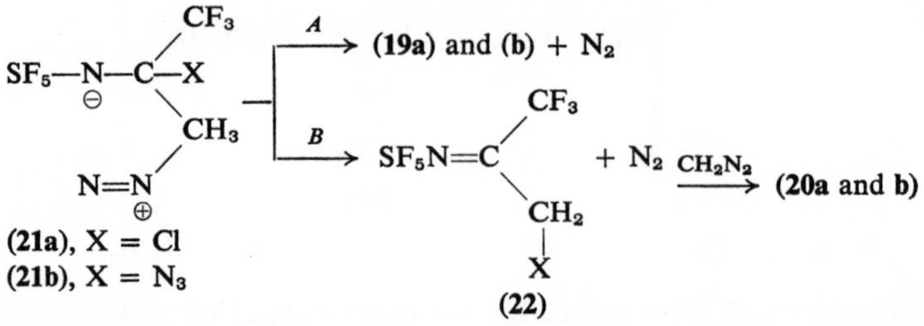

2-(2,4-dinitrophenyl)-3-methyl-2H-azirine (23) was treated with diazomethane (12) at room temperature, no nitrogen was evolved, and only one product was obtained, 1-(3-azido-2-methylpropenyl)-2,4-dinitrobenzene (24). The structures of the aziridines mentioned above were determined by their proton and fluorine nuclear magnetic resonance spectra.[162]

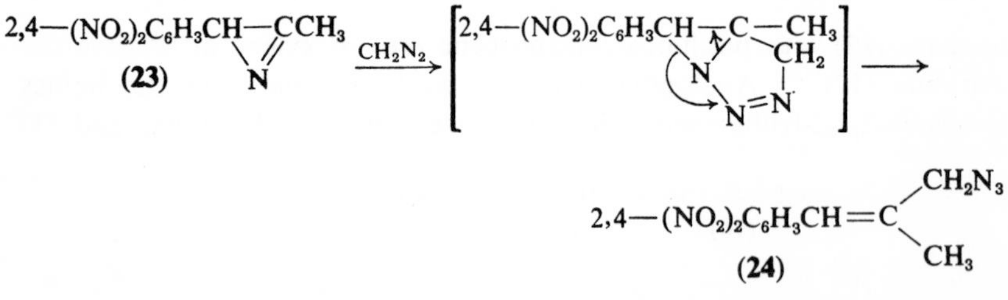

Recently, Deyrup and Greenwald[71] reported that benzophenone anil (25) was converted to 1,2,2-triphenyl-3,3-dichloroaziridine (26) by the reaction of potassium t-butoxide with chloroform at room temperature.

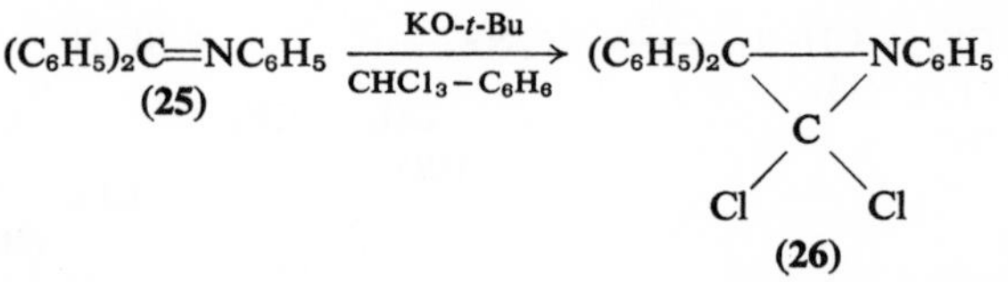

During the past several years, a growing interest in the chemistry of the electron-deficient monovalent nitrogen species referred to as a nitrene has developed.[1,123] Five types of nitrenes have been recognized: aryl,[125,199-206,203,210] sulfonyl,[68,105,220] acyl,[15,16,100,124,130,165,166,168] possibly vinyl,[207,209] and tentatively, alkyl.[22] Substituent groups have a pronounced effect upon nitrene reactions as seen in the different reaction products in the reactions of benzene with benzenesulfonylnitrene (27)[68,105] and carbethoxynitrene (28).[166] A reasonable explanation[210] of these

$$C_6H_5SO_2N: + C_6H_6 \longrightarrow C_6H_5SO_2NH-\langle\text{ring}\rangle$$
$$(27)$$

$$\underset{(28)}{C_2H_5O\overset{\displaystyle O}{\overset{\|}{C}}N: + C_6H_6 \longrightarrow C_2H_5O\overset{\displaystyle O}{\overset{\|}{C}}-N\langle\text{ring}\rangle}$$

observed differences is that the two nitrenes (27) and (28) are reacting in different electronic states, in one case as a triplet and in the other as a singlet. Available evidence concerning the nature of the electronic state of nitrenes is somewhat contradictory, but recent kinetic evidence obtained from a study[230] of the reaction of aryl and alkyl nitrenes supports the triplet state or radical hypothesis for these reacting nitrenes. Walker and Waters,[230] from their kinetic study of the thermal decomposition of aryl azides in cumene, toluene, styrene, and indene, have calculated that, in the case of the latter two olefins, the activation energy for triazoline formation followed by elimination of nitrogen to yield the aziridine is 15–20 kcal/mole lower than that for the aziridine formation by way of an intermediate nitrene.

Nitrenes are usually generated either by photolysis or pyrolysis of organic azides and thus appear to have a short lifetime. At liquid nitrogen temperatures, solid solutions of aryl and sulfonyl nitrenes prepared by photolysis of the corresponding azide appear to be stable indefinitely and are believed to possess triplet electronic ground states.[211,212,231] Nothing definitive, however, is known about the electronic state of the reacting nitrene.

When the nitrene intermediate (29) was photochemically generated in a solid argon matrix at 4°K in the presence of ethylene (30) and acetylene (31), ethylenimine (32) and keteneimine (33), respectively, were produced.[136]

$$\underset{(29)}{:NH} + \underset{(30)}{CH_2{=}CH_2} \longrightarrow \underset{\underset{(32)}{\overset{\displaystyle N}{\underset{H}{|}}}}{CH_2\text{——}CH_2}$$

$$\underset{(31)}{32 + CH{=}CH} \longrightarrow \underset{(33)}{CH_2{=}C{=}NH}$$

Boyer and Canter[35] reviewed alkyl and aryl azides and reported that their adducts with olefins and triazolines underwent loss of nitrogen with the formation of aziridines, as had been demonstrated earlier.[45,63] By introducing a nitro group in the *para* position of the *N*-phenyl substituent, the triazoline is so unstable that it decomposes at once.[42] It has also been noted that addition of azides to a double bond in a cyclic system in which there is considerable ring strain occurs more readily than addition to double bonds in conjugation with an aromatic system.[6-11,13,66,67,174,188] These reactions were performed, obviously, under conditions in which the nitrene was not generated, and therefore are not 1,2-cycloadditions.

Huisgen[127] reported that benzazide (34), when reacted with norbornene (35) at 40°C, gave the triazoline 1-benzoyl-4,5-dihydro-1,2,3-triazoline (36), which decomposed a little above room temperature into an *N*-acyl-ethylenimine (37) which was converted into the respective oxazoline (38) at higher temperatures. In contrast, when benzazide (34) was photolytically

decomposed[126] the acylnitrene intermediate (39) was trapped with dimethyl sulfoxide.[124] ApSimon and Edwards[16] and Lwowski and Mattingly[168] obtained the first successful unambiguous evidence that discrete acyl nitrene intermediates could be formed and then trapped. Photolysis of ethyl azidoformate (40) (which does not undergo the Curtius rearrangement)[2] in the presence of cyclohexene (41) and cyclohexane (42) gave 7-carbethoxy-7-azabicyclo[1.4.0]heptane (43) and the cyclohexyl-urethan (44), respectively. In the first case, the rate of nitrogen evolution was equal to that of the disappearance of the azide, excluding the possibility of triazoline formation. α-Elimination of *p*-nitrobenzenesulfonic acid from its *N*-hydroxyurethan ester (45) in cyclohexane, cyclohexene, or benzene leads to the same products as does the photodecomposition of ethyl azidoformate (40) in these substrates. In the reactions in cyclohexene,

3-cyclohexenylurethan (46) is formed as a by-product in the same amount relative to (43) [1:6] as with (44) [1:4.5].[166] That is, Hafner and König[100] reported that the photolysis of ethyl azidoformate (40) in the presence of benzene (47) afforded a 70% yield of N-ethoxycarbonylazepine (48) presumably via the aziridine (43). The same azepine was obtained from 45.[166] The azepine (48) was the first of the monocyclic azepine derivatives.[72,73,129,131,132] The nuclear magnetic resonance spectra of 48 showed, besides those for the protons of the ethyl group, characteristic signals (quartet at 5.8 $\tau$, triplet at 8.7 $\tau$), the multiplet of six ring protons at 3.7–4.7 $\tau$. When acetonitrile was used as the solvent, both reactions—the decomposition of ethyl azidoformate and N-p-nitrobenzenesulfonoxy-urethan—gave 2-ethoxy-5-methyl-1,3,4-oxadiazole.[164]

Further support for the intermediacy of the nitrene species was found in the study by Berry, Cornell and Lwowski[26] of the flash photolytic decom-

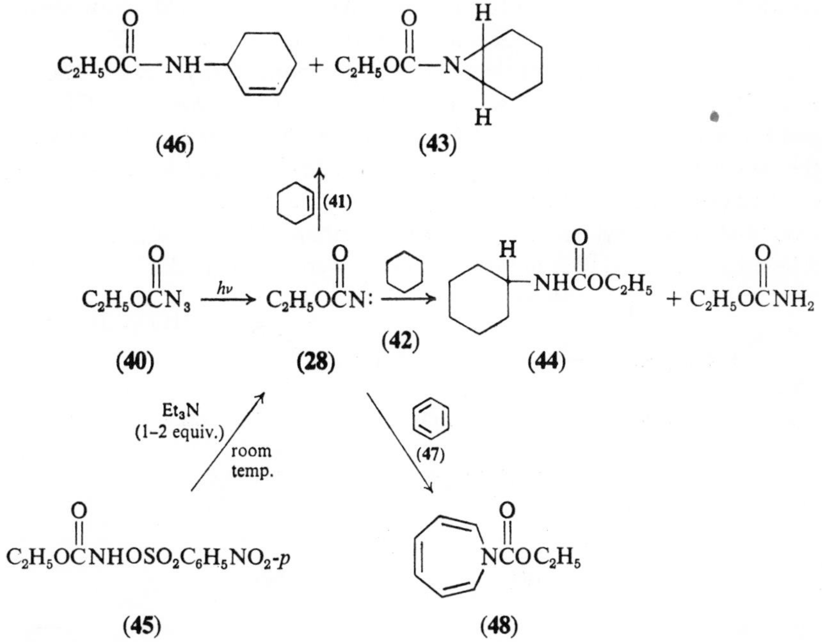

position of ethyl azidoformate in carbon dioxide. The transient decomposition product was found to be the NCO radical[74,75,122]; when the azide was photolyzed at high pressure in an atmosphere of cyclohexene vapor, none of the NCO radical was observed and the aziridine (43) was isolated. It was therefore concluded that the azide loses a molecule of nitrogen to give the unstable and reactive carbethoxynitrene (28), which may be trapped if a suitable substrate is present; otherwise its carbon–oxygen single bond breaks, yielding the NCO radical.

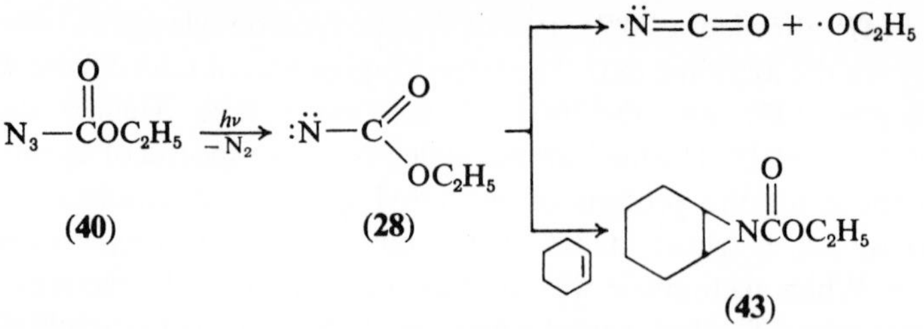

Recently, Lwowski and Mattingly,[167] in additional support for the nitrene intermediate formation, reported that the direct photolysis of a dilute solution of ethyl azidoformate in cyclohexene at room temperature resulted in the formation of the aziridine (43) in a 50% yield whose structure was confirmed by chemical analysis, infrared (C=O at 1720, ester at 1220 and 1268 cm$^{-1}$) and nuclear magnetic resonance (ethyl CH$_3$, $\tau$ 8.80($t$); ring CH$_2$ at 3 and 4, 8.6–8.9($m$); ring CH$_2$ at 2 and 5, 8.22($m$); ring CH at 1 and 6, 7.47($m$), and ethyl CH$_2$, 5.95($q$)) spectra. Other products found were the two isomeric urethans, 3-cyclohexenylurethan (46) and 4-cyclohexenylurethan (49), in a total yield of 12%, and a trace amount of the third isomer, 1-cyclohexenylurethan (50). The urethan (51) in 30% yield and 3,3'-biscyclohexenyl (52) in yields of 1–7% were also found.

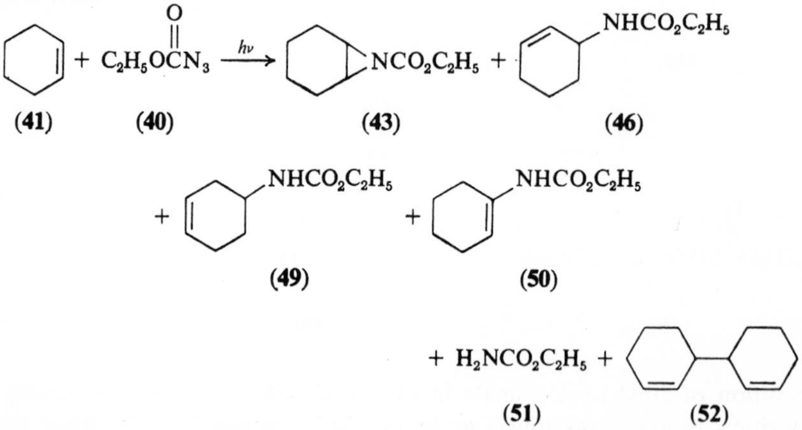

In the direct photolysis reaction, as previously viewed,[166,168] no triazoline was formed. If a triazoline intermediate was present, its decomposition must be fast compared to the rate of its formation; otherwise nitrogen evolution would lag behind the decrease in azide concentration.

The nitrene mechanism proposed earlier explains the products as well as, if not better than, any of the other plausible mechanisms and has a strong analogy in the reactions of carbenes. In particular, there is an exceptional parallel between the behavior of ethyl azidoformate upon photolysis and that of ethyl diazoacetate.[46,77,78,146,147,195,239] Upon irradiation, this diazo compound loses nitrogen to yield carbethoxycarbene, which undergoes an intermolecular reaction with the solvent.

Further support for the nitrene mechanism is found by observing that the rate of nitrogen evolution is the same in cyclohexane and cyclohexene, demonstrating that the solvent does not assist in the rate-determining step of the decomposition. It should be noted, however, that this does not exclude a photolytic azide mechanism of the type

$$R—N_3 \xrightarrow[\text{slow}]{h\nu} R—N_3^* \xrightarrow[\text{fast}]{\text{solvent}} \text{Product} + N_2$$

On the other hand, the rate of thermal decomposition of $n$-octadecyl azidoformate also is independent of the type of solvent,[179] supporting a primary formation of a carbalkoxy nitrene.

Even stronger support for the nitrene mechanism is found in the study of base-induced decomposition in various solvents, of $N$-$p$-nitrobenzene-sulfonoxyurethan (**45**). All evidence points to an $\alpha$-elimination mechanism such as the one shown here,[165,166] yielding the carbethoxynitrene (**28**).

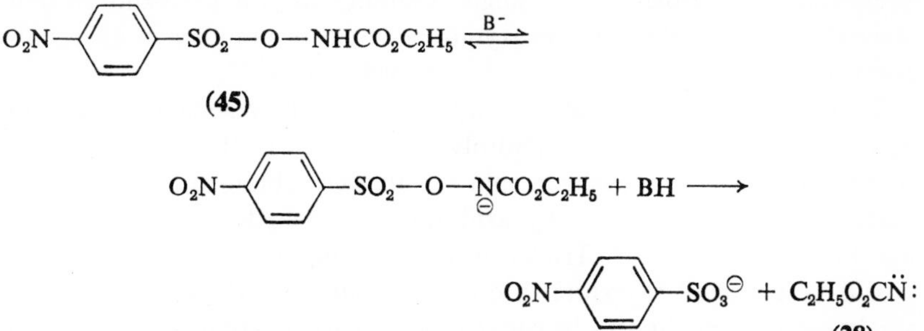

Accepting a nitrene-type intermediate immediately raises the question of its electronic state, as mentioned earlier in this section; that is, is the react-ing species a singlet having no unpaired electrons, or is it in a triplet state with two unpaired electrons? On the basis of quantum theory, upon absorption of a photon of irradiation the azide is most probably promoted to an excited singlet state. Since the lowest triplet state of elemental nitro-gen is about 140 kcal above the ground state, nitrogen should cleave from the excited singlet azide in the singlet state, leaving behind a singlet carbethoxynitrene.[167] In support of this conclusion, Berry, Cornell, and

Singlet with unpaired electrons:

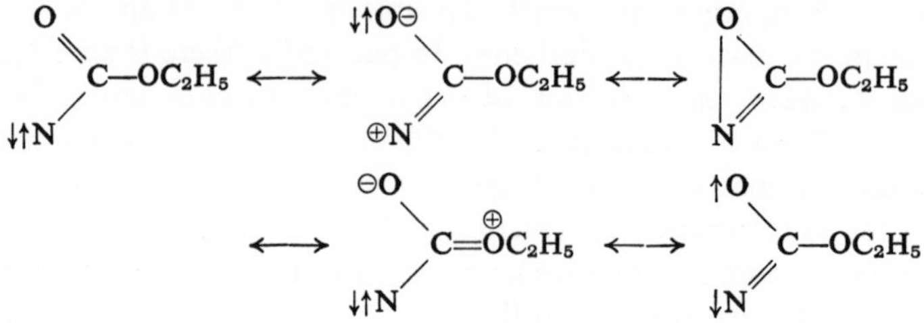

Triplet with unpaired electrons:

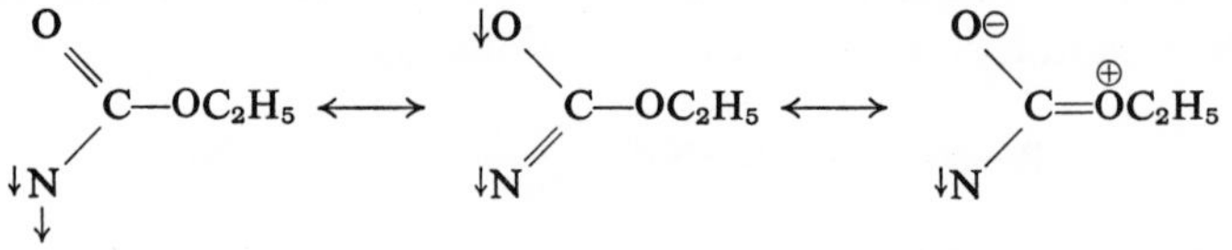

Lwowski[26] and Cornell[56] did not observe spectroscopically the formation of any triplet nitrogen upon flash photolysis of ethyl azidoformate. There is, however, a high probability that the excited nitrene will undergo spin inversion forming a triplet species. Spectroscopic evidence[120] in agreement with theoretical calculations[3] indicates that an unsubstituted nitrene $(:\ddot{N}—H)$ has a triplet ground state, but at present there is no reason for the preference of a triplet over a singlet ground state for carbethoxynitrene since it is possible that carbethoxynitrene could react either in its initially formed singlet state or first decay to a triplet species.[167]

Triplet nitrenes were detected by electron spin resonance spectrometry[211,212,222,231] during the photolysis at 77°K of alkyl, aryl, and sulfonyl azides, while no electron spin signals were obtained from azidoformates. During reactions of alkyl azidoformates, dehydrogenation products are found.[149,178-180,198] Triplet nitrenes giving rise to such products would be expected to exhibit a diradical character. On the other hand, singlet nitrenes might also be capable of dehydrogenating, and might lead to a triplet diradical pair on reactive collision; therefore, no conclusion as to the electronic multiplicity of the nitrene can be made on the basis of the nature of the reaction products alone.[167]

The addition of carbethoxynitrene (28) across the double bond of dihydropyran could be an interesting approach to the 2-aminodeoxy sugars.[1]

The generation of carbethoxynitrene (28) from N-(p-nitrobenzenesulfonoxy)urethan and triethylamine in cyclooctatetraene (53) afforded the aziridine (54)[170] whose nuclear magnetic resonance spectrum was similar to that of cyclooctatetraene epoxide[55] and shows a singlet at 6.90 τ (two

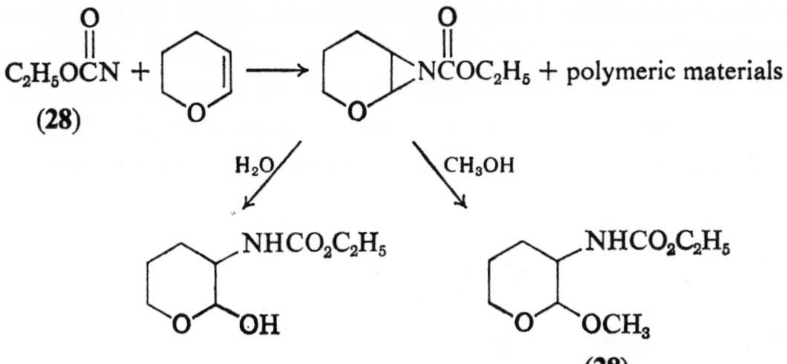

$$C_2H_5O\overset{O}{\overset{\|}{C}}N + \text{(structure)} \longrightarrow \text{(structure)} N\overset{O}{\overset{\|}{C}}OC_2H_5 + \text{polymeric materials}$$

(28)

$H_2O$ / \ $CH_3OH$

NHCO$_2$C$_2$H$_5$                    NHCO$_2$C$_2$H$_5$

OH                                        OCH$_3$

(28)

allylic protons), a multiplet at 3.95–4.15 $\tau$ (six olefinic protons), and signals for an ethyl group. The aziridine (54) rearranges readily within 30 min at 80°C giving the isomer (55), whose structure was determined by

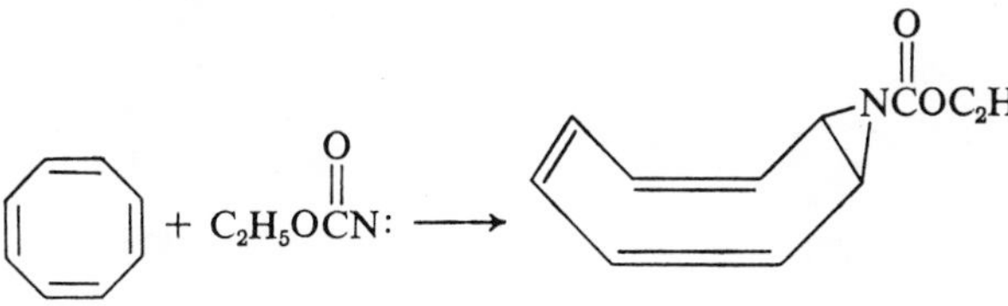

$$\text{(53)} + C_2H_5O\overset{O}{\overset{\|}{C}}N: \longrightarrow \text{(54)}$$

(53)          (28)                            (54)

ultraviolet ($\lambda_{max} = 228$ m$\mu$ ($\varepsilon = 1.23 \times 10^4$)), infrared ($\lambda_{max} = 5.81$ and 6.02 $\mu$), and nuclear magnetic resonance ($\tau = 6.23$ (H-4),* 4.83,* and 5.00 (H-3),* 3.77 (sharp singlet, H-5), 3.08,* and 3.25 (H-2),* in addition to a typical ethyl group absorption; and coupling constants ($J_{(H-4)-(H-5)} = 0$; $J_{(H-2)-(H-3)} = 10.5$ cps)) spectra. This observed valence-bond rearrangement is in striking contrast to the thermal behavior of cyclooctatetraene,[133] its epoxide,[41] and its carbene adducts.[18,143,224-226] It should be noted that Masamune and Castellucci[170] were able to trap an unstable intermediate, melting point 55°C, in the formation of the nitrene which was characterized

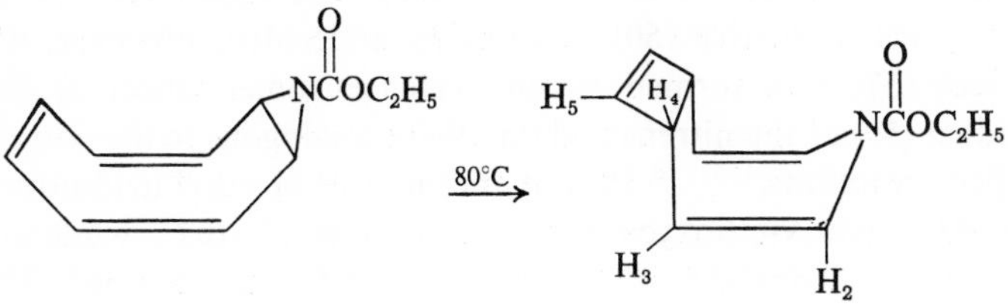

(54)                    $\xrightarrow{80°C}$                    (55)

* Fine splitting.

by its analysis and spectra as the triethylamine salt of *N*-(*p*-nitrobenzene-sulfonoxy)urethan.

Hafner and Kaiser[98] have reported that the thermolysis of the ethyl azidoformate (**40**) in thiophene (**56a**) or 2,5-dimethylthiophene (**56b**) resulted chiefly in *N*-ethoxycarbonyl pyrrols (**58**). The formation of **58**

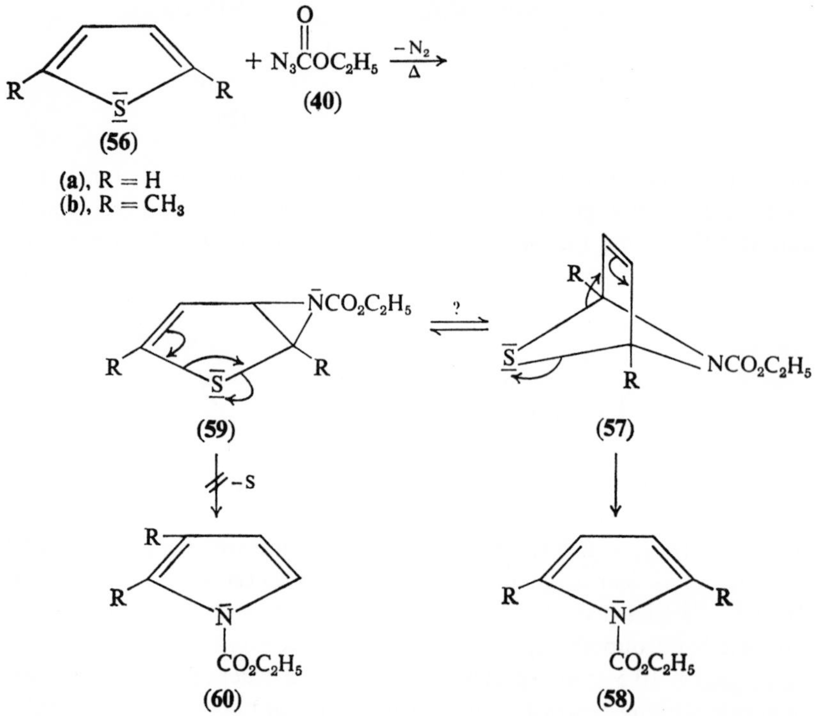

$$R \diagup\diagdown \underset{\underset{\displaystyle \text{(56)}}{\overset{\scriptstyle -}{S}}}{} \diagdown R \quad + \quad N_3\overset{\displaystyle O}{\overset{\displaystyle \|}{C}}OC_2H_5 \quad \xrightarrow[\Delta]{-N_2}$$
(**40**)

(**a**), R = H
(**b**), R = CH₃

was postulated as proceeding through a 1,4-addition of carbethoxynitrene (**28**) to thiophene to the adduct (**57**), since valence-isomerization of the 1,2-adduct (**59**) in the case of 2,5-dimethylthiophene should lead to the 2,3-dimethylpyrrol derivative (**60**). It remains undecided, however, whether the adduct (**57**) was formed by the valence-isomerization of the 1,2-cycloadduct (**59**) of the nitrene and thiophene analogous to the corresponding carbene reactions.[175,189,214] The thermolysis of ethyl azidoformate in pyrrole (**61**) gave *N*-ethoxycarbonyl-2-aminopyrrole (**62**), while in furan (**63**), *N*-ethoxycarbonyl-Δ³- or Δ⁴-pyrrolon-2 (**64**) was obtained. The formation of the derivatives of 2-aminopyrrole (**62**) and pyrrolon-2 (**64**) are also in accordance with the primary step resulting in the 1,4 (or 1,2) addition of ethoxycarbonylnitrene (**28**) to pyrrole or furan. The structures of

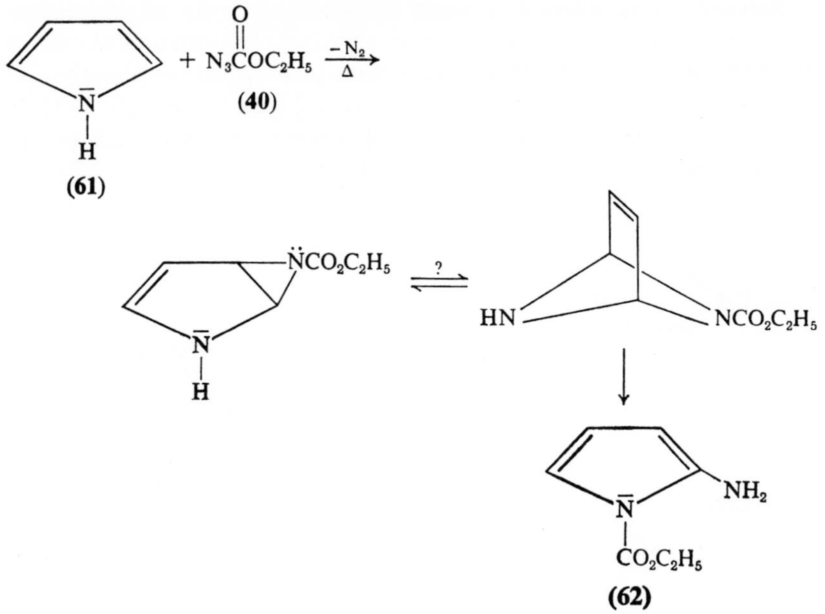

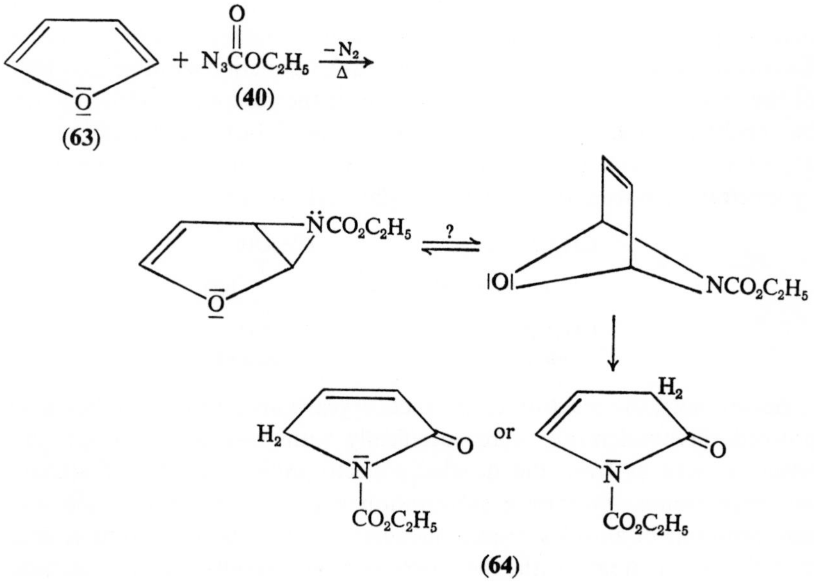

(61)    (40)

(62)

(63)    (40)

(64)

the addition products were confirmed by ultraviolet, infrared, and nuclear
magnetic resonance spectra.

Hafner,[99] in an attempt to study the stereoselectivity of the nitrene-addition to olefins, thereby obtaining additional information about the electronic state of this reactive intermediate, investigated the photolysis of methyl azidoformate in *cis*- and *trans*-butene-2 (**65a** and **b**) at $-30°C$. In both cases a mixture of diastereomers of *N*-methoxycarbonyl-2,3-methyl-aziridine (**66**) were obtained in 68–72% yield.

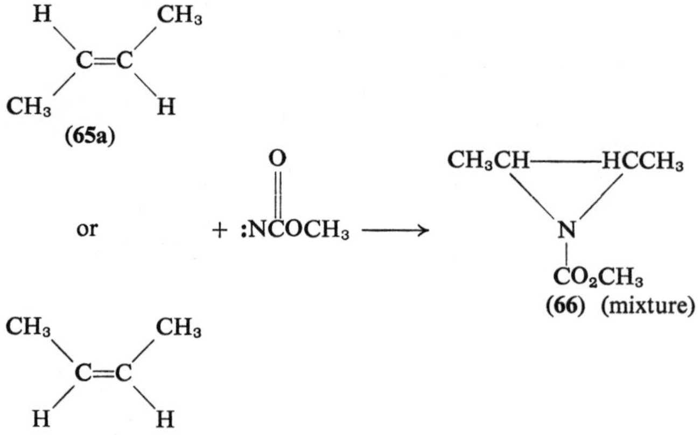

To determine the ratio of the *cis*- and *trans*-aziridines in the mixture, the reaction product from *cis*-butene-2 (**65b**) and the methoxycarbonylnitrene was decarboxylated to yield 87% of the *cis*-2,3-dimethylaziridine and 13% of the *trans*-isomer. The decarboxylation of the reaction product of *tran* butene-2 (**65a**) and the nitrene gave 92% *trans*-2,3-dimethylaziridine and 8% of the *cis*-isomer. The structures of the aziridines were determined by spectral analysis and chemical and physical properties.

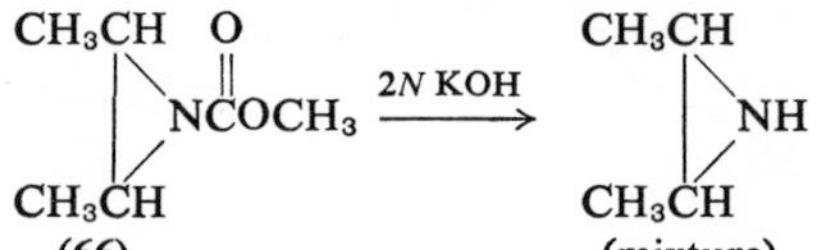

Accordingly, the reaction of the methoxycarbonylnitrene with butene-2 proceeds preponderantly stereospecifically with *cis*-addition. From this result, as well as from the decidedly electrophilic character of alkoxy-carbonylnitrenes—indicating substitution reactions except in *ortho* and *para* positions of anisoles[101] and phenols[181] and in the 1-position of azulenes[181]—in analogy with the corresponding results of the carbene chemistry,[81] it can be supposed that the nitrene produced from alkyl azidoformates preferably reacts in the singlet state.

The formation of small amounts of diastereomeric aziridine derivatives by the reaction of *cis*- as well as *trans*-butene-2 with the methoxycarbonyl-nitrene can be traced back possibly to a photochemical isomerization of (66).[99]

Similarly, 1,3-dienes react with alkoxycarbonylnitrenes photolytically produced from alkyl azidoformates with 1,2-cycloaddition.[99] For example, the photolysis of ethyl azidoformate (40) in butadiene (67) at $-30°C$ gave the $N$-ethoxycarbonyl-2-vinylaziridine (68) in 47% yield. The structure of (68) was confirmed by its nuclear magnetic resonance spectrum ($C_2H_5O$ (triplet at 8.73 $\tau$, quadruplet at 5.9 $\tau$); ring CH (multiplet at 6.97–7.30 $\tau$); ring $CH_2$ (two doublets at 7.62 and 7.67 $\tau$); vinyl protons (2 multiplets at 4.35–4.65 and 4.65–5.0 $\tau$)).

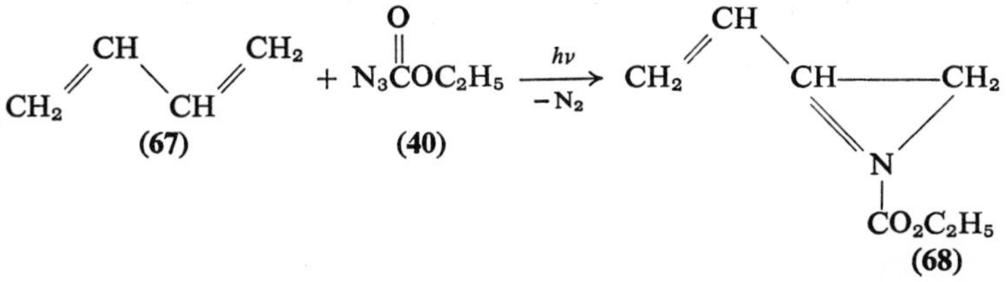

In 1926 Curtius and Bertho[62] reported that the decomposition of carbonyl azide (69) in the presence of benzene (47) resulted in the formation of pyridine, aniline, and what was described as a "Humuskörper," a brown amorphous substance of undetermined composition. Analogously, toluene gave 4-picoline, a mixture of *ortho*- and *para*-anisidine and a "Humuskörper"; *para*-xylene gave 2,5-lutidine and *para*-xylidine and a "Humuskörper"; *para*-cymene gave either 2-isopropyl-5-methyl- or 5-isopropyl-2-methylpyridine and carvacrylamine.

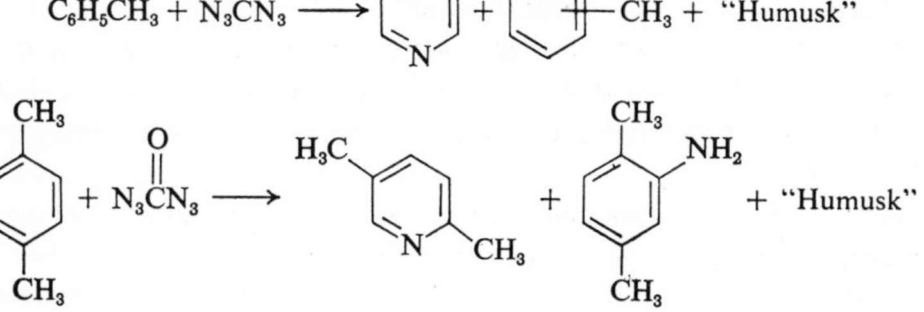

The mechanism proposed for the aniline formations involved the generation and subsequent reaction of the carbonyl dinitrene intermediate (70). The formation of pyridine in

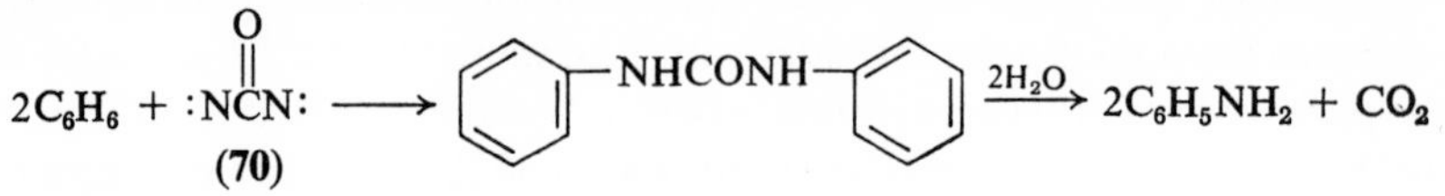

this reaction was formulated as following equation 1.

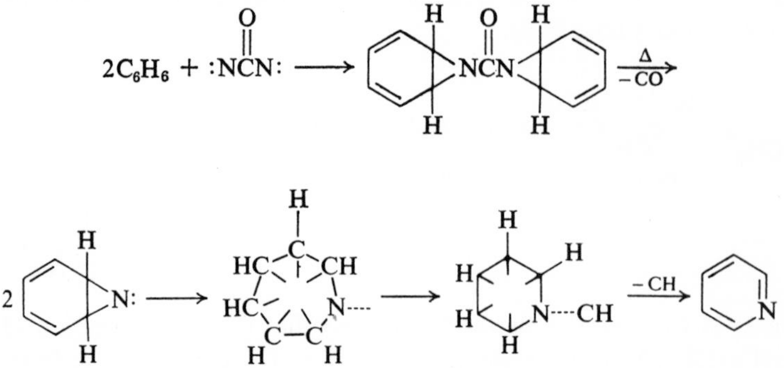

If the reaction really yields pyridine as reported, the rearrangement and elimination of a methylene group might be rationalized in modern terms,[1] as in equation 2. The reaction needs to be reinvestigated and the products unambiguously identified.

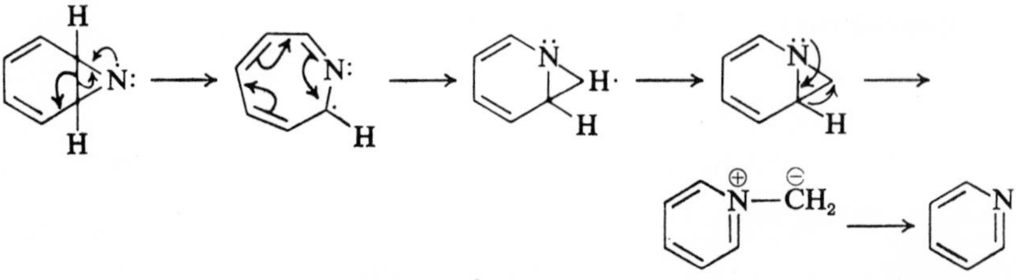

Bertho,[27] Bertho, Curtius, and Schmidt,[28] and Curtius and Schmidt[65] investigated the thermal decomposition of the sulfonyl azide (71) in the presence of para-xylene. The mechanism proposed the dinitrene intermediate ($NSO_2N$). The structures of the products need careful reinvestigation, in view of the azepine obtained by Hafner with ethyl azidoformate and benzene.

Thermal or photolytic decomposition of other sulfonyl azides with aromatic compounds have been reported.[4, 17, 39, 61, 68, 105, 124, 218, 220, 227] For example, benzenesulfonyl azide (72) and a refluxing saturated solution of anthracene in chlorobenzene yielded a mixture of anthracene mono-sulfonamides together with comparable amounts of *ortho-* and *para-*chlorobenzenesulfonamides. The main product of substitution of the anthracene was the 1-isomer (55% yield), while the 9-isomer was obtained in 15% yield. Some 2-isomer was also formed.[220] It was suggested that the sulfonylnitrene intermediate (27) added to the 1,2-bond, in agreement with calculated localization energies,[38] since normal free-radical substitution of anthracene, as well as electrophilic and nucleophilic substitution, take place exclusively at position 9.

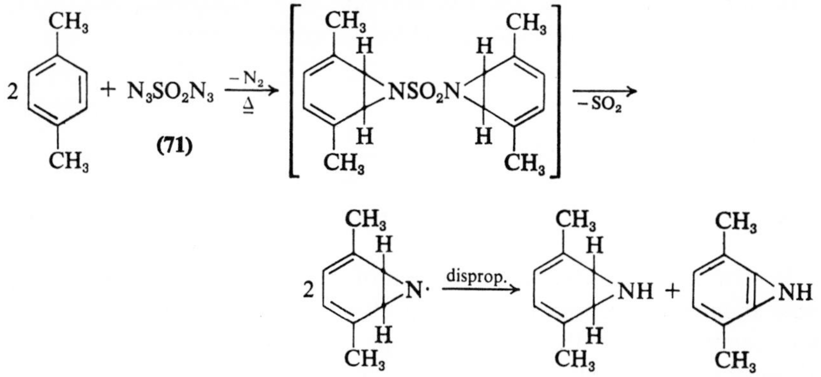

Azides of the type, $RN_3$ ($R = C_6H_5SO_2—$, $p\text{-}CH_3C_6H_4SO_2—$, $CH_3SO_2—$, $(C_6H_5)_2PO—$, $(C_2H_5)_2NSO_2—$, and $N_3SO_2C_6H_4OC_6H_4SO_2—$),

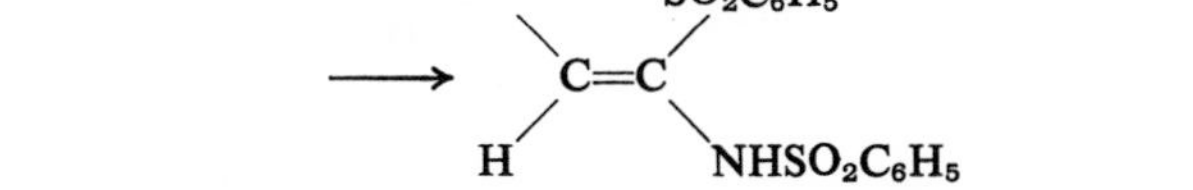

were reported to have reacted with bicyclic olefins (norbornene, dicyclopentadiene, 3,6-endomethylenetetrahydrophthalic anhydride, and 3,6-endooxytetrahydrophthalic anhydride) yielding aziridines and imines directly without evidence of the intermediate triazoline,[88,236,237] via the corresponding nitrene. For example, benzenesulfonyl azide (72) and norbornene (35) in acetonitrile were heated at 55–60°C for 2–3 hr giving the aziridine adduct (73), whose structure was supported by its infrared spectrum (λ = 6.8, 6.92, 7.4, 7.6, 7.8, 8.6, 8.87, 9.18, 9.67, 10.2, 10.7, 10.95, 11.35, 12.1, 13.85, 14.08 μ in chloroform).[88]

(25) (72) (73) (74)

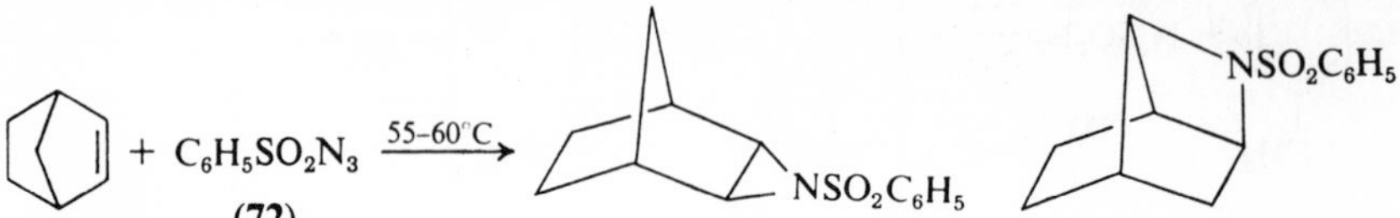

In view of the possible rearrangement of the aziridine (**73**) to **74**[37,91] the nuclear magnetic resonance spectrum of exo-2,3-epoxynorbornane[213,229] was compared with that of **73**. Except for aromatic hydrogen atoms, identical chemical shifts were observed [bridge $CH_2$ group 7, two doublets—one at 9.2–9.4 τ, the other at 8.8–8.9 τ; ring $CH_2$ groups 5 and 6, multiplet at 8.6–8.7 τ; bridgehead CH at C-1 and C-4, 7.6 τ; ring CH at C-2 and C-3, 7.1 τ; aromatic hydrogen, complex band at 2.0–2.5 τ].

(77)

(79)

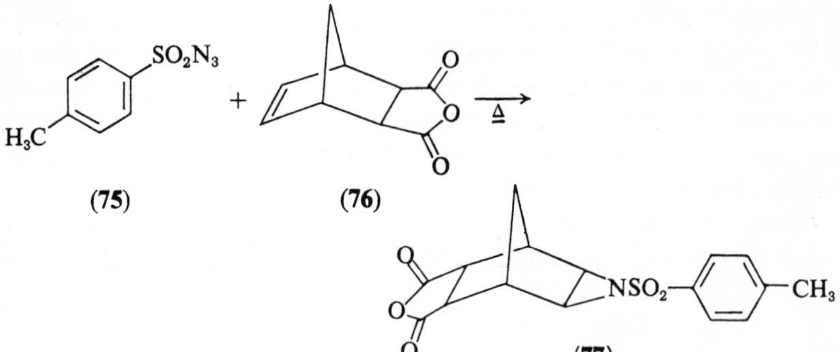

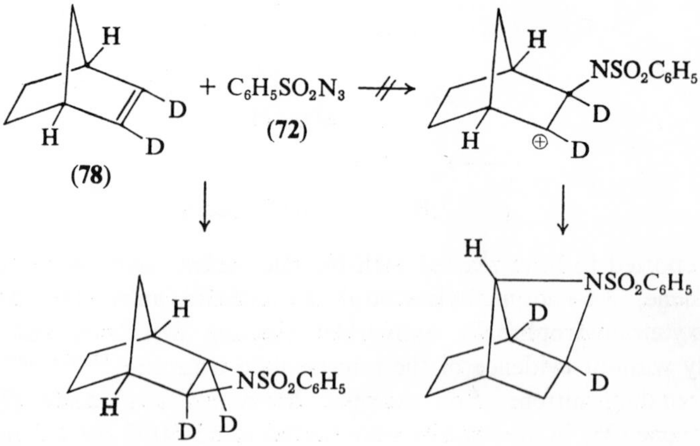

Structure **73** was supported with regard to exo configuration as well as presence of the aziridine ring. Similarly, *p*-toluenesulfonyl azide (**75**) was heated with endomethylenetetrahydrophthalic anhydride (**76**), yielding the aziridine (**77**) in 64.6% yield.

Recently, in defense of the structure of the aziridine (**73**), Franz, Osuch, and Dietrich[89] reported additional nuclear magnetic resonance and chemical evidence. The nuclear magnetic spectrum of the aziridine (**79**) prepared from 2,3-dideuterobicylco[2.2.1]-2-heptene (**78**) and benzenesulfonyl azide (**72**) conclusively established that rearrangement did not occur during this reaction and that carbonium ion intermediates were not involved. Further, a mechanism analogous to epoxidation[216] was proposed involving a concerted addition of the azide to the double bond of the olefin with concomitant loss of nitrogen.

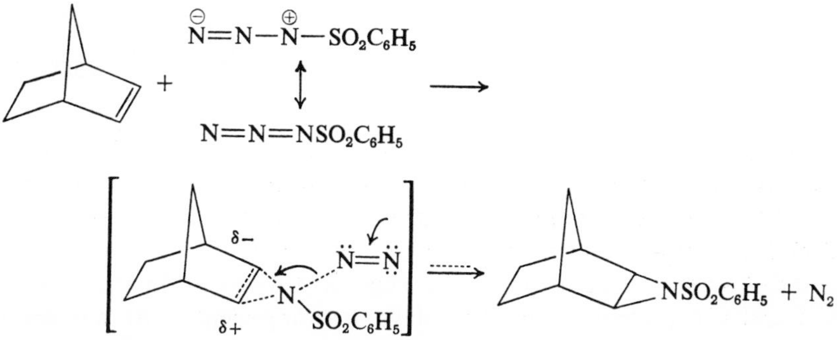

$$\overset{\ominus}{N}=N-\overset{\oplus}{N}-SO_2C_6H_5$$

$$N=N=NSO_2C_6H_5$$

$$[\quad] \dashrightarrow \quad NSO_2C_6H_5 + N_2$$

Benzoyl azide (**34**) was reported to react[238] with norbornene (**35**) at room temperature to give the aziridine (**37**).

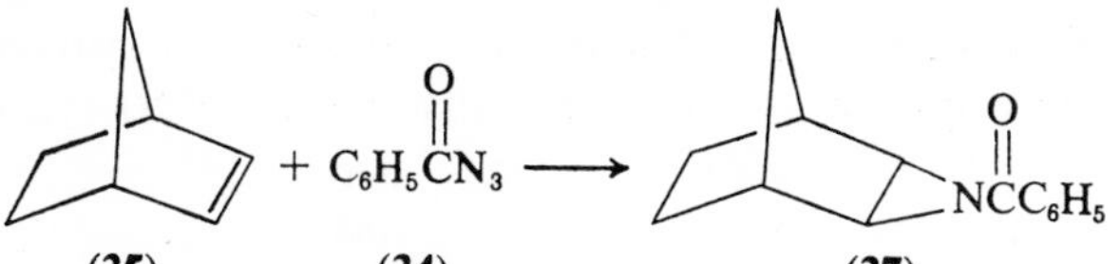

$$(35) \quad + \quad C_6H_5\overset{O}{\overset{\|}{C}}N_3 \quad (34) \quad \longrightarrow \quad (37)$$

Franz and Osuch[87] reported that the reaction of norbornadiene (**80**) and benzenesulfonyl azide (**72**) in ether gave 68% yield of an adduct to which structure **81** was assigned on the basis of chemical evidence and spectral analysis. Oehlschlager and Zalkow[173] reported, however, that the reaction yields initially the expected aziridine (**82**). The nitrogen insertion

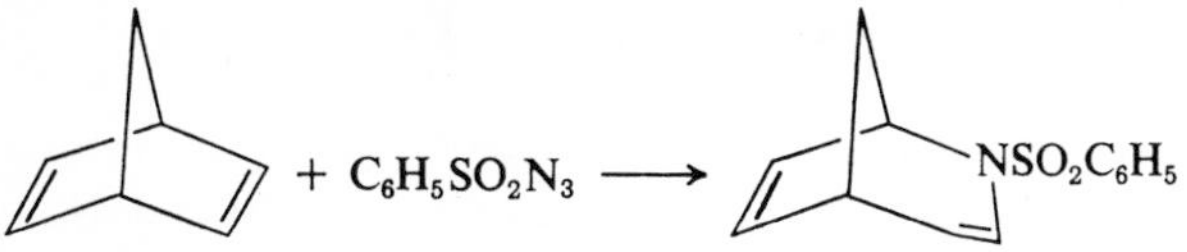

$$(80) \quad + \quad C_6H_5SO_2N_3 \quad (72) \quad \longrightarrow \quad NSO_2C_6H_5 \quad (81)$$

product of Franz and Osuch has been shown to arise by rearrangement of
the aziridine (82) and to be correctly represented as (81). The proton mag-

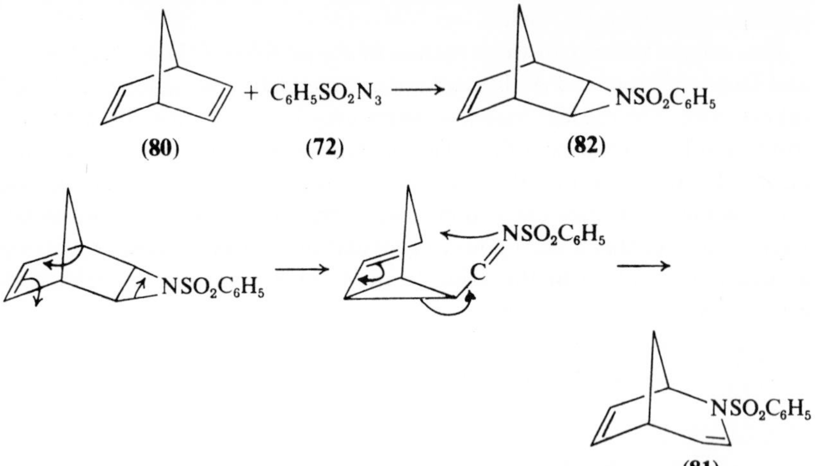

netic resonance of the aziridine (82) showed an AB quartet ($J = 8.5$ cps)
at δ 1.07 and 1.66 arising from C-7 protons, a broad multiplet centered at
2.96 due to bridgehead protons, and a sharp singlet at δ 3.18 for the C-2
and C-3 protons and a triplet ($J = 1.5$ cps) centered at δ 6.35 arising from
C-5 and C-6 protons. After three days, rearrangement to 81 was com-
pleted and the infrared and proton magnetic resonance spectra was
identical to those reported.[87]

The decomposition of cyanogen azide (83) to nitrogen and cyanonitrene
(84) at 40°C was reported.[14] The transient existence of cyanonitrene (84)
was established by the use of isotopically labeled ($^{15}$N) cyanogen azide

$$N_3CN \xrightarrow{\Delta} N_2 + :NCN$$
$$\text{(83)} \qquad\qquad \text{(84)}$$

prepared from KN*=N=N* and cyanogen chloride. When the decomposition was quenched with norbornene (35) in acetonitrile the cyano-

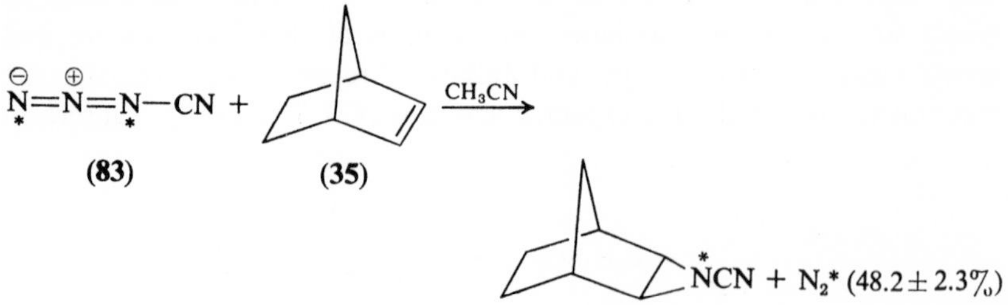

aziridine (85) resulted. Cyanonitrene (84) was observed recently in the flash photolysis of diazomethane[121] and cyanogen azide[176]; its ground state is $^3\Sigma_g{}^-$.

p-Diphenyl-N-tosylphosphazene azide (86) decomposes above 220° (a copper catalyst lowers the decomposition temperature to 120°) with the elimination of a molecule of nitrogen and the unstable nitrene intermediate (87).[32a] The unstable nitrene can also be formulated as a 1,3-dipole in a mesomeric structure.[128,130] Reaction with the strained double bond of dicyclopentadiene traps the intermediate as a crystalline adduct which could either be the aziridine (88) formed by the addition of the nitrene intermediate or the $\Delta^1$-1,2,5-phosphadiazoline (89) resulting from a 1,3-cycloaddition.

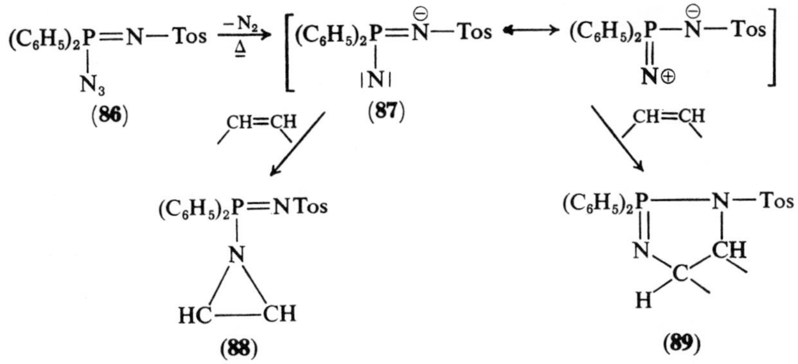

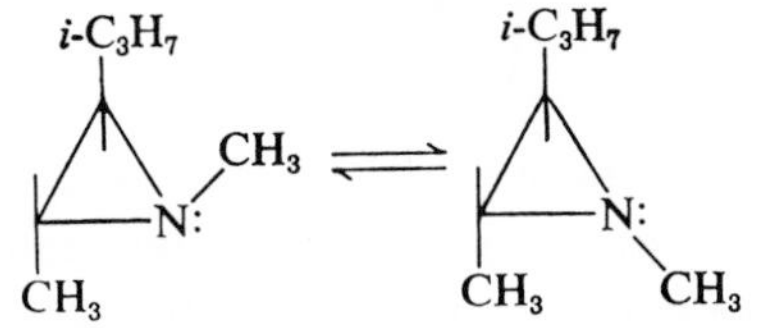

In an endeavor to understand more clearly the reactions of the aziridines, Hammett $\rho$ constants for the ethylenimine ring by substituted benzoic acids were determined for 2-ethylethylenimine ($-1.66 \pm 0.17$) and 2,2-dimethylethylenimine ($-1.50 \pm 0.17$).[177] A Hammett $\rho$ constant ($-1.47$) as well as a reaction mechanism were reported for the reaction of 1-acetylaziridine with anilines,[102] yielding the ring-opened adduct, O-ethyl-N-(2-anilinoethyl)urethan. Recently, in a study of the conformational equilibrium of trans-1,2-dimethyl-3-isopropylaziridine[34] at several temperatures by means of nuclear magnetic resonance spectroscopy, it was reported that for 90a → 90b in chloroform at 25°, $\Delta F$ (by extrapolation) $= -0.77$ kcal, $\Delta H = -0.24 \pm 0.05$ kcal, and $\Delta S = +1.8 \pm 0.2$ eu.

Aziridines have been reported to undergo isomerization reactions[32,47-49,57,59,63,69,70,83,93,95,106,107-117,134,135,140-142,187,217,221,223,233] resulting in ring-opening reactions mainly involving the cleavage of the carbon–nitrogen bond of the ring, forming such heterocyclic systems as oxazolines, imidazoline, imidazolidinones, thiazolines, pyrazolines, and triazolines, while other isomerizations form $N$-unsaturated amides, anils, and isocyanates. For example, 1,2,3-triphenylaziridine (91) with potassium $t$-butoxide in heptane or toluene at 180° in a sealed tube for three days formed 1,2-diphenylisoindoline (92) in 70% yield via the postulated mechanism shown here.[116]

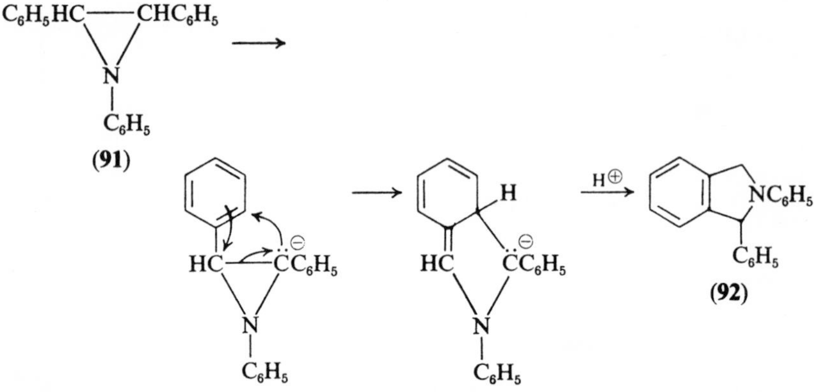

Although the reaction of diazomethane with ternary imine salts is a nucleophilic reaction and not a 1,2-cycloaddition, a brief summary will follow due to the interesting nature of the similarity of the reaction forming aziridinium salts to the formation of aziridines previously mentioned. The first report of the existence of an ethylenimonium or aziridinium compound was that of Marckwald and Frobenius,[169] as a result of the treatment of 1-$\beta$-chloroethylpiperidine hydrochloride with limited base. A more reasonable bispiperizinium salt structure was suggested.[31] During the

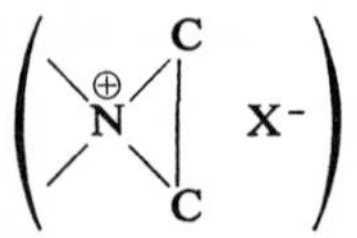

hydrolysis of certain $\alpha$-bromo-$\beta$-3-aminoketones, evidence has been provided for the intermediacy of the aziridinium cation,[58,60] and it has been recognized as the major intermediate in the chemical reactions of the nitrogen mustards, $\beta$-haloethyl-$tert$-amines.[19-21,36,51,94,96,104,144,184]

Aziridinium intermediates had only been trapped in the form of salts,[23,43,44,50,96,97,103,118,137] although the charged three-membered ring readily opened in the presence of most anions, including the halides.[20,52,53,92,119,197] Ternary iminium perchlorates, from acidification of the corresponding enaimines and iminium salts, are known to undergo nucleophilic attack with a variety of reagents.[84,152,183,215] The knowledge of three-membered ring formation by the action of diazomethane on certain carbon–sulfur, carbon–oxygen, and carbon–nitrogen double bond functions[79] and the above facts led Leonard and Jann[154,155] to report the following general method of preparing aziridinium salts (93). For example, 1-N-pyrrolidylcyclohexene (94) when treated with ethanolic perchloric

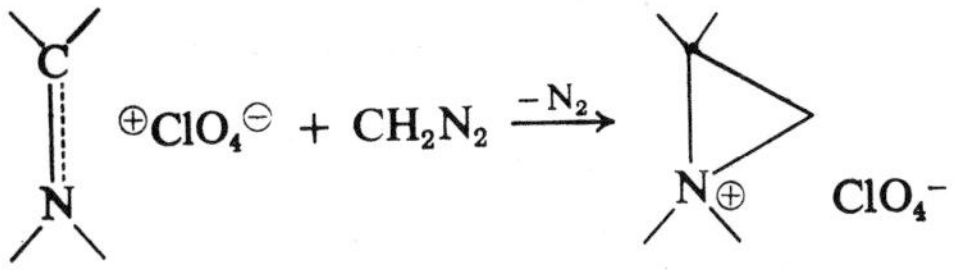

(93)

acid gave N-cyclohexylidene pyrrolidinium perchlorate (95) which readily reacted with diazomethane in methanol–ether solution at − 10° yielding the aziridinium salt (96), 2,2-pentamethylene-1,1-tetramethyleneaziridinium

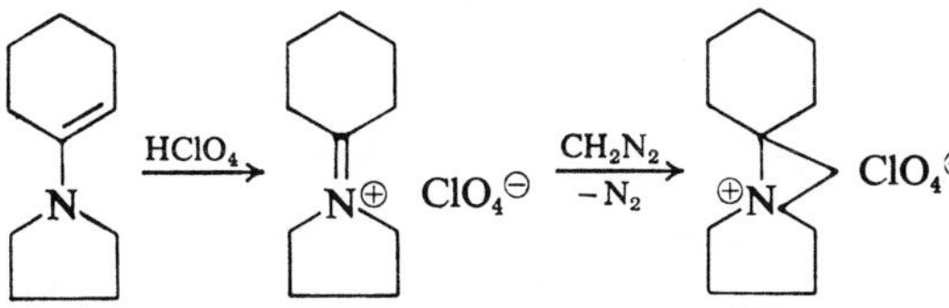

(94)            (95)            (96)

perchlorate, in 88–93% yields. The structure of the aziridinium salt (96) was determined by thiosulfate titration, infrared and nuclear magnetic resonance spectra, hydrolysis, and alcoholysis. Diazoethane reacted with N-cyclohexylidenepyrrolidinium perchlorate (95) to give an analogous product, 3-methyl-2,2-pentamethylene-1,1-tetramethyleneaziridinium per-

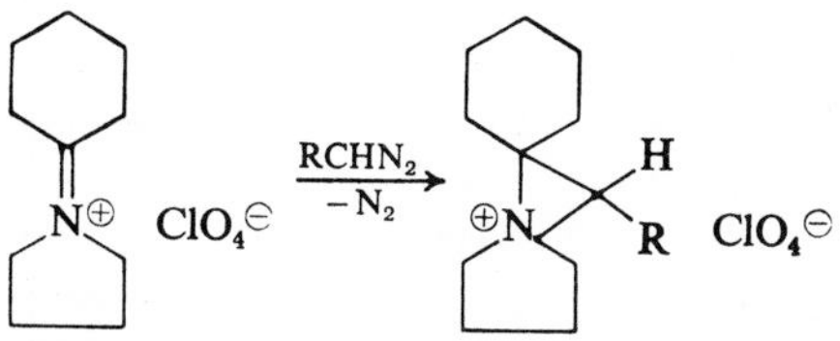

(95)            (97a), R = $CH_3$
               (97b), R = $C_2H_5$

chlorate (97), while diazopropane and (95) gave 3-ethyl-2,2-pentamethyl-ene-1,1-tetramethyleneaziridinium perchlorate (97b) (Table 2). Analogously, *N*-cyclohexylidenepiperidinium perchlorate treated with diazomethane gave 1,1-pentamethylene-2,2-pentamethyleneaziridinium perchlorate. The structures of the aziridinium salts were confirmed by their nuclear magnetic resonance spectra.

Extending this process, the addition of diazomethane to the ternary iminium grouping $\left(\underset{/}{\overset{\backslash}{N}}\overset{\oplus}{=}\underset{\backslash}{\overset{/}{C}}\right)$ contained in monocyclic, bicyclic, and tricyclic systems has been successful[156]; for example, 2-ethyl-1-methyl-$\Delta^1$-tetrahydropyridinium perchlorate (98)[151,163] and diazomethane in ethylene chloride and ether at 0°C gave the aziridinium perchlorate (99), 6-ethyl-1-methyl-1-azoniabicyclo[4.1.0]heptane perchlorate, while $\Delta^{5(10)}$-

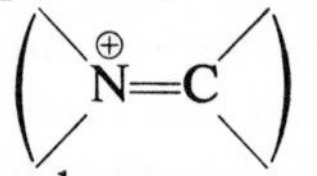

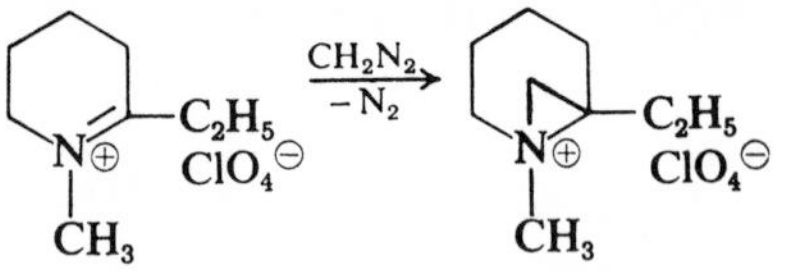

(98)                              (99)

dehydroquinolizidinium perchlorate (100)[153] gave 1-azoniatricyclo-[4.4.1.0]undecane perchlorate (101) (Table 2).

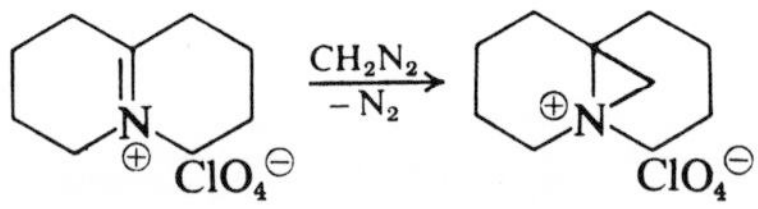

(100)                    (101)

Since the introduction of a general method for preparing aziridinium salts by Leonard and co-workers, expansion of the aziridinium ring by reactions with aldehydes[157] and ketones[159] to give the corresponding oxazolidinium salt and with nitriles[150] to give the imidazolinium salt, have been reported as well as the interconversion of substituted β-chloro-ethylamines and aziridinium salts.[158] For example, 5-azoniadispiro-[4.0.5.1]dodecane perchlorate (96) and aldehydes or ketones give the corresponding oxazolidinium salt (102) while 1-benzyl-1-ethyl-1-azonia-

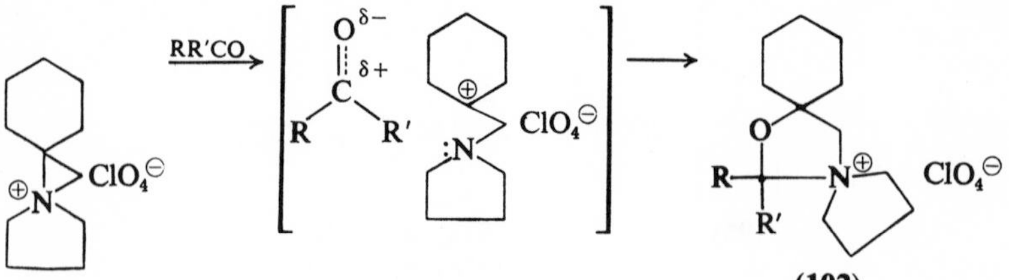

(102)

## Table 2

### Aziridinium Salts via Ternary Imine Salts and Diazo Compounds

| Imine salt | Diazo cpd. | Aziridinium salt | MP (°C) | Yield, (%) | Ref. |
|---|---|---|---|---|---|
| 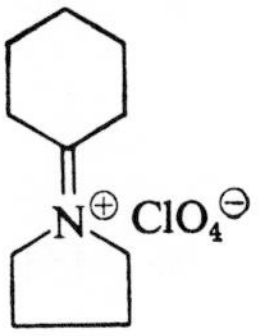 (cyclohexyl pyrrolidinium imine salt, $ClO_4^{\ominus}$) | $CH_2N_2$ | 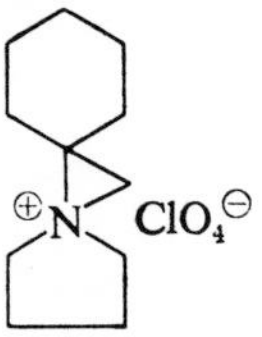 (spiro aziridinium salt, $ClO_4^{\ominus}$) | 132–133 | 88 | 154 |
| | | | 133–134 | 93 | 155 |
| 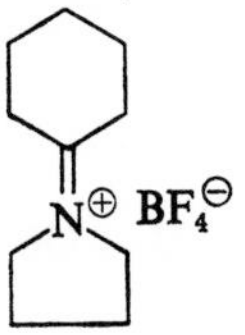 (cyclohexyl pyrrolidinium imine salt, $BF_4^{\ominus}$) | $CH_2N_2$ | 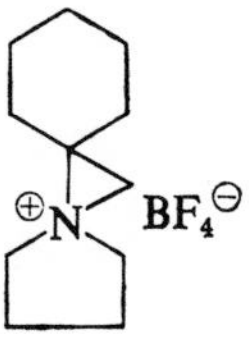 (spiro aziridinium salt, $BF_4^{\ominus}$) | 110–113 | 92 | 155 |
| 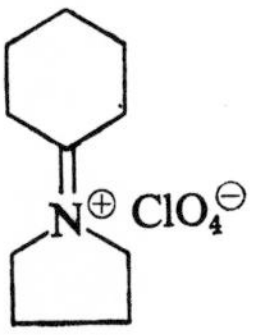 (cyclohexyl pyrrolidinium imine salt, $ClO_4^{\ominus}$) | $CH_3CH_2N_2$ | 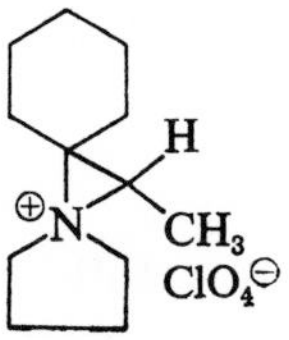 (aziridinium salt, H, $CH_3$, $ClO_4^{\ominus}$) | 166–166.5 | 40 | 155 |
| 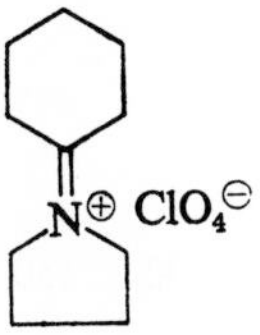 (cyclohexyl pyrrolidinium imine salt, $ClO_4^{\ominus}$) | $C_2H_5CHN_2$ | 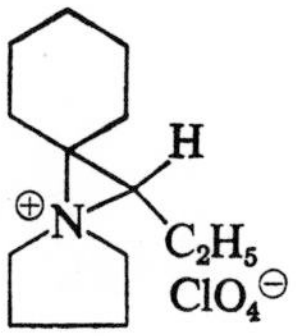 (aziridinium salt, H, $C_2H_5$, $ClO_4^{\ominus}$) | 204–205 | 70 | 155 |
| 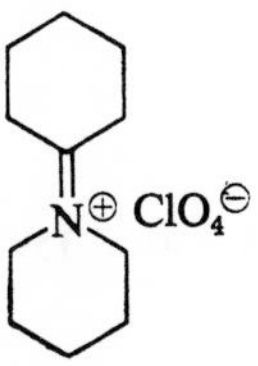 (cyclohexyl piperidinium imine salt, $ClO_4^{\ominus}$) | $CH_2N_2$ | 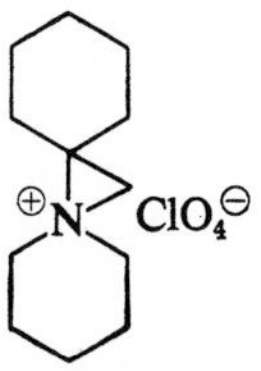 (spiro aziridinium salt, $ClO_4^{\ominus}$) | 236–238 | 73 | 155 |
| 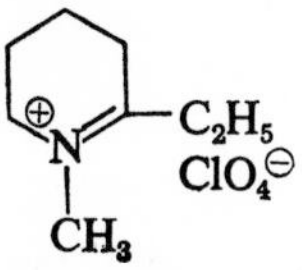 (N-methyl, $C_2H_5$ imine salt, $ClO_4^{\ominus}$, $CH_3$) | $CH_2N_2$ | 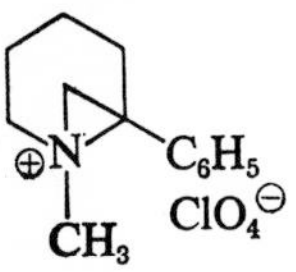 (aziridinium salt, $C_6H_5$, $ClO_4^{\ominus}$, $CH_3$) | 137–138 | 87 | 156 |

*(continued)*

**Table 2** (*continued*)

| Imine salt | Diazo cpd. | Aziridinium salt | MP (°C) | Yield (%) | Ref. |
|---|---|---|---|---|---|
| 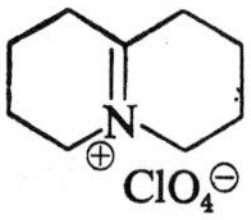 | $CH_2N_2$ | 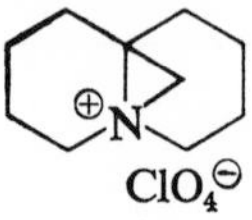 | 142–144 | 90 | 156 |
| 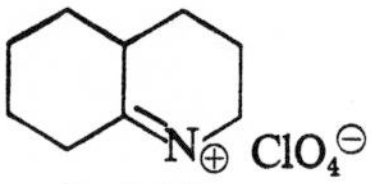 Ref. 160 | $CH_2N_2$ | 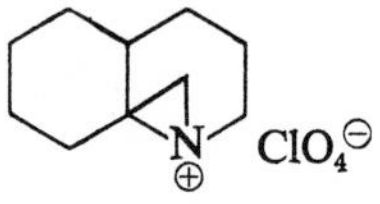 | 129–129.5 | 90 | 156 |
| 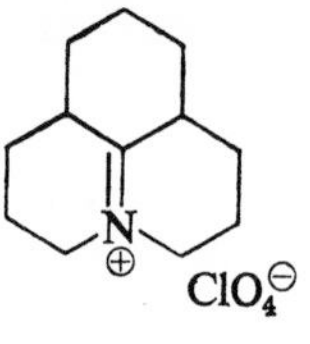 | $CH_2N_2$ | 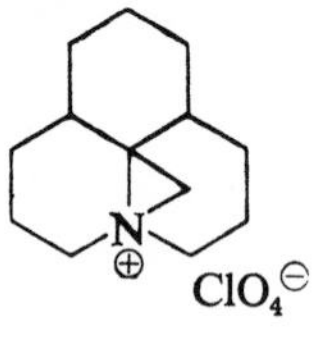 | 150–151 | 72 | 156 |
| 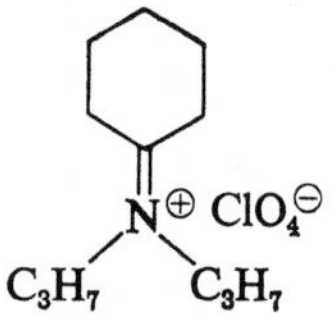 | $CH_2N_2$ | 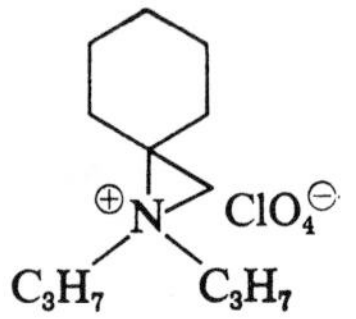 | — | — | 157 |
| 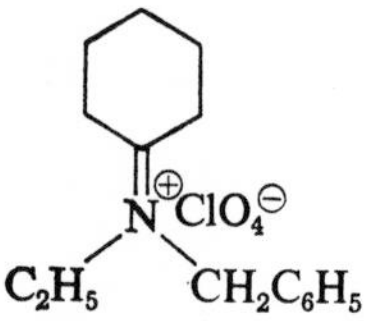 | $CH_2N_2$ | 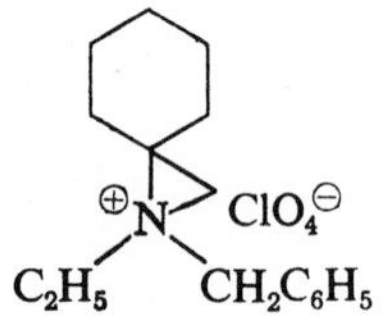 | — 115 | — 90 | 157 150 |
| 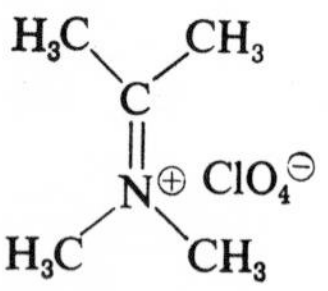 | $CH_2N_2$ | 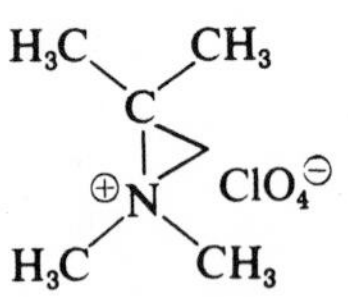 | 149–149.5 | 93 | 159 |
| 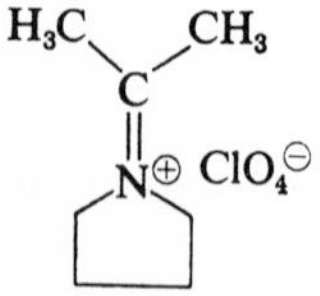 | $CH_2N_2$ | 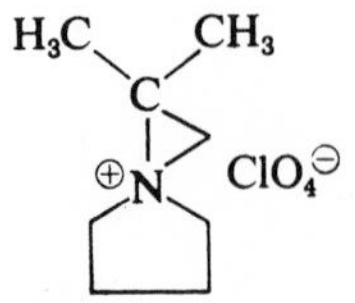 | 58–59 | 91 | 158 |

spiro[2.5]octane perchlorate (103) and an excess of acetonitrile give 3-benzyl-3-ethyl-2-methyl-1-aza-3-azoniaspiro[4.5]dec-1-ene     perchlorate (104).

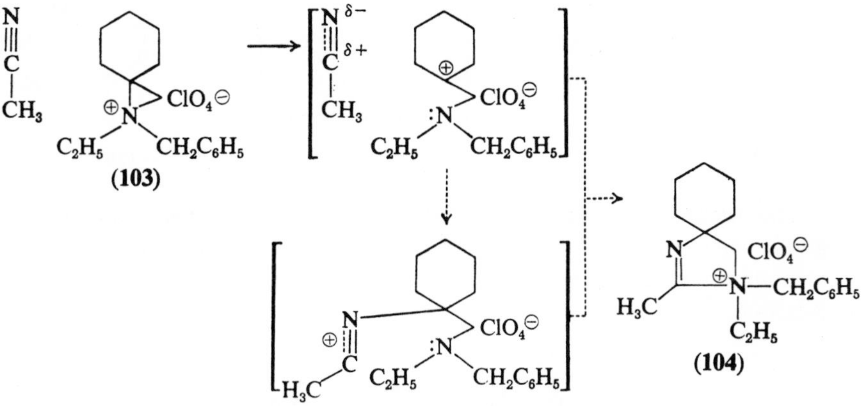

Recently increasing interest in α-lactams (aziridinones) has developed. In 1949, 1-phenylaziridinone was suggested as a possible intermediate in the reaction of phenyl isocyanate and diazomethane.[192] The claim that certain α-haloamides with sodium hydride produce aziridinones[186] has been questioned.[190] Spectral evidence of the existence of an aziridinone and its preparation were first found by Baumgarten and co-workers.[23-25] Aziridinones have also been reported as the products of the reaction of 2-bromo-2-methyl-N-t-butylpropionamide with potassium t-butoxide or metallic potassium.[193]

Sheehan and co-workers[190,194] reported that phenyl-isocyanate (105) and diphenyldiazomethane (106) under the influence of ultraviolet light gave 2,2-diphenylindoxyl (107), this reaction being the first example of the addition of a carbene to an isocyanate as well as the first photo-initiated reaction of an isocyanate. Individually, each reactant was converted into a characteristic irradiation product; that is, diphenyldiazomethane produced

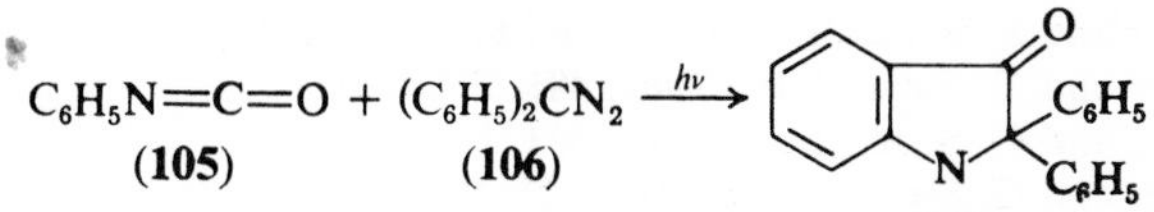

benzophenone azine[64] and phenylisocyanate gives the cyclic dimer 1,3-diphenyluretidione.[182]

The formation of the 2,2-diphenylindoxyl was explained by assuming that the photogenerated diphenylcarbene (108) from diphenyldiazomethane (106) added to phenylisocyanate (105) produced an α-lactam (109) which then collapsed to the indoxyl (107).

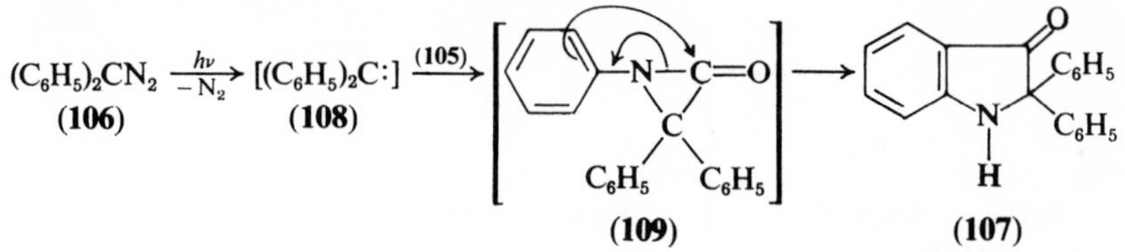

$$(C_6H_5)_2CN_2 \xrightarrow[-N_2]{h\nu} [(C_6H_5)_2C\colon] \xrightarrow{(105)}$$
(106)            (108)

(109)                    (107)

The nonphotochemical reaction of diazomethane with phenylisocyanate gives β-lactams[191,192] in which an α-lactam was postulated as an intermediate which reacted with a second molecule of diazomethane to form the β-lactam.

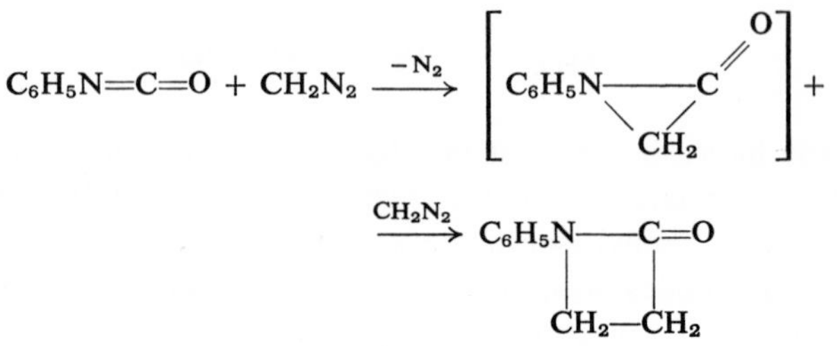

## REFERENCES

1. R. A. Abramovitch and B. A. Davis, *Chem. Rev.*, **64**, 149 (1964).
2. R. A. Abramovitch and B. A. Davis, *Chem. Rev.*, **64**, 169 (1964).
3. R. A. Abramovitch and B. A. Davis, *Chem. Rev.*, **64**, 178 (1964).
4. R. A. Abramovitch and J. Roy, in R. A. Abramovitch and B. A. Davis, *Chem. Rev.*, **64**, 173 (1964).
5. R. M. Acheson, *An Introduction to the Chemistry of Heterocyclic Compounds*, Interscience, New York, 1960, p. 6.
6. K. Alder and H. Finzenhagen, *Ann. Chem.*, **485**, 233 (1931).
7. K. Alder and W. Friedrichsen, *Ann. Chem.*, **501**, 1 (1933).
8. K. Alder and K. A. Hornung, *Ann. Chem.*, **515**, 165 (1935).
9. K. Alder and R. Rührmann, *Ann. Chem.*, **566**, 1 (1950).
10. K. Alder and S. Schneider, *Ann. Chem.*, **515**, 185 (1935).
11. K. Alder and G. Stein, *Ann. Chem.*, **485**, 211 (1931).
12. K. Alder and G. Stein, *Ann. Chem.*, **501**, 1 (1933).
13. K. Alder and G. Stein, *Chem. Abstr.*, **27**, 1003 (1933).
14. A. G. Anastassiou, H. E. Simmons, and F. D. Marsh, *J. Am. Chem. Soc.*, **87**, 2296 (1965).
15. J. W. ApSimon and O. Edwards, *Can. J. Chem.*, **40**, 896 (1962).
16. J. W. ApSimon and O. Edwards, *Proc. Chem. Soc.*, **1961**, 461.
17. J. N. Ashley, G. L. Buchanan, and A. P. T. Easson, *J. Chem. Soc.*, **1947**, 60.
18. K. F. Bangert and V. Boekelheide, *J. Am. Chem. Soc.*, **86**, 905 (1964).

19. P. D. Bartlett, J. W. Davis, S. D. Ross, and C. G. Swain, *J. Am. Chem. Soc.*, **69**, 2977 (1947).

20. P. D. Bartlett, S. D. Ross, and C. G. Swain, *J. Am. Chem. Soc.*, **69**, 2971 (1947).

21. P. D. Barlett, S. D. Ross, and C. G. Swain, *J. Am. Chem. Soc.*, **71**, 1415 (1949).

22. D. H. R. Barton and L. R. Morgan, Jr., *J. Chem. Soc.*, **1961**, 3313.

23. H. E. Baumgarten, *J. Am. Chem. Soc.*, **84**, 4975 (1962).

24. H. E. Baumgarten, J. F. Frierholzer, R. D. Clark, and R. D. Thompson, *J. Am. Chem. Soc.*, **85**, 3303 (1963).

25. H. E. Baumgarten, R. L. Zey, and U. Krolls, *J. Am. Chem. Soc.*, **83**, 4469 (1961).

26. R. S. Berry, D. Cornell, and W. Lwowski, *J. Am. Chem. Soc.*, **85**, 1199 (1963).

27. A. Bertho, *J. Prakt. Chem.*, **120**, 89 (1928).

28. A. Bertho, T. Curtius, and F. Schmidt, *Chem. Ber.*, **60**, 1717 (1927).

29. H. Bestian, *Ann. Chem.*, **566**, 210 (1950).

30. H. Bestian, in *Methoden der Organischen Chemie* (*Houben-Weyl*), Vol. XI/2, E. Müller, Ed., Georg Thieme, Stuttgart, 1958, p. 223.

31. H. Bestian, in *Methoden der Organischen Chemie* (*Houben-Weyl*), Vol. XI/2, E. Müller, Ed., Georg Thieme, Stuttgart, 1958, p. 234.

32. H. Bestian, J. Henya, A. Bauer, G. Ehlers, B. Hirsekorn, T. Jacobs, W. Noll, W. Weibezahn, and F. Romer, *Ann. Chem.*, **566**, 210 (1950).

32a. H. Bock and W. Wiegräbe, *Angew. Chem. Intern. Ed. Engl.*, **1**, 265 (1962).

33. A. T. Bottini and R. L. Van Etten, *J. Org. Chem.*, **30**, 575 (1965).

34. A. T. Bottini, R. L. Van Etten, and A. J. Davidson, *J. Am. Chem. Soc.*, **87**, 755 (1965).

35. J. H. Boyer and F. C. Canter, *Chem. Rev.*, **54**, 1 (1954).

36. E. Boyland and R. Nery, *J. Chem. Soc.*, **1961**, 679.

37. G. D. Brindell and S. J. Cristol, *Organic Sulfur Compounds*, Vol. I, N. Kharasch, Ed., Pergamon Press, New York, 1961, pp. 121–133.

38. R. D. Brown, *J. Chem. Soc.*, **1950**, 3249.

39. G. L. Buchanan and R. M. Levine, *J. Chem. Soc.*, **1950**, 2248.

40. G. D. Buckley, *J. Chem. Soc.*, **1954**, 1850.

41. G. Büchi and E. M. Burgess, *J. Am. Chem. Soc.*, **84**, 3104 (1962).

42. G. Caronna and S. Palazzo, *Gazz. Chim. Ital.*, **82**, 292 (1952).

43. N. B. Chapman and J. W. James, *J. Chem. Soc.*, **1954**, 2103.

44. N. B. Chapman, J. W. James, J. D. P. Graham and G. N. Lewis, *Chem. Ind.* (*London*), **1952**, 805.

45. F. D. Chattaway and G. D. Parkes, *J. Chem. Soc.*, **127**, 1307 (1925).

46. E. Chinoporos, *Chem. Rev.*, **63**, 247 (1963).

47. L. B. Clapp, *J. Am. Chem. Soc.*, **70**, 184 (1948).

48. L. B. Clapp, *J. Am. Chem. Soc.*, **73**, 2584 (1951).

49. L. B. Clapp, E. A. Rick, W. B. Moniz, and V. B. Schatz, *J. Am. Chem. Soc.*, **77**, 5116 (1955).

50. R. D. Clark and G. K. Helmkamp, *J. Org. Chem.*, **29**, 1316 (1964).

51. B. Cohen, E. R. Van Artsdalen, and J. Harris, *J. Am. Chem. Soc.*, **70**, 281 (1948).

52. B. Cohen, E. R. Van Artsdalen, and J. Harris, *J. Am. Chem. Soc.*, **74**, 1875 (1952).

53. B. Cohen, E. R. Van Artsdalen, and J. Harris, *J. Am. Chem. Soc.*, **74**, 1878 (1952).

54. A. G. Cook and E. K. Fields, *J. Org. Chem.*, **27**, 3686 (1962).

55. A. C. Cope, P. T. Moore, and W. R. Moore, *J. Am. Chem. Soc.*, **80**, 5505 (1958).

56. D. Cornell, Thesis, Yale University, 1964.

57. N. H. Cromwell, N. G. Barker, R. A. Wankel, P. J. Vanderhorst, F. W. Olson, and J. H. Anglin, Jr., *J. Am. Chem. Soc.*, **73**, 1044 (1951).

58. N. H. Cromwell and D. J. Cram, *J. Am. Chem. Soc.*, **65**, 301 (1943).
59. N. H. Cromwell and H. Hoeksema, *J. Am. Chem. Soc.*, **71**, 716 (1949).
60. N. H. Cromwell and I. H. Witt, *J. Am. Chem. Soc.*, **65**, 308 (1943).
61. T. Curtius, *J. Prakt. Chem.*, **125**, 303 (1930).
62. T. Curtius and A. Bertho, *Chem. Ber.*, **59**, 565 (1926).
63. T. Curtius and W. Dörr, *J. Prakt. Chem.*, **125**, 425 (1930).
64. T. Curtius and F. Rauterberg, *J. Prakt. Chem.*, **44**, 200 (1891).
65. T. Curtius and F. Schmidt, *Chem. Ber.*, **55**, 1571 (1922).
66. A. A. Danish and R. E. Lidov, *Anal. Chem.*, **22**, 702 (1950).
67. S. J. Davis and C. S. Rondestvedt, Jr., *Chem. Ind. (London)*, **1956**, 845.
68. O. C. Dermer and M. T. Edmison, *J. Am. Chem. Soc.*, **77**, 70 (1955).
69. A. S. Deutsch and P. E. Fanta, *J. Org. Chem.*, **21**, 892 (1956).
70. C. S. Dewey and R. A. Bafford, *J. Org. Chem.*, **30**, 495 (1965).
71. J. A. Deyrup and R. B. Greenwald, *Tetrahedron Letters*, **1965**, 321.
72. K. Dimroth and H. Freyschlag, *Chem. Ber.*, **89**, 2602 (1956).
73. K. Dimroth and H. Freyschlag, *Chem. Ber.*, **90**, 1628 (1957).
74. R. N. Dixon, *Can. J. Phys.*, **38**, 10 (1960).
75. R. N. Dixon, *Phil. Trans. Roy. Soc. (London)*, **252**, 165 (1959).
76. W. v. E. Doering and W. A. Henderson, Jr., *J. Am. Chem. Soc.*, **80**, 5274 (1958).
77. W. v. E. Doering and L. Knox, *J. Am. Chem. Soc.*, **78**, 4947 (1956).
78. W. v. E. Doering and L. Knox, *J. Am. Chem. Soc.*, **83**, 1989 (1961).
79. B. Eistert, *Newer Methods of Preparative Organic Chemistry*, Interscience, New York, 1948, pp. 513ff.
80. F. Eloy, *J. Org. Chem.*, **26**, 952 (1961).
81. R. M. Etter, H. S. Skovronek, and P. S. Skell, *J. Am. Chem. Soc.*, **81**, 1008 (1959).
82. P. E. Fanta, in *Compounds with Three- and Four-Membered Rings (The Chemistry of Heterocyclic Compounds*, Vol. 19, A. Weissberger, Ed.), Interscience, New York, 1964, p. 41.
83. P. E. Fanta and A. S. Deutsch, *J. Org. Chem.*, **23**, 72 (1958).
84. P. E. Fanta, L. P. Pandya, W. R. Groskopf, and H.-J. Su, *J. Org. Chem.*, **28**, 413 (1963).
85. E. K. Fields and J. M. Sandri, *Angew. Chem.*, **72**, 89 (1960).
86. E. K. Fields and J. M. Sandri, *Chem. Ind. (London)*, **1959**, 1216.
87. J. E. Franz and C. Osuch, *Chem. Ind. (London)*, **1964**, 2058.
88. J. E. Franz and C. Osuch, *Tetrahedron Letters*, **1963**, 837.
89. J. E. Franz, C. Osuch, and M. W. Dietrich, *J. Org. Chem.*, **29**, 2922 (1964).
90. J. S. Fruton, in *Three-, Four-, Five-, and Six-Membered Monocyclic Compounds Containing One O, N, and S Atom (Heterocyclic Compounds*, Vol. I, R. C. Elderfield, Ed.), Wiley, New York, 1950.
91. R. Fusco, G. Biazhetti, and D. Pocar, *Gazz. Chim. Ital.*, **91**, 933 (1961); *Chem. Abstr.*, **56**, 14020 (1962).
92. R. C. Fuson and C. L. Zirkle, *J. Am. Chem. Soc.*, **70**, 2700 (1948).
93. S. Gabriel and R. Stelzner, *Chem. Ber.*, **28**, 2929 (1895).
94. A. Gilman and F. S. Phillips, *Science*, **103**, 409 (1946).
95. A. A. Goldberg and W. Kelly, *J. Chem. Soc.*, **1948**, 1919.
96. C. Golumbic, J. S. Fruton, and M. Bergmann, *J. Org. Chem.*, **11**, 518 (1946), and following papers.
97. J. D. P. Graham, *Brit. J. Pharmacol.*, **12**, 489 (1957).
98. K. Hafner and W. Kaiser, *Tetrahedron Letters*, **1964**, 2185.

99. K. Hafner, W. Kaiser, and R. Puttner, *Tetrahedron Letters*, **1964**, 3953.

100. K. Hafner and C. König, *Angew. Chem.*, **75**, 89 (1963).

101. K. Hafner, D. Zinser, and K.-L. Mortiz, *Tetrahedron Letters*, **1964**, 1733.

102. C. E. Ham, *J. Org. Chem.*, **29**, 3052, (1964).

103. W. E. Hanby, G. S. Hartley, E. O. Powell, and H. N. Rydon, *J. Chem. Soc.*, **1947**, 519.

104. A. W. Hay, A. L. Thompson, and C. A. Winkler, *Can. J. Res.*, **26B**, 175 (1948).

105. J. F. Heacock and M. T. Edmison, *J. Am. Chem. Soc.*, **82**, 3460 (1960).

106. H. W. Heine, *Angew. Chem. Intern. Ed. Engl.*, **1**, 528 (1962).

107. H. W. Heine, *J. Am. Chem. Soc.*, **85**, 2743 (1963).

108. H. W. Heine and H. S. Bender, *J. Org. Chem.*, **25**, 461 (1960).

109. H. W. Heine and A. C. Booker, *J. Org. Chem.*, **27**, 2943 (1962).

110. H. W. Heine, M. E. Fetter, and E. M. Nicholson, *J. Am. Chem. Soc.*, **81**, 2202 (1959).

111. H. W. Heine and B. L. Kapur, *J. Am. Chem. Soc.*, **77**, 4892 (1955).

112. H. W. Heine, B. L. Kapur, J. L. Bove, R. W. Greiner, K. H. Klinger, and C. Mitch, *J. Am. Chem. Soc.*, **76**, 2503 (1954).

113. H. W. Heine, B. L. Kapur, and C. S. Mitch, *J. Am. Chem. Soc.*, **76**, 1173 (1954).

114. H. W. Heine, W. G. Kennyon, and E. M. Johnson, *J. Am. Chem. Soc.*, **83**, 2570 (1961).

115. H. W. Heine and Z. Proctor, *J. Org. Chem.*, **23**, 1554 (1958).

116. H. W. Heine and F. Scholer, *Tetrahedron Letters*, **1964**, 3667.

117. H. W. Heine and D. A. Tomalia, *J. Am. Chem. Soc.*, **84**, 993 (1962).

118. G. K. Helmkamp, R. D. Clark, and J. R. Koskinen, *J. Org. Chem.*, **30**, 666 (1965).

119. G. F. Hennion and P. E. Butler, *J. Org. Chem.*, **27**, 2088 (1962).

120. G. Herzberg, *Molecular Spectra and Molecular Structure*, Van Nostrand, Princeton, N.J., 1950, p. 369.

121. G. Herzberg and D. N. Travis, *Can. J. Phys.*, **42**, 1658 (1964).

122. R. Holland, W. D. Style, R. N. Dixon, and D. A. Ramsay, *Nature*, **182**, 336 (1958).

123. L. Horner, *Angew. Chem. Intern. Ed. Engl.*, **2**, 599 (1963).

124. L. Horner and A. Christmann, *Chem. Ber.*, **96**, 388 (1963).

125. L. Horner, A. Christmann, and A. Gross, *Chem. Ber.*, **96**, 399 (1963).

126. L. Horner, E. Spietschka, and A. Gross, *Ann. Chem.*, **573**, 17 (1951).

127. R. Huisgen, *Angew. Chem.*, **72**, 359 (1960).

128. R. Huisgen, *Naturw. Rundschau*, **14**, 43 (1961).

129. R. Huisgen and R. Appel, *Chem. Ber.*, **91**, 12 (1958).

130. R. Huisgen and H. Blaschke, *Tetrahedron Letters*, **1964**, 1409.

131. R. Huisgen, E. Laschtuvka, and F. Bayerlein, *Chem. Ber.*, **93**, 392 (1960).

132. R. Huisgen, E. Laschtuvka, I. Ugi, and A. Kammermeier, *Ann. Chem.*, **630**, 128 (1960).

133. R. Huisgen and F. Mietzsch, *Angew. Chem.*, **76**, 36 (1964); *Angew. Chem. Intern. Ed. Engl.*, **3**, 83 (1964).

134. Y. Iwakura and A. Nabeya, *J. Chem. Soc. Japan, Pure Chem. Sect.*, **77**, 773 (1963).

135. Y. Iwakura and A. Nabeya, *J. Org. Chem.*, **25**, 1118 (1960).

136. M. E. Jacox and D. E. Milligan, *J. Am. Chem. Soc.*, **85**, 278 (1963).

137. G. D. Jones, A. Langsjoen, Sr., M. M. C. Neumann, and J. Zomlefer, *J. Org. Chem.*, **9**, 125 (1944).

138. P. K. Kadaba and J. O. Edwards, *J. Org. Chem.*, **25**, 1431 (1960).
139. P. K. Kadaba and J. O. Edwards, *J. Org. Chem.*, **26**, 2331 (1961).
140. D. V. Kashelikar and P. E. Fanta, *J. Am. Chem. Soc.*, **82**, 4927 (1960).
141. D. V. Kashelikar and P. E. Fanta, *J. Am. Chem. Soc.*, **82**, 4930 (1960).
142. D. V. Kashelikar and P. E. Fanta, *J. Org. Chem.*, **26**, 1841 (1961).
143. T. J. Katz and P. J. Garratt, *J. Am. Chem. Soc.*, **85**, 2852 (1963).
144. J. F. Kerwin, G. E. Ullyot, R. C. Fuson, and C. L. Zirkle, *J. Am. Chem. Soc.*, **69**, 2961 (1947).
145. F. E. King, *J. Chem. Soc.*, **1949**, 1318.
146. W. Kirmse, *Angew. Chem.*, **67**, 439 (1955).
147. W. Kirmse, *Angew. Chem.*, **73**, 161 (1961).
148. I. L. Knunyants, N. P. Gambaryan, and E. M. Rokhlin, *Usp. Khim.*, **27**, 1361 (1958).
149. R. Kreher and G. H. Bockhorn, *Angew. Chem.*, **76**, 681 (1964).
150. N. J. Leonard and L. E. Brady, *J. Org. Chem.*, **30**, 817 (1965).
151. N. J. Leonard and F. P. Hauck, Jr., *J. Am. Chem. Soc.*, **79**, 5279 (1957).
152. N. J. Leonard and A. S. Hay, *J. Am. Chem. Soc.*, **78**, 1984 (1956).
153. N. J. Leonard, A. S. Hay, R. W. Fulmer, and V. W. Gash, *J. Am. Chem. Soc.*, **77**, 439 (1955).
154. N. J. Leonard and K. Jann, *J. Am. Chem. Soc.*, **82**, 6418 (1960).
155. N. J. Leonard and K. Jann, *J. Am. Chem. Soc.*, **84**, 4806 (1962).
156. N. J. Leonard, K. Jann, J. V. Paukstelis, and C. K. Steinhardt, *J. Org. Chem.*, **28**, 1499 (1963).
157. N. J. Leonard, E. F. Kiefer, and L. E. Brady, *J. Org. Chem.*, **28**, 2850 (1963).
158. N. J. Leonard and J. V. Paukstelis, *J. Org. Chem.*, **30**, 821 (1965).
159. N. J. Leonard, J. V. Paukstelis, and L. E. Brady, *J. Org. Chem.*, **29**, 3383 (1964).
160. N. J. Leonard, C. K. Steinhardt, and C. Lee, *J. Org. Chem.*, **27**, 4027 (1962).
161. A. L. Logothetis, *J. Org. Chem.*, **29**, 3049 (1964).
162. A. L. Logothetis, *J. Org. Chem.*, **29**, 3050 (1964).
163. R. Lukes and O. Grossman, *Collection Czech. Chem. Commun.*, **8**, 533 (1936).
164. W. Lwowski, A. Hartenstein, C. de Vita, and R. I. Smick, *Tetrahedron Letters*, **1964**, 2497.
165. W. Lwowski and T. J. Maricich, *J. Am. Chem. Soc.*, **86**, 3164 (1964).
166. W. Lwowski, T. J. Maricich, and T. W. Mattingly, Jr., *J. Am. Chem. Soc.*, **85**, 1200 (1963).
167. W. Lwowski and T. W. Mattingly, Jr., *J. Am. Chem. Soc.*, **87**, 1947 (1965).
168. W. Lwowski and T. W. Mattingly, Jr., *Tetrahedron Letters*, **1962**, 277.
169. W. Marckwald and O. Frobenius, *Chem. Ber.*, **34**, 3544 (1901).
170. S. Masamune and N. T. Castellucci, *Angew. Chem.*, **76**, 569 (1964); *Angew. Chem. Intern. Ed. Engl.*, **3**, 582 (1964).
171. W. L. Mosby, *Heterocyclic Systems with Bridgehead Nitrogen Atoms*, Interscience, New York, 1961, pp. 7–34.
172. A. Mustafa, *J. Chem. Soc.*, **1949**, 234.
173. A. C. Oehlschlager and L. H. Zalkow, *Chem. Commun.*, **1965**, 70.
174. W. E. Parham, W. T. Hunter, R. Hanson, and T. Lahr, *J. Am. Chem. Soc.*, **74**, 5646 (1952).
175. R. Pettit, *Tetrahedron Letters*, **1960**, 11.
176. G. J. Pontrelli and A. G. Anastassiou, *J. Chem. Phys.*, in press (1965).
177. D. H. Powers, Jr., V. B. Schatz, and L. B. Clapp, *J. Am. Chem. Soc.*, **78**, 907 (1956).

178. T. J. Prosser, A. F. Marcantonio, and D. S. Breslow, *Tetrahedron Letters*, **1964**, 2479.

179. T. J. Prosser, A. F. Marcantonio, C. A. Genge, and D. S. Breslow, *Tetrahedron Letters*, **1964**, 2483.

180. R. Puttner and K. Hafner, *Tetrahedron Letters*, **1964**, 3119.

181. R. Puttner and K. Hafner, in K. Hafner, W. Kaiser, and R. Puttner, *Tetrahedron Letters*, **1964**, 3953.

182. L. C. Raiford and H. B. Freyermuth, *J. Org. Chem.*, **8**, 230 (1943).

183. H. G. Reiber and T. D. Stewart, *J. Am. Chem. Soc.*, **62**, 3026 (1940).

184. S. D. Ross, *J. Am. Chem. Soc.*, **69**, 2982 (1947).

185. K. E. Russell, *J. Am. Chem. Soc.*, **77**, 3487 (1955).

186. S. Sarel and H. Leader, *J. Am. Chem. Soc.*, **82**, 4752 (1960).

187. F. C. Schaefer, *J. Am. Chem. Soc.*, **77**, 5922 (1955).

188. P. Scheiner, J. H. Schomaker, S. Deming, W. J. Libbey, and G. P. Nowack, *J. Am. Chem. Soc.*, **87**, 306 (1965).

189. G. O. Schenck and R. Steinmetz, *Ann. Chem.*, **668**, 199 (1963).

190. J. C. Sheehan and J. W. Frankenfeld, *J. Am. Chem. Soc.*, **83**, 4792 (1961).

191. J. C. Sheehan and P. T. Izzo, *J. Am. Chem. Soc.*, **70**, 1985 (1948).

192. J. C. Sheehan and P. T. Izzo, *J. Am. Chem. Soc.*, **71**, 4059 (1949).

193. J. C. Sheehan and I. Lengyel, *J. Am. Chem. Soc.*, **86**, 1356 (1964).

194. J. C. Sheehan and I. Lengyel, *J. Org. Chem.*, **28**, 3252 (1953).

195. P. S. Skell and R. M. Etter, *Proc. Chem. Soc.*, **1961**, 443.

196. P. S. Skell and A. Y. Garner, *J. Am. Chem. Soc.*, **78**, 5430 (1956).

197. W. A. Skinner, A. P. Martinez, H. F. Gram, L. Goodman, and B. R. Baker, *J. Org. Chem.*, **26**, 148 (1961).

198. M. F. Sloan, T. J. Prossor, N. R. Newburg, and D. S. Breslow, *Tetrahedron Letters*, **1964**, 2945.

199. P. A. S. Smith and J. H. Boyer, *J. Am. Chem. Soc.*, **73**, 2626 (1951).

200. P. A. S. Smith and B. B. Brown, *J. Am. Chem. Soc.*, **73**, 2435 (1951).

201. P. A. S. Smith and B. B. Brown, *J. Am. Chem. Soc.*, **73**, 2438 (1951).

202. P. A. S. Smith, B. B. Brown, R. K. Putney, and R. F. Reinisch, *J. Am. Chem. Soc.*, **75**, 6335 (1953).

203. P. A. S. Smith, J. M. Clegg, and J. H. Hall, *J. Org. Chem.*, **23**, 524 (1958).

204. P. A. S. Smith and J. H. Hall, *J. Am. Chem. Soc.*, **84**, 480 (1962).

205. G. Smolinsky, *J. Am. Chem. Soc.*, **82**, 4717 (1960).

206. G. Smolinsky, *J. Am. Chem. Soc.*, **83**, 2489 (1961).

207. G. Smolinsky, *J. Am. Chem. Soc.*, **83**, 4483 (1961).

208. G. Smolinsky, *J. Org. Chem.*, **26**, 4108 (1961).

209. G. Smolinsky, *J. Org. Chem.*, **27**, 3557 (1962).

210. G. Smolinsky and B. I. Feuer, *J. Am. Chem. Soc.*, **86**, 3085 (1964).

211. G. Smolinsky, L. C. Synder, and E. Wasserman, *Rev. Mod. Phys.*, **35**, 576 (1963).

212. G. Smolinsky, E. Wasserman, and W. A. Yager, *J. Am. Chem. Soc.*, **84**, 3220 (1960).

213. S. B. Soloway and S. J. Cristol, *J. Org. Chem.*, **25**, 327 (1960).

214. W. Steinkopf and H. Augestad-Jenson, *Ann. Chem.*, **428**, 154 (1922).

215. T. D. Stewart and W. E. Bradley, *J. Am. Chem. Soc.*, **54**, 4192 (1932).

216. D. Swern, in *Organic Reactions*, Vol. 7, R. Adams, Ed., Wiley, New York, 1953 p. 378.

217. P. B. Talukdar and P. E. Fanta, *J. Org. Chem.*, **24**, 526 (1959).

218. D. S. Tarbell and C. Weaver, *J. Am. Chem. Soc.*, **63**, 2939 (1941).

219. A. P. TerBog and A. F. Bickel, *Proc. Chem. Soc.*, **1958**, 283.
220. J. F. Tilney-Bassett, *J. Chem. Soc.*, **1962**, 2517.
221. M. Tisler, *Arch. Pharm.*, **291**, 457 (1958).
222. A. M. Trozollo, R. W. Murray, G. Smolinsky, W. A. Yager, and E. Wasserman, *J. Am. Chem. Soc.*, **85**, 2526 (1963).
223. A. B. Turner, H. W. Heine, J. Irving, and J. J. Bush, Jr., *J. Am. Chem. Soc.*, **87**, 1050 (1965).
224. E. Vogel, *Angew. Chem.*, **74**, 829 (1962).
225. E. Vogel, *Angew. Chem. Intern. Ed. Engl.*, **2**, 1 (1963).
226. E. Vogel, W. Wiedemann, H. Kiefer, and W. F. Harrison, *Tetrahedron Letters*, **1963**, 673.
227. A. Wagner, *Angew. Chem.*, **71**, 386 (1959).
228. W. M. Wagner, *Proc. Chem. Soc.*, **1959**, 229.
229. H. M. Walborsky and D. F. Loncrini, *J. Am. Chem. Soc.*, **76**, 5396 (1954).
230. P. Walker and W. A. Waters, *J. Chem. Soc.*, **1962**, 1632.
231. E. Wasserman, G. Smolinsky, and W. A. Yager, *J. Am. Chem. Soc.*, **86**, 3166 (1964).
232. W. West, *Chemical Applications of Spectroscopy*, Interscience, New York, 1956, p. 413.
233. H. W. Whitlock, Jr. and G. L. Smith, *Tetrahedron Letters*, **1965**, 1389.
234. K. L. Wolff, *Ann. Chem.*, **394**, 68 (1912).
235. P. Yates, D. G. Farnum, and D. W. Wiley, *Tetrahedron*, **18**, 881 (1962).
236. L. H. Zalkow and C. D. Kennedy, *J. Org. Chem.*, **28**, 3309 (1963).
237. L. H. Zalkow and A. C. Oehlschlager, *J. Org. Chem.*, **28**, 3303 (1963).
238. L. H. Zalkow, A. C. Oehlschlager, G. A. Cabat, and R. L. Hale, *Chem. Ind. (London)*, **1964**, 1556.
239. H. Zollinger, *Azo and Diazo Chemistry*, Interscience, New York, 1963, pp. 82, 110.

## 2. Silicon or Germanium

### a. Silacyclopropanes

It is known that carbene intermediates, $R_2C$:, react with $\diagup C{=}C\diagdown$ double-bonded compounds via a cycloaddition reaction to form an unstable cyclopropane ring[3,16] which undergoes rearrangement to propylene.[8,20,21] It appears then that if a silicon analog of carbene,

$R_2Si:$,[2,7,15,17,23,24,26-28] could be formed it would react in a similar manner—via a cycloaddition reaction—with ethylene to form a three-membered heterocyclic compound, silacyclopropane, containing a silicon atom in the ring, which would in all probability be unstable.

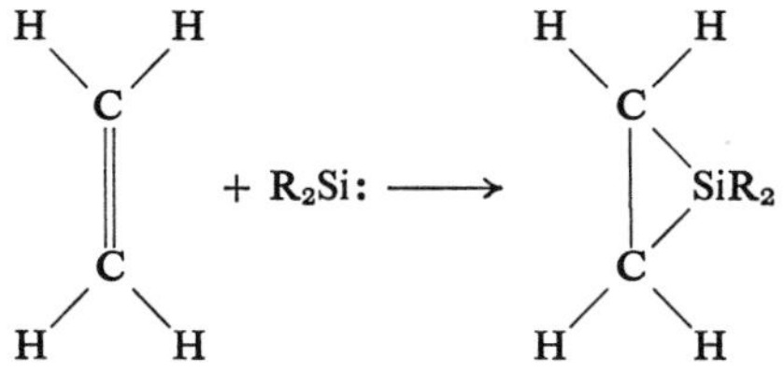

Recently, dimethylsilene, $(CH_3)_2Si:$, was synthesized as a short-lived intermediate by the reaction of sodium–potassium vapor and dimethyl-dichlorosilane at temperatures between 260° and 280° in a helium atmosphere (200 mm) resulting in polymeric products.[20,21] If trimethylsilane, $(CH_3)_3Si$—H, is added to the reaction mixture the dimethylsilene intermediate inserts into the Si—H bond to produce pentamethyldisilane.[10,11,19]

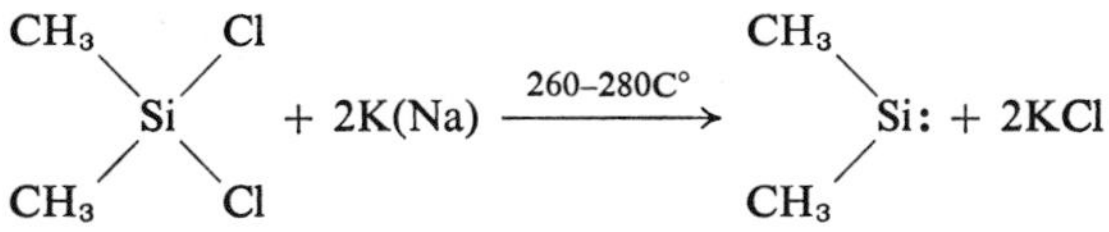

Previous reports claiming dimethylsilene intermediates in condensed systems are ambiguous.[9,25] Observations of the reaction of trimethylsilane and the dimethylsilene intermediate not only indicate the formation

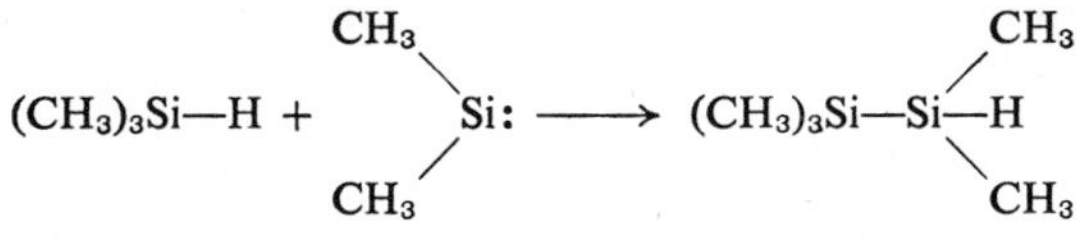

of a dimethylsilene intermediate, but also indicate it is in the singlet electronic configuration which for kinetic reasons is considered to be the ground state.[20,21]

Evidence for the existence of the dimethylsilene intermediate, $(CH_3)_2Si:$, has also been independently offered by Russian chemists.[12,13] They also used dimethyldichlorosilane, but treated it with lithium in tetrahydrofuran with ethylene being passed through the reaction mixture (at 0–10°C). Dimethyldichlorosilane, ethylene, metallic sodium, and benzene in a autoclave at 105–120°C also gave the silene intermediate. A third method of generating the dimethylsilene intermediate is the thermal degradation of polydimethylsilene, $[(CH_3)_2Si]_{55}$,[1] at 300°C[23] in the presence of ethylene

(*1*), resulting in silicon-containing heterocycles (*4, 5*), telomers (*2*), and polymers (*3*).

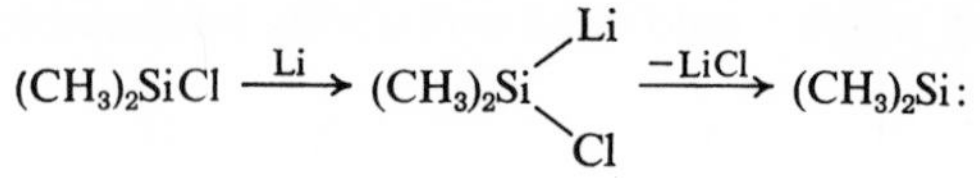

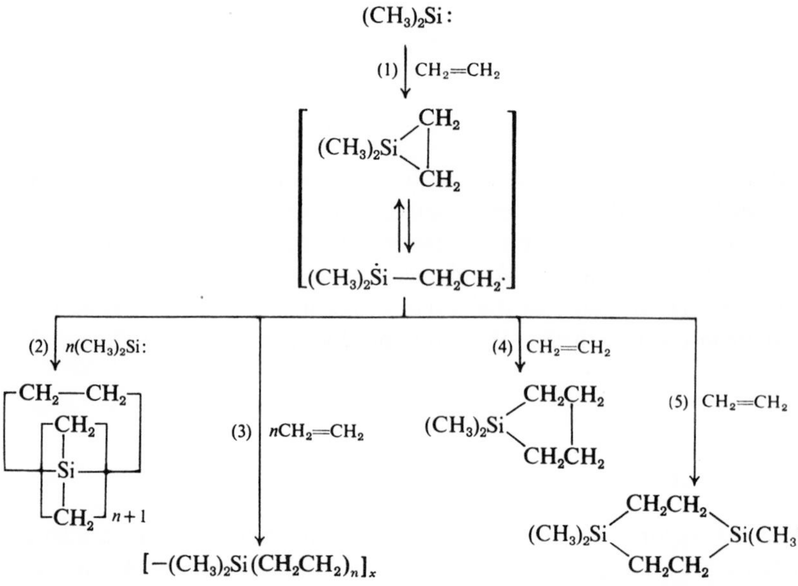

$$(CH_3)_2SiCl \xrightarrow{Li} (CH_3)_2Si\begin{smallmatrix} Li \\ \diagdown \\ Cl \end{smallmatrix} \xrightarrow{-LiCl} (CH_3)_2Si:$$

$$(CH_3)_2Si:$$

The assumption of the formation of the dimethylsilene intermediate is the only plausible explanation for the products mentioned above, since lithium does not add onto the $\diagup C{=}C\diagdown$ double bond of monoolefins under the reaction conditions employed [22] and ethylene does not react with silicon–lithium bonds at 105–120°C.[4, 29] Intermediary formation of silenes must always be expected when diorganyldichlorosilanes are treated with alkali metals.[5, 14, 15] Recently, H. Gilman and co-workers[6] investigated the use of 7-silanorbornadienes as precursors of silene intermediates. The most compelling evidence for the formation of the silene intermediate was

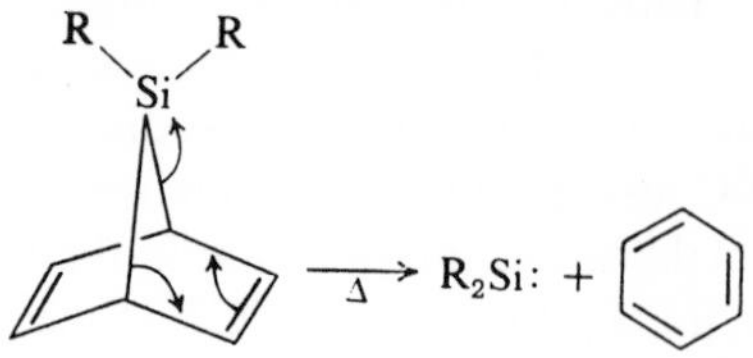

from the pyrolysis of 2,3-benzo-7,7-dimethyl-1,4,5,6-tetraphenyl-7-silanor-
bornadiene (1) at 300° giving 1,2,3,4-tetraphenylnaphthalene and amorphous dimethylsilyl polymer $[(CH_3)_2Si]_n$, as is shown here.

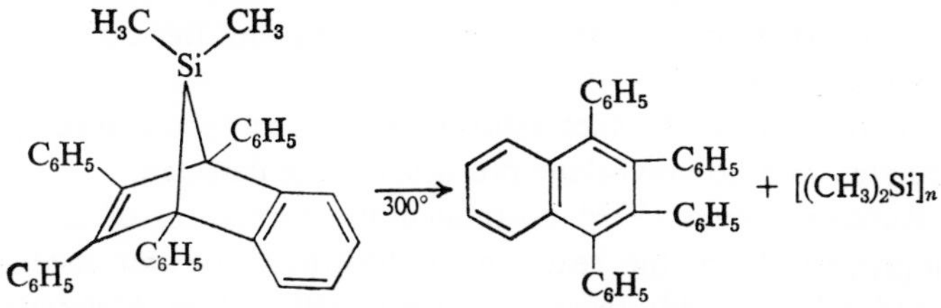

Referring again to the work by Skell and Goldstein[20,21] and that by
Nefedov and co-workers,[12,13] in both instances a very unstable silacyclopropane was postulated as being formed by the reaction of the dimethylsilene intermediate and ethylene. In the case of Skell's work the unstable
silacyclopropane is thought to undergo rearrangement to a vinylsilane:

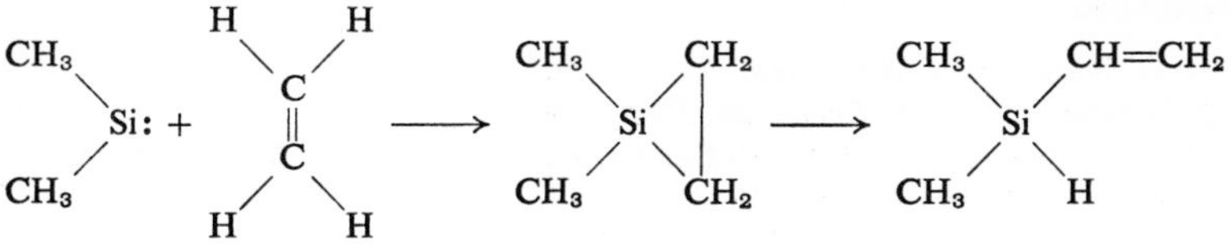

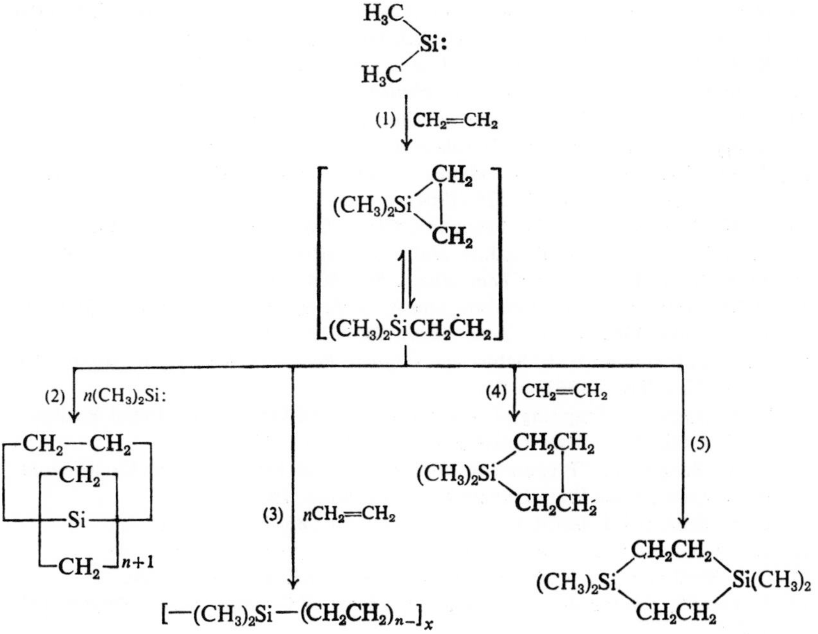

Rearrangement to olefinic products analogous to that of alkylcarbenes[8] is not favored by dimethylsilene due to the relative instability of the silicon-to-carbon double bond. The large difference in thermal stability of cyclopropanes and silacyclopropanes is attributed to strain enhanced in the latter by the large size of the silicon atom, making the carbon–silicon–carbon angle $\cong 48°$.[20,21]

There were, however, no successful attempts to trap the silacyclopropane intermediates, and no vinylsilane precursors were detected.

The Russian chemists[12,13] postulated the formation of an unstable silacyclopropane from the reaction of dimethylsilene intermediate and ethylene (1) which readily reacts with the dimethylsilene intermediate (2), with excess ethylene (3), with one mole of ethylene (4), and finally with itself (5) to form the corresponding products.

Thus, to this date there has been no success in isolating a three-membered heterocyclic compound containing silicon.

REFERENCES

1. C. A. Buckhard, *J. Am. Chem. Soc.*, **71** 963 (1949).
2. J. Diekmann, *J. Org. Chem.*, **28**, 2880 (1963).
3. W. v. E. Doering and A. K. Hoffmann, *J. Am. Chem. Soc.*, **77**, 6162 (1959).
4. V. Franzen, *Chem. Ber.*, **95**, 1964 (1962).
5. H. Gilman, *Angew. Chem.*, **74**, 950 (1962).
6. H. Gilman, S. G. Cottis, and W. H. Atwell, *J. Am. Chem. Soc.*, **86**, 1596 (1964).
7. H. Gilman and G. D. Litchenwalter, *J. Org. Chem.*, **24**, 1588 (1959).
8. R. A. Holroyd and F. E. Blacet, *J. Am. Chem. Soc.*, **79**, 4839 (1957).
9. F. Johnson and R. S. Gohlke, *Tetrahedron Letters*, **1962**, 1291.
10. K. Kramer and A. Wright, *Angew. Chem.*, **74**, 468 (1962).
11. K. Kramer and A. Wright, *Tetrahedron Letters*, **1962**, 1095.
12. O. M. Nefedov and M. N. Manakov, *Angew. Chem.*, **76**, 270 (1964); *Angew. Chem. Intern. Ed. Engl.*, **3**, 226 (1964).
13. O. M. Nefedov and M. N. Manakov, *Chem. Eng. News*, April 6, 1964, p. 40.
14. O. M. Nefedov, M. N. Manakov, and A. D. Petrov, *Izv. Akad. Nauk SSSR., Otd. Khim. Nauk*, **1961**, 1717; *Chem. Abstr.*, **56**, 3504 (1962).
15. O. M. Nefedov, M. N. Manakov, and A. D. Petrov, *Izv. Akad. Nauk SSSR, Otd. Khim. Nauk*, **1962**, 1228; *Chem. Abstr.*, **58**, 5713 (1963).
16. W. E. Parham and E. E. Schweizer, *Organic Reactions*, Vol. 13, R. Adams, Ed., Wiley, New York, 1963, p. 55.
17. D. J. Peterson, "Trapping of Organometallic and Organometallodial Radicals," Ph.D. thesis, Iowa State University, Ames, Iowa, 1962.
18. G. L. Schwebke, "Preparation and Stability of Perphenylated Cyclosilanes," Ph.D. thesis, Iowa State University, Ames, Iowa, 1964.
19. D. Seyferth and J. Burlitch, *J. Am. Chem. Soc.*, **85**, 2667 (1963).
20. P. S. Skell and E. J. Goldstein, *Chem. Eng. News*, April 6, 1964, p. 40.
21. P. S. Skell and E. J. Goldstein, *J. Am. Chem. Soc.*, **86**, 1442 (1964).
22. P. Vaculik, *Chemie der Monomeren*, Academy of Czechoslovakia, Prague, 1956, Vol. I.

23. M. E. Volpin, Yu. D. Koreshkov, V. G. Dulova, and D. N. Kursanov, *Tetrahedron*, **18**, 107 (1962).
24. M. E. Volpin and D. N. Kursanov, *Zh. Obshch. Khim.*, **32**, 1137 (1962).
25. R. West and R. E. Bailey, *J. Am. Chem. Soc.*, **85**, 2871 (1963).
26. E. Wiberg, O. Stecher, H. J. Andraschek, L. Kreuzblicher, and E. Staude, *Angew. Chem. Intern. Ed. Engl.*, **2**, 507 (1963).
27. D. Wittenberg, M. V. George, and H. Gilman, *J. Am. Chem. Soc.*, **81**, 4812 (1959).
28. W. G. Woods, *J. Org. Chem.*, **23**, 110 (1958).
29. K. Ziegler and H. G. Gellert, *Ann. Chem.*, **567**, 195 (1950).

### b. Silirenes

It has been proposed[25,29] that three-membered heterocyclic compounds of the type **2** can be prepared by replacing the $C^{\oplus}$—H group in the cyclopropenyl cation (**1b**)[2,5-9,13,16,26,27] by a heteroatom with an available orbital, particularly those heteroatoms with a vacant *p*-orbital or *d*-orbital.

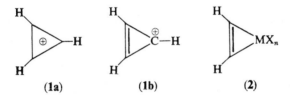

(1a)  (1b)  (2)

where M = heteroatom.

With silicon, as well as with germanium or tin, the possibility of *p-p-p* and *p-p-d* interaction in the three-membered heterocyclic system may occur. By replacing the $\diagup C^{\oplus}$—H in formula **1b** by $Si^{\oplus}$, $Ge^{\oplus}$, or $Sn^{\oplus}$ it was thought to give rise to systems of type **3**.[25] Numerous investigations, however, have

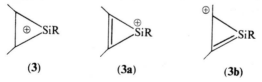

(3)  (3a)  (3b)

shown that silicon compounds do not form $R_3Si^{\oplus}$.[14] Also, stable multiple bonds of the type $\diagup Si{=}X$ are not formed from tetracovalent silicon, germanium or tin compounds, so that structures of type **3a** and **3b** are unstable, making **3** unlikely.[25] Data concerning dipole moments,[20] spectra, and reactivity of organosilicon compounds[14] indicate a relative stability of structures containing pentacovalent negatively charged silicon of the type $R_3Si^{\ominus}=C\!\!<$ produced by participation of the $3d$ orbitals of silicon. Volpin and co-workers[25] proposed that in three-membered cyclic systems of the type (4) the $2p$ electrons of the carbon atoms and the $3d$ orbital of the silicon atom interact leading to a stable system described by formula 4a.

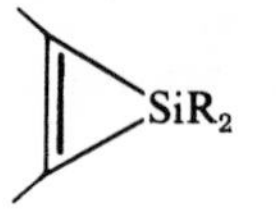

(4) 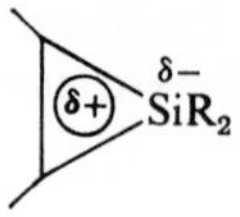                    (4a)

The most useful method of obtaining three-membered cyclopropyl derivatives is via the cycloaddition reaction of carbenes to double bonds.[11,23] Carbene intermediates have been used in cycloaddition reactions with —C≡C— triple bonds to synthesize unsaturated three-

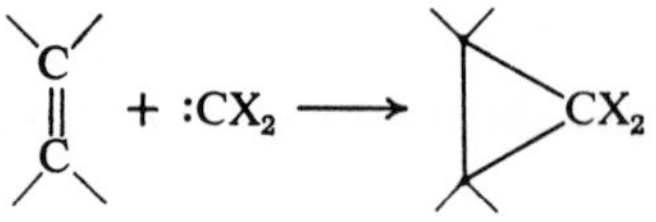

membered cycles as derivatives of cyclopropene,[3,12] or those of the cyclopropenyl system.[21,25,26]

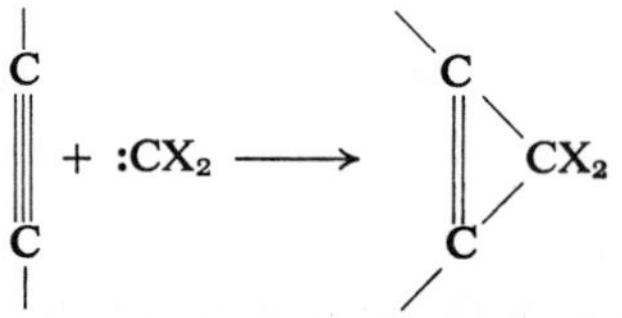

The similarity between the electron structure and the reactivity of the carbene intermediate, $R_2C$:, and their inorganic analogs—for example the silene intermediates, $R_2Si$:—suggests that it would undergo a cycloaddition reaction with multiple bonds to give a three-membered heterocyclic compound (5).

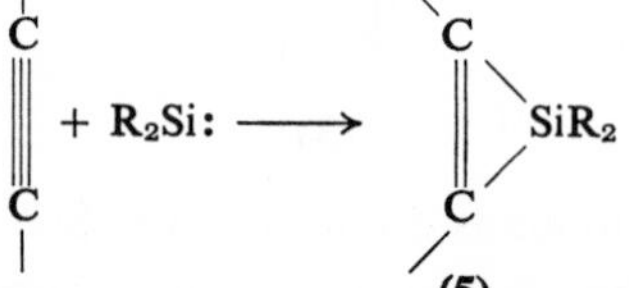

(5)

It was thought that if the dimethylsilene intermediate (see Section IIA–2a) was generated in the presence of diphenylacetylene, a three-membered ring (6) would arise via a cycloaddition reaction. A compound was isolated whose composition, molecular weight, infrared spectrum, and chemical evidence indicated that structure **6** was correct.[25, 28]

$$\begin{array}{c} C_6H_5 \\ | \\ C \\ ||| \\ C \\ | \\ C_6H_5 \end{array} + (CH_3)_2Si: \longrightarrow \begin{array}{c} C_6H_5 \\ \diagdown \\ \diagup \hspace{-0.4em} Si \hspace{-0.6em} \begin{array}{c} CH_3 \\ CH_3 \end{array} \\ C_6H_5 \end{array}$$

**(6)**

However, three discrepancies appearing in the Russian paper[25] led Johnson and Gohlke[18] to reinvestigate the nature of the products. The "aromatic character" was based on the stability of the system to the action of bromine, alkali, and strong acids and lack of catalytic hydrogen addition, as well as to heat and oxidation.[25, 18] These properties, with the exception of the inertness to bromine, are common to organometallic systems which are not heteroaromatic, especially in the organogermanium series[10] and to many substituted organosilicon compounds.[15] In regard to the action of bromine on **5**, it was found that the decoloration of bromine was almost complete after an hour at room temperature in carbon tetrachloride solution.

There was a large discrepancy in the determination of the molecular weight of the iodide (**5**) (R = I) ascribed to the association of the compound. And finally, the method used to prepare the silirene derivative (**6**) (reacting dichlorodimethylsilane and sodium in the presence of diphenylacetylene) was very similar to the procedure used in the preparation of metalloles (**7**),[1, 22] suggesting that the silirene could be a silole; also, the

$$\begin{array}{c} \quad R \quad R \\ C_6H_5 \diagdown \hspace{-0.4em} \diagup M \diagdown \hspace{-0.4em} C_6H_5 \\ | \qquad | \\ C_6H_5 \diagup \hspace{2em} \diagdown C_6H_5 \end{array}$$

formation of silirene (**6**) was accompanied by formation of a by-product, 1,2,3-triphenylnapthalene, often observed in the preparation of **7**.

A study by West and Bailey[30] has shown that the silicon compound reported by Volpin[25] has the "silirene" structure (**8**). Mass spectral studies[19] have confirmed the dimeric structure (**8**).

$$\begin{array}{c} H_3C \diagdown \hspace{-0.4em} \diagup CH_3 \\ C_6H_5 \diagdown \hspace{-0.4em} Si \diagdown \hspace{-0.4em} C_6H_5 \\ | \qquad | \\ C_6H_5 \diagdown \hspace{-0.4em} Si \diagdown \hspace{-0.4em} C_6H_5 \\ H_3C \diagup \hspace{-0.4em} \diagdown CH_3 \end{array}$$

**(8)**

Recently, Gilman and co-workers[17] found that the reaction of a dimethylsilene polymer[24] $[(CH_3)_2Si]_n$ with diphenylacetylene at 280–290° for 8 hr did not give 1,4-disilacyclohexadiene (**8**); therefore the reaction is not general for dimethylsilene polymers. Pyrolysis of 2,3-benzo-7,7-dimethyl-1,4,5,6-tetraphenyl-7-silanorbornadiene, a silene precursor, in the presence of diphenylacetylene gave 1,2,3,4-tetraphenylnaphthalene and **8**.[17] No

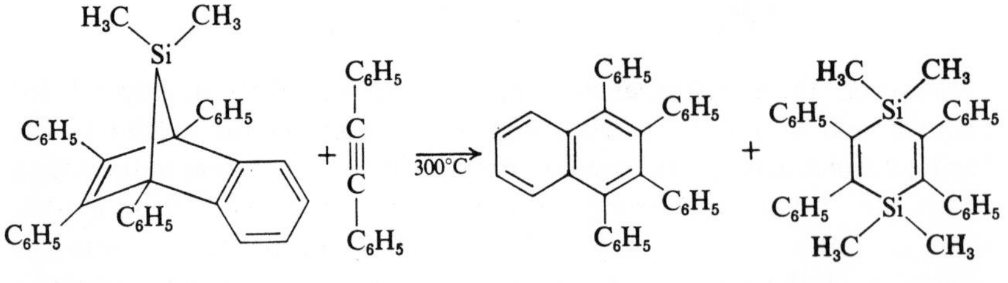

material corresponding to the silirene (**6**), however, was isolated, but it was assumed that if **6** was formed it could dimerize under the pyrolysis conditions employed to give an intermediate (**9**) followed by rearrangement to the observed 1,4-disilacyclohexadiene (**8**).[17] An intermediate similar to **9** may be involved in the rearrangement of bistriphenylcyclopropenyl to hexaphenylbenzene.[4] There has been no further experimental evidence to

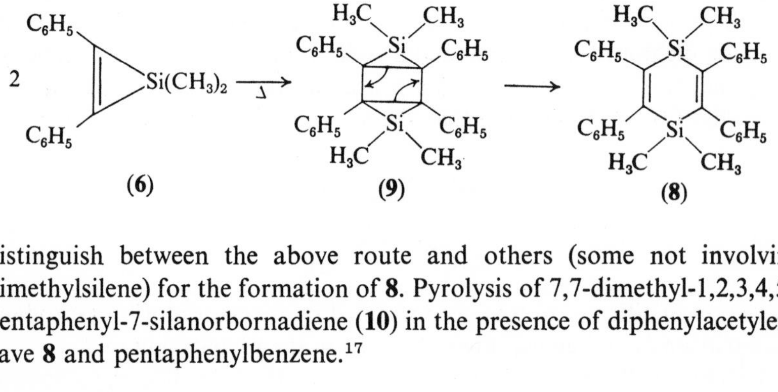

distinguish between the above route and others (some not involving dimethylsilene) for the formation of **8**. Pyrolysis of 7,7-dimethyl-1,2,3,4,5,-pentaphenyl-7-silanorbornadiene (**10**) in the presence of diphenylacetylene gave **8** and pentaphenylbenzene.[17]

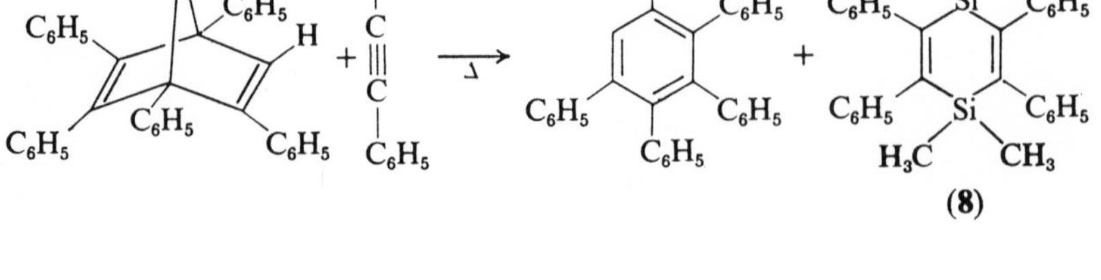

REFERENCES

1. E. H. Braye, W. Hübel, and I. Caplier, *J. Am. Chem. Soc.*, **83**, 4406 (1961).
2. R. Breslow, *J. Am. Chem. Soc.*, **79**, 5318 (1957).
3. R. Breslow and M. Battiste, *Chem. Ind. (London)*, **1958**, 1143.
4. R. Breslow and P. Gal, *J. Am. Chem. Soc.*, **81**, 4747 (1959).
5. R. Breslow, R. Haynie, and J. Mirra, *J. Am. Chem. Soc.*, **81**, 247 (1959).
6. R. Breslow and H. Höver, *J. Am. Chem. Soc.*, **82**, 2644 (1960).
7. R. Breslow and R. Peterson, *J. Am. Chem. Soc.*, **82**, 4426 (1960).
8. R. Breslow and R. Winter, *Abstr. Am. Chem. Soc. Mtg. New York, 1957*, p. 18-P.
9. R. Breslow and C. Yuan, *J. Am. Chem. Soc.*, **80**, 5991 (1958).
10. C. E. Coates, *Organo-Metallic Compounds*, Wiley, New York, 1961, pp. 164ff.
11. W. E. Doering and A. K. Hoffmann, *J. Am. Chem. Soc.*, **76**, 6162 (1959).
12. W. E. Doering and T. Mole, *Tetrahedron*, **10**, 65 (1960).
13. I. A. D'yakonov and M. I. Komendantov, *Vestn. Leningr. Univ.*, **11** (22), *Ser. Fiz. Khim.* (*4*), 166 (1956); *Chem. Abstr.*, **52**, 2762 (1958).
14. C. Eaborn, *Organosilicon Compounds*, Butterworths, London, 1960.
15. C. Eaborn, *Organosilicon Compounds*, Butterworths, London, 1960, pp. 122ff.
16. D. G. Farnum and M. Burr, *J. Am. Chem. Soc.*, **82**, 2651 (1960).
17. H. Gilman, S. G. Cottis, and W. H. Atwell, *J. Am. Chem. Soc.*, **86**, 1596 (1964).
18. F. Johnson and R. S. Gohlke, *Tetrahedron Letters*, **1962**, 1291.
19. F. Johnson and R. S. Gohlke, unpublished results presented at the IUPAC Meeting, London, July, 1963.
20. G. N. Kartsev, Ya. K. Syrkin, V. F. Mironov, and E. A. Chernyshev, *Dokl. Akad. Nauk SSSR*, **122**, 99 (1958); *Chem. Abstr.*, **54**, 23523 (1960).
21. D. N. Kursanov, M. E. Volpin, and Yu. D. Koreshkov, *Zh. Obshch. Khim.*, **30**, 2877 (1960); *Chem. Abstr.*, **55**, 16473 (1961).
22. F. C. Leavitt, T. A. Manuel, F. Johnson, L. U. Matternas, and D. S. Lehman, *J. Am. Chem. Soc.*, **82**, 5099 (1960).
23. W. E. Parham and E. E. Schweizer, *Organic Reactions*, Vol. 13, R. Adams, Ed., Wiley, New York, 1963, pp. 55ff.
24. G. L. Schwebke, "Preparation and Stability of Perphenylated Cyclosilanes," Ph.D. thesis, Iowa State University, Ames, Iowa, 1964.
25. M. E. Volpin, Yu. D. Koreshkov, V. G. Dulova, and D. N. Kursanov, *Tetrahedron*, **18**, 107 (1962).
26. M. E. Volpin, Yu. D. Koreshkov, and D. N. Kursanov, *Izv. Akad. Nauk SSSR, Otd. Khim. Nauk*, **1959**, 560; *Chem. Abstr.*, **53**, 21799 (1959).
27. M. E. Volpin, Yu. D. Koreshkov, and D. N. Kursanov, *J. Gen. Chem. USSR Engl. Transl.*, **30**, 2877 (1960).
28. M. Volpin and D. N. Kursanov, *Izv. Akad. Nauk. SSSR, Otd. Khim. Nauk*, **1960**, 1903; *Chem. Abstr.*, **55**, 14419 (1961).
29. M. E. Volpin and D. N. Kursanov, *Zh. Obshch. Khim.*, **32**, 1137 (1962); *Chem. Abstr.*, **58**, 1332 (1963).
30. R. West and R. E. Bailey, *J. Am. Chem. Soc.*, **85**, 2871 (1963).

### c. Germirenes

Using the same reasoning as that for the formation of the silirenes (see Section II-A-2b), Volpin and co-workers[5,12-17] postulated the formation of three-membered heterocyclic compounds containing a germanium atom—germirenes (1)—via a cycloaddition reaction of the divalent germanium intermediate[11,14,16] germene $R_2Ge:$, with multiple bonded compounds. The germene intermediates can be generated by the reaction

$$\begin{array}{c} R \\ | \\ C \\ ||| \\ C \\ | \\ R \end{array} + \begin{array}{c} R' \\ \diagdown \\ Ge: \\ \diagup \\ R' \end{array} \longrightarrow \begin{array}{c} R \diagdown \\ C \diagdown \\ || \quad GeR'_2 \\ C \diagup \\ R \diagup \end{array}$$

(1)

of $R_2GeCl_2$ with lithium.[9,10] Formation of the germene intermediate,

$$\begin{array}{c} R' \diagdown \quad Cl \diagup \\ Ge \\ R' \diagup \quad Cl \diagdown \end{array} + 2Li \longrightarrow \begin{array}{c} R' \diagdown \\ Ge: + 2LiCl \\ R' \diagup \end{array}$$

$GeHal_2$, has recently been reported to result from the trihalogermane etherates (2)[6-8] formed by the association of $HGeCl_3$ with diethyl ether or di-$n$-butyl ether.

$$HGeCl_3 + 2(C_2H_5)O \longrightarrow 2(C_2H_5)2O \cdot HGeCl_3$$

(2)

$$2(C_2H_5)_2O \cdot HGeCl_3 \rightleftharpoons [:GeCl_2] + 2(C_2H_5)_2O \cdot HCl$$

(2)

Volpin and co-workers found that diiodogermene, $:GeI_2$[11,14,16] does not noticeably react with diphenylacetylene either at room temperature or on being moderately heated but adds, via a cycloaddition reaction, to

$$\begin{array}{c} C_6H_5 \\ | \\ C \\ ||| \\ C \\ | \\ C_6H_5 \end{array} + :GeI_2 \longrightarrow \begin{array}{c} C_6H_5 \diagdown \\ C \diagdown \\ GeI_2 \\ C_6H_5 \diagup \end{array}$$

(3)

diphenylacetylene above 200°C giving rise to a very stable diiodo-germirene (3).[11,13,14,17] The diiodogermirene (3) was reacted with organomagnesium compounds to give the dialkylgermirene (4):

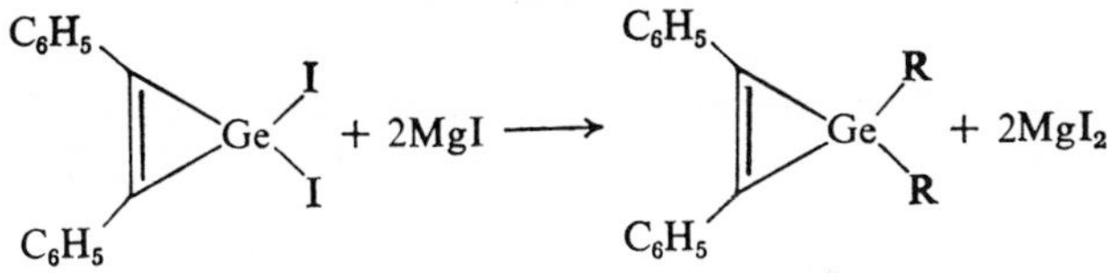

where R = $CH_3$, $C_2H_5$.[13,17]

Upon treatment of 3 with alkali the hydroxy-derivative (5) was obtained which was dehydrated to form a polymeric oxide (6).[13,17] Treatment of

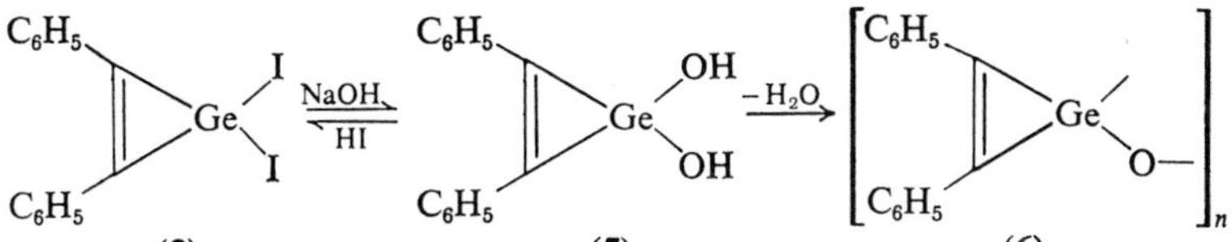

both the hydroxide (5) and the oxide (6) with hydrogen chloride or hydrogen bromide led to the dichloride (7) or the dibromide (8).[13,17]

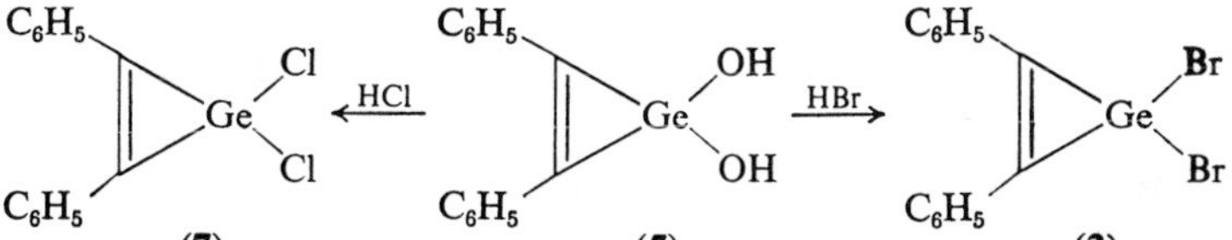

Recently, Johnson and Gohlke[1,2] reported that the germanium compound (1) reported by Volpin[13,14,17] was in reality dimeric in nature, probably of type 9 from the evidence shown by x-ray analysis, nuclear

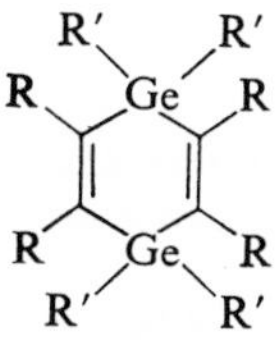

(9)

magnetic resonance, and mass spectra, and molecular weight determination using vapor phase osmometry.[3,4] Volpin and co-workers[18] reinvestigated a monocrystal of the three-membered structure (I, R = H, R = Cl).[12,13,17]

According to x-ray analysis the molecule consists of a plane centro-symmetrical six-membered ring ((9), R = H, R′ = Cl) with the following bond lengths: C=C, $1.3_5$ Å; Ge—C, $1.9_8$ Å; Ge—Cl, $2.1_5$ Å; and the following bond angles: C–Ge–C and C–C–Ge about 120°, Cl–Ge–Cl, 103°. An "electron-graphic"* investigation in the vapor state has confirmed structure 9 as having the parameters: Ge—Cl, $2.1_4$ Å; Ge—C, $1.9_3$ Å; C=C, 1.35 Å; and bond angles, Ge–C–C, 123 ± 2°; C–Ge–C, 113 ± 4°; Cl–Ge–Cl, 104 ± 3°.[18]

From the evidence presented there has been no successful attempt at isolating a germirene compound. Recently, however, the formation of an unstable three-membered cyclogermanium compound has been postulated in the cycloaddition reactions of dichlorogermene, $:GeCl_2$, and multiple-bonded compounds[8] such as acetylene (10), ethylene (11), and 1,3-butadiene (12). These unstable cyclogermanium intermediates react with the etherate (2) to form polymeric products.

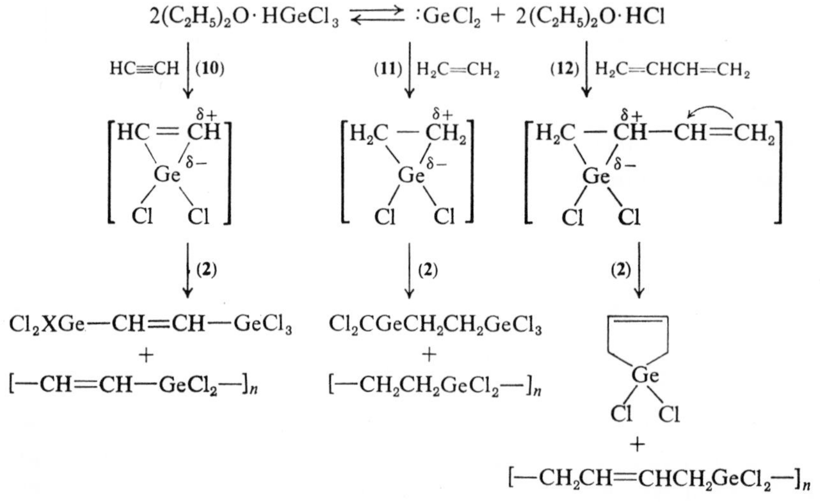

$$2(C_2H_5)_2O \cdot HGeCl_3 \rightleftharpoons \ :GeCl_2 + 2(C_2H_5)_2O \cdot HCl$$

REFERENCES

1. F. Johnson and R. S. Gohlke, *Tetrahedron Letters*, **1962**, 1291.
2. F. Johnson and R. S. Gohlke, unpublished results presented at IUPAC Meeting, London, July, 1963.
3. H. Gilman and G. L. Schwebke, *Advances in Organometallic Chemistry*, Vol. I, F. G. A. Stone and R. West, Eds., Academic Press, New York, 1964.
4. H. Gilman and G. L. Schwebke, *J. Am. Chem. Soc.*, **86**, 1061 (1963).

* The meaning of the word "electron-graphic" is not clear. It is believed that the true meaning was lost in translation and that the word refers to electron diffraction.

5. L. A. Leites, V. G. Dulova, and M. E. Volpin, *Izv. Akad. Nauk SSSR, Otd. Khim. Nauk*, **1963**, 731; *Chem. Abstr.*, **59**, 10104 (1963).

6. O. M. Nefedov and S. P. Kolesnikov, *Izv. Akad. Nauk SSSR, Otd. Khim. Nauk*, **1963**, 2068; *Chem. Abstr.*, **60**, 5534 (1964).

7. O. M. Nefedov, S. P. Kolesnikov, A. S. Chachatyrov, and A. D. Petrov, *Dokl. Akad. Nauk SSSR*, **154**, 1389 (1964); *Chem. Abstr.*, **60**, 12039 (1964).

8. O. M. Nefedov, S. P. Kolesnikov, and V. I. Sheichenko, *Angew. Chem. Intern. Ed. Engl.*, **3**, 508 (1964).

9. O. M. Nefedov and M. N. Manakov, *Angew. Chem.*, **76**, 270 (1964); *Angew. Chem. Intern. Ed. Engl.*, **3**, 226 (1964).

10. O. M. Nefedov and M. N. Manakov, *Chem. Eng. News*, April 6, 1964, p. 40.

11. D. Quane and R. S. Bottei, *Chem. Rev.*, **63**, 403 (1963).

12. M. E. Volpin, V. G. Dulova, and D. N. Kursanov, *Izv. Akad. Nauk SSSR, Otd. Khim. Nauk*, **1963**, 727; *Chem. Abstr.*, **59**, 10104 (1963).

13. M. E. Volpin, Yu. D. Koreshkov, V. G. Dulova, and D. N. Kursanov, *Tetrahedron*, **18**, 107 (1962).

14. M. E. Volpin and D. N. Kursanov, *Izv. Akad. Nauk SSSR, Otd. Khim. Nauk*, **1960**, 1903; *Chem. Abstr.*, **55**, 14419 (1961).

15. M. E. Volpin and D. N. Kursanov, *Zh. Obshch. Khim.*, **32**, 1137 (1962); *Chem. Abstr.*, **58**, 1332 (1963).

16. M. E. Volpin and D. N. Kursanov, *Zh. Obshch. Khim.*, **32**, 1142 (1962); *Chem. Abstr.*, **58**, 1332 (1963).

17. M. E. Volpin and D. N. Kursanov, *Zh. Obshch. Khim.*, **32**, 1455 (1962); Engl. trans., *Ibid.*, **32**, 1443 (1962); *Chem. Abstr.*, **58**, 9111 (1963).

18. M. E. Volpin, Yu. T. Struchkov, L. V. Vilkov, U. S. Mastyukov, V. G. Dulova, and D. N. Kursanov, *Bull. Acad. Sci., USSR, Div. Chem. Sci., Engl. Transl.*, **1963**, 1909.

### 3. Sulfur

#### a. Thiiranes and Thiirane 1,1-Dioxides

Thiiranes,* or episulfides, have been reported as intermediates in the reactions of thio compounds and diazomethanes.[22,58,63-65,71,72] These intermediates decomposed to give unsaturated compounds (Table 1); for example, thiobenzophenone (1) combined with diphenyldiazomethane (2) via a cycloaddition reaction resulting in the formation of the thiirane (3), 2,2,3,3-tetraphenylthiirane, which decomposed into tetraphenylethylene (4)[71] and sulfur upon heating. The cleavage of similar three-membered

$$(C_6H_5)_2C{=}S + (C_6H_5)_2CN_2 \xrightarrow{-N_2}$$

(1)  (2)

(3)  (4)

* For a review of thiiranes see Ref. 53.

rings had previously been observed by Staudinger and Pfenninger[69] when the episulfone (6) 2,2,3,3-tetraphenylthiirane 1,1-dioxide obtained from diphenyldiazomethane (2) and sulfur dioxide (5) decomposed upon heating to give tetraphenylethylene (4) and sulfur dioxide (5).

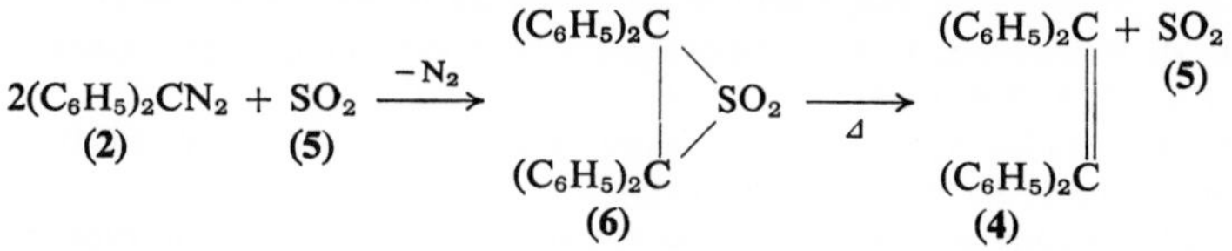

$$2(C_6H_5)_2CN_2 + SO_2 \xrightarrow{-N_2}$$
(2)          (5)

Diphenyldiazomethane (2) also reacted with dithiobenzoic acid esters (7); however, no thiirane derivative (8) was isolated.[71] Only its decomposition product, tetraphenylethylene (4), was isolated. A similar decomposition was observed in the reactions of carbon disulfide (10) and isothiocyanates (11).[71] In all three cases it was assumed that the carbon–sulfur double bond reacted with the diazo compounds; the resulting thiirane derivatives decomposed with evolution of heat into unsaturated compounds which were thought to result from the dimerization of diphenylcarbene (9),[71] that is,

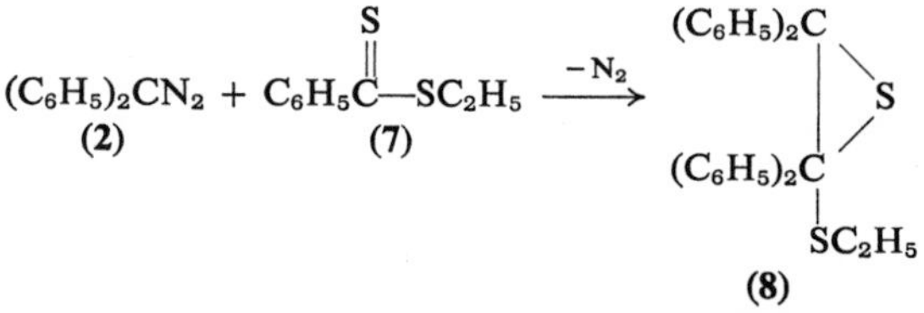

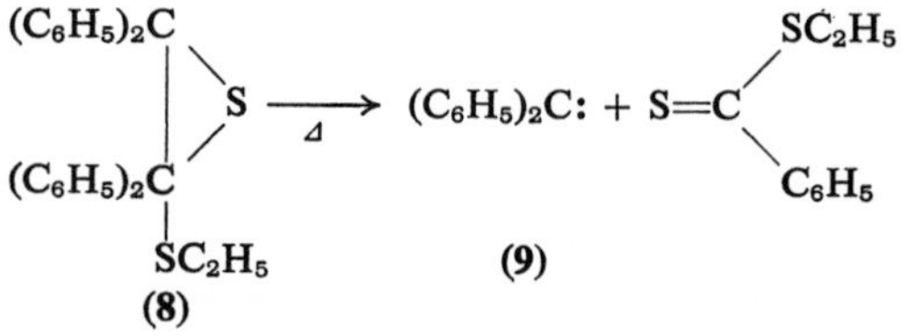

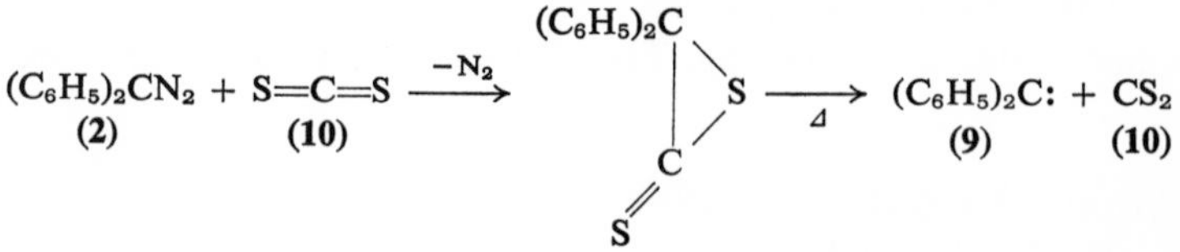

$$(C_6H_5)_2CN_2 + R\!-\!N\!=\!C\!=\!S \xrightarrow{-N_2}$$

$$\begin{array}{c} (C_6H_5)_2C \\ \diagdown \\ \quad\quad S \\ \diagup \\ C \\ \parallel \\ R\!-\!N \end{array}$$

$$\text{(2)} \qquad \text{(11)} \qquad\qquad R\!-\!N$$

$$\xrightarrow{\varDelta} (C_6H_5)_2C\!: + R\!-\!N\!=\!C\!=\!S$$
$$\text{(9)} \qquad\quad \text{(11)}$$

$$2(C_6H_5)_2C\!: \longrightarrow (C_6H_5)_2C\!=\!C(C_6H_5)_2$$
$$\text{(9)} \qquad\qquad\qquad \text{(4)}$$

In addition, diphenyldiazomethane (2) and thiophosgene (12) reacted via a cycloaddition reaction to form the thiirane (13), 2,2-diphenyl-3,3-dichlorothiirane,[72] which undergoes a decomposition analogous to that of the thiiranes previously mentioned,[69, 71] forming diphenyldichloroethylene (14) and sulfur. Diphenylenediazomethane (15) and thiophosgene (12)

$$(C_6H_5)_2CN_2 + Cl\!-\!\overset{\overset{\displaystyle S}{\parallel}}{C}\!-\!Cl \xrightarrow{-N_2} \begin{array}{c} (C_6H_5)_2C \\ \big| \quad\diagdown \\ \quad\quad S \\ \big| \quad\diagup \\ Cl_2C \end{array} \xrightarrow{\varDelta} (C_6H_5)_2C\!=\!CCl_2 + S$$

$$\text{(2)} \qquad\quad \text{(12)} \qquad\qquad\qquad \text{(13)} \qquad\qquad\qquad \text{(14)}$$

produces the thiirane (16), 2,2-diphenylene-3,3-dichlorothiirane, which decomposed analogously on long standing into the ethylene derivative (17).[72] Similarly, from diphenylenediazomethane (15) and thiobenzoyl

$$\xrightarrow{-N_2} \begin{array}{c} (C_6H_4)_2C \\ \big| \quad\diagdown \\ \quad\quad S \\ \big| \quad\diagup \\ Cl_2C \end{array} \xrightarrow{\Delta} (C_6H_4)_2C\!=\!CCl_2 + S$$

$$\text{(12)} \qquad\qquad \text{(16)} \qquad\qquad \text{(17)}$$

chloride (18) was obtained the thiirane (19), 2,2-diphenylene-3-phenyl-3-chlorothiirane, which decomposed into the ethylene compound (20), diphenylenephenylchloroethylene, and sulfur.[72]

$$+ C_6H_5\overset{\overset{\displaystyle S}{\parallel}}{C}\!-\!Cl \xrightarrow{-N_2} \begin{array}{c} (C_6H_4)_2C \\ \big| \quad\diagdown \\ \quad\quad S \\ \big| \quad\diagup \\ (C_6H_5)_2C \end{array} \xrightarrow{\Delta} (C_6H_4)_2C\!=\!\overset{\overset{\displaystyle Cl}{\big|}}{C}C_6H_5 + S$$

$$\text{(15)} \qquad\quad \text{(18)} \qquad\qquad\qquad \text{(19)} \qquad\qquad\qquad \text{(20)}$$

It was reported[64,76] that phenyldiazomethane (21) reacted with trithio-carboxylic acid diaryl esters (22) to give 1,1-bis(arylthio)-2-phenylethylene sulfides (23) (Table 1A).

$$
\text{C}_6\text{H}_5\text{CHN}_2 + \text{RS}-\overset{\overset{\text{S}}{\|}}{\text{C}}-\text{SR} \longrightarrow
\begin{array}{c}
\text{H} \\
| \\
\text{C}_6\text{H}_5\text{C} \\
| \\
\text{RSC} \\
| \\
\text{RS}
\end{array}\!\!\!\diagdown\!\!\!\diagup\!\text{S}
$$

(21)            (22)                                   (23)

Prior to 1962 there was little known about the action of elementary sulfur on diazoalkanes. It has been reported[41,61,63] that sulfur reacts almost quantitatively with diaryldiazomethane (24) to form tetraaryl-ethylene sulfides (23) (Table 1A). The formation of the ethylene sulfide (25)

$$
2\text{Ar}_2\text{CN}_2 + \text{S} \longrightarrow \text{Ar}_2\text{C}\underset{\text{S}}{\diagdown\diagup}\text{CAr}_2 + 2\text{N}_2
$$

(24)                                          (25)

was assumed to occur according to equations a and b, in which a diaryl-thioketone (26) is formed (equation a) which then reacts with the second molecule of the diaryldiazomethane (24) to form the ethylene sulfide (25)

$$
\text{Ar}_2\text{CN}_2 + \text{S} \longrightarrow \text{Ar}_2\text{C}{=}\text{S} + \text{N}_2 \qquad\qquad\text{(a)}
$$

(24)                       (26)

$$
\text{Ar}_2\text{C}{=}\text{S} + \text{Ar}_2\text{CN}_2 \longrightarrow \text{Ar}_2\text{C}\underset{\text{S}}{\diagdown\diagup}\text{CAr}_2 + \text{N}_2 \qquad\text{(b)}
$$

(26)       (24)                       (25)

(equation b).[61] Reaction b had been previously described by Staudinger and Siegwart.[71] In both reactions a and b it was found that the diaryl-carbene intermediate Ar$_2$C: was formed by the thermal decomposition of the diaryldiazomethane and subsequently reacted with sulfur (equation a) and the diarylthioketone (26) (equation b).[1,41,56,61] For example, diphenyl-diazomethane (2) and sulfur form tetraphenylethylene sulfide or 2,2,3,3-tetraphenylthiirane (3) in 90–95% yield (Table 1A).[61] Schönberg and co-workers[60,61] obtained the same tetraarylethylene sulfides (25) by reacting

$$
(\text{C}_6\text{H}_5)_2\text{CN}_2 + \text{S} \xrightarrow{-\text{N}_2} (\text{C}_6\text{H}_5)_2\text{C}: + \text{S} \longrightarrow (\text{C}_6\text{H}_5)_2\text{C}{=}\text{S}
$$

(2)                                                                (1)

$$
(\text{C}_6\text{H}_5)_2\text{C}{=}\text{S} + (\text{C}_6\text{H}_5)_2\text{C}: \longrightarrow (\text{C}_6\text{H}_5)_2\text{C}\underset{\text{S}}{\diagdown\diagup}\text{C}(\text{C}_6\text{H}_5)_2
$$

(1)                                                  (3)

## Table 1A

Thiiranes via Cycloaddition of Diazo Compounds and Thio Compounds

| Diazo compound | Thio compound | Cycloadduct | MP (°C) | Ref. |
|---|---|---|---|---|
| $(C_6H_5)_2CN_2$ | $(C_6H_5)_2C{=}S$ | $(C_6H_5)_2C\!\!<\!\!^{S}_{}\!\!>\!\!C(C_6H_5)_2$ | 175 | 71 |
| | | $(C_6H_5)_2C\!\!<\!\!^{S}_{}\!\!>\!\!C(C_6H_5)_2$ | 178–179 | 71 |
| $(C_6H_4)_2CN_2$ | $(C_6H_5)_2C{=}S$ | 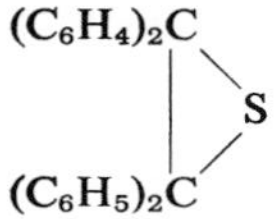 $(C_6H_4)_2C\!\!<\!\!^{S}_{}\!\!>\!\!C(C_6H_5)_2$ | 190–200 (dec) | 71 |
| $(C_6H_5)_2CN_2$ | $(p\text{-}CH_3OC_6H_4)_2C{=}S$ | 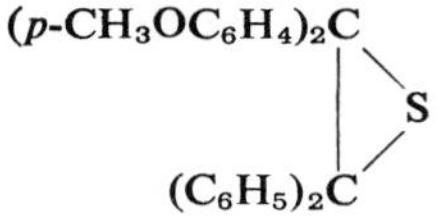 $(p\text{-}CH_3OC_6H_4)_2C\!\!<\!\!^{S}_{}\!\!>\!\!C(C_6H_5)_2$ | 100 (dec) | 71 |
| $(C_6H_5)_2CN_2$ | $[p\text{-}(CH_3)_2NC_6H_4]_2C{=}S$ | 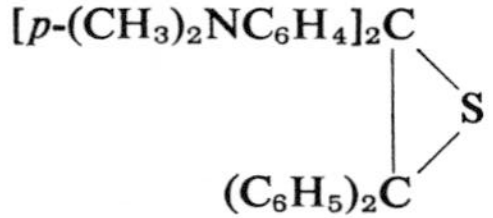 $[p\text{-}(CH_3)_2NC_6H_4]_2C\!\!<\!\!^{S}_{}\!\!>\!\!C(C_6H_5)_2$ | 164–165 | 71 |
| $(C_6H_5)_2CN_2$ | $Cl_2C{=}S$ | 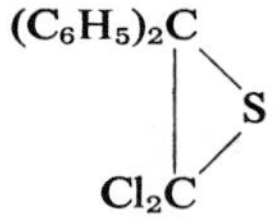 $(C_6H_5)_2C\!\!<\!\!^{S}_{}\!\!>\!\!CCl_2$ | 89–90 | 72 |

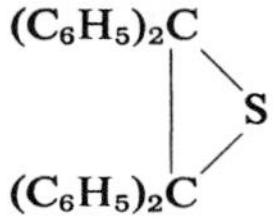

(continued)

**Table 1A** (*continued*)

| Diazo compound | Thio compound | Cycloadduct | MP (°C) | Ref. |
|---|---|---|---|---|
| $(C_6H_4)_2CN_2$ | $Cl_2C{=}S$ | 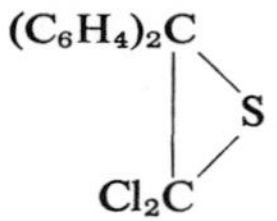 $(C_6H_4)_2C\!\!\diagdown\!\!\underset{Cl_2C}{\overset{S}{\diagup}}$ | 97 | 72 |
| $(C_6H_5)_2CN_2$ | 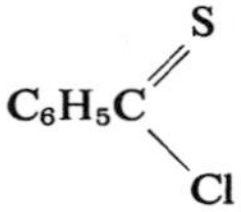 $C_6H_5C(={S})\!-\!Cl$ | 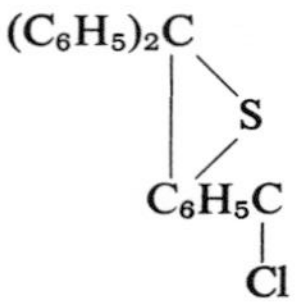 $(C_6H_5)_2C\!\!\diagdown\!\!\underset{C_6H_5C-Cl}{\overset{S}{\diagup}}$ | 70–71 | 72 |
| $(C_6H_4)_2CN_2$ | 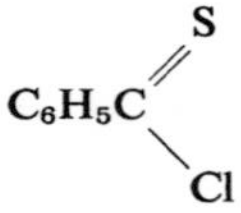 $C_6H_5C(={S})\!-\!Cl$ | 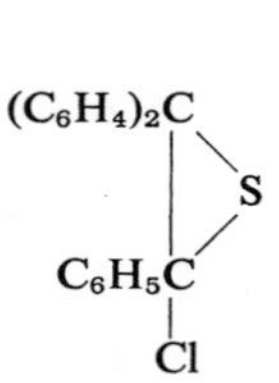 $(C_6H_4)_2C\!\!\diagdown\!\!\underset{C_6H_5C-Cl}{\overset{S}{\diagup}}$ | 125–126 | 72 |
| $C_6H_5CHN_2$ | $(2{,}4\text{-}Cl_2C_6H_3S)_2C{=}S$ | 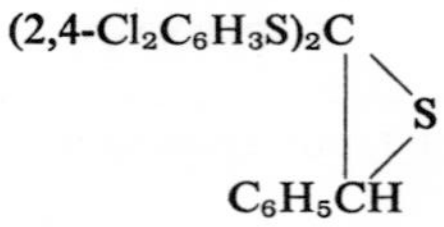 $(2{,}4\text{-}Cl_2C_6H_3S)_2C\!\!\diagdown\!\!\underset{C_6H_5CH}{\overset{S}{\diagup}}$ | 104–105 | 76 |

| | | | | |
|---|---|---|---|---|
| $C_6H_5CHN_2$ | $(3,4\text{-}Cl_2C_6H_3S)_2C{=}S$ | 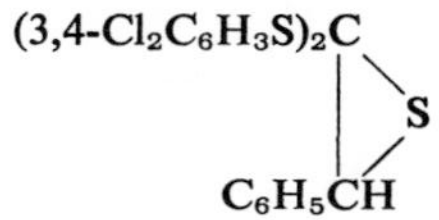 $(3,4\text{-}Cl_2C_6H_3S)_2C$ $\overset{S}{\diagup\!\!\diagdown}$ $C_6H_5CH$ | 100.5–101.5 | 76 |
| $C_6H_5CHN_2$ | $(2,5\text{-}Br_2C_6H_3S)_2C{=}S$ | 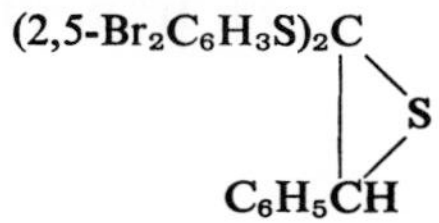 $(2,5\text{-}Br_2C_6H_3S)_2C$ $\overset{S}{\diagup\!\!\diagdown}$ $C_6H_5CH$ | 136.5–137.5 | 76 |
| $(C_6H_5)_2CN_2$ | S | 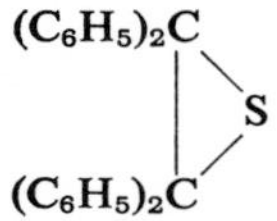 $(C_6H_5)_2C$ $\overset{S}{\diagup\!\!\diagdown}$ $(C_6H_5)_2C$ | 177–179[a] | 61 |
| | | | 178 | 41 |
| $(p\text{-}CH_3OC_6H_4)_2CN_2$ | S | 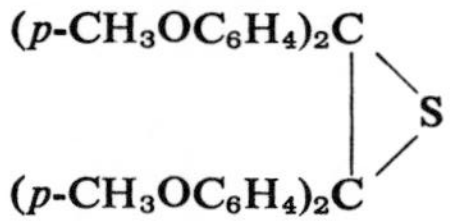 $(p\text{-}CH_3OC_6H_4)_2C$ $\overset{S}{\diagup\!\!\diagdown}$ $(p\text{-}CH_3OC_6H_4)_2C$ | 216–218[b] | 61 |
| $(p\text{-}CH_3OC_6H_4)_2CN_2$ | $(p\text{-}CH_3OC_6H_4)_2C{=}S$ | 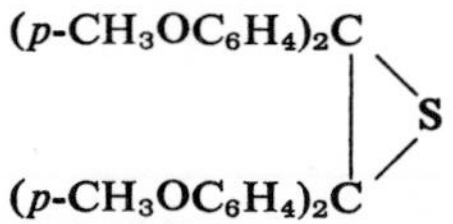 $(p\text{-}CH_3OC_6H_4)_2C$ $\overset{S}{\diagup\!\!\diagdown}$ $(p\text{-}CH_3OC_6H_4)_2C$ | 216–218[b] | 61 |

*(continued)*

**Table 1A** (*continued*)

| Diazo compound | Thio compound | Cycloadduct | MP (°C) | Ref. |
|---|---|---|---|---|
| 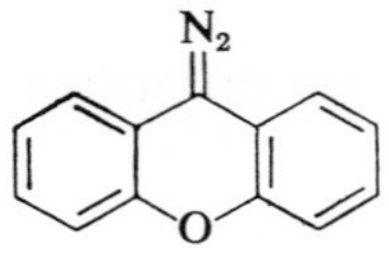 | S | 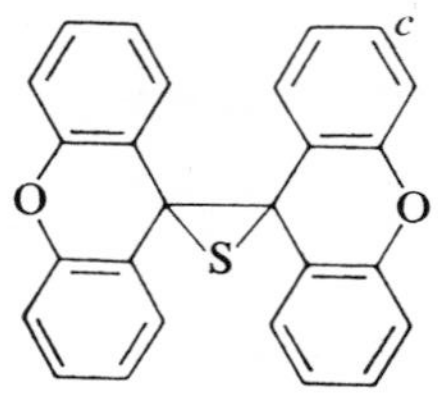 | 201–202 | 41, 61 |
| | | | 201–202 | 61 |
| | | | 206–207 | 41 |
| $CH_3(C_6H_5)CN_2$ | $[p\text{-}(CH_3)_2NC_6H_4]_2C{=}S$ | 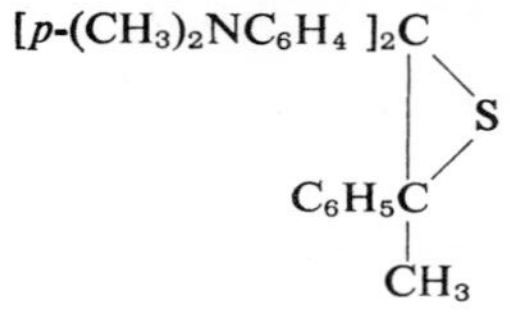 $[p\text{-}(CH_3)_2NC_6H_4\ ]_2C$<br>$C_6H_5C$ — $CH_3$<br>(S bridge) | 134 | 60 |

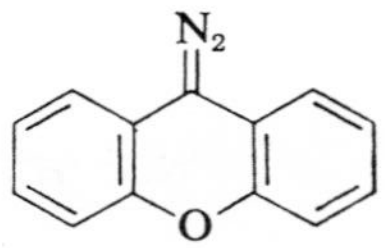

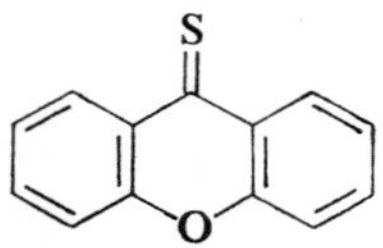

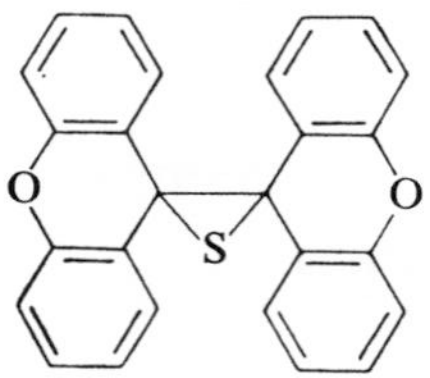

| | | | | |
|---|---|---|---|---|
| $CH_3(p\text{-}CH_3C_6H_4)CN_2$ | $[p\text{-}(CH_3)_2NC_6H_4]_2C{=}S$ | 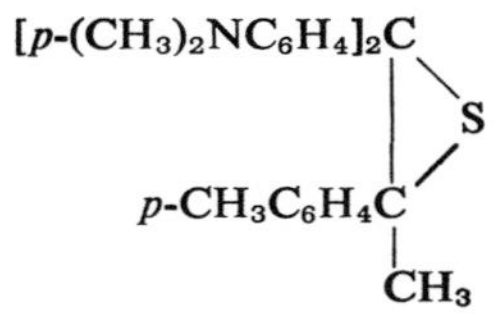 $[p\text{-}(CH_3)_2NC_6H_4]_2C\overset{\displaystyle S}{\triangle}C(p\text{-}CH_3C_6H_4)CH_3$ | 124 | 60 |
| $(p\text{-}ClC_6H_4)_2CN_2$ | $[p\text{-}(CH_3)_2NC_6H_4]_2C{=}S$ | 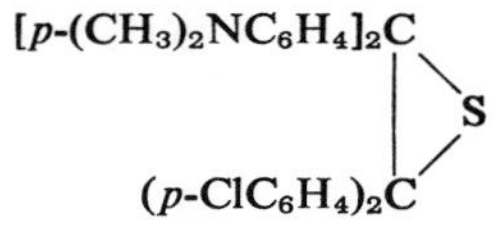 $[p\text{-}(CH_3)_2NC_6H_4]_2C\overset{\displaystyle S}{\triangle}C(p\text{-}ClC_6H_4)_2$ | 180 | 60 |
| $2,5\text{-}(CH_3)_2C_6H_3(C_6H_5)CN_2$ | $[p\text{-}(CH_3)_2NC_6H_4]_2C{=}S$ | 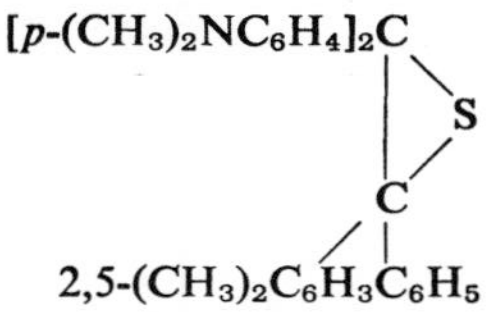 $[p\text{-}(CH_3)_2NC_6H_4]_2C\overset{\displaystyle S}{\triangle}C\,2,5\text{-}(CH_3)_2C_6H_3C_6H_5$ | 189 | 60 |
| $(p\text{-}CH_3C_6H_4)_2CN_2$ | $[p\text{-}(CH_3)_2NC_6H_4]_2C{=}S$ | 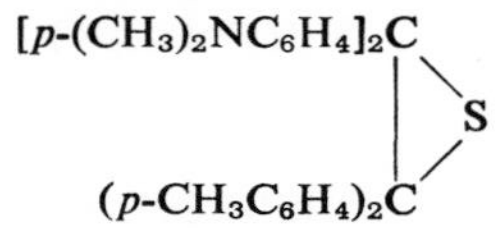 $[p\text{-}(CH_3)_2NC_6H_4]_2C\overset{\displaystyle S}{\triangle}C(p\text{-}CH_3C_6H_4)_2$ | 164 | 60 |
| $(C_6H_5)_2CN_2$ | $(C_6H_5S)_2C{=}S$ | 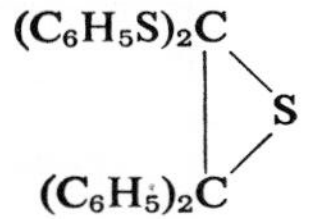 $(C_6H_5S)_2C\overset{\displaystyle S}{\triangle}C(C_6H_5)_2$ | 135 | 64 |

(continued)

**Table 1A** (*continued*)

| Diazo compound | Thio compound | Cycloadduct | MP (°C) | Ref. |
|---|---|---|---|---|
| $(p\text{-}CH_3C_6H_4)_2CN_2$ | $(p\text{-}CH_3C_6H_4S)_2C{=}S$ | 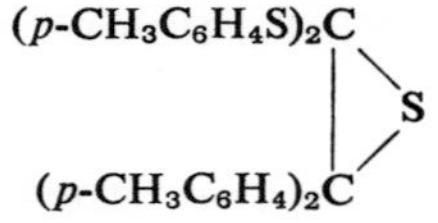 $(p\text{-}CH_3C_6H_4S)_2C\overset{S}{\diagup\diagdown}(p\text{-}CH_3C_6H_4)_2C$ | 134–135 | 64 |
| $(C_6H_4)_2CN_2$ | 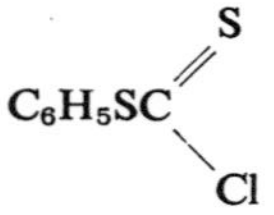 $C_6H_5SC(\overset{S}{=})Cl$ | 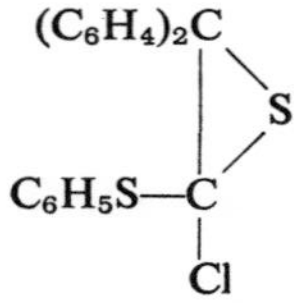 $(C_6H_4)_2C\overset{S}{\diagup\diagdown}\underset{C_6H_5S}{C}{-}Cl$ | 110 | 64, 65 |
| $(C_6H_4)_2CN_2$ | 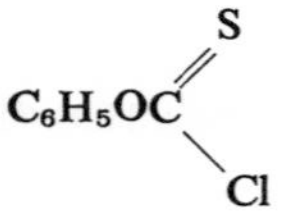 $C_6H_5OC(\overset{S}{=})Cl$ | 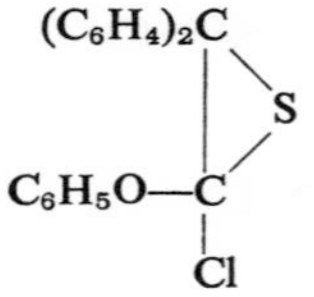 $(C_6H_4)_2C\overset{S}{\diagup\diagdown}\underset{C_6H_5O}{C}{-}Cl$ | — | 64, 65 |

| | | | | |
|---|---|---|---|---|
| $(p\text{-ClC}_6\text{H}_4)_2\text{CN}_2$ | | $(\text{C}_6\text{H}_4\text{Cl-}p)_2$ | 170 | 60 |
| $(o\text{-ClC}_6\text{H}_4)_2\text{CN}_2$ | | $(\text{C}_6\text{H}_4\text{Cl-}o)_2$ | 195 | 60 |
| $p\text{-NO}_2\text{C}_6\text{H}_4(\text{C}_6\text{H}_5)\text{CN}_2$ | | $\text{C}_6\text{H}_5$ / $\text{C}_6\text{H}_4\text{NO}_2\text{-}p$ | 182 | 60 |
| $p\text{-C}_6\text{H}_5\text{C}_6\text{H}_4(\text{C}_6\text{H}_5)\text{CN}_2$ | | $\text{C}_6\text{H}_5$ / $\text{C}_6\text{H}_4\text{C}_6\text{H}_5\text{-}p$ | — | 60 |

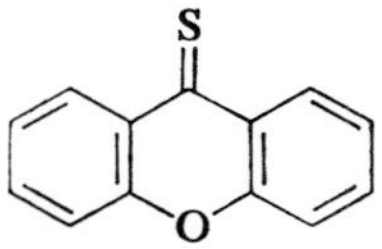

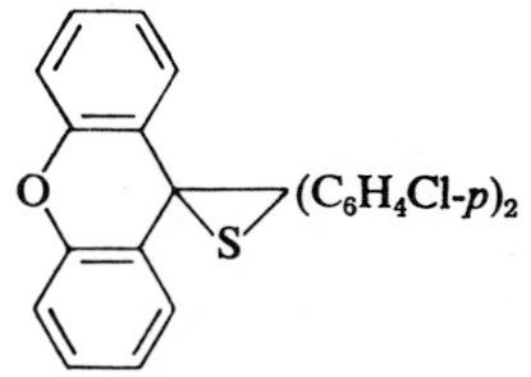

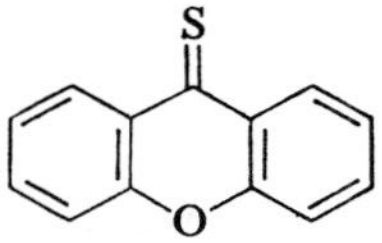

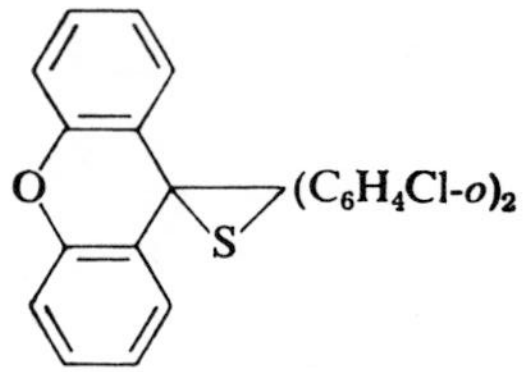

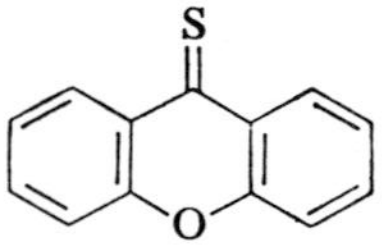

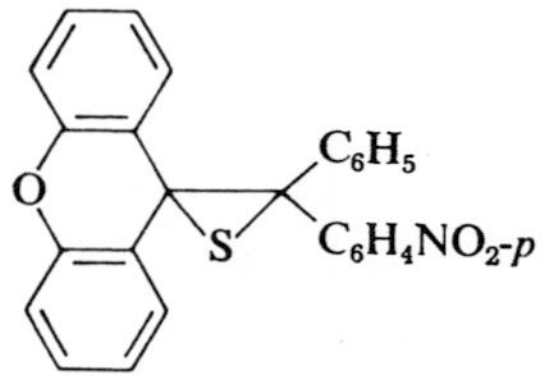

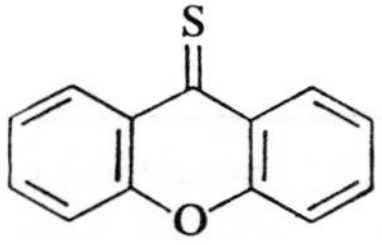

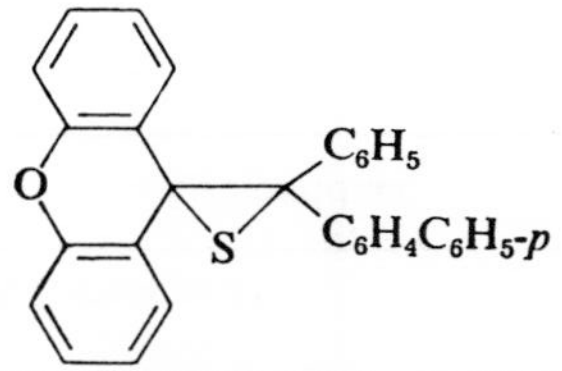

*(continued)*

**Table 1A** (*continued*)

| Diazo compound | Thio compound | Cycloadduct | MP (°C) | Ref. |
|---|---|---|---|---|
| $CH_3(C_6H_5)CN_2$ | 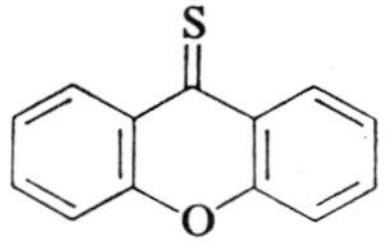 | 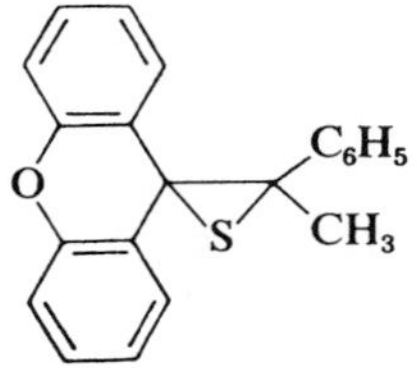 | 105 | 60 |
| $(p\text{-}CH_3C_6H_4)_2CN_2$ | 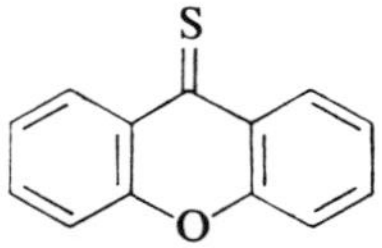 | 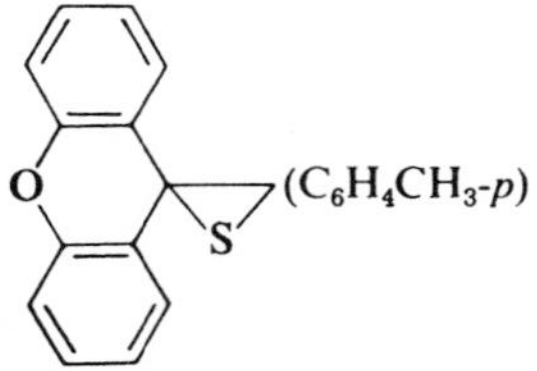 | 176 | 60 |
| 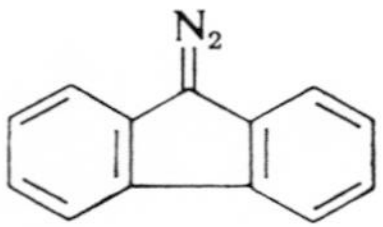 | 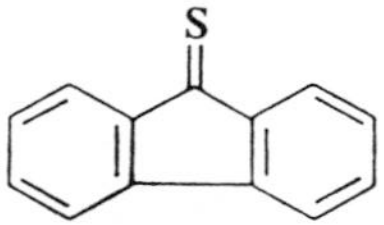 | 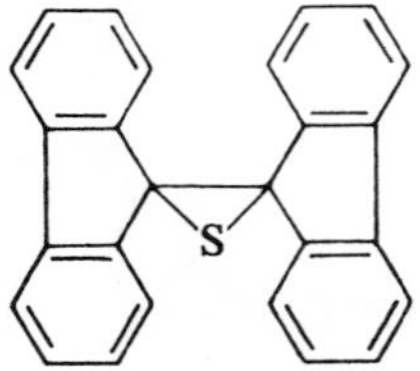 | 162–163 | 41 |

| | | | | |
|---|---|---|---|---|
| 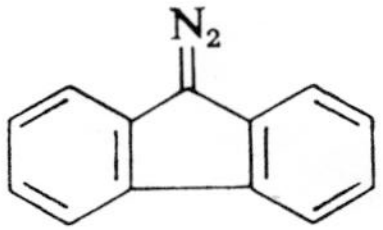 | S | | | 162–163 | 41 |
| 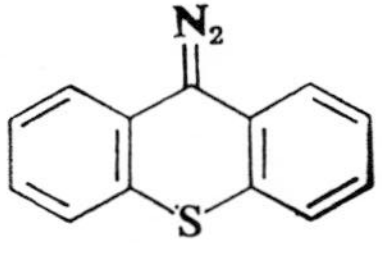 | S | | | above 360 | 41 |
| | | | | above 360 | 41, 63 |

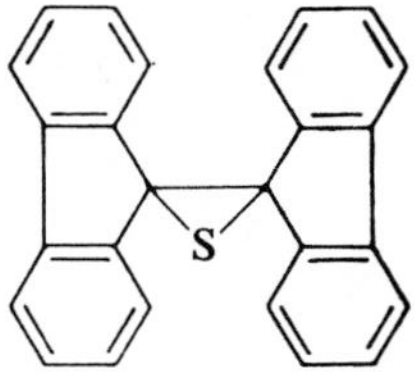

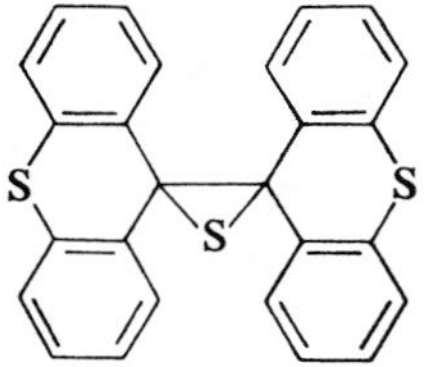

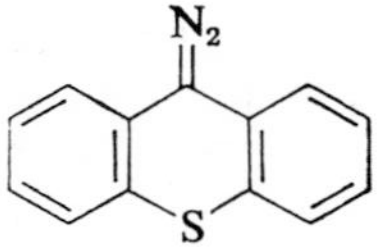

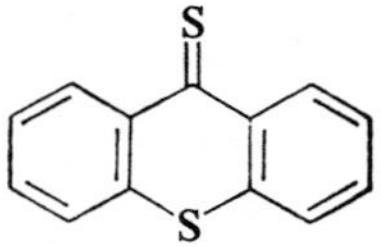

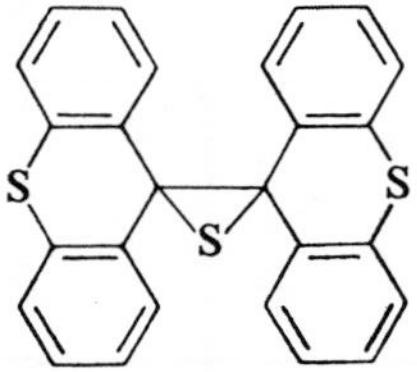

(continued)

**Table 1A** (*continued*)

| Diazo compound | Thio compound | Cycloadduct | MP (°C) | Ref. |
|---|---|---|---|---|
| 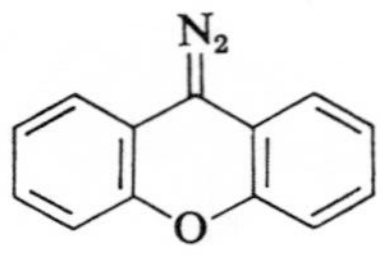 | 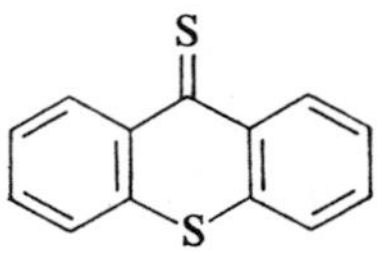 | 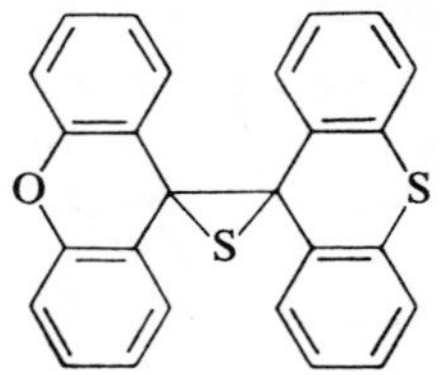 | 208 | 41 |
| 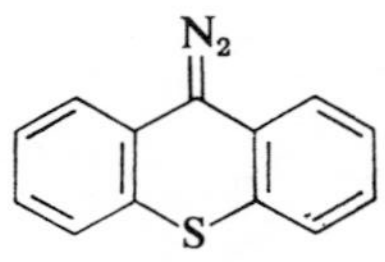 | 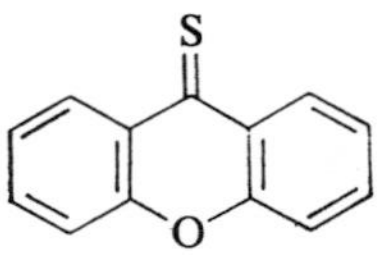 | 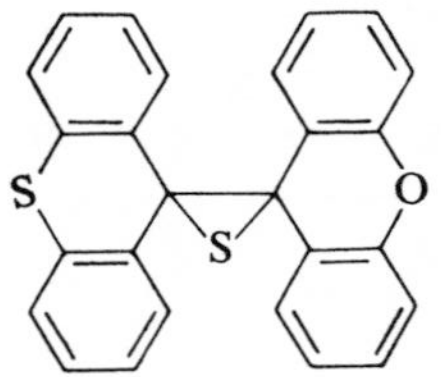 | 205 (dec) | 63 |
| 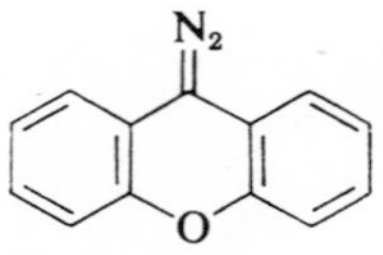 | 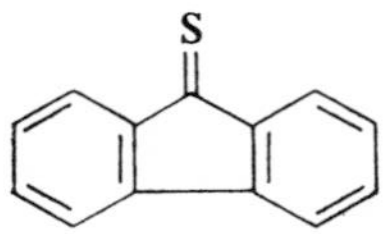 | 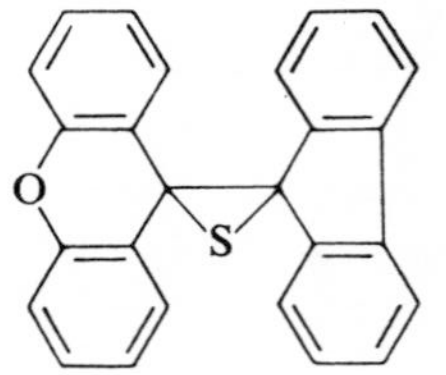 | 198 | 41 |

| | | | | |
|---|---|---|---|---|
| 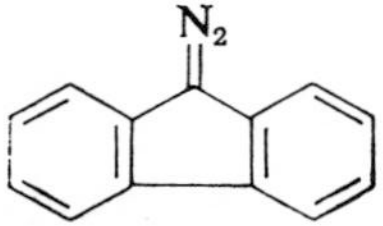 | 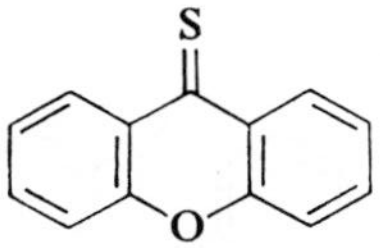 | 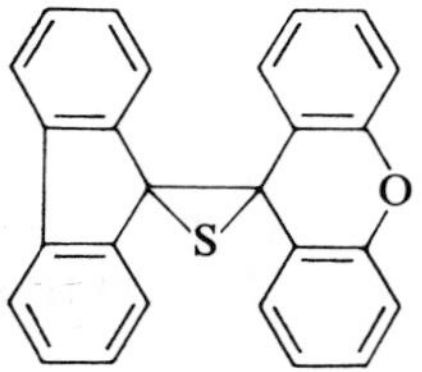 | 198 | 41, 63 |
| 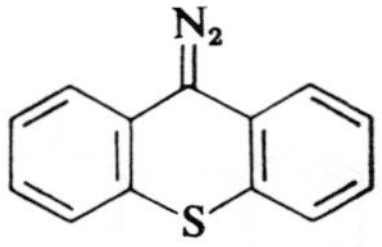 | 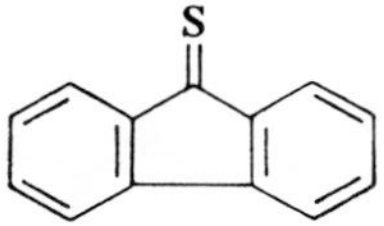 | 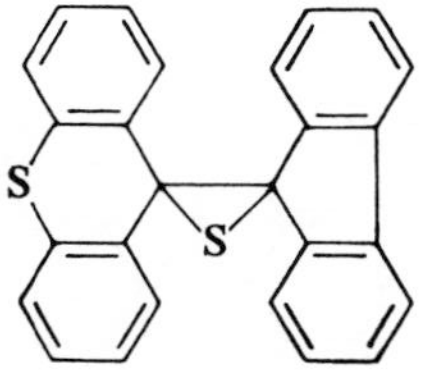 | 240 | 41 |
| $(C_6H_4)_2CN_2$ | 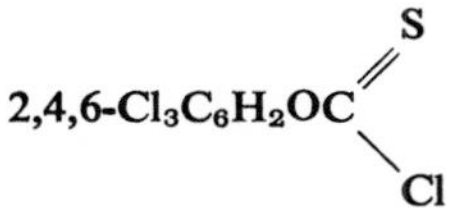 | 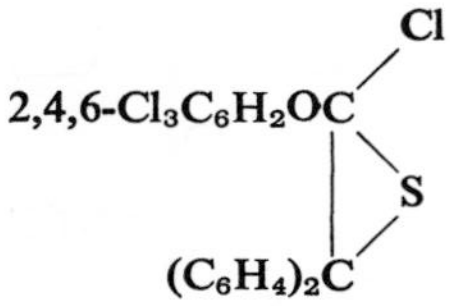 | — | 65 |
| $(C_6H_5)_2CN_2$ | 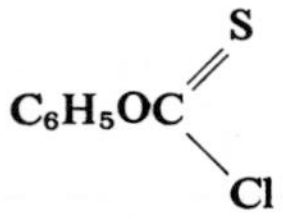 | 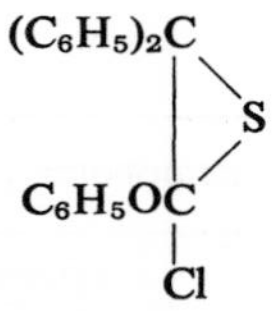 | 78 | 65 |

(continued)

**Table 1A** (*continued*)

| Diazo compound | Thio compound | Cycloadduct | MP (°C) | Ref. |
|---|---|---|---|---|
| $(C_6H_5)_2CN_2$ | 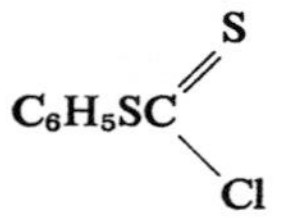 $C_6H_5SC(=S)Cl$ | 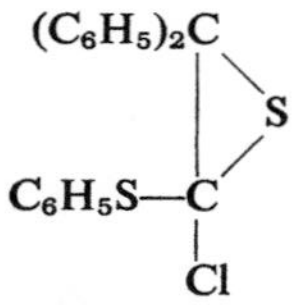 | 99–100 | 65 |
| 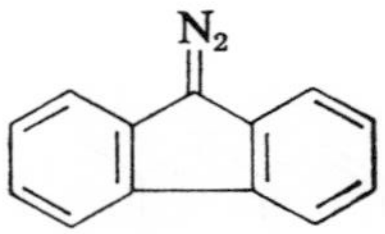 | 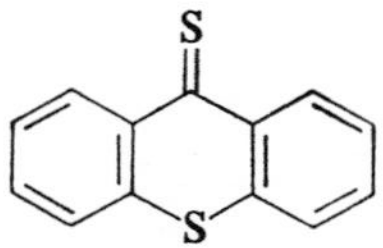 | 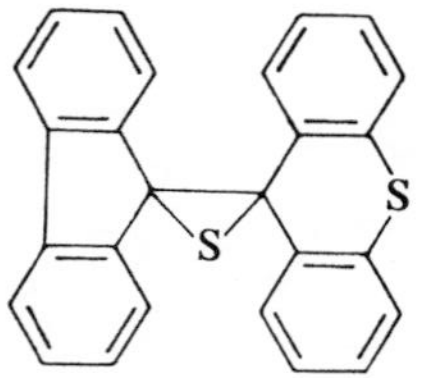 | 240 | 63 |
| $(C_6H_5)_2CN_2$ | 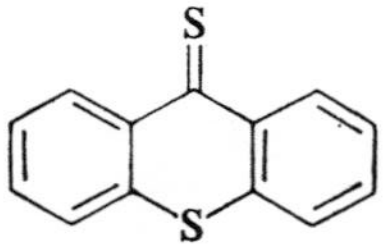 | 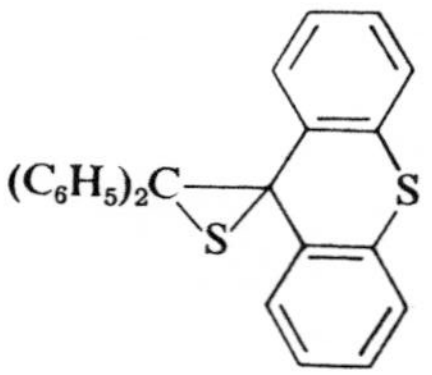 | 208 | 63 |

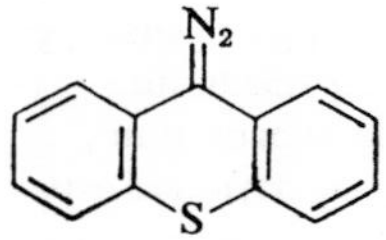

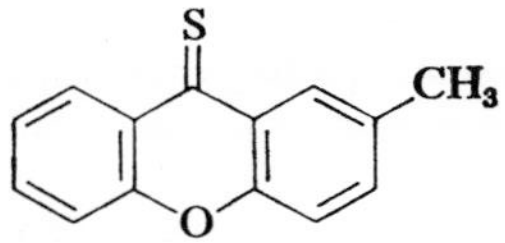

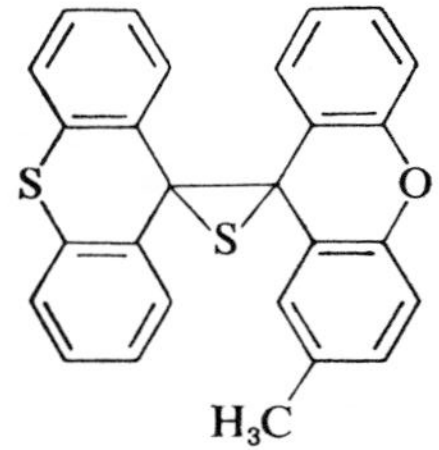

63

63

63

44

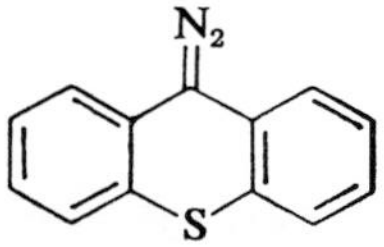

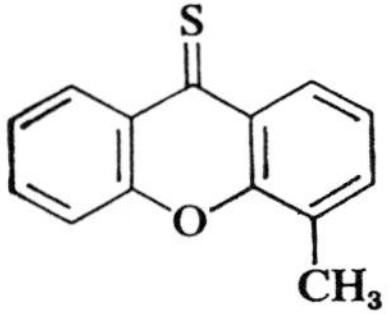

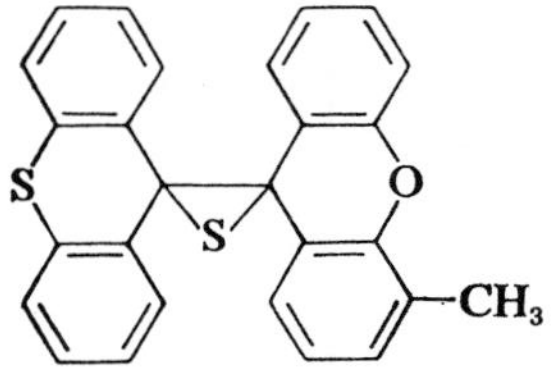

210 (dec)

190 (dec)

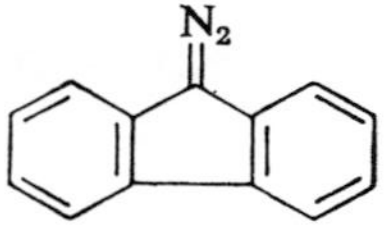

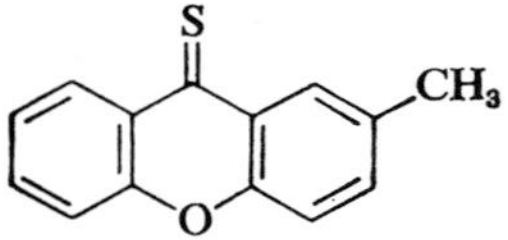

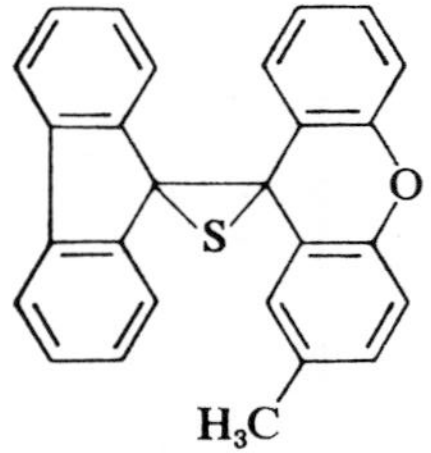

168

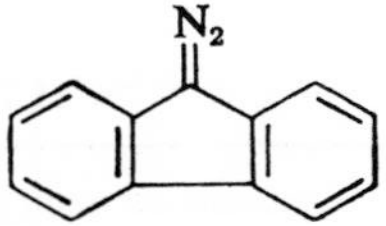

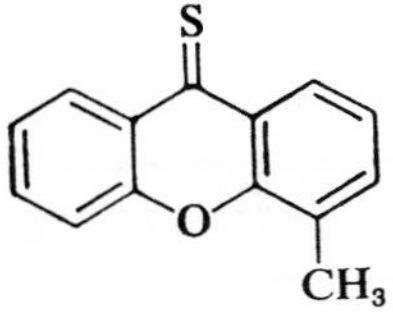

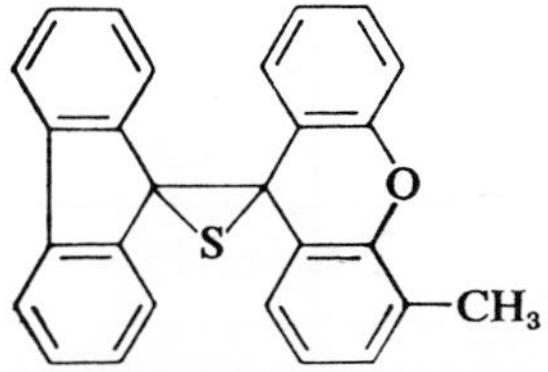

(dec)

(continued)

**Table 1A** (*continued*)

| Diazo compound | Thio compound | Cycloadduct | MP (°C) | Ref. |
|---|---|---|---|---|
| $CH_2N_2$ | $CF_2{=}S$ | 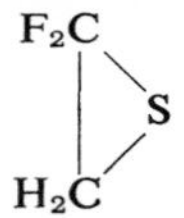 | (dec) | 44 |
| $(C_6H_5)_2CN_2$ | $F_2C{=}S$ | 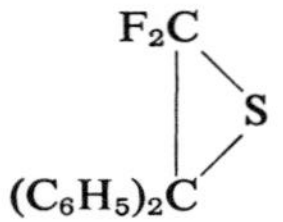 | (dec) | 44 |
| $(C_6H_5)_2CN_2$ | $(F_3C)_2C{=}S$ | 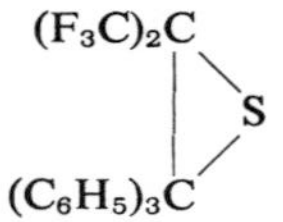 | 79–80[d] | 45 |
| $C_2H_5O_2CCHN_2$ | $(F_3C)_2C{=}S$ | 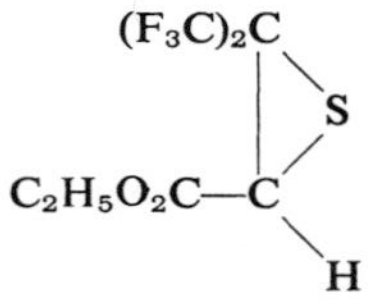 | 87–89[e] | 45 |

[a] Mp 178–179° and yield 90–95% reported in literature.[59]

[b] Mp 210° and 90–95% yield reported in literature.[62]

[c] Also reported by Reid and Klug.[54]

[d] $F^{19}$ nmr spectrum contained a single unsplit resonance line at $-6.81$ ppm.

[e] $F^{19}$ nmr spectrum showed two quadruplets of equal intensity at $-10.00$ and $-8.2$ ppm. The proton nmr spectrum showed a singlet at 4.52 ppm in addition to absorption due to an ethyl group.

the diaryldiazomethane (24) with the corresponding thioketone (26) (Table 1A). It was also found that thiiranes are directly synthesized from ketohydrazones when the latter compounds are allowed to react with elemental sulfur in the presence of mercuric oxide and alkali (Table 1C).[42] It was assumed that the hydrazone was first dehydrogenated by mercuric oxide yielding the corresponding diazoalkanes, which reacted with sulfur to give the cyclic sulfide. The formation was postulated to occur via the formation of a carbene intermediate.[41] Atomic sulfur in the ($^1D$) metastable state was generated at 25°C, by the *in situ* photolysis of gaseous carbonyl sulfide (27) in the wavelength region, 2550–2290 Å.[37,38,75] Upon addition of ethylene (28), 1,1-difluoroethylene, or propylene to the system, the corresponding cyclic sulfides (29) are formed[75,82] in yields varying from 60 to 100%, and mercaptans are formed as by-products by the sulfur atoms in the ($^1D$) state undergoing insertion reactions into the carbon–hydrogen bonds.[37–39,82] The value of the relative rate constants $k_{C_3H_6}/k_{C_2H_4}$ for the addition reaction was equal to 3.6, while the relative rate constants for the addition to olefin compared to the abstraction reaction from the carbonyl sulfide were found to be a function of the added olefin pressure. The mechanism was proposed as is shown here.[75,82]

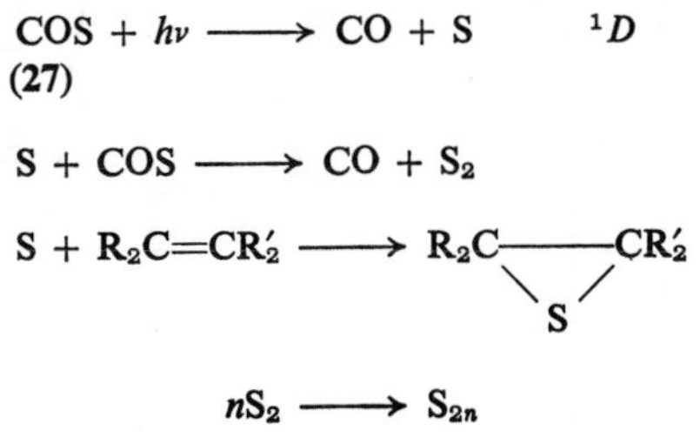

$$COS + h\nu \longrightarrow CO + S \qquad ^1D$$
(27)

$$S + COS \longrightarrow CO + S_2$$

$$S + R_2C{=}CR_2' \longrightarrow R_2C\underset{\diagdown S \diagup}{\phantom{xxx}}CR_2'$$

$$nS_2 \longrightarrow S_{2n}$$

or

$$COS + h\nu \longrightarrow CO + S(^1D)$$
(27)

$$S(^1D) + COS \longrightarrow CO + S_2$$

$$S(^1D) + C_2H_4 \longrightarrow H_2C\underset{\diagdown S_* \diagup}{\phantom{xxx}}CH_2$$
(28)

$$S(^1D) + C_2H_4 \longrightarrow C_2H_4{*} + S(^3p)$$

$$S(^3p) + C_2H_4 \longrightarrow H_2C\underset{\diagdown S \diagup}{\phantom{xxx}}CH_2$$
(29)

$$S(^3p) + COS \longrightarrow CO + S_2$$

$$nS_2 \longrightarrow S_{2n}$$

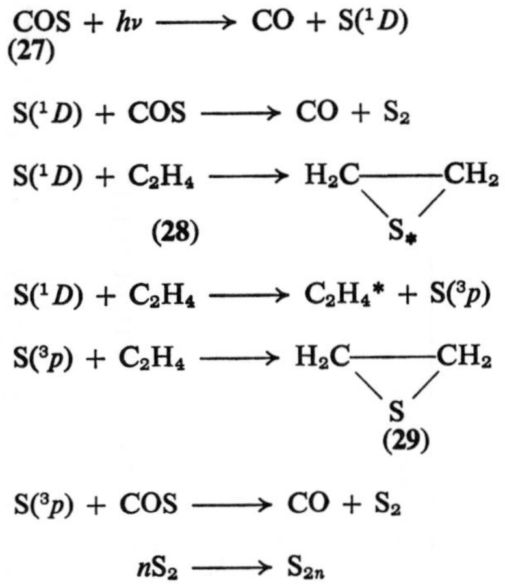

**Table 1B**
Thiiranes via Cycloaddition of Olefins and Sulfur

| Olefin | Cycloadduct | BP (°C/mm) | $t_{nD}$ | Ref. |
|---|---|---|---|---|
| $CH_3CH=CH_2$ | 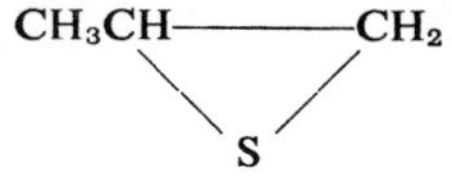 | 75–77 | [19]1.4730 | 32 |
| 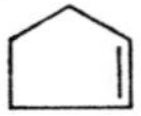 | 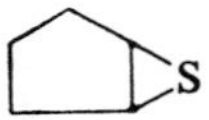 | 67–68/16 | [20]1.5309 | 32 |
| $n\text{-}C_8H_{17}CH=C[(CH_2)_7CO_2H]H$ | 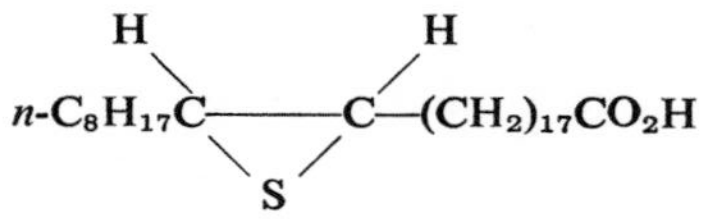 | — | — | 9, 11, 12 |
| $n\text{-}C_5H_{11}CH=C(H)CH_2CH=CH[(CH_2)_7CO_2H]$ | 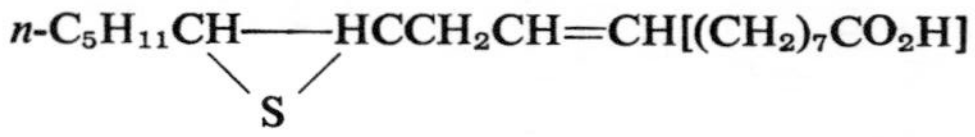 | — | — | 10 |

**Table 1C**

**Thiiranes via Cycloaddition Reactions of Ketohydrazones with Sulfur[42]**

| Ketohydrazone | Cycloadduct |
|---|---|
| Benzophenone | 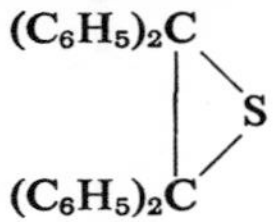 |
| Thiaxanthone | 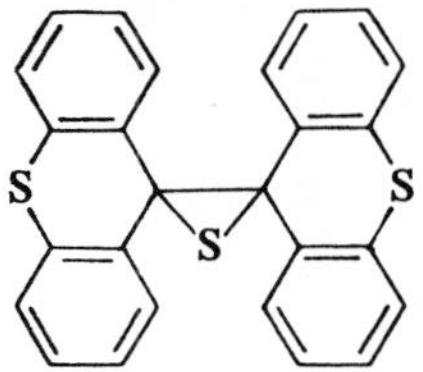 |
| Fluorenone | 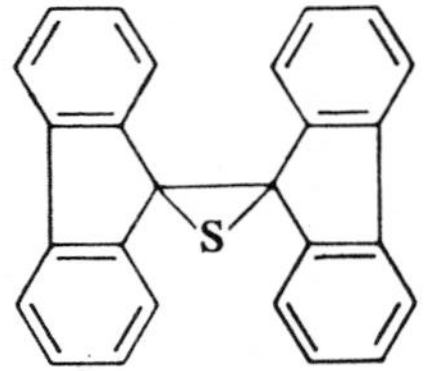 |
| Xanthone | 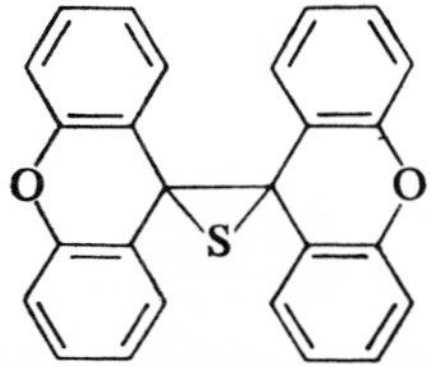 |

Thiiranes were also reported in the reactions of olefins (such as ethylene, propylene, and cyclohexene); and ethyltetrasulfide, $(C_2H_5)_2S_4$, as the source of free sulfur at 150°C[32]; and by the heating at 135–200°, in the presence of iodine catalyst, of unsaturated fatty acids and unsaturated glycerides with sulfur (Table 1B).[9–12] Martin[43] also reported the formation of a fluorothiirane in the reaction of hexafluoropropene and sulfur which subsequently dimerized.

Other methods of preparation of thiiranes involving, for example, cyclizations, additions, and substitution and decomposition reactions, are more common than the cycloaddition reactions.[3,4,6–8,13–16,18,23,46,47,52,54,55,59,62,66,67,73,78,83]

The conjugative properties and electronic spectra of styrene–thiirane have recently been discussed.[74] It was shown that, relative to benzene, styrene–thiirane is electron-withdrawing. Thus a p-methoxy substituent was observed to shift conjugatively and enhance the ultraviolet "primary" absorption bands of phenylthiirane, whereas a p-nitro substituent showed the reverse effect. These observations were in agreement with second-order resonance effects and clarified various observations dealing with the unsaturation properties of the three-membered ring system.

In relatively recent studies of the reactions of thiiranes,[18,29,73] Dittmer and Levy found that thiiranes could be oxidized to form thiirane 1-oxide and thiirane 1,1-dioxides. Only one thiirane 1-oxide had been previously reported,[68] but its structure was not adequately characterized. Although several thiirane 1,1-dioxides (episulfones) are known,[28,31,47,50,51,70,79] none had been prepared by oxidation of a thiirane.[5,71]

Dibenzoylstilbene episulfide (30) was oxidized with 30% hydrogen peroxide in glacial acetic acid; the thiirane 1-oxide (31) was obtained when the oxidation was done with a limited amount of hydrogen peroxide at room temperature, while the thiirane 1,1-dioxide (32) was obtained if a greater quantity of hydrogen peroxide and steam-bath temperatures were used.[18] The structure of the thiirane 1-oxide (31) was inferred from its composition and molecular weight, its mode of preparation, and the strong sulfoxide absorption band in the infrared at 1065 cm$^{-1}$. Its ultraviolet absorption spectrum is similar to that of the thiirane 1,1-dioxide (32), and its proton magnetic resonance spectrum is similar to that of the thiirane (30) and the thiirane 1,1-dioxide (32). The infrared absorption for the sulfoxide group was found to be at a greater frequency than is usual for acyclic sulfoxides (1060–1040 cm$^{-1}$ in solution and 10–20 cm$^{-1}$ lower in solid states),[2,18] and may be attributed to a greater s-character in the sulfur–

$$C_6H_5CO(C_6H_5)C\underset{S}{\overset{}{\diagdown\diagup}}C(C_6H_5)COC_6H_5 \quad \xrightarrow[\text{CH}_3\text{COOH}]{\text{H}_2\text{O}_2}$$
(30)

$$C_6H_5CO(C_6H_5)C\underset{SO}{\overset{}{\diagdown\diagup}}C(C_6H_5)COC_6H_5 +$$
(31)

$$C_6H_5CO(C_6H_5)C\underset{SO_2}{\overset{}{\diagdown\diagup}}C(C_6H_5)COC_6H_5$$
(32)

oxygen bond.[17] Two isomeric thiirane 1-oxides (31) melting points about 170° and 145°C, respectively, were obtained; however, their stereochemistry was not determined.

The structure of the thiirane 1,1-dioxide (32) was characterized by its composition, molecular weight, and proton magnetic resonance, infrared, and ultraviolet spectra.* The infrared absorption for the sulfone group (1315, 1145 cm$^{-1}$) was similar to the absorption of ethylene sulfone (1310, 1168 cm$^{-1}$).[31]

As mentioned earlier, Staudinger and Pfenninger[70] observed that diphenyldiazomethane (2) in an inert solvent readily reacted with sulfur dioxide (5) producing the tetraphenylethylene sulfone (6), 2,2,3,3-tetraphenylthiirane 1,1-dioxide, or benzophenone (33) in the presence of excess sulfur dioxide (5). The mechanism proposed by Staudinger and Pfenninger[70] involved the initial formation of the diphenylsulfene

$$(C_6H_5)_2CN_2 + SO_2 \longrightarrow$$
$$\quad\ (2)\qquad\quad (5)$$

$$\left[\begin{array}{c}C_6H_5 \\ \diagdown \\ \diagup \\ C_6H_5\end{array} C{=}SO_2\right] \quad \underset{(34)}{\underbrace{\qquad\qquad\qquad\qquad}} \quad$$

$$\xrightarrow{(C_6H_5)_2CN_2} (C_6H_5)_2C\underset{SO_2}{\overset{}{\diagdown\diagup}}C(C_6H_5)_2$$
(6)

$$\xrightarrow{SO_2} (C_6H_5)_2C{=}O$$
(33)

* For ultraviolet spectra of sulfone groups see Refs. 24–26.

(34)[34-36,81] followed by the reaction with a second molecule of diphenyl-diazomethane, or with excess sulfur dioxide with the loss of "$S_2O_3$." When the reaction was performed in hydroxylic solvents the products were those derivable by direct addition of the solvent to the sulfene (as in the manner of ketenes); that is, in water, the sulfonic acid, and in methanol and ethanol, the corresponding esters of sulfonic acid.[70] Staudinger and Pfenninger[70] also reported that when the thiirane 1,1-dioxide (6) was heated in a neutral medium a new, stable, sulfone (35) was formed which formed tetraphenylethylene isomeric hydrocarbons when heated. The formation of this sulfone (35) was thought to have been caused by the instability of the three-membered ring of the thiirane 1,1-dioxide (6) with rearrangement resulting in the extension of the ring similar to the rearrangement of hexaphenylethane to benzyhydryltetraphenylmethane.[27,77] More

$$(C_6H_5)_2C\text{————}C(C_6H_5)_2 \xrightarrow{\ \Delta\ } (C_6H_5)_2C\text{—}C_6H_4CHC_6H_5$$

$$\overset{\diagdown}{\phantom{x}} SO_2 \overset{\diagup}{\phantom{x}} \qquad\qquad \overset{\diagdown}{\phantom{x}} SO_2 \overset{\diagup}{\phantom{x}}$$

$$(6)\qquad\qquad\qquad\qquad (35)$$

recently the reaction of diphenyldiazomethane and sulfur dioxide in the presence of an amine was shown to yield the sulfonamide.[36]

Stilbestrol[19-21] and a number of analogs have been synthesized by pyrolysis of the thiirane 1,4-dioxide initially formed by reacting the disubstituted diazomethane with sulfur dioxide (Table 2),[79] for example,

### Table 2

Intermediate Thiirane 1,1-Dioxides formed by the Cycloaddition Reaction of Diazo Compounds and Sulfur Dioxide in the Preparation of Stilbestrols[79]

$$2RR'CN_2 + SO_2 \xrightarrow{-N_2} RR'C\text{————}CRR'$$

$$\overset{\diagdown}{\phantom{x}} SO_2 \overset{\diagup}{\phantom{x}}$$

| R | R' | MP (°C) | Yield (%) |
|---|---|---|---|
| $p$-CH$_3$OC$_6$H$_4$ | C$_2$H$_5$ | dec at room temperature | 70 |
| $p$-BrC$_6$H$_4$ | C$_2$H$_5$ | 100–110 dec | — |
| $p$-NH$_2$C$_6$H$_5$ | C$_2$H$_5$ | — | — |

($p$-methoxyphenyl)ethyldiazomethane (36) was converted by sulfur dioxide (5) into 70% of the very unstable 2,3-bis($p$-methoxyphenyl)-2,3-diethylthiirane 1,1-dioxide (37), which was converted at 80–120°C to trans-1,1'-bis($p$-methoxyphenyl)-1,1'-diethylethylene (38), which gives diethylstilbestrol (39) when treated with alcoholic potassium hydroxide.

$$p\text{-CH}_3\text{OC}_6\text{H}_4-\text{CN}_2 + \text{SO}_2 \xrightarrow{-\text{N}_2} p\text{-CH}_3\text{OC}_6\text{H}_4-\overset{\overset{\displaystyle \text{C}_2\text{H}_5}{|}}{\text{C}}\underset{\underset{\displaystyle \text{SO}_2}{\diagup}}{\diagdown}\overset{\overset{\displaystyle \text{C}_2\text{H}_5}{|}}{\text{C}}-\text{C}_6\text{H}_4\text{OCH}_3\text{-}p$$

$$\underset{\displaystyle \text{C}_2\text{H}_5}{|}$$

(36)                    (5)                                              (37)

$$(37) \xrightarrow[80-120^\circ]{} p\text{-CH}_3\text{OC}_6\text{H}_4-\overset{\overset{\displaystyle \text{C}_2\text{H}_5}{|}}{\text{C}}=\underset{\underset{\displaystyle \text{C}_2\text{H}_5}{|}}{\text{C}}-\text{C}_6\text{H}_4\text{OCH}_3\text{-}p$$

(38)

$$(38) + \text{alc. KOH} \longrightarrow p\text{-HOC}_6\text{H}_4-\overset{\overset{\displaystyle \text{C}_2\text{H}_5}{|}}{\text{C}}=\underset{\underset{\displaystyle \text{C}_2\text{H}_5}{|}}{\text{C}}-\text{C}_6\text{H}_4\text{OH-}p$$

(39)

The thiirane 1,1-dioxides discussed thus far were unstable intermediates which could not be isolated. Hesse and co-workers[30,31] were able to isolate thiirane 1,1-dioxide (41) during the reaction of sulfur dioxide (5) and diazomethane (40) (Table 3) in inert solvents. Again, a sulfene inter-

**Table 3**

Preparation of Thiirane 1,1-Dioxides via Cycloaddition Reaction of Diazo Compounds and Sulfur Dioxide

| Compound | Cycloadduct | MP (°C) | Yield (%) | Ref. |
|----------|-------------|---------|-----------|------|
| $\text{CH}_2\text{N}_2$ | $\text{H}_2\text{C}\diagdown\diagup\text{CH}_2$ over $\text{SO}_2$ | 19 | — | 30, 31 |
| $\text{CH}_3\text{CHN}_2$ | $\text{CH}_3\text{CH}$ ... $\text{SO}_2$ / $\text{HCCH}_3$ *trans* | — | 78 | 47 |
| | $\text{CH}_3\text{CH}$ ... $\text{SO}_2$ / $\text{CH}_3\text{CH}$ *cis* | — | 22 | |

mediate (42) was formed by the reaction of one molecule of diazomethane and sulfur dioxide; the intermediate (42) then reacts with the second molecule of diazomethane (40) to form thiirane 1,1-dioxide (41).[30,31] The

$$2CH_2N_2 + SO_2 \xrightarrow{-N_2} \quad H_2C\text{———}CH_2$$
$$\underset{SO_2}{\diagdown\diagup}$$

(40)      (5)                    (41)

structure of thiirane 1,1-dioxide was characterized by chemical analysis and by its infrared absorption spectrum.

$$CH_2N_2 + SO_2 \xrightarrow{-N_2} [CH_2{=}SO_2] \xrightarrow[-N_2]{CH_2N_2} H_2C\text{———}CH_2$$
$$\underset{SO_2}{\diagdown\diagup}$$

(40)      (5)              (42)                    (41)

Using an adaptation of the method used in preparing thiirane 1,1-dioxide (41).[30,31] Neureiter and Bordwell[47] isolated the postulated intermediate, 2,3-dimethylthiirane 1,1-dioxide (44), resulting from the reaction of an ethereal solution of diazoethane (43) with sulfur dioxide (5). The thiirane dioxide (44) was found to be the *cis*-isomer (44a), *cis*-2,3-dimethylthiirane

$$2CH_3CHN_2 + SO_2 \longrightarrow CH_3CH\text{———}CHCH_3$$
$$\underset{SO_2}{\diagdown\diagup}$$

(43)      (5)                       (44)

1,1-dioxide; the corresponding *trans* isomer (44b) was also obtained. The structures of the isomeric thiirane 1,1-dioxides were determined by microanalysis and nuclear magnetic resonance, and infrared spectra. The *cis*-thiirane 1,1-dioxide underwent rapid decomposition when warmed

$$\begin{array}{cc} H \quad\quad H \\ CH_3\blacktriangleright C\text{———}C\blacktriangleleft CH_3 \\ \underset{SO_2}{\diagdown\diagup} \end{array} \qquad \begin{array}{cc} H \quad\quad CH_3 \\ CH_3\blacktriangleright C\text{———}C\blacktriangleleft H \\ \underset{SO_2}{\diagdown\diagup} \end{array}$$

(44a)                    (44b)

neat, or in solution to give 100% *cis*-2-butene (45a). The thiirane 1,1-dioxide mixture decomposed into a mixture of 78% *trans*-2-butene

$$\begin{array}{cc} H \quad\quad H \\ CH_3\blacktriangleright C\text{———}C\blacktriangleleft CH_3 \\ \underset{SO_2}{\diagdown\diagup} \end{array} \xrightarrow{\Delta} \begin{array}{cc} H \quad H \\ CH_3\blacktriangleright C{=}C\blacktriangleleft CH_3 \end{array}$$

(44a)                    (45a)

(45b) and 22% *cis*-2-butene (45a),[47] whose composition was identical with the thiirane 1,1-dioxide isomer distribution in the mixture as determined by nuclear magnetic resonance.

$$CH_3CH\text{———}CHCH_3 \longrightarrow \begin{array}{c} H \;\; H \\ CH_3\blacktriangleright C{=}C\blacktriangleleft CH_3 \end{array} \longrightarrow \begin{array}{c} H \;\; CH_3 \\ CH_3\blacktriangleright C{=}C\blacktriangleleft H \end{array}$$
$$\underset{SO_2}{\diagdown\diagup}$$

(44)                    (45a)                    (45b)

Recently, it was found that sulfenes, $R'$—$CH$=$SO_2$ (**47**),[33,49] which are produced by dehydrochlorination of primary alkanesulfonyl chlorides (**46**) with triethylamine react readily *in situ* with diazoalkanes (**48**) at 0°C to form isolable thiirane 1,1-dioxides (**49**) (Table 4).[48] Thermal elimination

### Table 4

Preparation of Thiirane 1,1-Dioxides via Cycloaddition Reaction of Sulfenes and Diazo Compounds

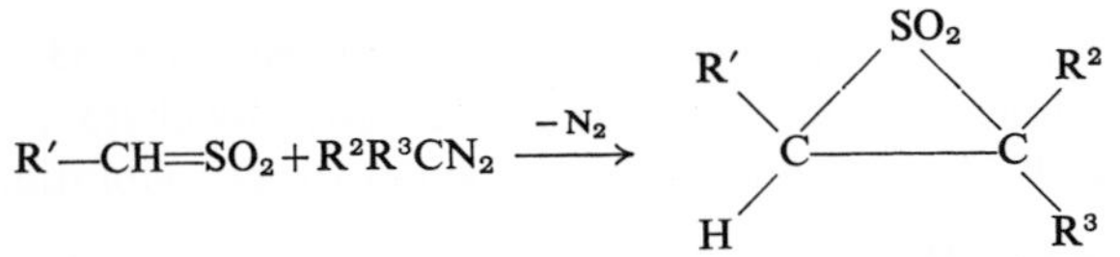

$$R'\text{—}CH\text{=}SO_2 + R^2R^3CN_2 \xrightarrow{-N_2}$$

| R' | R² | R³ | Yield (%) | MP, °C (BP, °C/mm) |
|---|---|---|---|---|
| H | H | H | 64 | 19 |
| $C_2H_5$ | H | H | 95 | (80/0.2; dec) |
| $C_6H_5$ | H | H | 35 | 39 (dec) |
| $C_6H_5CH_2$ | H | H | 99 | 49–51 |
| $C_6H_5CH_2$ | $CH_3$ | $C_2H_5$ | 76 | 77–78 |
| 7,7-Dimethyl-2-oxobicyclo[2,2,1]hept-1-yl | H | H | 94 | 83–85 |
| 7,7-Dimethyl-2-oxobicyclo[2,2,1]hept-1-yl | H | $CH_3$ | 36 | 77–79 |

of sulfur dioxide from the latter produces unsymmetrically substituted olefins (**50**) in good yields,[48] as is illustrated here.

$$R'\text{—}CH_2SO_2Cl \xrightarrow{Et_3N} R'\text{—}CH\text{=}SO_2$$
$$(46) \qquad\qquad (47)$$

$$R'\text{—}CH\text{=}SO_2 + R^3R^2CN_2 \xrightarrow{-N_2} R'\text{—}C\text{—}C\text{—}R^2$$
$$(47) \qquad (48) \qquad (49)$$

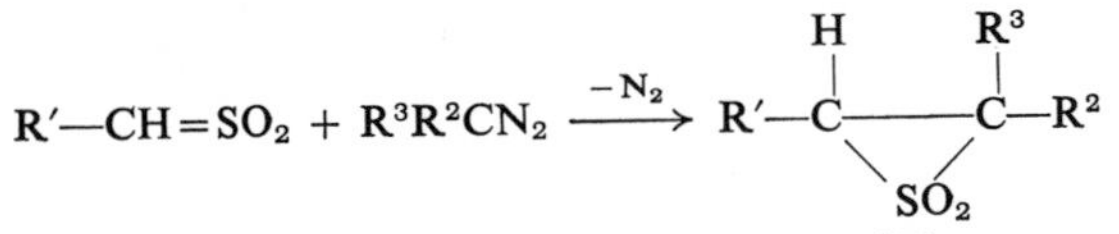

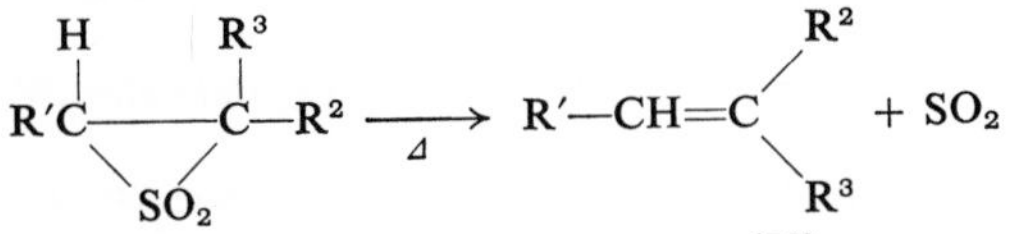

$$(49) \xrightarrow{\Delta} R'\text{—}CH\text{=}C + SO_2$$
$$(49) \qquad\qquad (50)$$

When phenylethanesulfonyl chloride (**51**) was added to a solution of diazomethane (**40**) and triethylamine cooled in ice, triethylamine hydrochloride precipitated with simultaneous evolution of nitrogen and formation of 2-benzylthiirane 1,1-dioxide (52) in 99% yield.[48] The thiirane 1,1-dioxide (52) released sulfur dioxide slowly at room temperature and

$$C_6H_5CH_2CH_2SO_2Cl + (C_2H_5)_3N \longrightarrow C_6H_5CH_2CH{=}SO_2 + (C_2H_5)_3NHCl$$
$$(51)$$

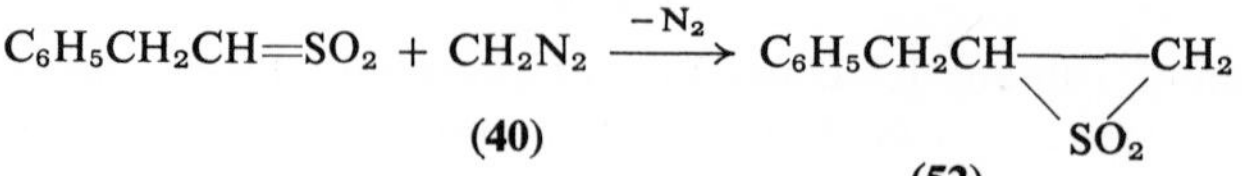

$$C_6H_5CH_2CH{=}SO_2 + CH_2N_2 \xrightarrow{-N_2} C_6H_5CH_2CH{\diagdown \diagup}CH_2$$
$$(40) \qquad\qquad\qquad\qquad SO_2$$
$$(52)$$

rapidly on heating to 80°C yielding 97% of allybenzene (53). The structures of the thiirane 1,1-dioxides were determined by characteristic infrared bands at 3080 cm$^{-1}$ due to the carbon–hydrogen vibration from the

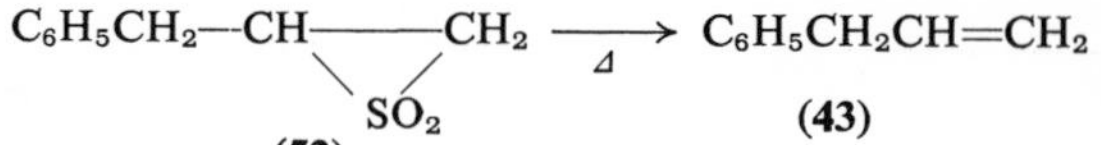

$$C_6H_5CH_2{-}CH{\diagdown \diagup}CH_2 \xrightarrow{\Delta} C_6H_5CH_2CH{=}CH_2$$
$$SO_2 \qquad\qquad (43)$$
$$(52)$$

three-membered ring and the intense sulfone band at 1160 and 1305 cm$^{-1}$.

Finally, Volpin and co-workers[40,80] postulated that three-membered rings containing sulfur of types 54–57 were stabilized by $p$–$p$–$d$ interaction. However, no other reference to this type of three-membered ring system has been found.

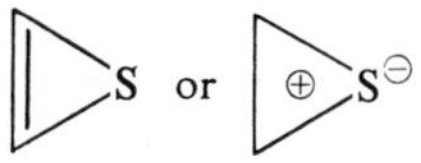

(54)

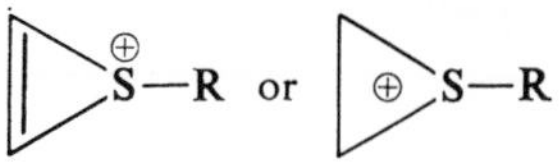

(55)

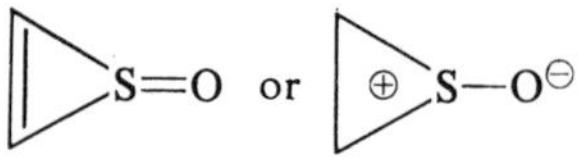

(56)

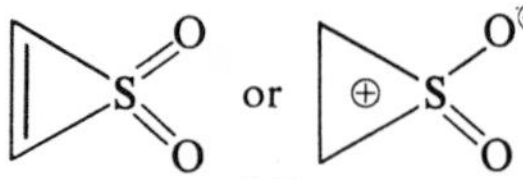

(57)

REFERENCES

1. G. M. Badger and B. J. Christie, *Current Trends in Heterocyclic Chemistry*, Butterworths, London, 1958.
2. L. J. Bellamy, *The Infra-Red Spectra of Complex Molecules*, Wiley, New York, 1962, p. 359.
3. F. G. Bordwell and H. M. Anderson, *J. Am. Chem. Soc.*, 75, 4959 (1953).
4. F. G. Bordwell and G. D. Cooper, *J. Am. Chem. Soc.*, 73, 5187 (1951).
5. C. C. J. Culvenor, W. Davies, and N. S. Heath, *J. Chem. Soc.*, 1949, 282.
6. C. C. J. Culvenor, W. Davies, and K. H. Pausacker, *J. Chem. Soc.*, 1946, 1050.
7. K. Dachlauer and L. Jackel, *Fr. Pat.* 797,621 (1936).

8. K. Dachlauer and L. Jackel, *Ger. Pat.* 636,708 (1936).
9. F. E. Dearborn, *U.S. Pat.* 2,169,293 (1939).
10. F. E. Dearborn, *U.S. Pat.* 2,237,096 (1941).
11. F. E. Dearborn, *U.S. Pat.* 2,333,093 (1943).
12. F. E. Dearborn, *U.S. Pat.* 2,427,717 (1947).
13. M. Delépine, *Bull. Soc. Chim. France*, **27**, 740 (1920).
14. M. Delépine, *Compt. Rend.*, **172**, 36 (1920).
15. M. Delépine and P. Jaffeaux, *Bull. Soc. Chim. France*, **29**, 136 (1921).
16. M. Delépine and P. Jaffeaux, *Compt. Rend.*, **172**, 158 (1921).
17. W. B. De More, H. O. Pritchard, and N. Davidson, *J. Am. Chem. Soc.*, **81**, 5874 (1959).
18. D. C. Dittmer and G. C. Levy, *J. Org. Chem.*, **30**, 636 (1965).
19. E. C. Dodds, L. Goldberg, W. Lawson, and R. Robinson, *Nature*, **141**, 247 (1938).
20. E. C. Dodds, L. Goldberg, W. Lawson, and R. Robinson, *Nature*, **142**, 34 (1938).
21. E. C. Dodds, L. Goldberg, W. Lawson, and R. Robinson, *Proc. Roy. Soc. (London)*, **127B**, 140 (1939).
22. B. Eistert, in *Newer Methods of Preparative Organic Chemistry*, Interscience, New York, 1948, p. 513.
23. M. G. Ettlinger, *J. Am. Chem. Soc.*, **72**, 4792 (1950).
24. E. A. Fehnel and M. Caramack, *J. Am. Chem. Soc.*, **71**, 84 (1949).
25. E. A. Fehnel and M. Caramack, *J. Am. Chem. Soc.*, **71**, 231 (1949).
26. E. A. Fehnel and M. Caramack, *J. Am. Chem. Soc.*, **72**, 1292 (1950).
27. M. Gomberg, *Chem. Ber.*, **35**, 3914 (1902).
28. C. P. Hager and R. M. Burgison, *J. Am. Pharm. Assoc.*, **39**, 7 (1950).
29. G. K. Helmkamp and D. J. Pettitt, *J. Org. Chem.*, **27**, 2942 (1962).
30. G. Hesse and S. Majmudar, *Chem. Ber.*, **93**, 1129 (1960).
31. G. Hesse, E. Reichold, and S. Majmudar, *Chem. Ber.*, **90**, 2106 (1957).
32. S. O. Jones and E. E. Reid, *J. Am. Chem. Soc.*, **60**, 2452 (1938).
33. J. F. King and T. Durst, *Tetrahedron Letters*, **1963**, 585.
34. J. F. King, P. de Mayo, E. Morkved, A. B. M. A. Sattar, and A. Stoessl, *Can. J. Chem.*, **41**, 100 (1963).
35. H. Kloosterziel and H. J. Backer, *Rec. Trav. Chim.*, **71**, 1235 (1952).
36. H. Kloosterziel, M. H. Deinema, and H. J. Backer, *Rec. Trav. Chim.*, **71**, 1228 (1952).
37. A. R. Knight, O. P. Strausz, and H. E. Gunning, *J. Am. Chem. Soc.*, **85**, 1207 (1963).
38. A. R. Knight, O. P. Strausz, and H. E. Gunning, *J. Am. Chem. Soc.*, **85**, 2349 (1963).
39. A. R. Knight, O. P. Strausz, S. M. Malm, and H. E. Gunning, *J. Am. Chem. Soc.*, **86**, 4243 (1964).
40. D. N. Kursanov and M. E. Volpin, *Zh. Vses. Khim. Obshch. im D. I. Mendeleeva*, **7**, 282 (1962); *Chem. Abstr.*, **58**, 4389 (1963).
41. N. Latif and I. Fathy, *J. Org. Chem.*, **27**, 1633 (1962).
42. N. Latif, I. Fathy, and B. Haggag, *Tetrahedron Letters*, **1965**, 1155.
43. K. Martin, *J. Chem. Soc.*, **1964**, 2944.
44. W. J. Middleton, E. G. Howard, and W. H. Sharkey, *J. Org. Chem.*, **30**, 1375 (1965).
45. W. J. Middleton and W. H. Sharkey, *J. Org. Chem.*, **30**, 1384 (1965).
46. N. P. Neureiter and F. G. Bordwell, *J. Am. Chem. Soc.*, **81**, 578 (1959).
47. N. P. Neureiter and F. G. Bordwell, *J. Am. Chem. Soc.*, **85**, 1209 (1963).

48. G. Opitz and K. Fischer, *Angew. Chem.*, **77**, 41 (1965); *Angew. Chem. Intern. Ed. Engl.*, **4**, 70 (1965).
49. G. Opitz and K. Fischer, *Z. Naturforsch.*, **18b**, 775 (1963).
50. L. A. Paquette, *J. Am. Chem. Soc.*, **86**, 4085 (1964).
51. L. A. Paquette, *J. Am. Chem. Soc.*, **86**, 4089 (1964).
52. C. C. Price and P. F. Kirk, *J. Am. Chem. Soc.*, **75**, 2396 (1953).
53. D. D. Reynolds and D. L. Fields, in *Compounds with Three- and Four-Membered Rings* (*The Chemistry of Heterocyclic Compounds*, Vol. 19, A. Weissberger, Ed.), Interscience, New York, 1964, p. 576.
54. W. Reid and H. Klug, *Chem. Ber.*, **94**, 368 (1961).
55. S. Sarel, L. Pohoryles, and R. Shoshan, *J. Org. Chem.*, **24**, 1873 (1959).
56. V. W. Schlenk, *Ann. Chem.*, **394**, 182 (1912).
57. A. Schönberg, *Ann. Chem.*, **454**, 39 (1927).
58. A. Schönberg, *Methoden der Organischen Chemie* (*Houben-Weyl*), Vol. IX, Georg Thieme Verlag, Stuttgart, 1955, p. 158.
59. A. Schönberg and M. Z. Barakat, *J. Chem. Soc.*, **1939**, 1074.
60. A. Schönberg, A. Fateen, and A. Sammour, *J. Am. Chem. Soc.*, **79**, 6020 (1957).
61. A. Schönberg and E. Frese, *Chem. Ber.*, **95**, 2810 (1962).
62. A. Schönberg and O. Schütz, *Chem. Ber.*, **60**, 2351 (1927).
63. A. Schönberg and M. M. Sidky, *J. Am. Chem. Soc.*, **81**, 2259 (1959).
64. A. Schönberg and L. v. Vargha, *Ann. Chem.*, **483**, 176 (1930).
65. A. Schönberg and L. v. Vargha, *Chem. Ber.*, **64**, 1390 (1931).
66. S. Searles, Jr., H. R. Hays, and E. F. Lutz, *J. Org. Chem.*, **27**, 2832 (1962).
67. S. Searles, Jr. and E. F. Lutz, *J. Am. Chem. Soc.*, **80**, 3168 (1958).
68. S. B. Soloway, *U.S. Pat.* 2,694,073 (1954).
69. H. Staudinger and F. Pfenninger, *Chem. Ber.*, **49**, 1930 (1916).
70. H. Staudinger and F. Pfenninger, *Chem. Ber.*, **49**, 1941 (1916).
71. H. Staudinger and S. Siegwart, *Helv. Chim. Acta*, **3**, 833 (1920).
72. H. Staudinger and S. Siegwart, *Helv. Chim. Acta*, **3**, 840 (1920).
73. J. M. Stewart, *J. Org. Chem.*, **29**, 1655 (1964).
74. L. A. Strait, R. Ketcham, D. Jambotkar, and V. P. Shah, *J. Am. Chem. Soc.*, **86**, 4628 (1964).
75. O. P. Strausz and H. E. Gunning, *J. Am. Chem. Soc.*, **84**, 4080 (1963).
76. E. Taeger, Z. El-Hewehi, and F. Runge, *J. Prakt. Chem.*, **18**, 269 (1962).
77. A. E. Tschitschibabin, *Chem. Ber.*, **37**, 4709 (1904).
78. E. E. van Tamelen, *J. Am. Chem. Soc.*, **73**, 3444 (1951).
79. L. v. Vargha and E. Kovacs, *Chem. Ber.*, **75**, 794 (1942).
80. M. E. Volpin, Yu. D. Koreshkov, V. G. Dulova, and D. N. Kursanov, *Tetrahedron*, **18**, 107 (1962).
81. E. Wedekind and D. Schenk, *Chem. Ber.*, **44**, 198 (1911).
82. H. A. Wiebe, A. R. Knight, O. P. Strausz, and H. E. Gunning, *J. Am. Chem. Soc.*, **87**, 1443 (1965).
83. M. A. Youtz and P. P. Perkins, *J. Am. Chem. Soc.*, **51**, 3508 (1929).

## B. TWO HETEROATOMS

### 1. Nitrogen Only

#### a. Diaziridines and Diazirines

During the early 1900's, it was not clear whether diazo compounds were acyclic or cyclic. In an attempt to prepare isomeric diazo compounds and hydrazones, Staudinger[69] reported that azo compounds should react with ethylene derivatives forming diaziridines (2), rings with one carbon and two nitrogen atoms, analogous to the reaction of 9-diazofluorene (1) with ethylene derivatives to form the corresponding cyclopropanes. Staudinger suggested that by suitably choosing substituents (2, R's), it would be possible to substitute hydrogen atoms, thus obtaining a "hydrazi" compound (3). The diaziridine (3) was presumed to be isomeric with the linear compound (4) and to be capable of being oxidized to the diazo compound (a diazirine) (5), which Staudinger believed was different from the diazo compound (1). Staudinger was not in agreement with the cyclic structures reported for diazo compounds by Curtius.[13,44] For example, the diethyl azocarboxylate (6), when treated with the diazo compound (1), resulted in

$(C_6H_4)_2C$———N—R         $(C_6H_4)_2C$———N—H         $(C_6H_4)_2C$=NNH$_2$

           N                              N                              (4)

           |                              |

           R                              H

          (2)                            (3)

$(C_6H_4)_2C$———N

            N

           (5)

the formation of diethyl "hydrazilfluorenedicarboxylate" (7), which hydrolyzed to the ketone (8) and the hydrazine (9) when refluxed with concentrated hydrochloric acid.

$(C_6H_4)_2CN_2$ + $C_2H_5O_2C$—N $\xrightarrow{-N_2}$ $C_2H_5O_2CN$———$NCO_2C_2H_5$

                    $C_2H_5O_2C$—N                           $C(C_6H_4)_2$

        (1)              (6)                          (7)

                              HCl ↓ H$_2$O

              $(NHCO_2C_2H_5)_2$ + $(C_6H_4)_2C$=O

                    (9)                      (8)

Similarly, the diaziridine, triethyl "hydrazimethanecarboxylate" (12) was reported[12] to have been prepared via the insertion of the carbene intermediate, carbethoxymethylene (11), generated by the thermal decomposition of ethyl diazoacetate (10), into the nitrogen–nitrogen double bond of diethyl azocarboxylate (6).

$$N_2CHCO_2C_2H_5 \xrightarrow{\Delta} :CHCO_2C_2H_5 + N_2$$
$$(10) \qquad\qquad\qquad (11)$$

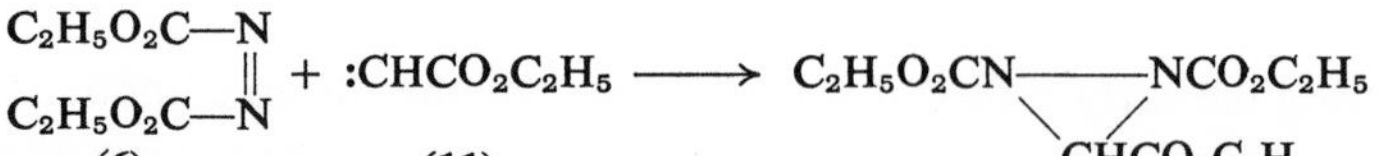

However, in a recent review of three-membered rings containing two heteroatoms, Schmitz[53] reported that erroneous cyclic structural assignments were often formulated for hydrazones, nitrones, and aliphatic diazo compounds, and that prior to 1950 no three-membered rings containing two heteroatoms had ever been prepared.

Specifically, diaziridines were discovered independently by three research groups in the late 1950's.[2,3,42,50,55]

Schmitz[54] described the synthesis of a hexahydrotetrazine derivative (13) from 3,4-dihydroisoquinoline (14) and chloramine (15); however, when the reaction was repeated using N-chloromethylamine (16) the expected tetrazine derivative was not obtained. Instead, the diaziridine derivative (17)[50,55] was obtained. The diaziridine (17) dimerized in dilute acid to the tetrazine derivative (18). Prior to this discovery diaziridines

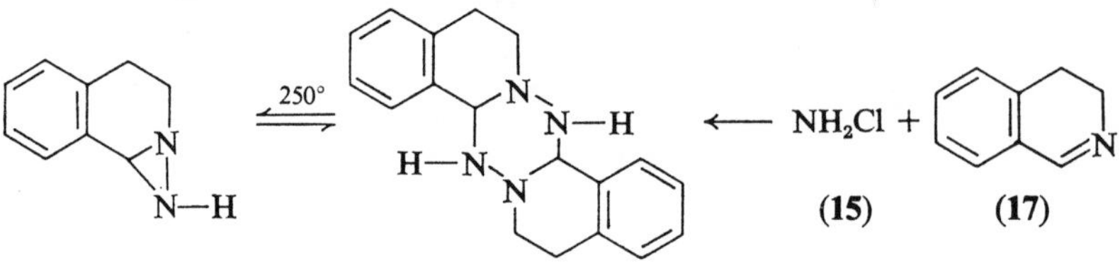

(13)

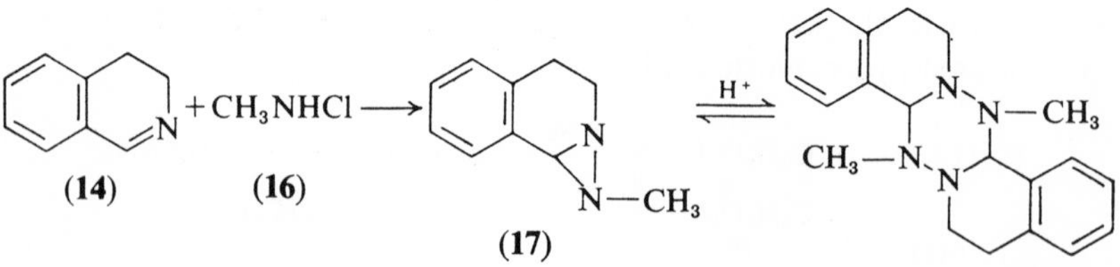

were assumed to have been formed by the reaction of azodicarbonyl compounds and aliphatic diazo compounds.[24,37,69]

While attempting a Raschig hydrazine synthesis in the gas phase and to trap the hydrazine formed with acetone, Abendroth and Henrich[2,3] obtained an isomer of acetone hydrazone which was assigned the diaziridine structure (**19**). Paulsen[42,43] reported analogous products from the diethyl ketone and from methyl ethyl ketone.

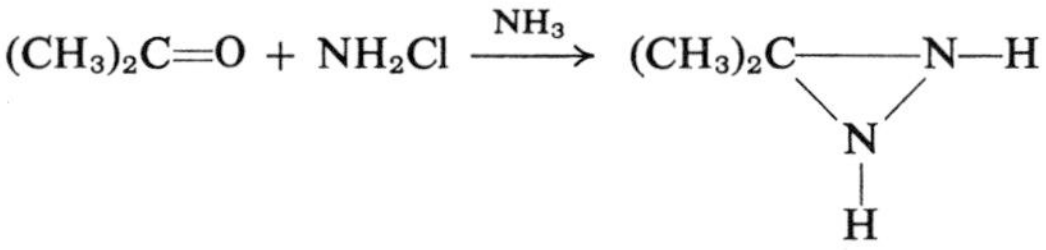

$(CH_3)_2C{=}O + NH_2Cl \xrightarrow{NH_3} (CH_3)_2C$
N—H
N
H

**(19)**

The smoothness of the formation of diaziridines as well as the general applicability of the synthesis[49] has proved surprising. The reaction with 3,4-dihydroisoquinoline (**14**) was quite applicable to aliphatic Schiff bases. In all investigations, chloramine or alkylchloramines transferred the nitrogen–hydrogen (or alkyl) residue to the Schiff bases, regardless of whether the Schiff base was derived from aldehydes, ketones, or cyclic ketones.[51,52,55–58,68]

During the reaction of aliphatic aldehydes (also benzaldehyde) with ammonia and chloramine, the diaziridine formation was accompanied by a further condensation yielding the triazolidine ring[56]; that is,

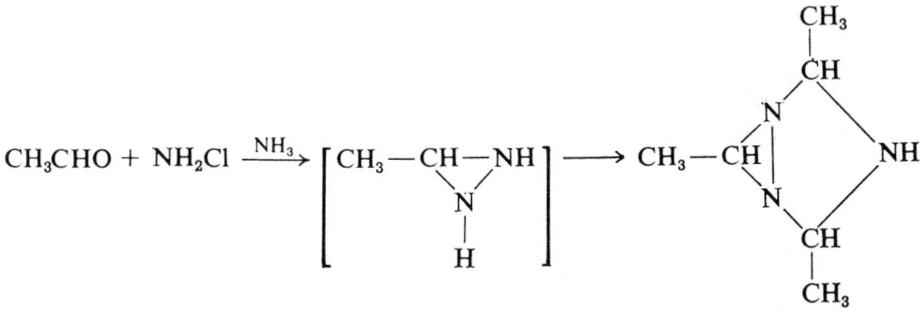

$CH_3CHO + NH_2Cl \xrightarrow{NH_3}$
$CH_3$—CH—NH
N
H
$CH_3$—CH
NH
CH
$CH_3$
N
N
CH
$CH_3$

Ketone–ammonia mixtures and Schiff bases reacted with hydroxylamine or alkylhydroxylamine-*O*-sulfonic acids resulting in diaziridine derivatives.[1,61,66] Likewise, mixtures of carbonyl compounds and primary amines may be used rather than the Schiff bases:

O
+ $H_2N$—R
$H_2N$—$OSO_3H$
NH
NH

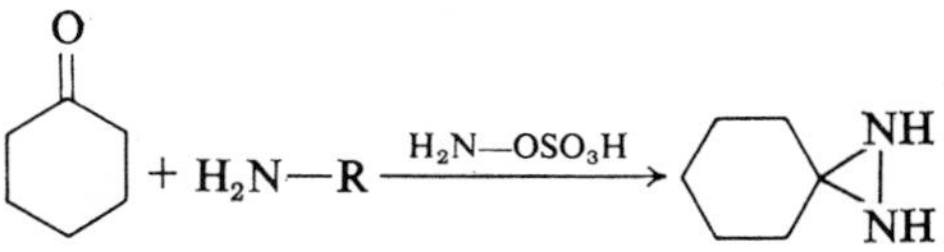

**Table 1**
Diaziridines

### A. From Schiff Bases and Chloramines

| Schiff base | Chloramines | Diaziridine | BP (°C/mm) | MP (°C/mm) | Yield | Ref. |
|---|---|---|---|---|---|---|
| 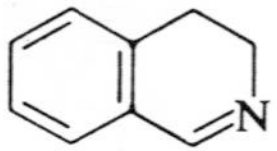 (3,4-dihydroisoquinoline) | $CH_3NHCl$ | 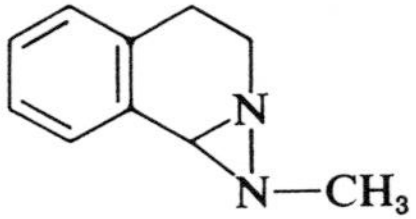 (N–$CH_3$ diaziridine) | 111.5–113/10 | — | 50 | 50 52 55 |
| 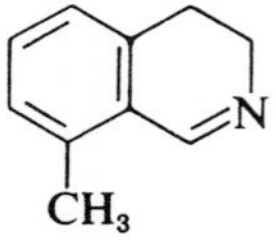 ($CH_3$-substituted dihydroisoquinoline) | $CH_3NHCl$ | 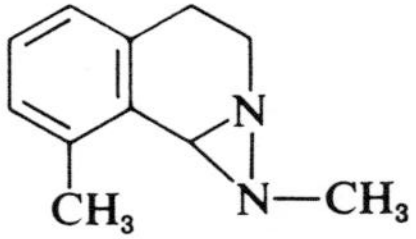 (N–$CH_3$ diaziridine, $CH_3$) | 126.5–128.5/11 | 68.5–70 | — | 50 55 |
| 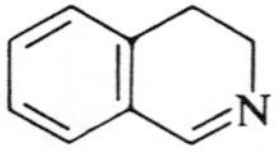 (3,4-dihydroisoquinoline) | $NH_2Cl$ | 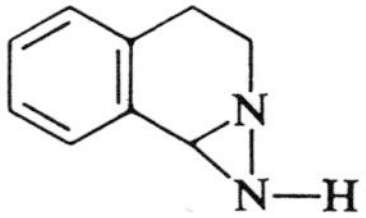 (N–H diaziridine) | — | 72 | 10–30 | 50 |
| $C_6H_{13}CH = NC_6H_9$ | $NH_2Cl$ | 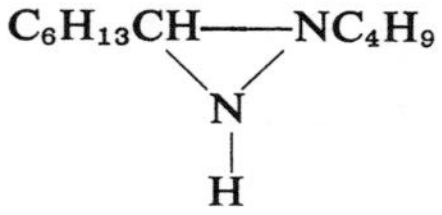 $C_6H_{13}CH$—$NC_4H_9$ (N–H) | 70–73/1 | 15.5–16 | 53 | 52 58 |
| 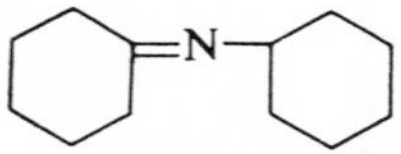 (dicyclohexyl ketimine) | $NH_2Cl$ | 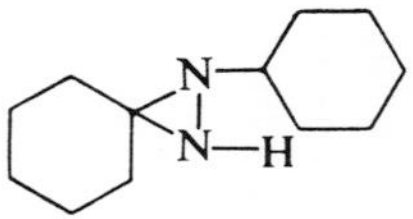 (dispiro N–N–H diaziridine) | — — | — — | — 71 | 52 58 |

| Imine | Reagent | Product | b.p. (°C/mm) | m.p. (°C) | Yield % | Yield % |
|---|---|---|---|---|---|---|
| $C_3H_7CH=NC_4H_9$ | $C_4H_9NCl$ | 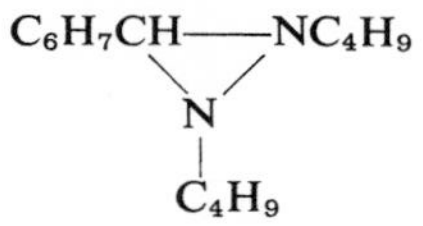 $C_6H_7CH{-}NC_4H_9$, $N{-}C_4H_9$ | — | — | — | 52 |
|  |  |  | 64–66/0.02 | — | 71 | 68 |
| 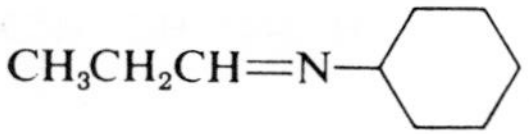 $CH_3CH_2CH=N{-}C_6H_{11}$ (cyclohexyl) | $NH_2Cl$ | 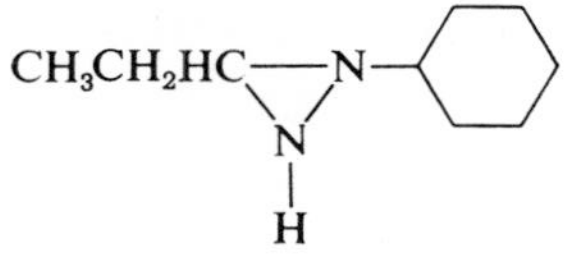 cyclohexyl–N, $CH_3CH_2HC{-}$, N–H | 99–100/12 | 28 | 55 | 58 |
| 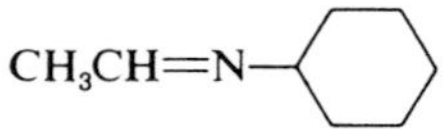 $CH_3CH=N{-}C_6H_{11}$ (cyclohexyl) | $NH_2Cl$ | 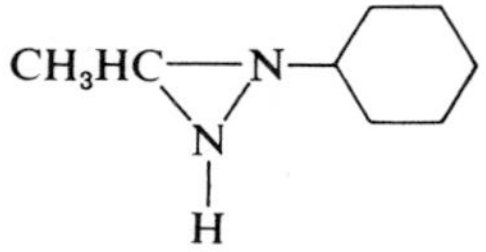 cyclohexyl–N, $CH_3HC{-}$, N–H | 34–36/0.2 | 30 | 46 | 58 |
| 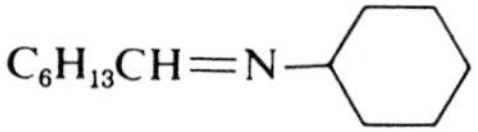 $C_6H_{13}CH=N{-}C_6H_{11}$ (cyclohexyl) | $NH_2Cl$ | 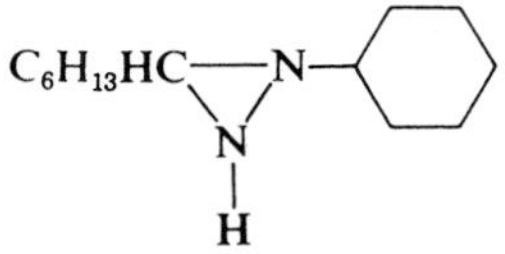 cyclohexyl–N, $C_6H_{13}HC{-}$, N–H | 114/0.2 | 17–18 | 54 | 58 |
| $C_3H_7CH=NCH_2C_6H_5$ | $NH_2Cl$ | 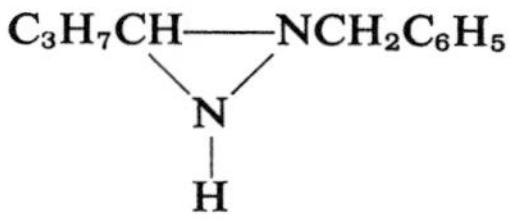 $C_3H_7CH{-}NCH_2C_6H_5$, N–H | 100–103/0.6 | 12–13 | 26 | 58 |
| $CH_3CH=NC_2H_5$ | $NH_2Cl$ | 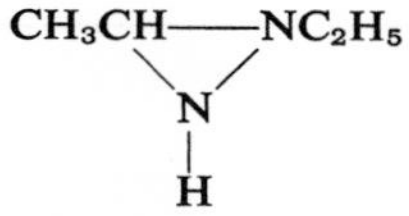 $CH_3HC{-}NC_2H_5$, N–H | 103.5–104 | — | 18 | 58 |

(continued)

**Table 1** (*continued*)

| Schiff base | Chloramines | Diaziridine | BP (°C/mm) | MP (°C/mm) | Yield | Ref. |
|---|---|---|---|---|---|---|
| 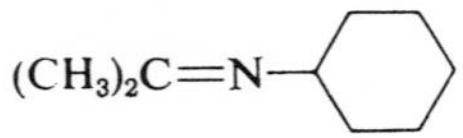 $(CH_3)_2C{=}N$–cyclohexyl | $NH_2Cl$ | 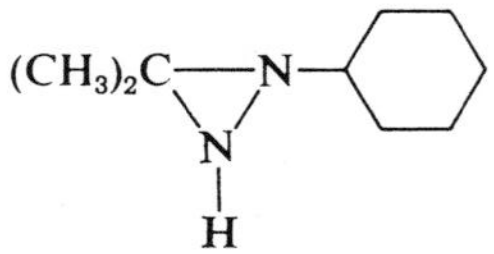 | 47–48 | 16–17 | 64 | 58 |
| $(CH_3)_2C{=}NC_3H_7$-$i$ | $NH_2Cl$ | 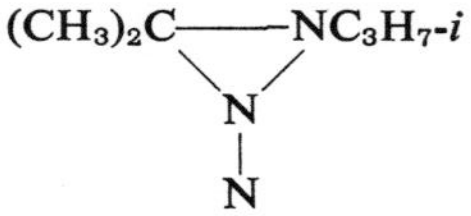 | 54–55/60 | −11 to −9 | 40 | 58 |
| $CH_3CH{=}NC_4H_9$ | $C_4H_9NHCl$ | 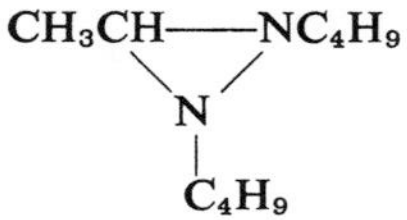 | 50–51/1.5 | — | 64 | 68 |
| 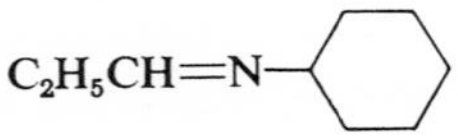 $C_2H_5CH{=}N$–cyclohexyl | $CH_3NHCl$ | 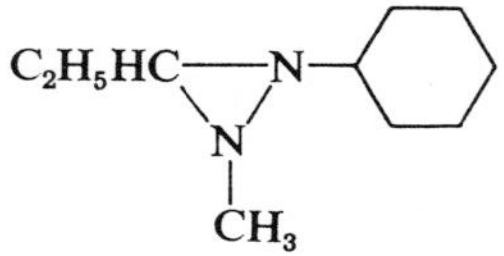 | 92–93/12 | — | 57 | 68 |
| $C_6H_{13}CH{=}NC_4H_9$ | $CH_3NHCl$ | 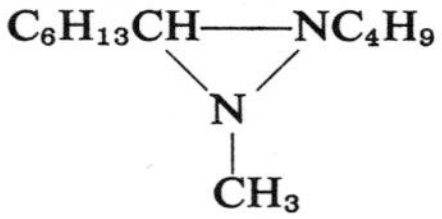 | 79–81/0.6 | — | 63 | 68 |

| | | | | | | |
|---|---|---|---|---|---|---|
| $C_6H_{13}CH{=}NC_4H_9$ | $C_4H_9NHCl$ | 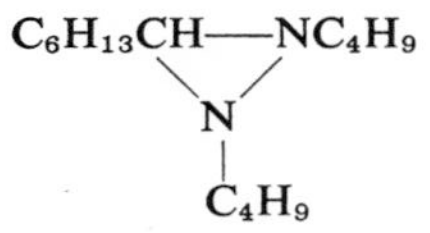 $C_6H_{13}CH{-}NC_4H_9$ / $N{-}C_4H_9$ | 106–107/0.8 | — | 53 | 68 |
| $C_6H_{13}CH{=}NCH_3$ | $CH_3NHCl$ | 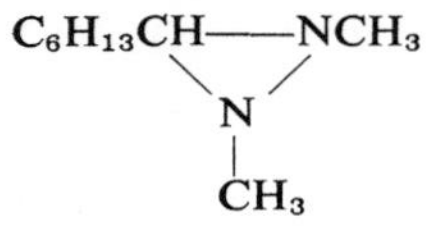 $C_6H_{13}CH{-}NCH_3$ / $N{-}CH_3$ | 42–43/1 | — | 68 | 68 |
| $C_3H_7CH{=}NC_4H_9$ | $CH_3NHCl$ | 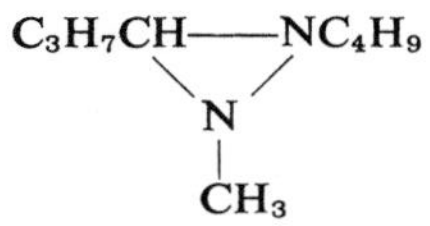 $C_3H_7CH{-}NC_4H_9$ / $N{-}CH_3$ | 49–51/0.02 | — | 42 | 68 |
| $C_3H_7CH{=}NC_4H_9$ | $C_3H_7NHCl$ | 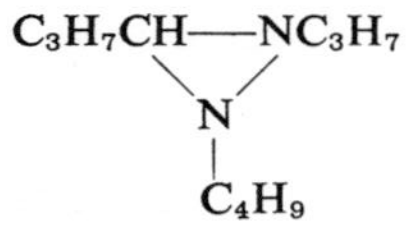 $C_3H_7CH{-}NC_3H_7$ / $N{-}C_4H_9$ | 60–62/0.02 | — | 50 | 68 |
| $C_3H_7CH{=}NC_4H_9$ | $C_2H_5NHCl$ | 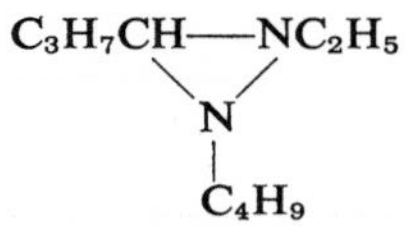 $C_3H_7CH{-}NC_2H_5$ / $N{-}C_4H_9$ | 55–57/0.02 | — | 55 | 68 |

**Table 1** (*continued*)

**B. From Carbonyl Compounds with Chloramines or Hydroxylamine-O-sulfonic Acids**

| Carbonyl compound | Chloramines, sulfonic acids | Diaziridine | BP (°C/mm) | MP (°C) | Yield (%) | Ref. |
|---|---|---|---|---|---|---|
| $(CH_3)_2C{=}O$ | $Cl_2$, $NH_3$ | 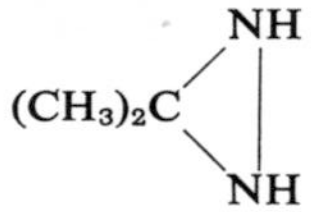 $(CH_3)_2C$ with NH, NH ring | — | — | — | 2 |
| $CH_3(C_2H_5)C{=}O$ | $Cl_2$, $NH_3$ | 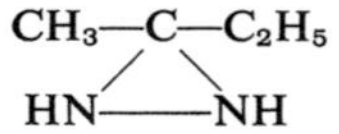 $CH_3{-}C{-}C_2H_5$ / $HN{-}NH$ | 32/17 | 21.5/22 | 99 | 43 |
| $(C_2H_5)_2C{=}O$ | $Cl_2$, $NH_3$ | 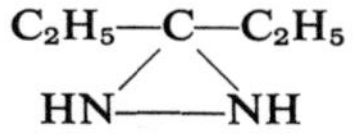 $C_2H_5{-}C{-}C_2H_5$ / $HN{-}NH$ | 58/24 | 56 | 95–97 | 43 |
| $CH_3(n{-}C_3H_7)C{=}O$ | $Cl_2$, $NH_3$ | 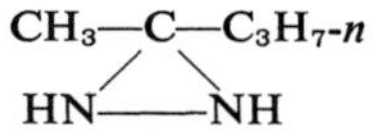 $CH_3{-}C{-}C_3H_7{-}n$ / $HN{-}NH$ | 48/15 | ~ −10 | — | 43 |
| $CH_3(i{-}C_3H_7)C{=}O$ | $Cl_2$, $NH_3$ | 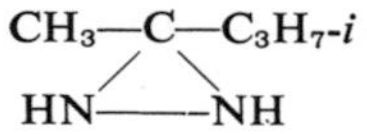 $CH_3{-}C{-}C_3H_7{-}i$ / $HN{-}NH$ | 67/50 | 55–56 | — | 43 |
| $CH_3CHO$ | $ClNH_2$, $NH_3$ | 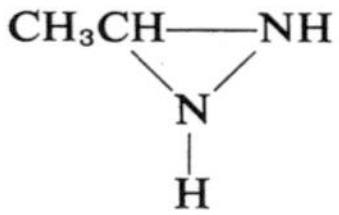 $CH_3CH{-}NH$ / $N{-}H$ | — | — | — | 56, 62 |

| | | Product | B.p./mm | M.p. | Yield | Refs. |
|---|---|---|---|---|---|---|
| $C_2H_5CHO$ | $ClNH_2$, $NH_3$ | 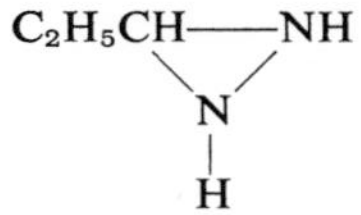 $C_2H_5CH{-}NH$, $N{-}H$ (aziridine) | — | — | — | 56, 62 |
| $C_6H_5CHO$ | $ClNH_2$, $NH_3$ | 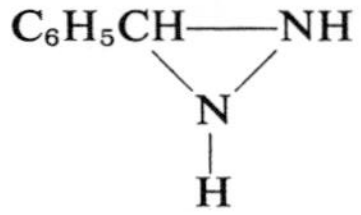 $C_6H_5CH{-}NH$, $N{-}H$ | — | — | — | 56 |
| $(n\text{-}C_3H_7)_2C{=}O$ | $NH_2OSO_3H$, $NH_3$ | 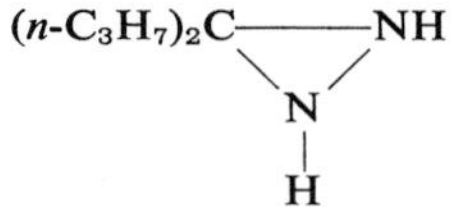 $(n\text{-}C_3H_7)_2C{-}NH$, $N{-}H$ | 73–74/11 | −1 to +1 | 33 | 61 |
| $(CH_3)_2C{=}O$ | $NH_2OSO_3H$, $NH_3$ | 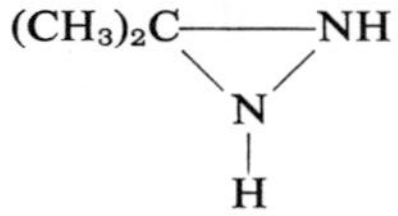 $(CH_3)_2C{-}NH$, $N{-}H$ | — | 44 | — | 61 |
| $CH_3(C_6H_5)C{=}O$ | $NH_2OSO_3H$, $NH_3$ | 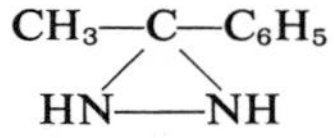 $CH_3{-}C{-}C_6H_5$, $HN{-}NH$ | 73–80/0.2 | 41–42 | 9 | 61 |
| $n\text{-}C_3H_7CHO$ | $NH_2Cl$, $NH_3$ | 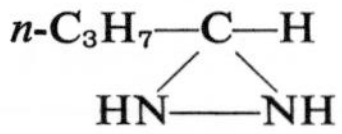 $n\text{-}C_3H_7{-}C{-}H$, $HN{-}NH$ | — | — | — | 62 |

(continued)

Table 1 (*continued*)

| Carbonyl compound | Chloramines, sulfonic acids | Diaziridine | BP (°C/mm) | MP (°C) | Yield (%) | Ref. |
|---|---|---|---|---|---|---|
| $CH_2O$ | $NH_2Cl$, $NH_3$ | 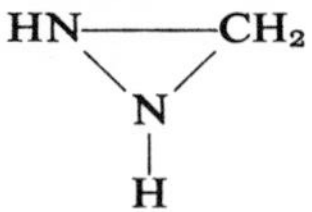 HN—CH$_2$ / N—H | — | — | — | 62 |
| 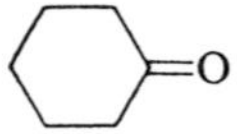 cyclohexanone | $NH_3$, $CH_3NHOSO_3H$ |  cyclohexane NH, N—CH$_3$ | 42–43/1.5 | 34–36 | 45 | 66 |
| 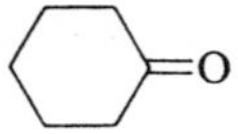 cyclohexanone | $NH_3$, $NH_2OSO_3H$ |  cyclohexane NH, NH | 70–80/0.01 | 105 | 67 | 66 |
| 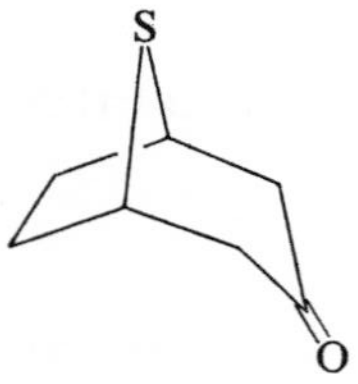 thiabicyclic ketone | $NH_2OSO_3H$, $NH_3$ | 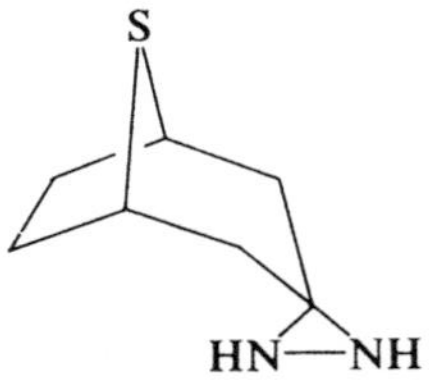 thiabicyclic HN—NH | — | 169–171 | 33 | 70 |
| 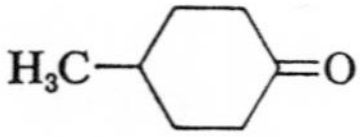 4-methylcyclohexanone ($H_3C$) | $NH_2OSO_3H$, $NH_4OH$ | 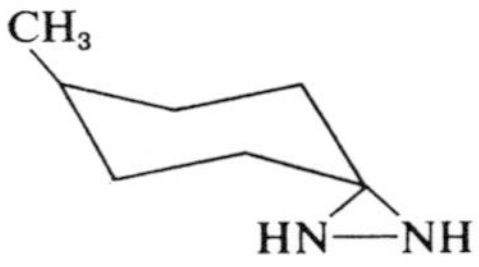 4-methyl HN—NH ($CH_3$) | — | 81–82 | 37 | 70 |

Numerous diaziridines have been prepared by this method, ranging in yields from 50 to 80% (Table 1). The diaziridine (21) was found to result from the reaction of cyclohexanone (20) with methylamine and hydroxylamine-$O$-sulfonic acid or with ammonia and methylhydroxylamine-$O$-sulfonic acid.[66] The equivalence of the two nitrogen atoms was determined by the labeling with methyl groups.

The mechanism first described for diaziridine synthesis was the cyclo-addition of an imene (22) or alkylimene (also termed nitrene intermediate) to a carbon–nitrogen double bond analogous to the synthesis of cyclo-propanes from olefins and carbenes[14] and the old mechanism for the Raschig hydrazine synthesis,[46-48] equation a. This mechanism has often been used.[6-10, 21, 25-27, 31, 40, 43, 71] Recently, however, it has been proven

that the nitrene intermediate (22) is not the reactive species in the reaction.[4, 6, 19, 23, 68, 72] The equilibrium between the nitrene intermediate (22) and the sulfate (equation a) from the hydroxylamine-$O$-sulfonic acid in the presence of a base does not exist[67] because it does not incorporate radioactive sulfur from a solution of active sulfate by isotope exchange. There remains, though, the possibility of an irreversible decomposition of the hydroxylamine-$O$-sulfonic acid into the nitrene intermediate (22) and sulfate; thus the formation of the diaziridine in a subsequent reaction would not be rate-determining but would proceed at the same rate as the decomposition of hydroxylamine-$O$-sulfonic acid in the absence of a Schiff base. It has been found[65] that the diaziridine from cyclohexanone, ammonia, and hydroxylamine-$O$-sulfonic acid was formed within one hour at 0°C, whereas only half of a given amount of the sulfonic acid is decomposed in 0.1$N$ sodium hydroxide solution after about 20 hr at 20°C, thus indicating that the Schiff base attacks the sulfonic acid as such before the irreversible decomposition of the acid to the nitrene occurs.

Since chlorine-36 was not incorporated, there exists no equilibrium between the chloramine and the nitrene,[5] and the reaction must therefore be due to an attack of the Schiff base on the chloramine. The closure of the diaziridine results by the formation of a geminal compound (23), arising from hydroxylamine-$O$-sulfonic acid either by addition to a Schiff base or by aminoalkylation with a carbonyl compound and an amine; thus, the formation of the diaziridine (24) appears to be an intramolecular $S_N2$ reaction and not a cycloaddition, as formerly believed.

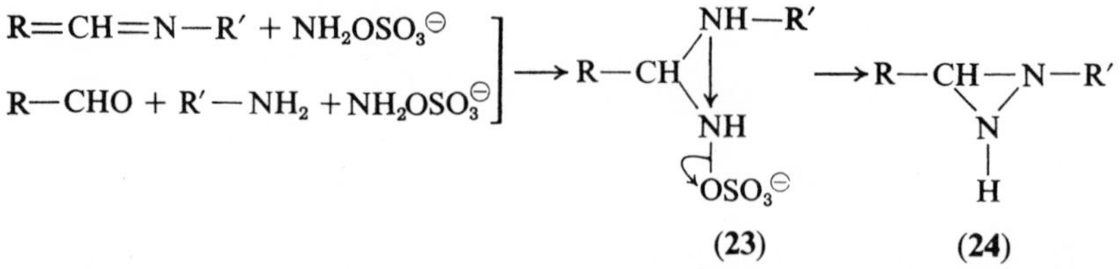

(23)          (24)

Although diazirines are not prepared by means of a cycloaddition reaction, they are of interest and their synthesis will be briefly discussed. Cyclic diazo compounds with three-membered rings—diazirines—had previously been widely discussed as tentative structures for known diazo compounds (see page 87), but it has been only in the last four years that diazirines have actually been prepared. The first published indications of their existence[41,61,64] were viewed with caution. However, not only was the structure of the diazirines determined[45,63,66] but it was found that the cyclic isomers 25 and 26 were frequently more readily available than the linear aliphatic diazo compounds. For instance, 3-diazopentane (27) has never been described, and diazocyclohexane (28) is only known in solution,[22] while the cyclic isomers were obtained in good yield by the dehydrogenation of the saturated three-membered rings (diaziridines).[28,41,60–62] Other diazirines were prepared from acetone, methyl ethyl ketone, methyl phenyl ketone, 4-heptanone, formaldehyde, acetalde-

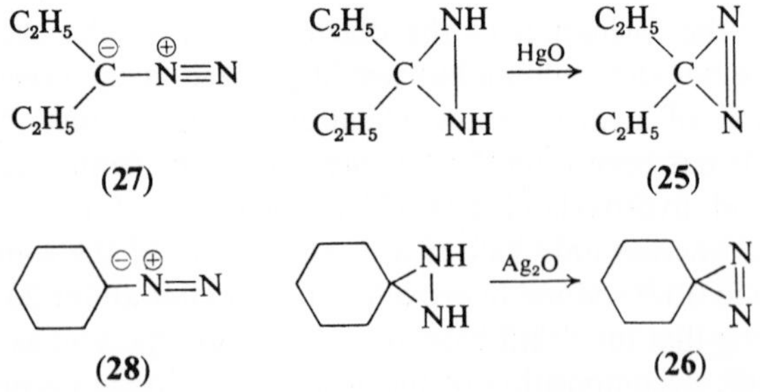

(27)          (25)

(28)          (26)

hyde, propionaldehyde, $n$-butyraldehyde, cyclopentanone, and cyclo-heptanone.[49,61,62] Intermediates in the two-stage process of preparing diazirines from aldehydes are the bicyclic diaziridines (29), whose five-membered rings are easily cleaved by hydrolysis without damage to the

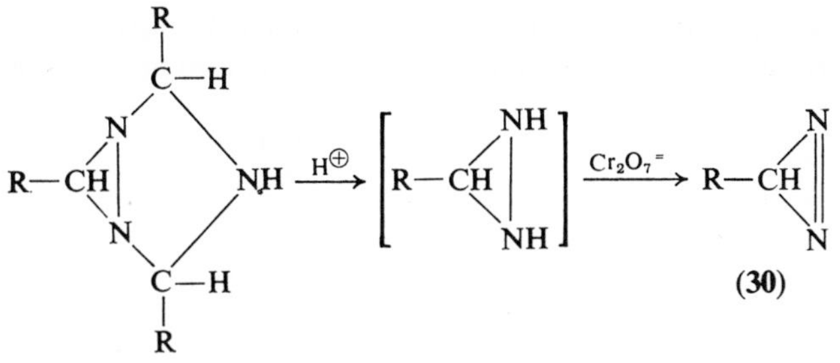

(29)          (30)

three-membered ring[62]; in the presence of dichromate the diazirines (30)

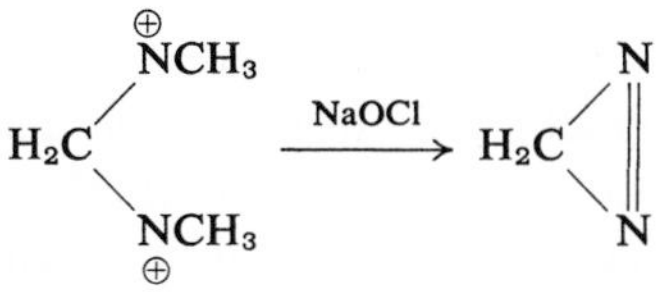

(31)          (32)

are formed in 70–95% yield. The diazirine (32) was prepared by adding methyldiammonium sulfate (31)[29] to a hypochlorite solution.[38] Diazirine

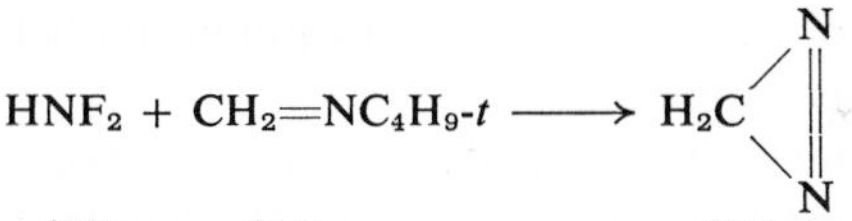

$$HNF_2 + CH_2=NC_4H_9\text{-}t \longrightarrow H_2C$$

(33)          (34)          (32)

(32) was also prepared by treating difluoramine (33) with *t*-butylazomethine (34).[20] Spectroscopic measurements of bond lengths and bond angles confirmed the structure of the diazirine (32).[15,45] The cyclic diazo compounds are so markedly different from the linear compounds that confusion between the two types is impossible, for in certain respects they appear to be the exact opposites. For instance, linear aliphatic diazo compounds absorb in the visible region, but the cyclic compounds are colorless and absorb only below 360 mμ.[30,32] However, the two types of diazo compounds have one common property; they explode violently on overheating. Diazirines appear to be rather more stable than the linear isomers; the activation energy for the decomposition of dimethyldiazirine was found to be 33.2 kcal/mole.[17]

Recently nuclear magnetic resonance studies of diazirines were used in the conformational analysis of six-membered carbocyclic rings.[70] The nuclear magnetic resonance spectra of 8-thiabicyclo[3.2.1]octane-3-spiro-3'-diazirine (35) and 1,2-diaza-6-methylspiro[2.5]-1-octene (36) were determined because of the large chemical shift difference between the axial and equatorial protons of the methylene groups adjacent to the spiro carbon atoms. These differences (1.57 and 1.40 ppm, respectively, in

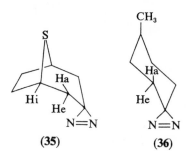

(35)                (36)

carbon tetrachloride) reflected the shielding of the equatorial protons resulting from the magnetic anisotropy of the diazirine ring. The large chemical shift difference of 35 was used, employing double irradiation techniques, to determine that the geminal and vicinal spin–spin coupling constants were opposite in sign ($J_{a,e}$ = −15.2, $J_{1,a}$ = +2.6, and $J_{1,e}$ = +4.2 cps). The temperature dependence of the large chemical shift difference between the comparable protons in the diazirine (36) was used to determine accurate values for $\Delta S$ (0.42 ± 0.14 eu) and $\Delta H$ (−1.91 ± 0.04 kcal/mole) for the conformational equilibrium between the two chair conformers of this compound.

Until recently no perfluorinated diazirines had been reported. Mitsch[34] reported the properties and the structural identity of difluorodiazirine (37). The method of preparation, however, was not available. The structure (37) for the difluorodiazirine was confirmed by its elemental analysis,

$$\begin{array}{c} F\diagdown \quad N \\ \phantom{F}C\diagup \quad \| \\ F\diagup \quad \phantom{C} N \end{array}$$
(37)

molecular weight determination, fluorine nuclear magnetic resonance spectrum, mass-spectral cracking pattern, ultraviolet spectrum (sharp peaks between 2820 and 3515 Å ($\varepsilon$ = 646.9 liters/mole-cm at 3515 Å)), gas phase infrared spectrum (bands at 1563, 1282, 805, 502, 1248, 481, 1091, and 544 cm$^{-1}$) and the Raman spectrum (band at 451 cm$^{-1}$).[11,34] Difluorodiazirine (37) was assumed to have the geometry and axes as shown by 38.[11]

Difluorodiazirine[33-36] as diazirine[18] and substituted diazirines[16,39,59]

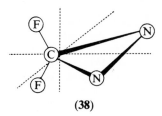

(38)

were decomposed to the corresponding carbene either thermally or by ultraviolet irradiation, for example,

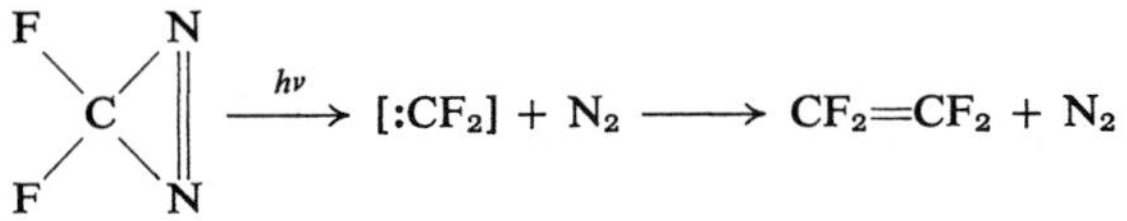

$$\underset{F}{\overset{F}{\diagdown}}C\underset{N}{\overset{N}{\diagup}} \xrightarrow{h\nu} [:CF_2] + N_2 \longrightarrow CF_2{=}CF_2 + N_2$$

The formation of carbenes was easily demonstrated due to their tendency to attack a $\beta$-carbon–hydrogen bond and form cyclopropanes; for example, difluorodiazirine (37) was photolytically decomposed in the presence of cis-butene-2 yielding 1,1-difluoro-2,3-cis-dimethylcyclopropane (39).[33]

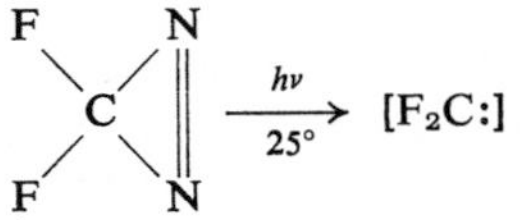

$$\underset{F}{\overset{F}{\diagdown}}C\underset{N}{\overset{N}{\diagup}} \xrightarrow[25°]{h\nu} [F_2C:]$$

(37)

$$[:CF_2] + \underset{H}{\overset{CH_3}{\diagup}}C{=}C\underset{H}{\overset{CH_3}{\diagdown}} \longrightarrow$$

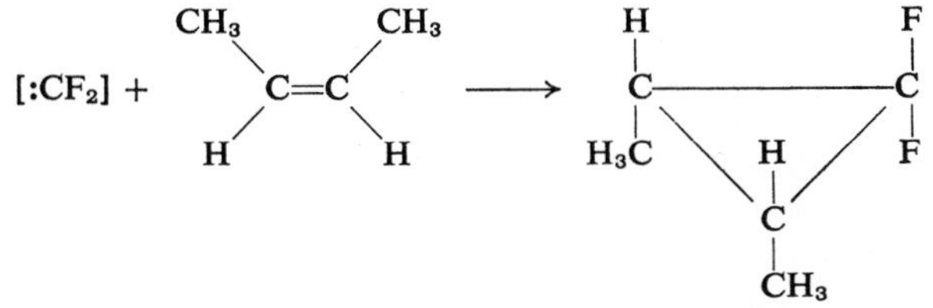

(39)

REFERENCES

1. H. J. Abendroth, *Angew. Chem.*, **73**, 67 (1961).
2. H. J. Abendroth and G. Henrich, *Angew. Chem.*, **71**, 283 (1959).
3. H. J. Abendroth and G. Henrich, *Ger. Pat.* 1,082,889 (1958).
4. R. A. Abramovitch and B. A. Davis, *Chem. Rev.*, **64**, 149 (1964).
5. M. Anbar and G. Yagil, *J. Am. Chem. Soc.*, **84**, 1790 (1962).
6. Z. B. R. Appel, W. Büchner and E. Guth, *Ann. Chem.*, **618**, 53 (1958).
7. L. F. Audrieth, H. Zimmer, M. Zimmer, and R. A. Rowe, *J. Am. Chem. Soc.*, **77**, 790 (1955).
8. L. F. Audrieth and L. H. Diamond, *J. Am. Chem. Soc.*, **77**, 3131 (1955).
9. L. F. Audrieth and R. A. Rowe, *J. Am. Chem. Soc.*, **77**, 4726 (1955).

10. L. F. Audrieth and R. A. Rowe, *J. Am. Chem. Soc.*, **78**, 563 (1956).

11. C. W. Bjork, N. C. Craig, R. A. Mitsch, and J. Overend, *J. Am. Chem. Soc.*, **87**, 1186 (1965).

12. E. Chinoporos, *Chem. Rev.*, **63**, 235 (1963).

13. T. Curtius, *J. Prakt. Chem.*, **39**, 107 (1889).

14. W. v. E. Doering and A. K. Hoffmann, *J. Am. Chem. Soc.*, **76**, 6162 (1954).

15. R. Ettinger, *J. Chem. Phys.*, **40**, 1693 (1964).

16. H. M. Frey and I. D. R. Stevens, *J. Am. Chem. Soc.*, **84**, 2647 (1962).

17. H. M. Frey and I. D. R. Stevens, *J. Chem. Soc.*, **1962**, 3865.

18. H. M. Frey and I. D. R. Stevens, *Proc. Chem. Soc.*, **1962**, 79.

19. R. Gösl and A. Meuwsen, *Chem. Ber.*, **92**, 2521 (1959).

20. W. H. Graham, *J. Am. Chem. Soc.*, **84**, 1063 (1962).

21. J. Harley-Mason, *Chem. Ind. (London)*, **1962**, 888.

22. K. Heyns, A. Heins and G. Seemann, *Ann. Chem.*, **634**, 49 (1960).

23. L. Horner and A. Christmann, *Angew. Chem. Intern. Ed. Engl.*, **2**, 599 (1963).

24. L. Horner and E. Lingnau, *Ann. Chem.*, **591**, 21 (1954).

25. J. Jander, *Naturwissenschaften*, **42**, 178 (1955).

26. J. Jander, *Z. Anorg. Allg. Chem.*, **280**, 264 (1955).

27. J. Jander, *Z. Anorg. Allg. Chem.*, **280**, 276 (1955).

28. A. Jankowski and S. R. Paulsen, *Angew. Chem.*, **76**, 229 (1964).

29. P. Knudsen, *Chem. Ber.*, **47**, 2698 (1914).

30. A. Lau, E. Schmitz, and R. Ohme, *Z. Physik. Chem.*, **223**, 417 (1963).

31. A. Lüttringhaus, J. Jander, and R. Schneider, *Chem. Ber.*, **92**, 1756 (1959).

32. J. A. Merritt, *Can. J. Phys.*, **40**, 1683 (1962).

33. R. A. Mitsch, *J. Am. Chem. Soc.*, **87**, 758 (1965).

34. R. A. Mitsch, *J. Heterocyclic Chem.*, **1**, 59 (1964).

35. R. A. Mitsch, *J. Heterocyclic Chem.*, **1**, 233 (1964).

36. R. A. Mitsch, *J. Heterocyclic Chem.*, **1**, 271 (1964).

37. E. Müller, *Chem. Ber.*, **47**, 3001 (1914).

38. R. Ohme and E. Schmitz, *Chem. Ber.*, **97**, 297 (1964).

39. C. G. Overberger and J.-P. Anselme, *J. Org. Chem.*, **29**, 1188 (1964).

40. C. G. Overberger and J.-P. Anselme, *Tetrahedron Letters*, **1963**, 1405.

41. S. R. Paulsen, *Angew. Chem.*, **72**, 781 (1960).

42. S. R. Paulsen, Belg. Pat. 588, 352 (1959).

43. S. R. Paulsen and G. Huck, *Chem. Ber.*, **94**, 968 (1961).

44. H. v. Pechmann, *Chem. Ber.*, **27**, 1888 (1894).

45. L. Pierce and V. Dobyns, *J. Am. Chem. Soc.*, **84**, 2651 (1962).

46. F. Raschig, *Chem. Ber.*, **40**, 4580 (1907).

47. F. Raschig, *Schwefel- und Stickstoffstudien*, Verlag Chemie, Berlin, 1924.

48. F. Raschig, *Z. Angew. Chem.*, **20**, 2065 (1907).

49. E. Schmitz, *Advan. Heterocyclic Chem.*, **2**, 83 (1963).

50. E. Schmitz, *Angew. Chem.*, **71**, 127 (1959).

51. E. Schmitz, *Angew. Chem.*, **72**, 579 (1960).

52. E. Schmitz, *Angew. Chem.*, **73**, 23 (1961).

53. E. Schmitz, *Angew. Chem. Intern. Ed. Engl.*, **3**, 333 (1964).

54. E. Schmitz, *Chem. Ber.*, **91**, 1495 (1958).

55. E. Schmitz, *Chem. Ber.*, **95**, 676 (1962).

56. E. Schmitz, *Chem. Ber.*, **95**, 688 (1962).

57. E. Schmitz, Ger. Pat. 1,107,238 (1959).

58. E. Schmitz and D. Habisch, *Chem. Ber.*, **95**, 680 (1962).

59. E. Schmitz, D. Habisch, and A. Stark, *Angew. Chem.*, **75**, 723 (1963); *Angew. Chem. Intern. Ed. Engl.*, **2**, 548 (1963).
60. E. Schmitz and R. Ohme, *Angew. Chem.*, **73**, 115 (1961).
61. E. Schmitz and R. Ohme, *Chem. Ber.*, **94**, 2166 (1961).
62. E. Schmitz and R. Ohme, *Chem. Ber.*, **95**, 795 (1962).
63. E. Schmitz and R. Ohme, *Kernenergie*, **5**, 357 (1962).
64. E. Schmitz and R. Ohme, *Tetrahedron Letters*, **1961**, 612.
65. E. Schmitz, R. Ohme, and R. D. Schmidt, in E. Schmitz, *Angew. Chem. Intern. Ed. Engl.*, **3**, 333 (1964).
66. E. Schmitz, R. Ohme, and R. D. Schmidt, *Chem. Ber.*, **95**, 2714 (1962).
67. E. Schmitz, R. Ohme, and S. Schramm, in E. Schmitz, *Angew. Chem. Intern. Ed. Engl.*, **3**, 333 (1964).
68. E. Schmitz and K. Schinkowski, *Chem. Ber.*, **97**, 49 (1964).
69. H. Staudinger and A. Gaule, *Chem. Ber.*, **49**, 1961 (1916).
70. J. J. Uebel and J. C. Martin, *J. Am. Chem. Soc.*, **86**, 4618 (1964).
71. M. E. Volpin, Yu. D. Koreshkov, V. G. Dulova, and D. N. Kursanov, *Tetrahedron*, **18**, 107 (1962).
72. G. Yagil and M. Anbar, *J. Am. Chem. Soc.*, **84**, 1797 (1962).

## 2. Oxygen and Nitrogen

### a. Oxaziranes*

It appears plausible that carbonyl compounds and nitrene intermediates may react to form three-membered heterocyclic compounds, oxaziridines,[26, 11] containing carbon, oxygen, and nitrogen in the ring via a typical cycloaddition reaction:

The action of N-methylhydroxylamine-O-sulfonic acid, as well as N-chloroalkylamines, on carbonyl compounds in alkaline solutions seems to provide a new synthesis of the oxaziridines by the reaction path mentioned above if a nitrene intermediate is generated. Other known syntheses of oxaziridines involve the oxidation of imines by peracids,[9, 10, 14, 19, 22] irradiation of nitrones,[8, 18, 20, 30] and ionization of imines.[7, 25]

L. F. Audrieth and co-workers, employing the Raschig hydrazine synthesis[23, 24] for the preparation of unsymmetrically substituted hydrazines

---

* The previously designated oxaziranes are to be termed oxaziridines in accordance with the *Ring Index* and the Definitive Rules for Fundamental Heterocyclic Systems in IUPAC, *Nomenclature of Organic Chemistry*, 1957.

from chloramine,[3-6] and J. Jander[15-17] confirmed the mechanism involving nitrene intermediates proposed originally by Raschig. The reaction path given by Audrieth and Jander consisted of the removal of a proton from the chloramine (a) in basic solution, followed by the loss of a chloride ion yielding the nitrene, :ṄH (b). U. Wannagat and H. Kohen[31] were able to

$$H_2NCl \xrightarrow{OH^-} HNCl^- + H_2O \tag{a}$$

$$HNCl^- \longrightarrow H\ddot{N}: + Cl^- \tag{b}$$

combine the nitrene, generated in a glow discharge at pressures of 0.02 mm and a secondary voltage of 0.9–1.0 kV, in the gaseous state with ammonia

$$NH_3 \longrightarrow :\ddot{N}H + N_2 \quad (e) \tag{c}$$

$$H\ddot{N}: \xrightarrow{NH_3} H_2N-NH_2 \tag{d}$$

to hydrazine (c, d). The nitrene is also formed from N-chloromethylamine derivatives in the presence of base.[21]

$$CH_3NHCl \xrightarrow{OH^-} CH_3\ddot{N}:$$

If one assumes the formation of a nitrene from chloramine or N-substituted chloramine derivatives in the presence of a base, then the formation of the oxaziridines from carbonyl compounds and chloramine or N-substituted chloramines[27,28] may involve a typical cycloaddition reaction. Analogously, it appears that the methylhydroxylamine-O-sulfonic acid and hydroxylamine-O-sulfonic acid in the presence of a base may proceed through a nitrene intermediate to form an oxaziridine.[2,27]

$$H_2NOSO_3H \xrightarrow{OH^-} :\ddot{N}H$$

By reacting **1** with benzaldehyde, 2-methyl-3-phenyloxaziridine (**2**) is obtained in 38% yield.[27]

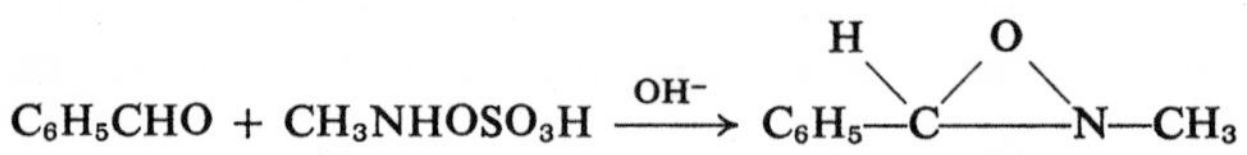

$$C_6H_5CHO + CH_3NHOSO_3H \xrightarrow{OH^-} C_6H_5-C \overset{H}{\underset{}{\diagup}} \overset{O}{\underset{}{\diagdown}} N-CH_3$$
$$\text{(1)} \qquad\qquad\qquad\qquad \text{(2)}$$

Cyclohexanone reacts with **1** to give 2-methyl-3,3-pentamethylene-oxaziridine, (**3**, Y = CH_3) in 35% yield. Acetone, butyraldehyde, acetophenone, and m-nitrobenzaldehyde were found to react analogously.

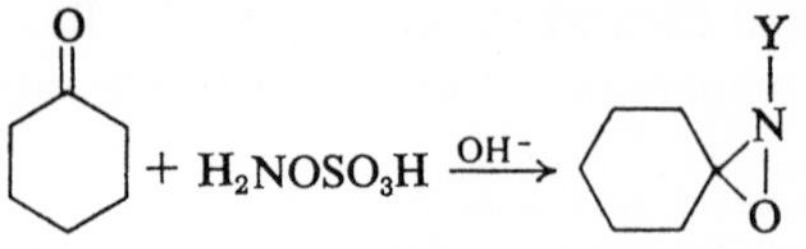

(3)

Cyclohexanone and hydroxylamine-*O*-sulfonic acid react to form a very unstable oxaziridine, (**3**, Y = H, 20% yield).[27,29]

*N*-Chloromethylamine reacts with benzaldehyde with oxaziridine formation[27,28]:

$$C_6H_5CHO + CH_3NHCl \xrightarrow{OH^-} C_6H_5-\overset{\displaystyle H}{\underset{\displaystyle}{C}}\overset{\displaystyle O}{\underset{\displaystyle}{}}N-CH_3$$

$$(2)$$

However, Horner and Christmann,[13] in a discussion of nitrene (H$\ddot{\text{N}}$:) formation have pointed out that the question is still undecided whether compounds containing the —$\ddot{\text{N}}$HX grouping react in the presence of bases via nitrene intermediates (equation e) or by an $S_N2$ mechanism (equation f). Path f appears to be more likely in a number of instances, based on the

$$H_2N-X \xrightarrow[-H_2O]{OH^-} (H-N-X)^- \longrightarrow (H-\ddot{N}:) + X^- \qquad (e)$$

$$(H-\ddot{N}:) + :B \longrightarrow H-\overset{-}{N}-\overset{+}{B}$$

$$(H-N-X)^- + :B \longrightarrow (B\cdots N-H\cdots X)^- \longrightarrow H-\overset{-}{N}-\overset{+}{B} + X^-$$
$$(X = Cl, HSO_4) \quad (f)$$

following evidence. According to a kinetic investigation,[32] the reaction between chloramine and ammonia in strong base is first order in both reactants, and since it is base-independent up to a pH of 14, the Bodenstein $S_N2$ mechanism seems to be the most plausible one. At higher alkalinities the following mechanism is suggested.

$$OH^- + NH_2Cl \rightleftharpoons NHCl^- + H_2O \text{ (preequil.)}$$

$$NH_3 + NHCl^- \xrightarrow{slow} N_2H_4 + Cl^-$$

Since chloride ions have no retarding effect on the reaction rate, a fast preequilibrium NHCl$^- \rightarrow$ :$\ddot{\text{N}}$H + Cl$^-$ with a slow H$\ddot{\text{N}}$: + NH$_3$ reaction was excluded. Also eliminated was a slow decomposition step NHCl$^- \rightarrow$ :NH + Cl$^-$ by the first-order dependence of the rate upon the ammonia concentration.[1]

A considerable amount of evidence favors the $S_N2$ mechanism for the

$$\overset{\displaystyle \diagdown}{\underset{\displaystyle \diagup}{C}}=X-R + NH_2Cl \longrightarrow \overset{\displaystyle \diagdown}{\underset{\displaystyle \diagup}{C}}-X-R \longrightarrow \overset{\displaystyle \diagdown}{\underset{\displaystyle \diagup}{C}}-X-R$$

reaction of chloramine rather than the formation of a free nitrene intermediate. Nevertheless, these reactions should be regarded as perhaps a nucleophilic addition or substitution reaction. The rate of product formation depends upon the nature of the substrate; this would not be expected if the nitrene intermediate was formed in the rate-determining step.[1]

A somewhat similar situation exists for the reactions of hydroxylamine-$O$-sulfonic acid. These reactions probably involve an attack by the undissociated hydroxylamine-$O$-sulfonic acid, that is, [1,2,12]

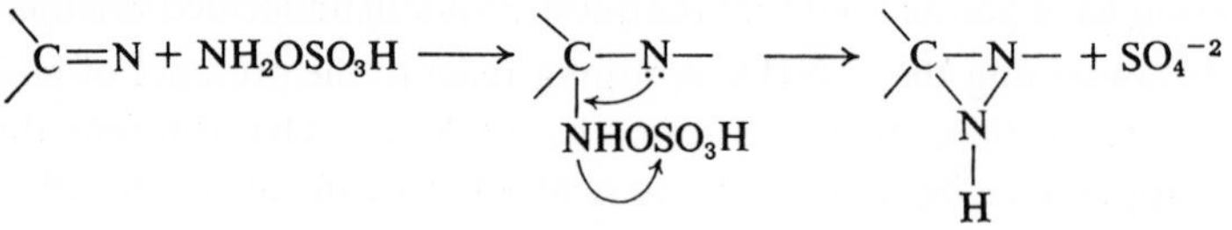

$$\text{C=N} + NH_2OSO_3H \longrightarrow \text{C}-\text{N}- \longrightarrow \text{C}-\text{N}- + SO_4^{-2}$$

### Table 1

Preparation of Oxaziridines: by the Reaction between Carbonyl Compounds and Chloramine, $N$-Chloroalkylamines, or $N$-Methylhydroxylamine-$O$-sulfonic Acid

$$\underset{R\text{——}N\text{-}Y}{\overset{O}{\triangle}}$$

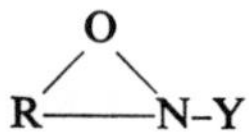

| R | Y— | BP (°C/mm) | Yield (%) | Ref. |
|---|---|---|---|---|
| $C_6H_5CH$ | $CH_3$ | 66/1.5 | 38 | 27 |
|  |  |  | 15 | 28 |
| $C_6H_{10}$ | H |  | 20 | 27 |
|  |  |  | 50 | 29 |
| $C_6H_{10}$ | $CH_3$ | 53/8 | 35 | 27 |
|  |  |  | 85 | 28 |
| $C_6H_{10}$ | $C_2H_5$ |  | 10 | 28 |
| $(CH_3)_2C$ | $CH_3$ |  | 30 | 27 |
|  |  |  |  | 28 |
| $CH_3CH_2CH_2CH$ | $CH_3$ |  |  | 27 |
| $C_6H_5(CH_3)C$ | $CH_3$ |  |  | 27 |
| $m\text{-}NO_2C_6H_4CH$ | $CH_3$ |  |  | 27 |
| $p\text{-}CH_3C_6H_9$ | $CH_3$ |  | 65 | 28 |
| $C_5H_8$ | $CH_3$ |  | 22 | 28 |
| $CH_3(C_2H_5)C$ | $CH_3$ |  | 30 | 28 |
| $p\text{-}CH_3OC_6H_4CH$ | H |  | 14 | 28 |
| $CH_3(C_2H_5)C$ | H |  | 10 | 29 |
| $(CH_3)_2C$ | H |  | 15 | 29 |
| $CH_3(C_5H_{11})C$ | H |  | 16 | 29 |
| $CH_3[CH_2C(OH)(CH_3)_2]C$ | H |  | 10 | 29 |

REFERENCES

1. R. A. Abramovitch and B. A. Davis, *Chem. Rev.*, **64**, 149 (1964).
2. Z. B. R. Appel, W. Büchner, and E. Guth, *Ann. Chem.*, **618**, 53 (1958).
3. L. F. Audrieth, H. Zimmer, M. Zimmer, and R. A. Rowe, *J. Am. Chem. Soc.*, **77**, 790 (1955).
4. L. F. Audrieth and L. H. Diamond, *J. Am. Chem. Soc.*, **77**, 3131 (1955).
5. L. F. Audrieth and R. A. Rowe, *J. Am. Chem. Soc.*, **77**, 4726 (1955).
6. L. F. Audrieth and R. A. Rowe, *J. Am. Chem. Soc.*, **78**, 563 (1956).
7. J. S. Belew and J. T. Person, *Chem. Ind. (London)*, **1959**, 1246.
8. R. Bonnet, V. M. Clark, and A. R. Todd, *J. Chem. Soc.*, **1959**, 2102
9. W. D. Emmons, *J. Am. Chem. Soc.*, **78**, 6208 (1956).
10. W. D. Emmons, *J. Am. Chem. Soc.*, **79**, 5739 (1957).
11. W. D. Emmons, in *Compounds with Three- and Four-Membered Rings* (*The Chemistry of Heterocyclic Compounds*, Vol. 19, A. Weissberger, Ed.), Interscience, New York, 1964, pp. 624ff.
12. R. Gösl and A. Meuwsen, *Chem. Ber.*, **92**, 2521 (1959).
13. L. Horner and A. Christmann, *Angew. Chem. Intern. Ed. Engl.*, **2**, 599 (1963).
14. L. Horner and E. Juergens, *Chem. Ber.*, **90**, 2184 (1957).
15. J. Jander, *Naturwissenschaften*, **42**, 178 (1955).
16. J. Jander, *Z. Anorg. Allgem. Chem.*, **280**, 264 (1955).
17. J. Jander, *Z. Anorg. Allgem. Chem.*, **280**, 276 (1955).
18. M. Kamlet and L. Kaplan, *J. Org. Chem.*, **22**, 576 (1957).
19. H. Krimm, *Chem. Ber.*, **91**, 1057 (1958).
20. F. Kröhnke, *Ann. Chem.*, **604**, 203 (1957).
21. A. Lüttringhaus, J. Jander, and R. Schneider, *Chem. Ber.*, **92**, 1756 (1959).
22. A. Padwa, *Tetrahedron Letters*, **1964**, 2001.
23. F. Raschig, *Chem. Ber.*, **40**, 4580 (1907).
24. F. Raschig, *Z. Angew. Chem.*, **20**, 2065 (1907).
25. A. H. Riebel, R. E. Erickson, C. J. Abshire, and P. S. Bailey, *J. Am. Chem. Soc.*, **82**, 1801 (1960).
26. E. Schmitz, *Angew. Chem. Intern. Ed., Engl.*, **3**, 333 (1964).
27. E. Schmitz, R. Ohme, and D. Murawski, *Angew. Chem.*, **73**, 708 (1961).
28. E. Schmitz, R. Ohme, D. Murawski, and S. Schramm, *Monatsber. Deut. Akad. Wiss. Berlin*, **6**, 347 (1964); *Chem. Abstr.*, **61**, 16057 (1964).
29. E. Schmitz, R. Ohme, and S. Schramm, *Chem. Ber.*, **97**, 2521 (1964).
30. J. S. Splitter and M. Calvin, *J. Org. Chem.*, **23**, 651 (1958).
31. U. Wannagat and H. Kohen, *Angew. Chem.*, **69**, 783 (1957).
32. G. Yagil and M. Anbar, *J. Am. Chem. Soc.*, **84**, 1797 (1962).

### 3. Phosphorus and Oxygen or Sulfur

#### a. Phosphiranes

In further studies of ketenes, Staudinger and Meyer[10] reported that triethylphosphine (**1**) and diphenylketene (**2**) readily combined with one another to give the cycloadduct 1,1,1-triethyl-3,3-diphenylphosphiran-2-one (**3**), while no reaction occurred with triphenylphosphine (**4**). The phosphirane (**3**) was extremely unstable and decomposed into its components upon heating at 80–100°C corresponding to other cycloadducts of

$$(C_2H_5)_3P + (C_6H_5)_2C{=}C{=}O \longrightarrow (C_2H_5)_3P\text{------}C(C_6H_5)_2$$

**(1)**                     **(2)**

$$\begin{array}{c} \backslash \;\; / \\ C \\ \| \\ O \end{array}$$

**(3)**

$$(C_6H_5)_3P + (C_6H_5)_2C{=}C{=}O \longrightarrow \text{No reaction}$$
**(4)**                     **(2)**

diphenylketene reactions.[9] Upon further investigation, Staudinger[10] reported that the cycloaddition product of triethylphosphine (**1**) and di-

$$(C_2H_5)_3P\text{------}C(C_6H_5)_2 \xrightarrow{\;\Delta\;} (C_2H_5)_3P + (C_6H_5)_2C{=}C{=}O$$

$$\begin{array}{c} \backslash \;\; / \\ C \\ \| \\ O \end{array}$$
                                          **(1)**                **(2)**

**(3)**

phenylketene (**2**) was not phosphirane (**3**) but the oxaphosphirane (**5**) because of the highly reactive character of the carbonyl group of the

$$(C_2H_5)_3P + (C_6H_5)_2C{=}C{=}O \longrightarrow (C_2H_5)_3P\text{------}C{=}C(C_6H_5)_2$$

**(1)**                     **(2)**                                 $\backslash\;/$
                                                                    O

**(5)**

diphenylketene molecule. Staudinger designated this new class of compounds in the phosphorus series as phosphiniketenium compounds to differentiate them from the Wedekind type compound,[12] the aminoketenium compound (**6**).

$$(C_2H_5)_3N\text{------}C{=}C(CH_3)_2$$
$$\backslash\;/$$
$$O$$

**(6)**

The structure of Staudinger and Meyer is almost certainly wrong and probably should be[6]

$$R_3\overset{\oplus}{P}\text{---}C{=}C(C_6H_5)_2 \longleftrightarrow R_3\overset{\oplus}{P}\text{---}\overset{\ominus}{C}\text{---}C(C_6H_5)_2$$
$$\qquad\quad |\qquad\qquad\qquad\qquad\qquad \|$$
$$\qquad\quad O\ominus\qquad\qquad\qquad\qquad\;\; O$$

rather than the heterocycle, for which no precedent exists. Sasse[7] refers to the products as betaines; however, he gives no structures. The only other papers that were found on this or related subjects were the reaction of ketenes with alkyl phosphonates[2] yielding dialkyl vinylphosphonates, $(RO)_2P(O)C(OCOCH_3){=}CH_2$, and the reaction of ketenes with triethyl phosphite.[5]

$$(C_2H_5O)_3P + 2(C_6H_5)_2C{=}C{=}O \longrightarrow (C_6H_5)_2C{=}\overset{\oplus}{C}\text{---}O\text{---}\overset{\ominus}{P}(OC_2H_5)_3 \longrightarrow$$

dimer of diphenylketene $+ C_6H_5C{\equiv}CC_6H_5 + (C_2H_5O)_3PO$

Hoffman[1] had reported that triethylphosphine combined with carbon disulfide and phenylisocycanate; therefore, it was possible for it to undergo reactions with multiple double-bonded compounds. Hoffman interpreted these compounds as urea derivatives; however, Staudinger[10] reported that this formulation was incorrect and that the structure for the carbon disulfide addition product postulated by Jacobson[4] (7) was the correct assignment. Staudinger reported that the carbon disulfide addition

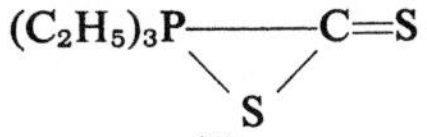

$$(C_2H_5)_3P\text{———}C{=}S$$
$$\diagdown\ \diagup$$
$$S$$
$$(7)$$

product (7) acted as the ketene addition product (5); that is, in solution it was somewhat more stable, but upon heating it dissociated completely as did the phenylisocyanate addition product. In the following table, Staudinger compiled the addition products of triethylphosphine with compounds having double bonds:

| Addition product | Stability | Color |
|---|---|---|
| 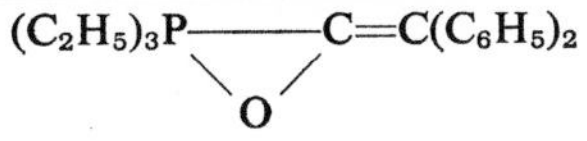 $(C_2H_5)_3P\text{———}C{=}C(C_6H_5)_2$ over $O$ | Unstable | Bright yellow |
| 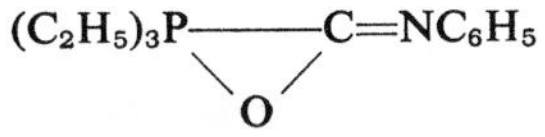 $(C_2H_5)_3P\text{———}C{=}NC_6H_5$ over $O$ | Unknown | — |
| 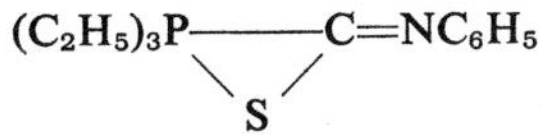 $(C_2H_5)_3P\text{———}C{=}NC_6H_5$ over $S$ | Fairly stable | Yellow |
| 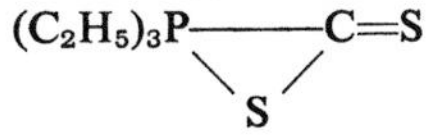 $(C_2H_5)_3P\text{———}C{=}S$ over $S$ | Fairly stable | Red |
| 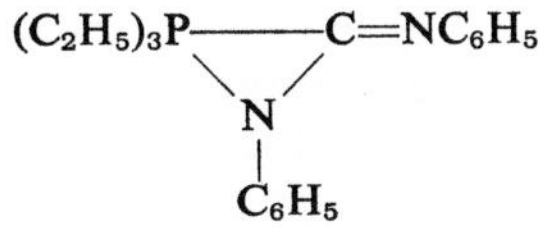 $(C_2H_5)_3P\text{———}C{=}NC_6H_5$ over $N$, $C_6H_5$ | Unknown | — |

It is interesting to note that tertiary amines were reported to give entirely analogously constructed products. For example, the addition product of carbon disulfide and trimethylamine was reported[8] to have the structure 8. According to its reported behavior it corresponds to the above

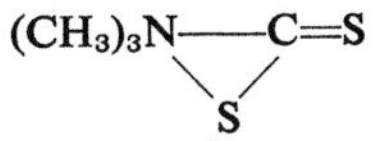

$$(CH_3)_3N\text{———}C{=}S$$
$$\diagdown\ \diagup$$
$$S$$
$$(8)$$

addition products. However, obviously it should be reinvestigated, as should

Wedekind's ketenium compound (6) obtained from dimethylketene and trimethylamine.

More recently, Volpin and co-workers[3,11] reported that in the case of three-membered rings that contain phosphorus a *p–p–d* type interaction would be expected as in (9) and (10). Phosphonium salts of the type (10)

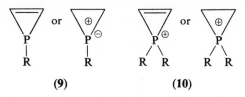

(9)                    (10)

appear to be stable. Volpin and co-workers also assumed compounds of the type (11) could be formed. There have, unfortunately, been no other references supporting these assertions.

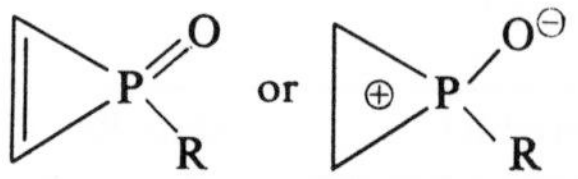

(11)

## REFERENCES

1. A. W. Hoffmann, *Ann. Chem.* (*Suppl.*), **1**, 27 (1861).
2. J. Kennedy and G. M. Meaburn, *Chem. Ind.* (*London*), **1956**, 930.
3. D. N. Kursanov and M. E. Volpin, *Zh. Vses. Khim. Obshch. im D. I. Mendeleeva*, **7**, 282 (1962).
4. V. Meyer and P. Jacobson, *Lehrbuch der organische Chemie*, Vol. I, p. 427.
5. T. Mukaiyama, H. Nambu, and M. Okamoto, *J. Org. Chem.*, **27**, 3651 (1962).
6. L. D. Quin, private communication.
7. L. Sasse, *Houben-Weyl*, Vol. 12, Part 1, p. 111.
8. E. Schmidt, *Ann. Chem.*, **267**, 261 (1892).
9. H. Staudinger, *Ann. Chem.*, **356**, 64 (1907).
10. H. Staudinger and J. Meyer, *Helv. Chim. Acta*, **2**, 612 (1919).
11. M. E. Volpin, Yu. D. Koreshkov, V. G. Dulova, and D. N. Kursanov, *Tetrahedron*, **18**, 107 (1962).
12. E. Wedekind and M. Miller, *Chem. Ber.*, **42**, 1296 (1909).

# III. Synthesis of Heterocyclic Four-Membered Ring Systems

## A. ONE HETEROATOM

### 1. Oxygen

#### a. Oxetanes

Paterno and Chieffi[66] reported that oxetanes (originally named trimethylene oxides) are formed via cycloaddition reactions when mixtures of tri- or tetrasubstituted olefins and aldehydes or ketones are exposed to sunlight.

$$
R-\underset{\displaystyle \overset{\displaystyle O}{\|}}{C}-R +
\underset{\underset{R}{\diagdown} \underset{R'}{\diagup}}{\overset{\overset{R}{\diagup} \overset{R}{\diagdown}}{\underset{C}{\overset{C}{\|}}}}
\xrightarrow{h\nu}
\text{ or }
$$

Since it was known that aldehydes react with monosubstituted terminal olefins in the presence of light or peroxides to form ketones,[57] and because there was no general procedure for synthesizing highly substituted trimethylene oxides, Büchi et al.[20] reinvestigated Paterno's reaction to determine the structure of the products obtained. They examined the products obtained by ultraviolet irradiation of benzaldehyde, acetophenone, and n-butyraldehyde with 2-methyl-2-butene.

To substantiate the structure of the irradiation product (1) from the reaction of benzaldehyde (2) and 2-methyl-2-butene (3), phenyllithium (4) which had been reported to react with trimethylene oxide to yield 85% of 3-phenylpropanol,[77] was reacted with 1. It was assumed that the phenyl anion would attack the less substituted α-carbon by analogy to the results obtained with ethylene oxides[25]; thus, two different alcohols, 5a or 5b, would be expected to be formed depending on whether the irradiation product was 1a or 1b. However, neither alcohol could be isolated from the

111

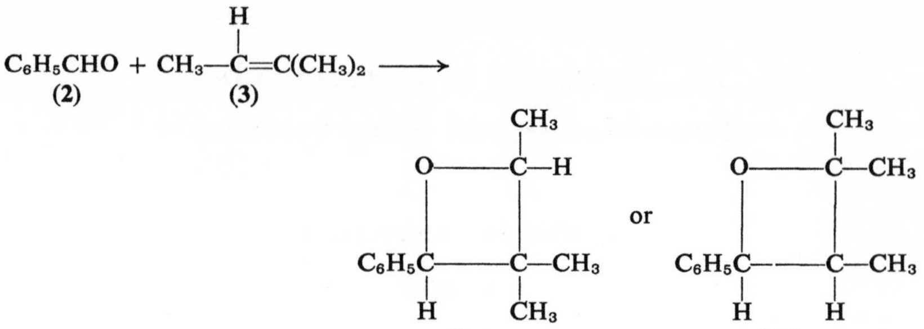

$$C_6H_5CHO + CH_3\overset{H}{\underset{}{\underset{(3)}{C}}}=C(CH_3)_2 \longrightarrow$$

(2)          (3)

(1a)          or          (1b)

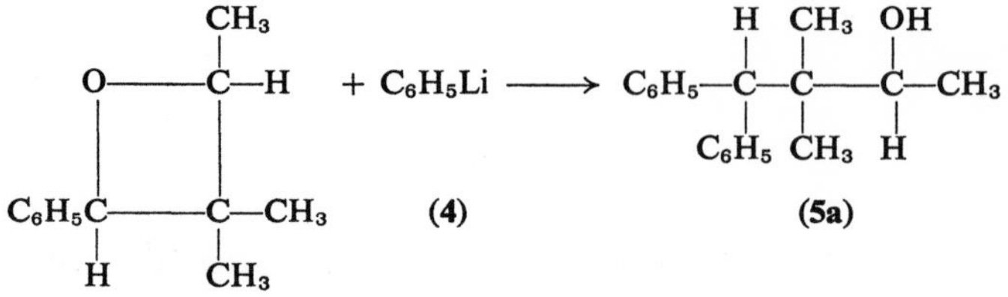

(1a)          (4)          (5a)

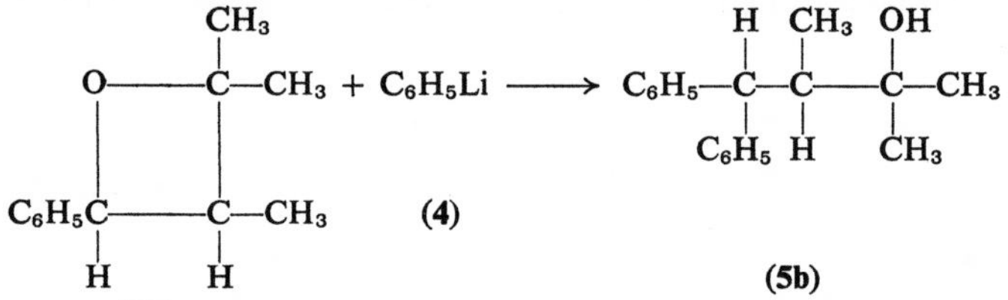

(1b)          (4)          (5b)

reaction mixture, and chromatography resulted in the isolation of only biphenyl and a small amount of triphenylcarbinol which was believed to have been formed by a Cannizzaro reaction of traces of benzaldehyde[33] either initially present or formed by the decomposition of 1 during the reaction.[20]

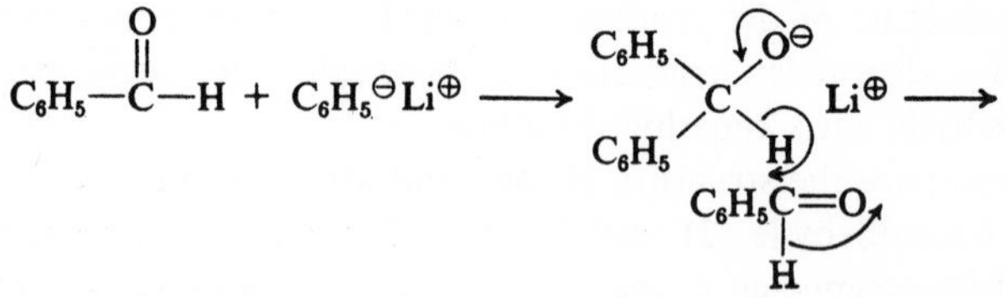

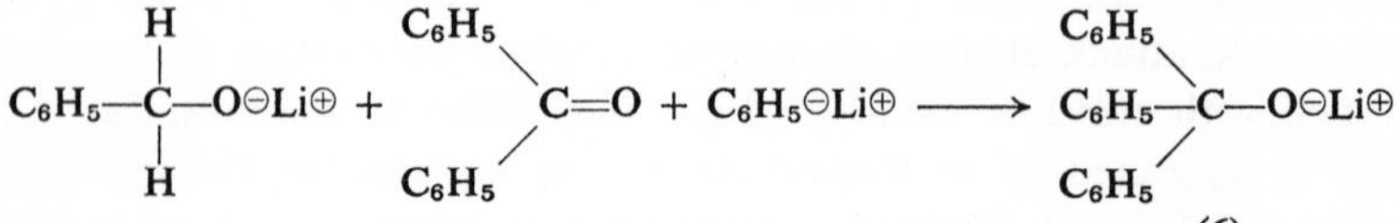

(6)

Considering the fact that LiAlH$_4$ reductions are relatively susceptible to steric effects, it would seem reasonable in view of the ethylene oxide reaction[89] that the hydride ion would attack the less substituted $\alpha$-carbon of **1**. No detectable reaction, however, took place even at 140°C.[20]

Since the reactions of unsubstituted oxetane are very susceptible to acid catalysis,[78] it was considered possible that highly substituted oxetanes[20] might cleave in the same manner as di-*tert*-1,3-diols into ketones and olefins.[26] That is, isomer **1** would cleave in two directions, forming acetaldehyde and benzaldehyde, as well as olefins, while isomer **1a** would give olefins together with acetone and benzaldehyde. The oxetane (**1**) was cleaved to the carbonyl compounds acetaldehyde and benzaldehyde, and to the olefin. No acetone was detected thereby confirming the structure of the oxetane (**1**) to be that of 2,3,3-trimethyl-4-phenyloxetane (**1**).[20]

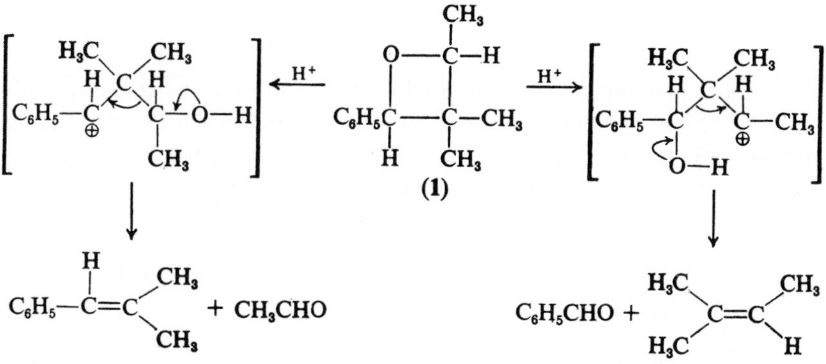

The irradiation product from acetophenone and 2-methyl-2-butene and that from *n*-butyraldehyde and 2-methyl-2-butene were determined in an analogous manner to be 2,3,3,4-tetramethyl-4-phenyloxetane and 2,2,3-trimethyl-4-*n*-propyloxetane, respectively.[20]

The mechanism proposed by Büchi et al.[20] to explain the formation of isomer **1** involves the diradical triplet (**7**), and not the radical (**8**) proposed

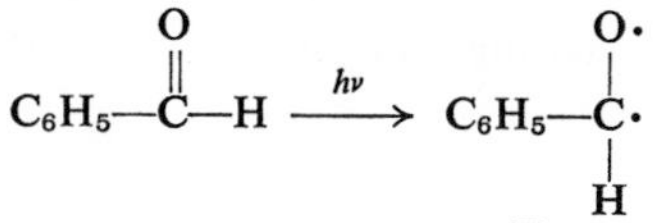

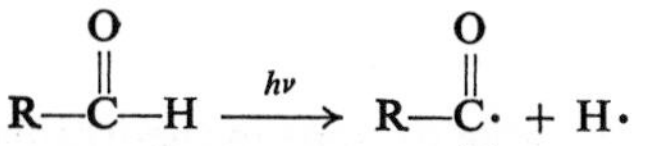

by Kharasch et al.[57] in the reactions of aldehydes with terminal olefins to form ketones. The cycloaddition was assumed to proceed to form the more stable intermediate (9) rather than the intermediate (10).

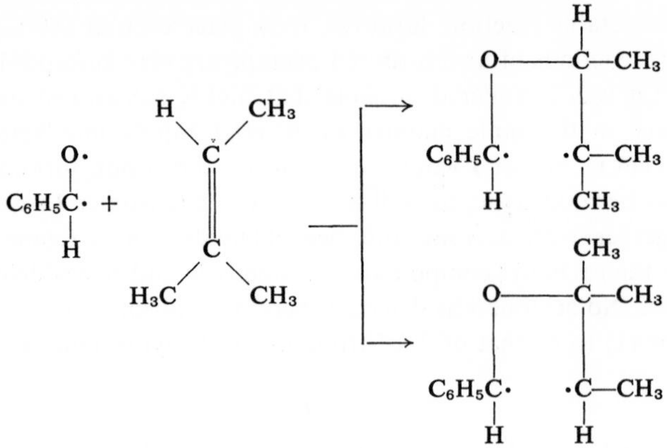

(9)

(10)

A similar mechanism was proposed for the reaction of benzaldehyde (2) and acetophenone (12) with dibutylacetylene (11),[2] in which an unstable oxetene (13 and 14) is formed which decomposes into either the starting material (path 3) or into the products (path 4) (15,16).[21,81] The intermediate oxetene (13) could not be isolated.

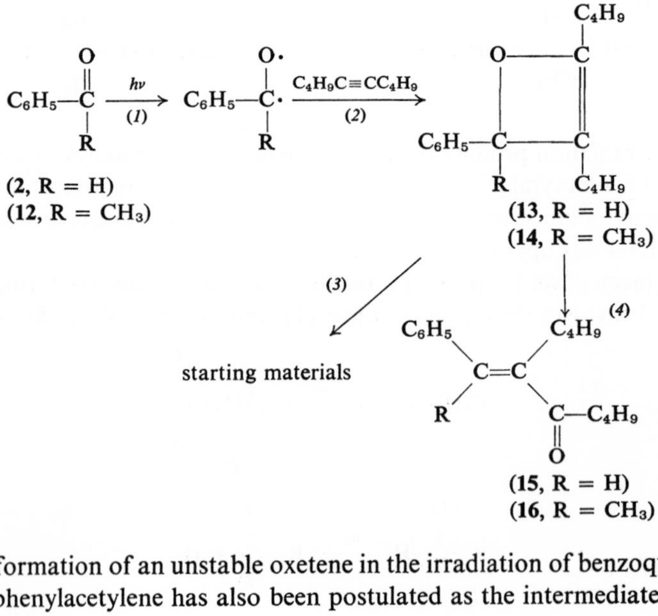

(2, R = H)
(12, R = CH₃)

(13, R = H)
(14, R = CH₃)

(15, R = H)
(16, R = CH₃)

The formation of an unstable oxetene in the irradiation of benzoquinone and diphenylacetylene has also been postulated as the intermediate in the reaction[17]:

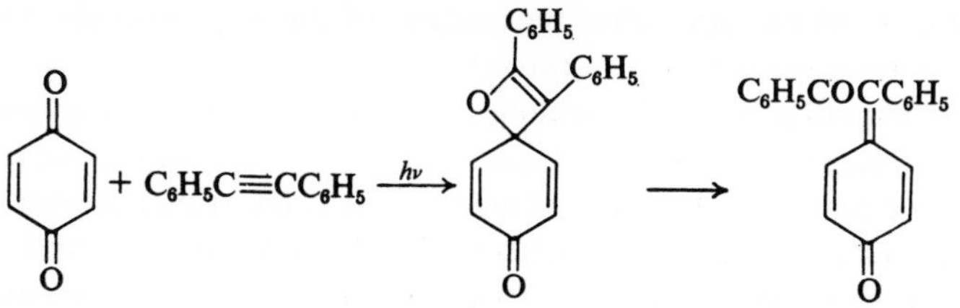

Ketones react with alkoxyacetylenes in the presence of boron trifluoride catalyst to give $\alpha,\beta$-unsaturated esters for which the formation of an oxete (oxetene), a cyclic intermediate, had been postulated.[90] However, no such intermediate has been isolated. Recently, Middleton[63] found that hexafluoroacetone reacts with ethyoxyacetylene without added catalyst to give the oxete intermediate at low temperatures. The oxete intermediate can be isolated in 85% yield, but it slowly isomerizes to the ester if stored at room temperature. The oxete was identified by its fluorine nuclear magnetic resonance and infrared spectra.

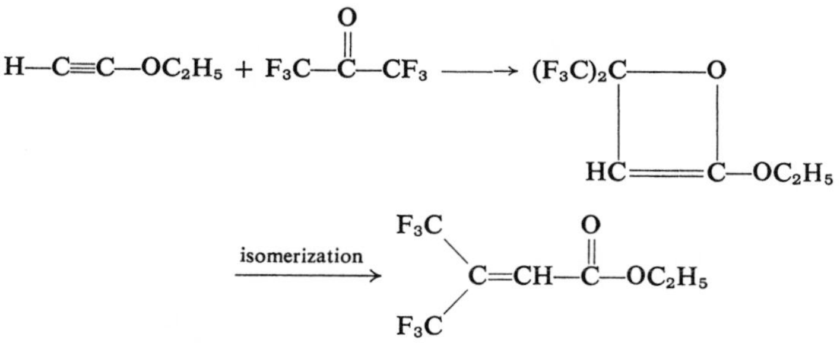

In an attempt to understand the properties of excited states, Arnold, Hinman, and Glick[7] investigated the mechanism of the photocycloaddition of carbonyl compounds to olefins with particular attention to the character of the excited state involved. It was found that the carbonyl $n,\pi^*$ state is necessary for the formation of the oxetane, but may not be sufficient. With this information it was possible to define the scope and limitations of this reaction.†

Arnold and co-workers[7] found that "ketones which are not reduced upon irradiation in isopropyl alcohol cannot be expected to form oxetanes in the presence of olefins." The reduction of ketones by irradiation involves hydrogen abstraction from the alcohol by the $n,\pi^*$ state of the ketone,[10,12,56,64,67,68,75] implying that the addition to the olefin also requires the $n,\pi^*$ state. Since the addition of the $n,\pi^*$ state of the carbonyl

† For a recent review on organic photochemistry which covers oxetanes see Refs. 47 and 67.

compounds to olefins completes the analogy of this state with alkoxy radicals which are known both to abstract hydrogen from and to add to olefins,[91] a competing reaction yielding carbinol[62] or pinacol may become prominent.[7] Ketones in the $\pi,\pi^*$ triplet state[16, 44, 65] are unreactive in both of the above reactions. It was concluded[7] that if the triplet energy of the olefin is below that of the carbonyl compound, triplet–triplet transfer may take place to the elimination of the formation of the oxetanes. For example, when benzophenone, which has a triplet energy of 70 kcal,[58] was irradiated in the presence of dienes that have triplet energies around 60 kcal,[58] products derived from the $\pi \rightarrow \pi^*$ triplet diene[45, 48, 49, 88] were formed.[7] Scharf and Korte[73] found that when acetone was irradiated in the presence of norbornene, norbornene dimers and 2-exoacetonylnorbornane[70] were formed. This was not the case, however, when a mixture of benzophenone

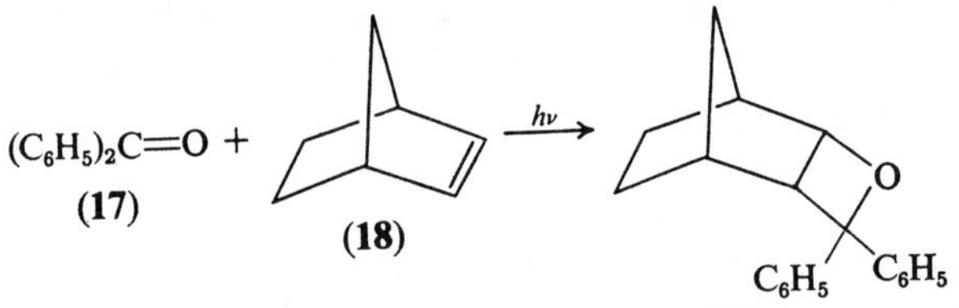

(17) and norbornene (18) are irradiated[7, 73]; the oxetane (19) was obtained in fair yield.

The oxetane formation then involves the sequence shown below.[7] It

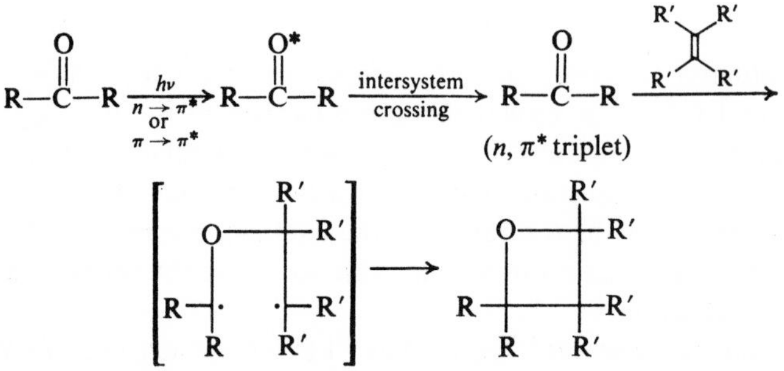

should be noted that the $n,\pi^*$ singlet and triplet states both have diradical character, that is, an unpaired electron on oxygen.[56] In some cases[64] the reduction of benzophenone has been shown to involve the $n,\pi^*$ triplet, while in others it may involve either or both.[15]

Arnold and co-workers[7] found other oxetanes in small amounts besides the major products; this was in contrast to the fact that only one isomeric oxetane—that expected from the more stable diradical intermediate—was reported by previous workers.[20, 61] The oxetanes were characterized by elemental analysis and infrared and nuclear magnetic resonance spectra.

In a recent study of the "Paterno-Büchi" reaction the nature of the low-lying triplet states[93] of aromatic carbonyl compounds was determined by spectrophosphorimetry, and the possible correlation between the course of this photochemical reaction of these carbonyl compounds with the nature of their low-lying triplet states was reported. For example, when benzaldehyde (20, R = H) is irradiated with 2-methyl-2-butene, the isomeric oxetanes (21) and (22) in a 1.6:1 ratio were detected by nuclear magnetic resonance analysis of the oxetane fraction.[93] The reaction was retarded by

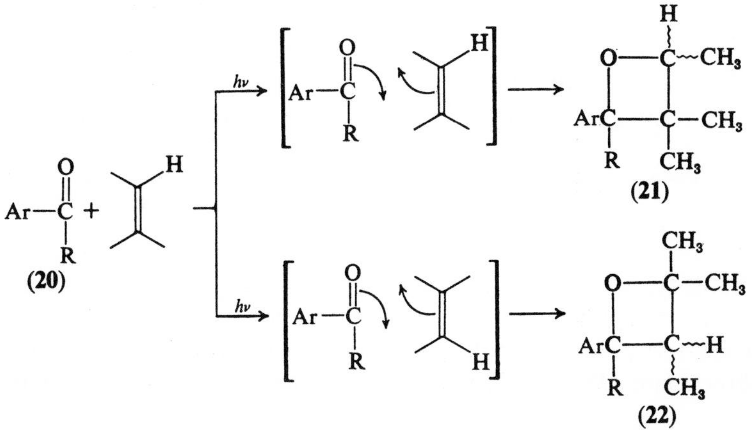

the addition of a paramagnetic salt, ferric tris-dipivaloylmethide, indicating that a triplet state is a reactive intermediate. The phosphorescence emissions of benzaldehyde, acetophenone, benzophenone, 2-naphthaldehyde, 2-acetonaphthone, and 2-naphthyl phenyl ketone at 77°K in MICP or EPA glass were also examined. In the case of benzaldehyde, acetophenone, and benzophenone, Yang and co-workers'[93] observations corresponded to those reported in the literature,[28, 65] indicating that the nature of the low-lying triplet state of these compounds is $n \rightarrow \pi^*$ in nature[54, 65] and may be the reactive species†. On the other hand, the phosphorescence emissions of 2-naphthaldehyde and 2-acetonaphthone, previously reported by McClure[65] and by Ermolaev and Terenin,[27] and that of 2-naphthyl phenyl ketone were confirmed by Yang and co-workers,[93] indicating that the low-lying triplet states of these compounds are $\pi \rightarrow \pi^*$ in nature. The direction of the cycloaddition reactions of 1-naphthaldehyde, 2-naphthaldehyde, and 2-naphthyl phenyl ketone with 2-methyl-2-butene to form

† For further proof of the $n,\pi^*$ triplet states of the carbonyl compounds as the reactive species in the cycloaddition reactions with olefins see Ref. 7.

oxetanes of types (21) and (22) suggests that the reactions proceed through an electron-deficient oxygen, implying that the reactive species is $n \to \pi^*$ in nature.[93] It was found that 1- and 2-acetonaphthone were unreactive, indicating the nature of low-lying triplet states responsible for the chemical behavior of the compounds. It has also been postulated that the low-lying triplet state for 9-anthraldehyde is $\pi \to \pi^*$ in nature and the excitation energy is mainly localized in the aromatic system[36-38,93]; however, when 9-anthraldehyde (24) was irradiated in 2-methyl-2-butene, the main product was an oxetane (25) indicating that the reaction proceeds through the $n \to \pi^*$ excited state.[93]

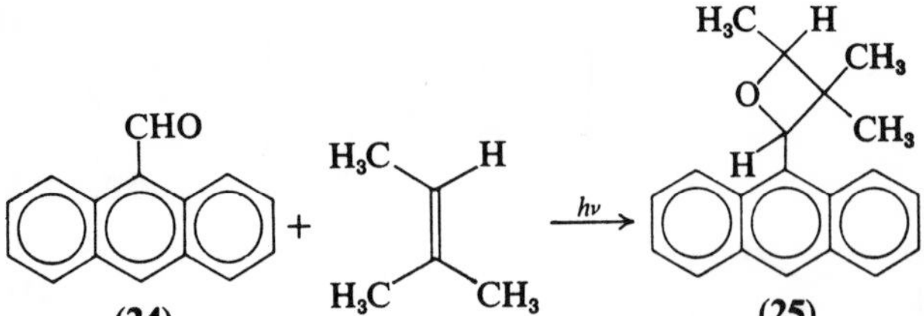

Recently, Bryce-Smith and Gilbert[18] reported a new synthesis for oxetanes involving the photoinduced cycloaddition of p-quinones to olefins; for example, p-benzoquinone (26) and cis-cyclooctene (27) readily give the spiro-oxetane (28) in 90% yields. The oxetane structures were confirmed

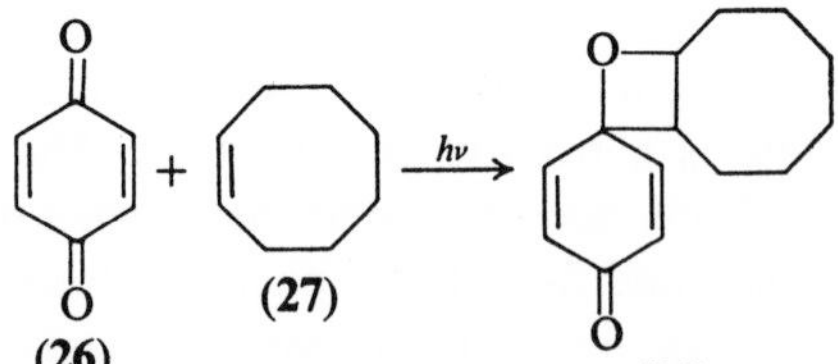

by nuclear magnetic resonance, infrared, ultraviolet, and mass spectra.

Since polyfluorooxetanes are virtually unknown,† Harris and Coffman[51] irradiated a refluxing mixture of a terminal fluoroolefin and either a fluoroaldehyde, a fluoroacyl fluoride, or a fluoroketone, resulting in the cycloaddition of the carbonyl function to the olefin to form a polyfluoro-oxetane in excellent yields. The isomeric oxetanes (see Table 4) obtained as

† Only two polyfluorooxetanes had been reported previously. They were hexafluoro-oxetane, prepared by the electrolytic fluorination of oxetane[56]; and 2-H-pentafluoro-oxetane, prepared by the reaction of oxygen with 1,1,2,2,3-pentafluoropropane at 500°.[52]

products were characterized by their fluorine nuclear magnetic resonance patterns.

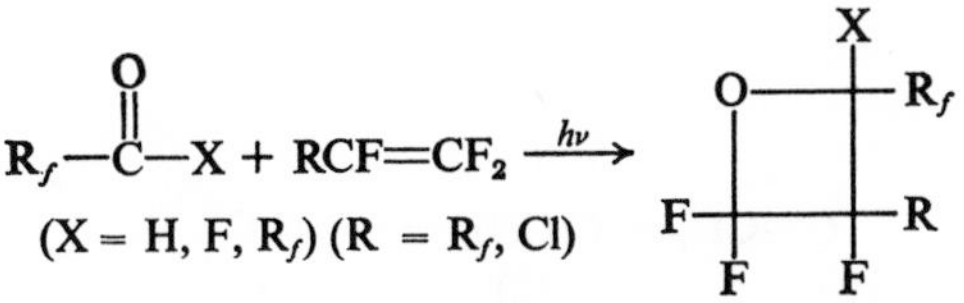

$$R_f{-}\overset{\overset{\text{O}}{\|}}{C}{-}X + RCF{=}CF_2 \xrightarrow{h\nu}$$

$$(X = H, F, R_f)\ (R = R_f, Cl)$$

More recently it was reported[14] that irradiation of mixtures of acetaldehyde (29) and a fluorinated ethylene (30) resulted in complex mixtures from which the ketone derived from addition of an acetyl radical to the $CF_2$ group of the olefin, and the oxetane (31) derived from cycloaddition of the aldehyde to the olefin, were isolated by vapor–liquid partition

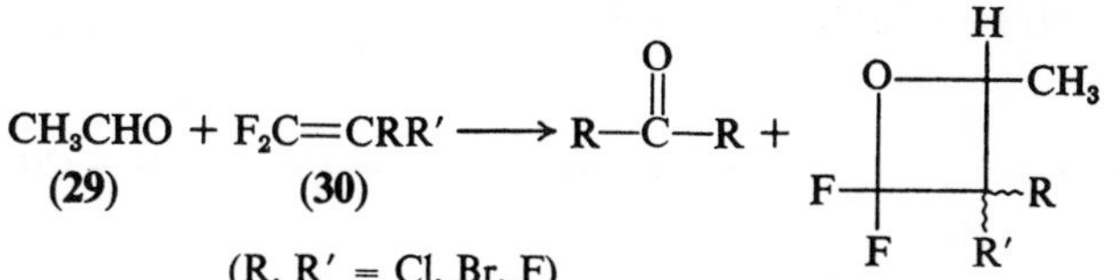

$$CH_3CHO + F_2C{=}CRR' \longrightarrow R{-}\overset{\overset{\text{O}}{\|}}{C}{-}R +$$

$$(29) \qquad (30)$$

$$(R, R' = Cl, Br, F)$$

chromatography. The structures of the oxetanes (31) were characterized by fluorine nuclear magnetic resonance, infrared, and mass spectra. (See Table 3.)

The reaction between carbonyl cyanide (32) and 1,1-diphenylene (33) was reported[1,2] to have formed an oxetane derivative (34a) (originally named 1,3-epoxypropane) via the cycloaddition of the carbonyl of the reagent to the double bond of the olefin. The oxetane (34b) had been proposed by Thesing and Witzel[86] for the reaction. The structure of the oxetane (34a) was determined by chemical evidence and infrared spectral

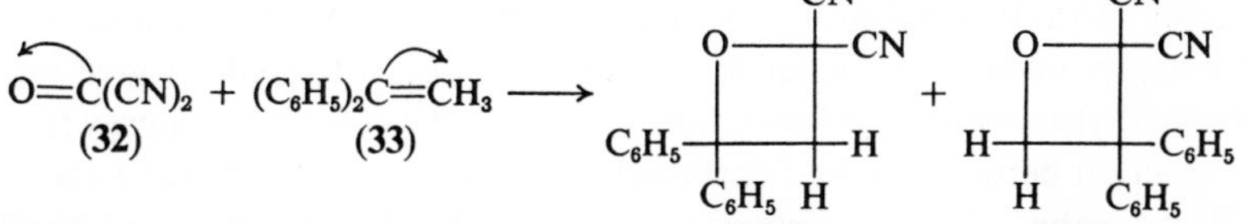

$$O{=}C(CN)_2 + (C_6H_5)_2C{=}CH_3 \longrightarrow$$

$$(32) \qquad (33)$$

measurements. In addition, the cycloaddition reaction between carbonyl cyanide (32) and 1,1-di-p-tolylethylene (35) led to the formation of the oxetane (36) whose structure was determined by chemical evidence.[1,2] It was also found that butadiene and 2,3-dimethylbutadiene form oxetanes by a 1,2-cycloaddition as well as dihydropyran derivatives[4] via a 1,4-cycloaddition. In further investigations of the reactions of carbonyl cyanide and olefins in the presence of acids it was reported[1,5] that an oxetane would form only when there was no hydrogen in the allylic position.

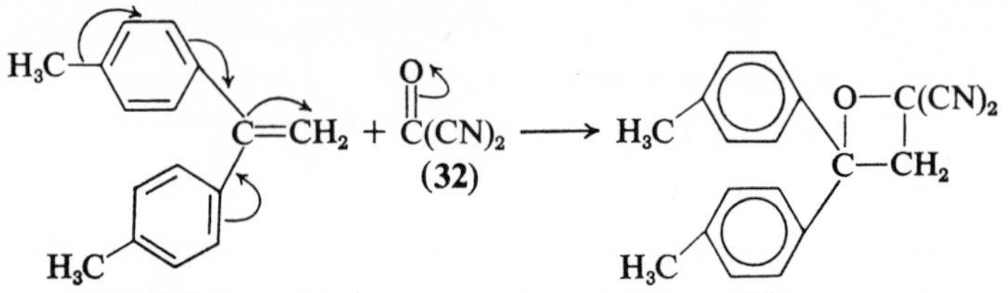

Singer and Bartlett[82] have observed the photocycloaddition of six aromatic aldehydes and ketones across the carbon–carbon double bond of dimethyl-$N$-(2-cyano-2-propyl)-keten-imine (37) to give iminooxetanes (38) and (39) (see Table 4). The $\beta$-adducts were identified by infrared and

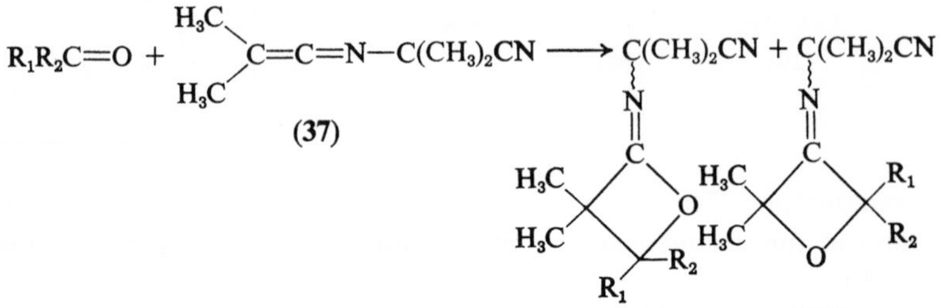

nuclear magnetic resonance spectra, after isolation by Florisil chromatography, while the $\alpha$-adducts were not isolable in this manner since they readily hydrolyze to their corresponding amides on Florisil. Singer and Bartlett[82] also reported an $n \rightarrow \pi^*$ configuration for the lowest-lying triplet state for the carbonyl compounds that reacted and a $\pi \rightarrow \pi^*$ configuration for those that did not give a photoadduct.[7,20,21,93] It was also noted that compounds with higher triplet energies ($E_{s-t}$) tended to give more tetramethylsuccinonitrile formation as a result of a competing energy transfer reaction between excited carbonyl compounds and the ground state of (37).[82] Further work is being explored using the ketene-imines in photocycloaddition reactions.[83]

In conclusion, Beereboom and von Wittenau[13] have reported that the light-catalyzed reaction of fumaronitrile (37) and acetone (38) provides a mixture of cis- and trans-oxetanedinitriles (39). The structures of the isomeric oxetanes were determined by infrared and nuclear magnetic resonance spectra and acidic hydrolysis.

The chemistry of oxetanes has been briefly reviewed.[79,85,92] The Raman

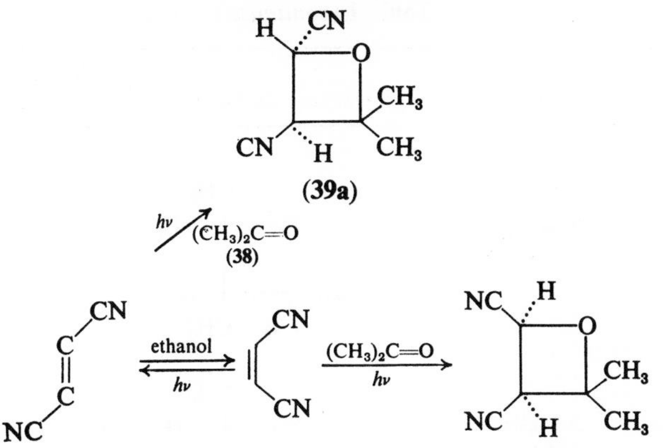

(39a)

$hv$ / (CH₃)₂C=O
(38)

(39b)

and microwave spectroscopy and electron diffraction of oxetanes have been discussed.[6, 23, 29, 31, 32, 35, 42, 43, 94, 95] The mass[34] and nuclear magnetic resonance[41, 53, 69, 71, 80, 84, 87] spectra of several oxetanes have been reported. Oxetane and 2,2-dimethyloxetane show ultraviolet absorption maxima at 183 and 173 m$\mu$, respectively[59]; there is little absorption above 220 m$\mu$. The far ultraviolet absorption of oxetanes has been discussed in terms of excited states.[30]

The infrared absorption spectra for numerous oxetanes have been recorded and show that a strong absorption band at approximately 10.2 $\mu$ is characteristic of this class of compounds.[11, 22, 40, 71]

### Table 1
Preparation of Oxetanes by the Photocycloaddition of Carbonyl Compounds to Alkenes

| Carbonyl compound | Alkene | Oxetane derivative | Yield (%) | MP, °C (BP, °C/mm) | Ref. |
|---|---|---|---|---|---|
| Benzaldehyde | 2-Methyl-2-butene | 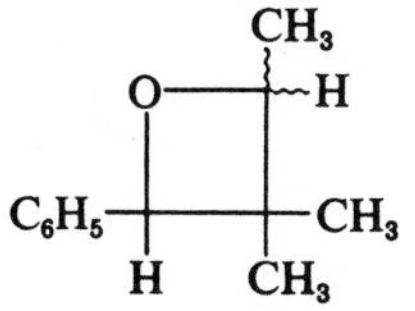 | 10 | (44/0.2) | 20 |
|  |  |  | 58 | 109–110 | 8 |
|  |  |  | 40 | 106–109 | 7 |
|  |  |  |  | 110–111 | 66 |
| Acetophenone | 2-Methyl-2-butene | 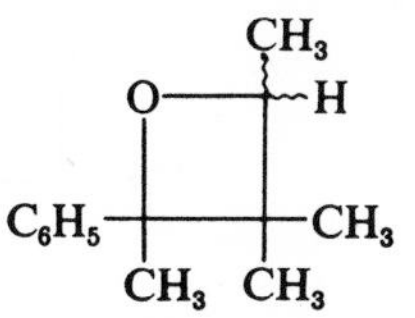 | 4.4 | (42/0.2) | 20 |
|  |  |  | 90.0 | — | 93 |

(continued)

**Table 1** (*continued*)

| Carbonyl compound | Alkene | Oxetane derivative | Yield (%) | MP, °C (BP, °C/mm) | Ref. |
|---|---|---|---|---|---|
| Acetophenone | 2-Methyl-2-butene | 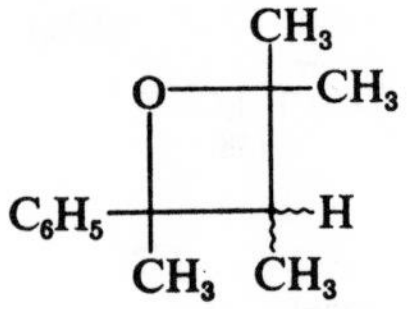 | 10.0 | — | 93 |
| n-Butyraldehyde | 2-Methyl-2-butene | 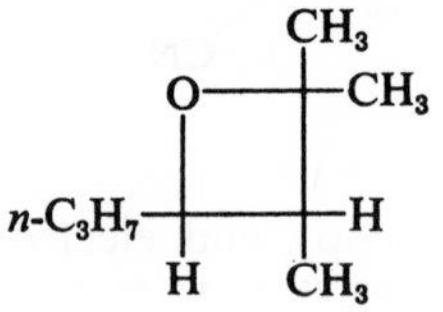 | 6.5 | 62–64/23 | 20 |
| Benzophenone | Furan | 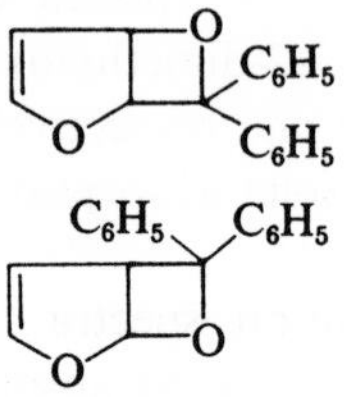 | — | — | 47, 74 |
| | | | quant. | | |
| Benzophenone | Octadiene | 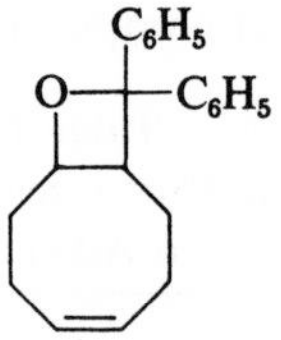 | — | — | 39, 47 |
| Benzophenone | Norbornene | 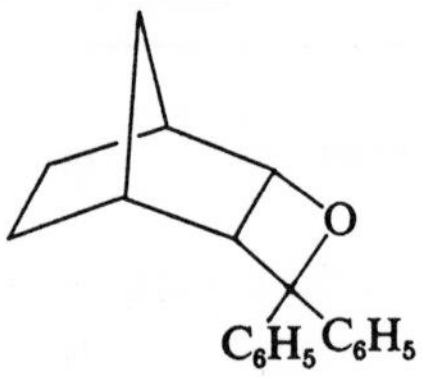 | 80<br>50 | 121<br>128–129 | 73<br>7 |
| Benzophenone | Propylene | 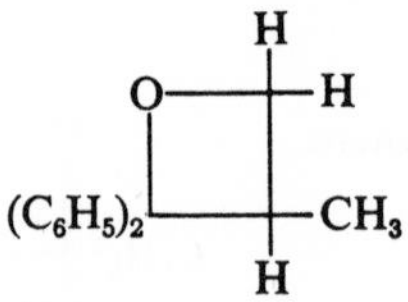 | 5 | 92–95 | 7 |

(*continued*)

**Table 1** (*continued*)

| Carbonyl compound | Alkene | Oxetane derivative | Yield (%) | MP, °C (BP, °C/mm) | Ref. |
|---|---|---|---|---|---|
| Benzophenone | Isobutylene | 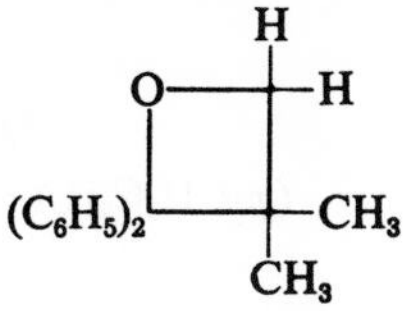 (structure: oxetane, $(C_6H_5)_2$, H, H, CH$_3$, CH$_3$) | 93 | 88.5–90 | 7 |
| Benzophenone | *Cis* or *trans*-butene | 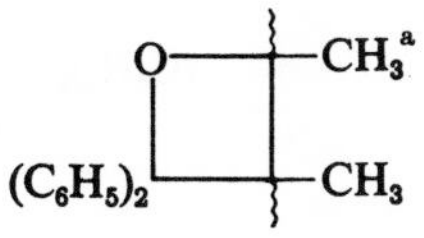 (structure: oxetane, $(C_6H_5)_2$, CH$_3$[a], CH$_3$) | 79 | 91.5–94 | 7 |
| Benzophenone | Tetramethyl-ethylene | 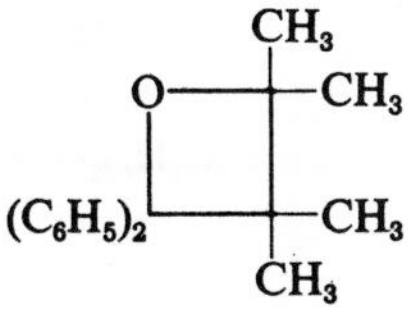 (structure: oxetane, $(C_6H_5)_2$, CH$_3$, CH$_3$, CH$_3$, CH$_3$) | 70 | 123–125 | 7 |
| 4,4′-Dimethyl-benzophenone | Isobutylene | 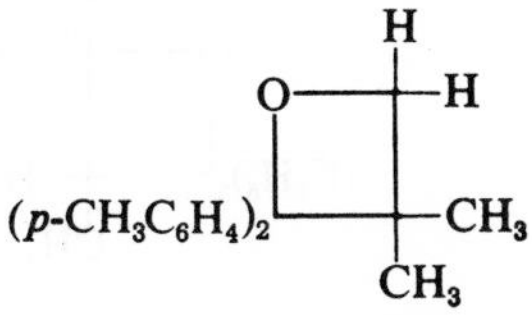 (structure: oxetane, $(p\text{-}CH_3C_6H_4)_2$, H, H, CH$_3$, CH$_3$) | 74 | 81 | 7 |
| 4,4′-Dimethoxy-benzophenone | Isobutylene | 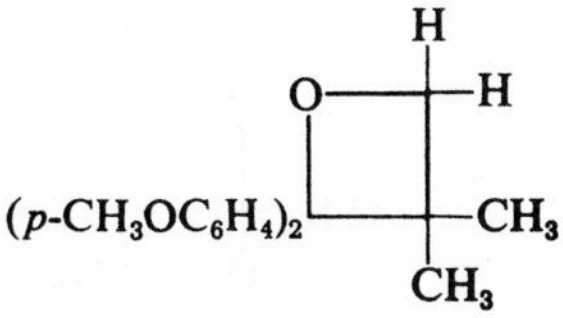 (structure: oxetane, $(p\text{-}CH_3OC_6H_4)_2$, H, H, CH$_3$, CH$_3$) | 80 | — | 7 |
| 4-Chlorobenzo-phenone | Isobutylene | 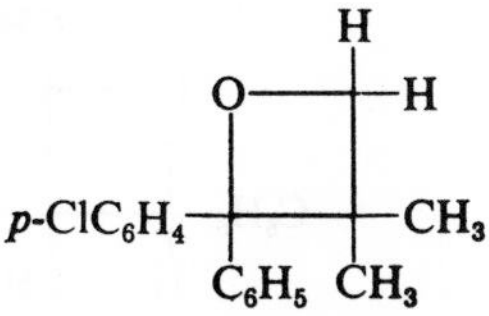 (structure: oxetane, $p\text{-}ClC_6H_4$, $C_6H_5$, H, H, CH$_3$, CH$_3$) | 76 | 75–76 | 7 |
| 4-Methylbenzo-phenone | Isobutylene | 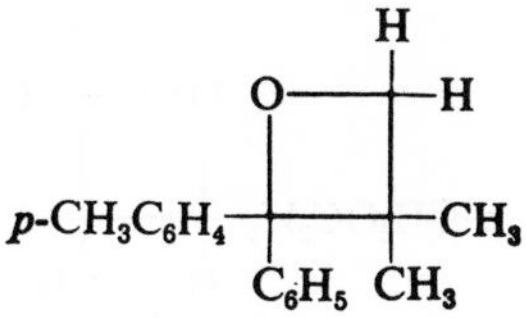 (structure: oxetane, $p\text{-}CH_3C_6H_4$, $C_6H_5$, H, H, CH$_3$, CH$_3$) | 81 | 67–68 | 7 |

(*continued*)

**Table 1** (*continued*)

| Carbonyl compound | Alkene | Oxetane derivative | Yield (%) | MP, °C (BP, °C/mm) | Ref. |
|---|---|---|---|---|---|
| 4,4′-Dimethyl-benzophenone | Norbornene | 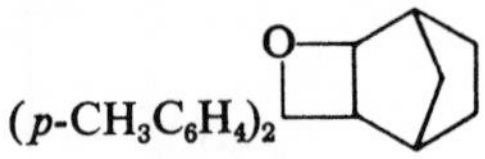 $(p\text{-}CH_3C_6H_4)_2$ | 16 | 117–123 | 7 |
| Benzophenone | 1-Methyl-cyclohexene | 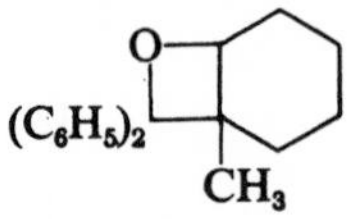 $(C_6H_5)_2$ CH$_3$ | 40 | 126–127 | 7 |
| Benzophenone | 2-Methyl-2-butene | 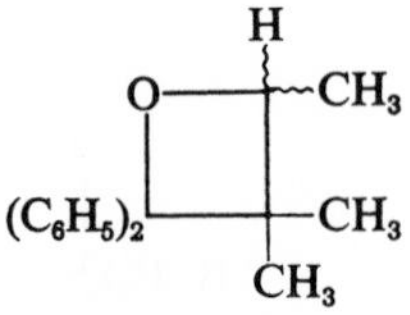 $(C_6H_5)_2$ | 54 / 90 | — / — | 8 / 93 |
| | | 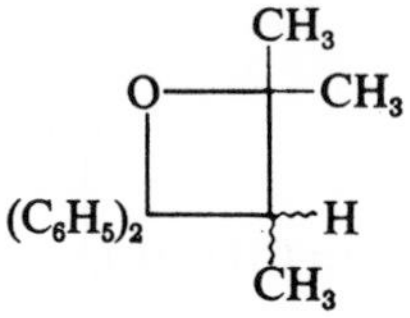 $(C_6H_5)_2$ | 10 / — | — / 110–111 | 93 / 66 |
| Benzaldehyde | 2-Methyl-2-butene | 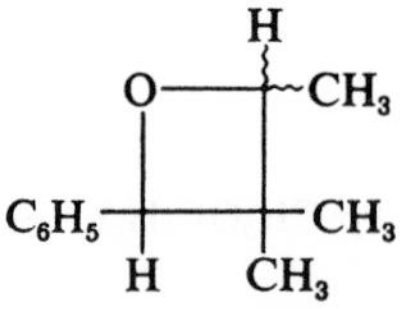 $C_6H_5$ | 64% (isomers 1.6:1) | — | 93 |
| | | 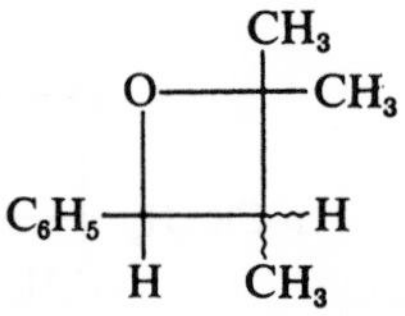 $C_6H_5$ | | | |
| *p*-Methoxy-benzaldehyde | 2-Methyl-2-butene | 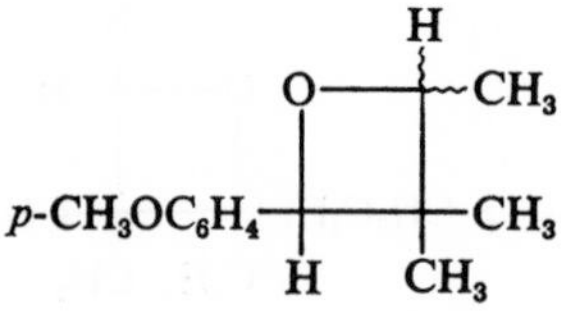 $p\text{-}CH_3OC_6H_4$ | — | — | 93 |

(*continued*)

**Table 1** (*continued*)

| Carbonyl compound | Alkene | Oxetane derivative | Yield (%) | MP, °C (BP, °C/mm) | Ref. |
|---|---|---|---|---|---|
| *p*-Methoxy-benzaldehyde | 2-Methyl-2-butene | 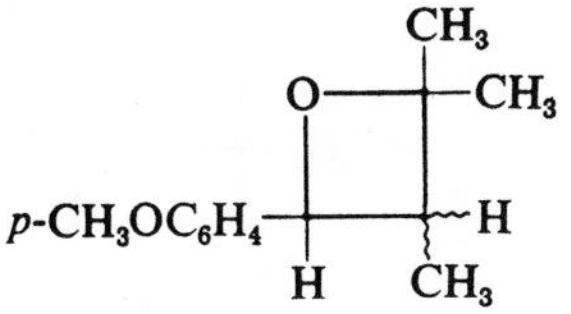 | — | — | 93 |
| 1-Naphthalde-hyde | 2-Methyl-2-butene | 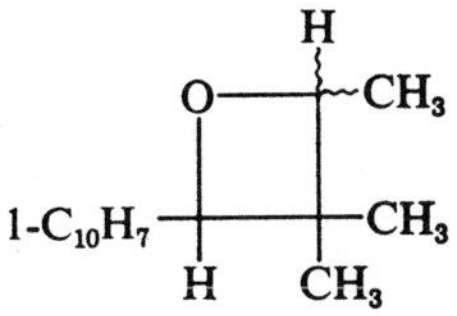 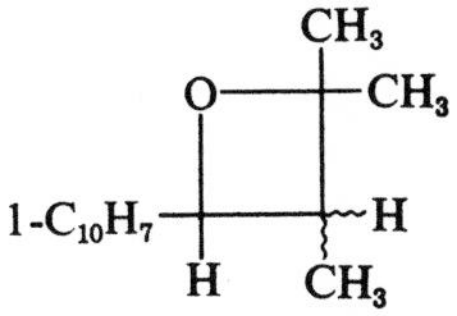 | 70 (3:2 isomers) | — | 93 |
| | | | | | |
| 2-Naphthyl-phenyl ketone | 2-Methyl-2-butene | 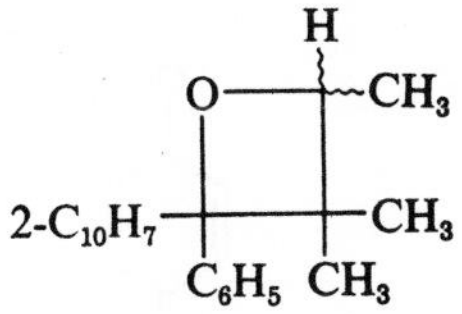 | 62 | 135–136 | 93 |
| 2-Naphthalde-hyde | 2-Methyl-2-butene | 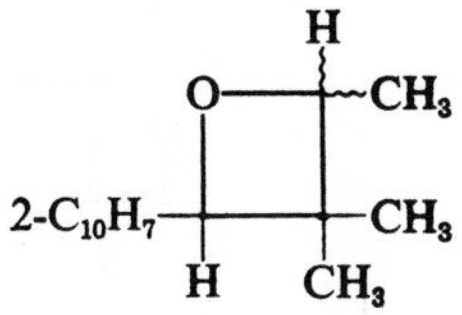 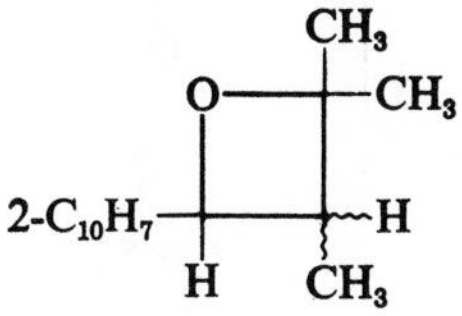 | 70 (3:2 isomers) | — | 93 |

(*continued*)

**Table 1** (*continued*)

| Carbonyl compound | Alkene | Oxetane derivative | Yield (%) | MP, °C (BP, °C/mm) | Ref. |
|---|---|---|---|---|---|
| 9-Anthraldehyde | 2-Methyl-2-butene | 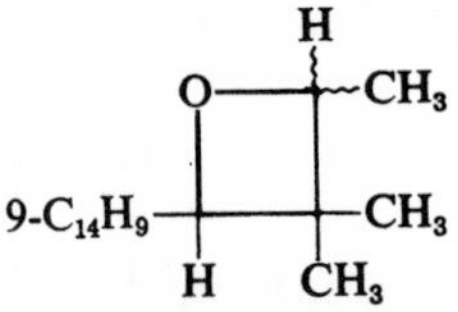 | — | 160–163 | 93 |
| *p*-Benzoquinone | *cis*-Cyclooctene | 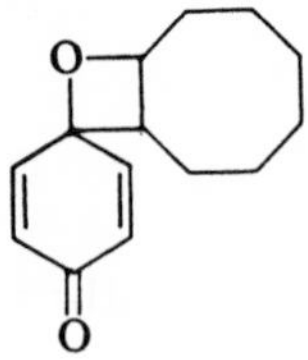 | 90 | — | 18 |
| *p*-Benzoquinone | Cyclohexene | 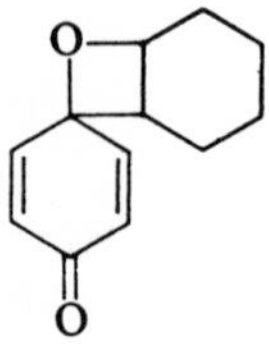 | 90+ | — | 18 |
| *p*-Benzoquinone | Cyclo-octa-1,5-diene | 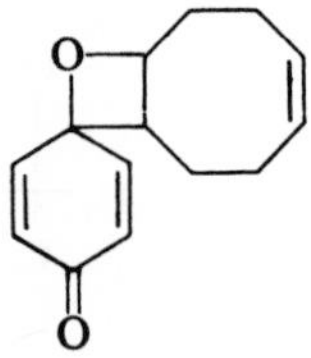 | 90+ | — | 18 |
| *p*-Benzoquinone | Cyclo-octa-tetraene | 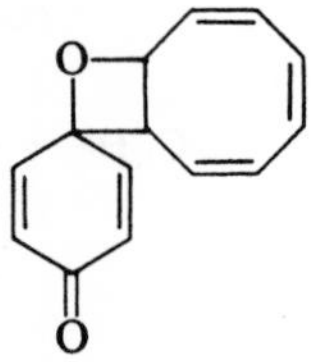 | 30 | — | 18 |
| *p*-Benzoquinone | Norbornadiene | 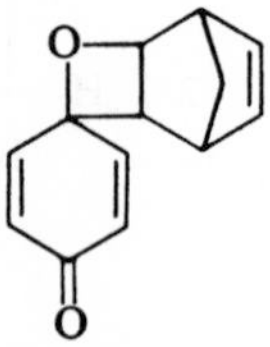 | 90+ | — | 18 |

(*continued*)

**Table 1** (*continued*)

| Carbonyl compound | Alkene | Oxetane derivative | Yield (%) | MP, °C (BP, °C/mm) | Ref. |
|---|---|---|---|---|---|
| *p*-Benzoquinone | Oct-1-ene | 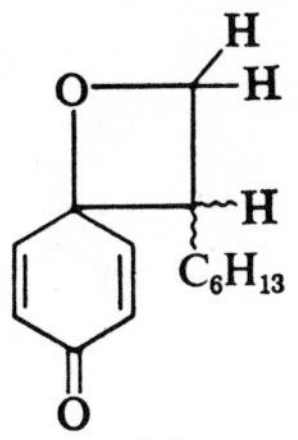 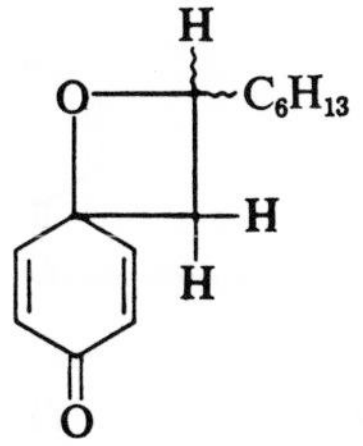 | 90+ | — | 18 |
| Chloranil | *cis*-Cyclooctene | 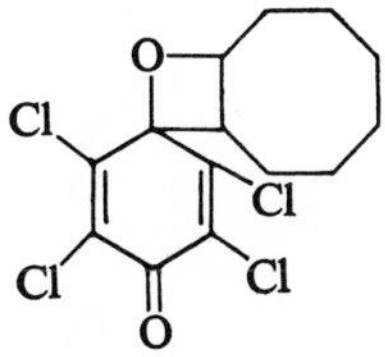 | 90+ | (189–191/ 0.05) | 18,19 |
| *p*-Benzoquinone | Oct-2-ene | 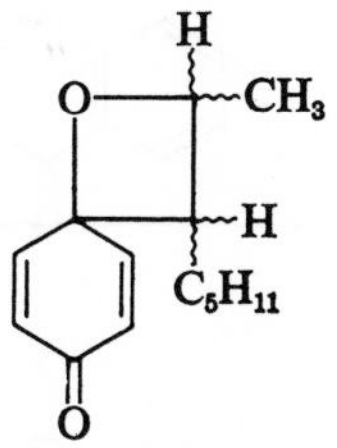 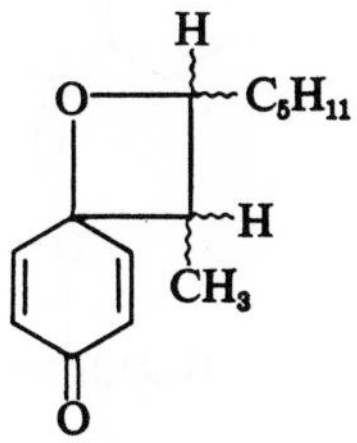 | 90+ | — | 18 |

(*continued*)

**Table 1** (*continued*)

| Carbonyl compound | Alkene | Oxetane derivative | Yield (%) | MP, °C (BP, °C/mm) | Ref. |
|---|---|---|---|---|---|
| Chloranil | Cyclo-octa-1,5-diene | 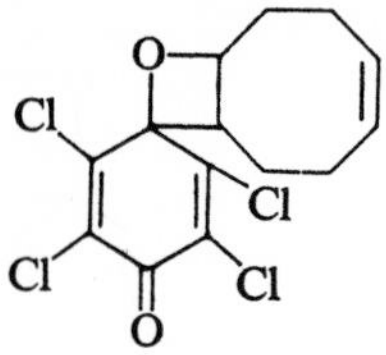 | 90+ | — | 18 |
| p-Toluquinone | cis-Cyclooctene | 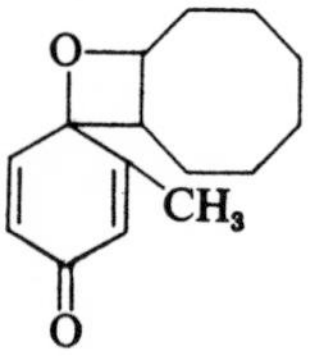 | 90+ | — | 18 |
| p-Toluquinone | Cyclo-octa-1,5-diene | 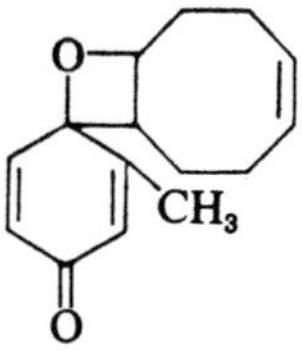 | 90+ | — | 18 |
| Naphtha-1,4-quinone | cis-Cyclooctene | 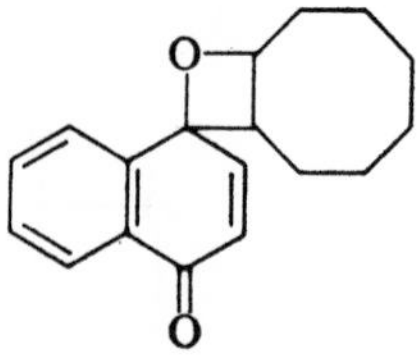 | 90+ | — | 18 |
| Naphtha-1,4-quinone | Cyclo-octa-1,5-diene | 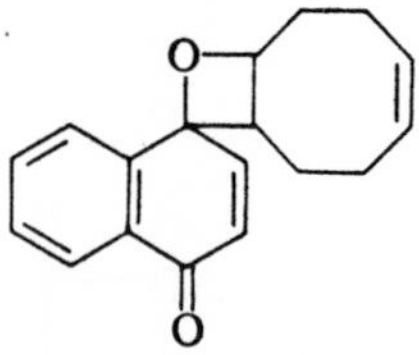 | 90+ | — | 18 |
| Carbonyl cyanide | 1,1-Diphenyl-ethylene | 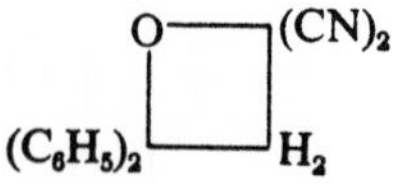 | 58 | 107.5–108.5 | 3 |

(*continued*)

**Table 1** (*continued*)

| Carbonyl compound | Alkene | Oxetane derivative | Yield (%) | MP, °C (BP, °C/mm) | Ref. |
|---|---|---|---|---|---|
| Carbonyl cyanide | 1,1-Di-*p*-tolyethylene | 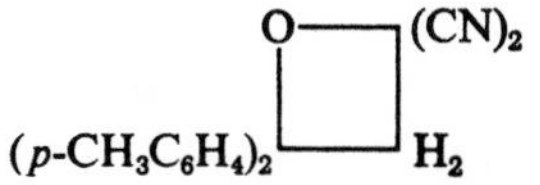 $(p\text{-}CH_3C_6H_4)_2$ ⊏⊐ $(CN)_2$ $H_2$ (oxetane) | 66 | 94–95.5 | 3 |
|  | 2-phenylvinyl | 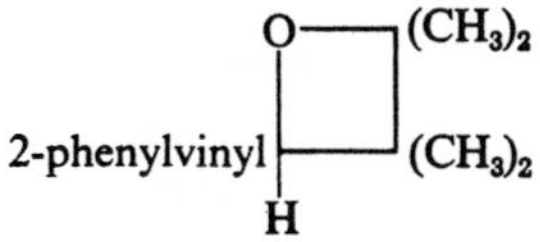 H $(CH_3)_2$ ⊏⊐ $(CH_3)_2$ (oxetane) | — | 320–340 | 66 |
| Acetone | Fumaronitrile | 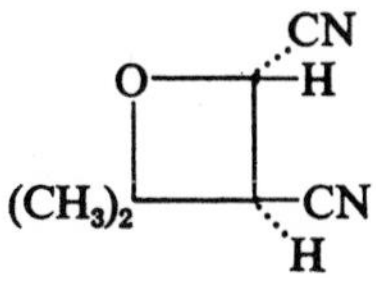 $(CH_3)_2$ ⊏⊐ with CN, H, CN, H (oxetane) | 64 | 41–42.3 | 13 |
|  |  | 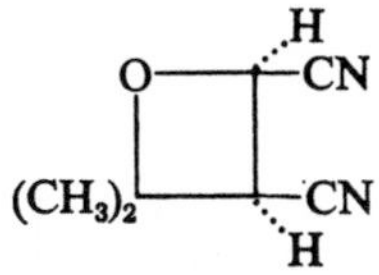 $(CH_3)_2$ ⊏⊐ with H, CN, CN, H (oxetane) | 22.5 | 59.5–60.2 | 13 |

<sup></sup> a The same oxetane was formed from both *cis*- and *trans*-butene. Olefin isomerization may be the result of triplet–triplet transfer by a nonefficient process that allows both reactions to occur.[7,46,72]

**Table 2**

Ultraviolet Radiation-Induced Cycloadditions of Polyfluorocarbonyl Compounds to Polyfluorolakenes

| Carbonyl compound | Alkene | Oxetane derivative | Yield (%) | BP (°C/mm) | Ref. |
|---|---|---|---|---|---|
| $CF_3CHO$ | $CF_2{=}CFCF_3$ | 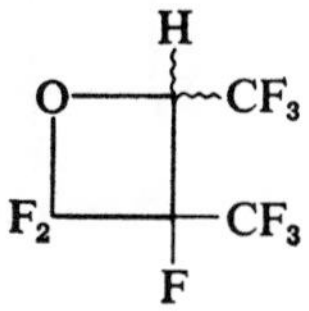 H $F_2$ ⊏⊐ $CF_3$, $CF_3$, F (oxetane) *cis* and *trans* (~1:1) | 32 | 38–39 (*trans*) 41–42 (*cis*) | 51 |

(*continued*)

**Table 2** (*continued*)

| Carbonyl compound | Alkene | Oxetane derivative | Yield (%) | BP (°C/mm) | Ref. |
|---|---|---|---|---|---|
| $CF_3CHO$ | $CF_2{=}CF(CF_2)_2H$ | 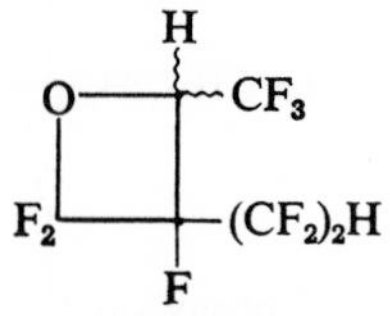 (structure) *cis* and *trans* | 66 | 72 (*trans*)<br>89 (*cis*) | 51 |
| $H(CF_2)_4CHO$ | $CF_2{=}CFCF_3$ | 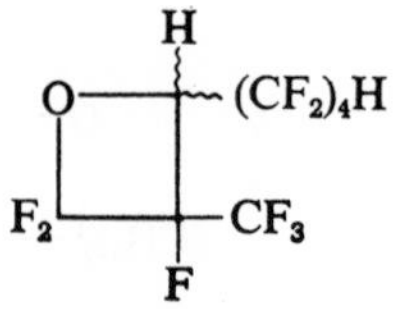 (structure) *cis* and *trans* (~1:1) | 59 | 124 (*trans*)<br>128 (*cis*) | 51 |
| $C_3F_7CHO$ | $CF_2{=}CFCF_3$ | 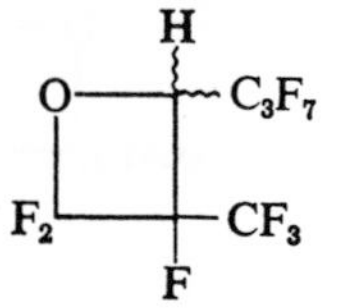 (structure) *cis* and *trans* (~1:1) | 37 | 83 (*trans*)<br>86 (*cis*) | 51 |
| $CF_3CHO$ | $CF_2{=}CFCl$ | 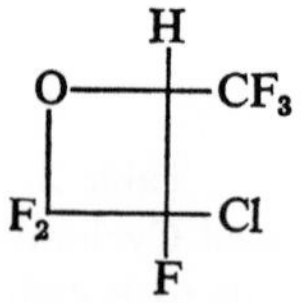 (structure) + polymer | 14 | 53 | 51 |
| $H(CF_2)_4CHO$ | $CF_2{=}CFCl$ | 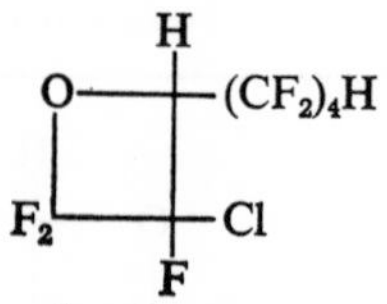 (structure) + polymer | 15 | 136 | 51 |

(*continued*)

**Table 2** (*continued*)

| Carbonyl compound | Alkene | Oxetane derivative | Yield, (%) | BP (°C/mm) | Ref. |
|---|---|---|---|---|---|
| $ClCF_2COCF_2Cl$ | $CF_2{=}CFCl$ | 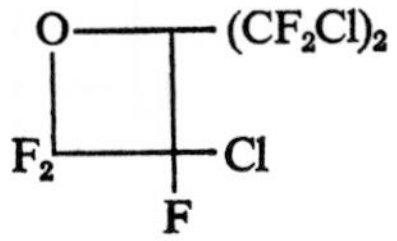 oxetane ring: $O$—$(CF_2Cl)_2$ / $F_2$—$Cl$, $F$  + polymer | 11 | 120 | 51 |
| $ClCF_2COCF_2Cl$ | $CF_2{=}CFCF_3$ | 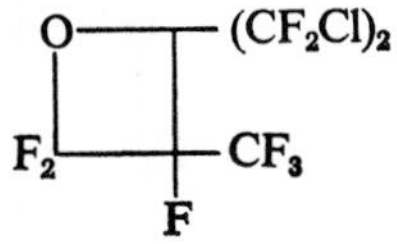 oxetane ring: $O$—$(CF_2Cl)_2$ / $F_2$—$CF_3$, $F$ | 56 | 107.5 | 50, 51 |
| $ClCF_2COCF_2Cl$ | $CF_2{=}CFC_5H_{11}$ | 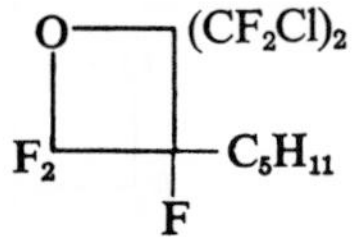 oxetane ring: $O$—$(CF_2Cl)_2$ / $F_2$—$C_5H_{11}$, $F$ | 47 | 182–184 / 179–182 | 51 / 50 |
| $Cl_2CFCOCFCl_2$ | $CF_2{=}CFCF_3$ | 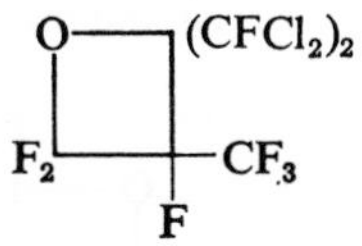 oxetane ring: $O$—$(CFCl_2)_2$ / $F_2$—$CF_3$, $F$ | 39 | 171–172 | 51 |
| $CF_3COCF_3$ | $CF_2{=}CFCF_3$ | 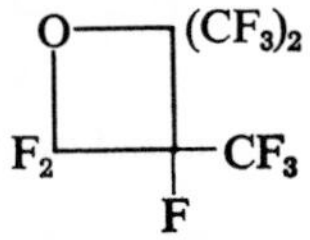 oxetane ring: $O$—$(CF_3)_2$ / $F_2$—$CF_3$, $F$ | 50 | 51–52 | 51 |
| $C_2F_5COC_2F_5$ | $CF_2{=}CFCF_3$ | 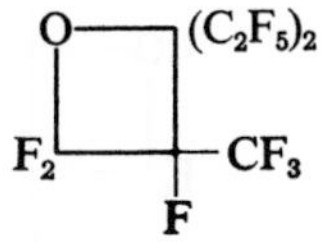 oxetane ring: $O$—$(C_2F_5)_2$ / $F_2$—$CF_3$, $F$ | 46 | 97 | 51 |
| $C_3F_7COC_3F_7$ | $CF_2{=}CFCF_3$ | 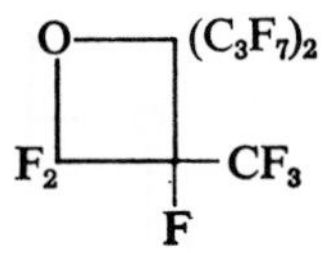 oxetane ring: $O$—$(C_3F_7)_2$ / $F_2$—$CF_3$, $F$ | 62 | 136 / 127–136 | 51 / 50 |

(continued)

**Table 2** (*continued*)

| Carbonyl compound | Alkene | Oxetane derivative | Yield (%) | BP (°C/mm) | Ref. |
|---|---|---|---|---|---|
| $C_3F_7COC_3F_7$ | $CF_2=CFC_5F_{11}$ | 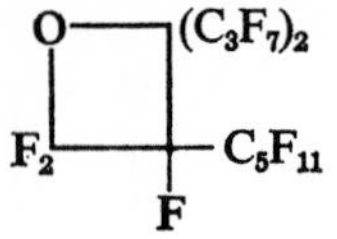 [oxetane ring: O–$(C_3F_7)_2$ top right, $F_2$ bottom left, C–$C_5F_{11}$ bottom right, $F$ below] | 32 | 199–201 / 183–185 | 51 / 50 |
| 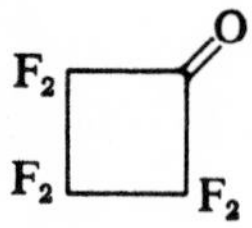 [cyclobutanone: $F_2$, $F_2$, $F_2$, C=O ring] | $CF_2=CFCF_3$ | 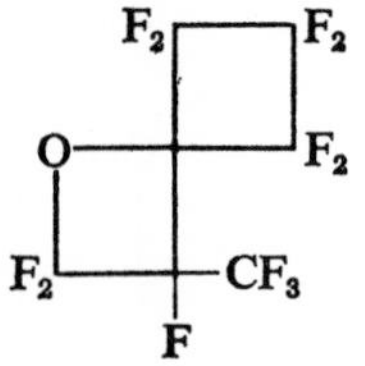 [fused bicyclic oxetane: $F_2$ $F_2$ top, $F_2$ right, O left, $F_2$ bottom left, $CF_3$ bottom right, $F$ below] | 33 | 68–69 | 50, 51 |
| $CF_3COF$ | $CF_2=CFCF_3$ | 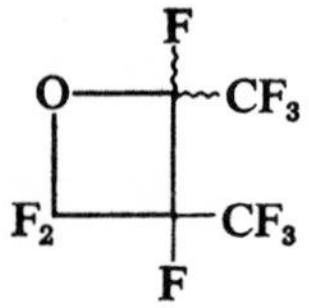 [oxetane: O–C($F$)–$CF_3$ top, $F_2$ bottom left, C–$CF_3$ bottom right, $F$ below] *cis* and *trans* (65:35) | 38 | 25 | 51 |
| $C_3F_7COF$ | $CF_2=CFCF_3$ | [oxetane: O–C($F$)–$C_3F_7$ top, $F_2$ bottom left, C–$CF_3$ bottom right, $F$ below] *cis* and *trans* (~1:1) | 73 / 42 | 80 (less prevalent struct.) / 78 (more prevalent struct.) | 51 / 24 |
| $C_3F_7COF$ | $CF_2=CF(CF_2)_2H$ | 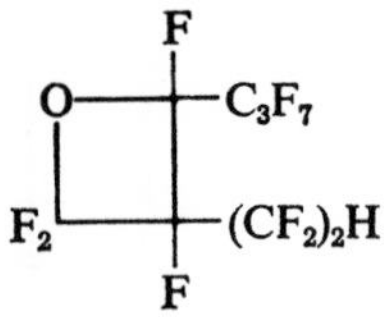 [oxetane: O–C($F$)–$C_3F_7$ top, $F_2$ bottom left, C–$(CF_2)_2H$ bottom right, $F$ below] | 35 | 109–111 | 24, 51 |
| $H(CF_2)_4COF$ | $CF_2=CFCF_3$ | 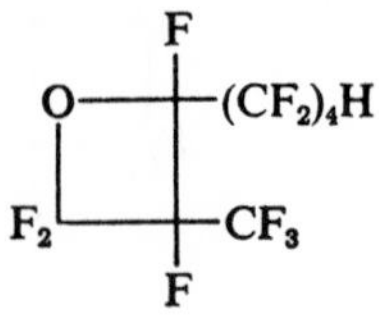 [oxetane: O–C($F$)–$(CF_2)_4H$ top, $F_2$ bottom left, C–$CF_3$ bottom right, $F$ below] | 48 | 111–118.5 | 24, 51 |

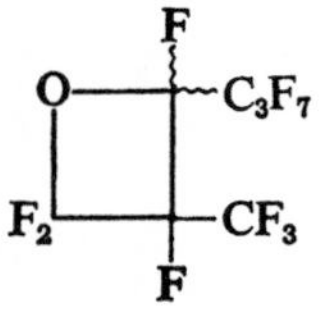

(*continued*)

**Table 2** (*continued*)

| Carbonyl compound | Alkene | Oxetane derivative | Yield (%) | BP (°C/mm) | Ref. |
|---|---|---|---|---|---|
| $H(CF_2)_4COF$ | $CF_2{=}CF(CF_2)_2H$ | 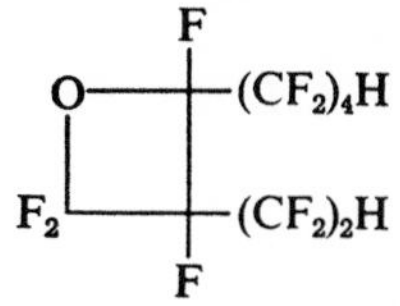 F / O—$(CF_2)_4H$ / $F_2$—$(CF_2)_2H$ / F | 61 | 79–94/98 | 51 |
| $C_7H_{15}COF$ | $CF_2{=}CFCF_3$ | 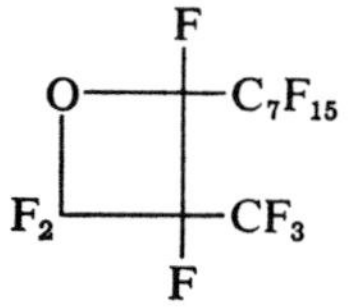 F / O—$C_7F_{15}$ / $F_2$—$CF_3$ / F | 91 | 161<br>162–166 | 51<br>24 |
| $FOC(CF_2)_3COF$ | $CF_2{=}CFCF_3$ | 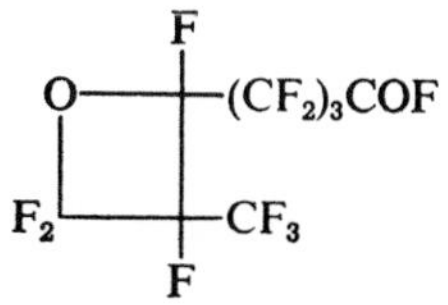 F / O—$(CF_2)_3COF$ / $F_2$—$CF_3$ / F | 34 | 102–104 | 51 |
| | | 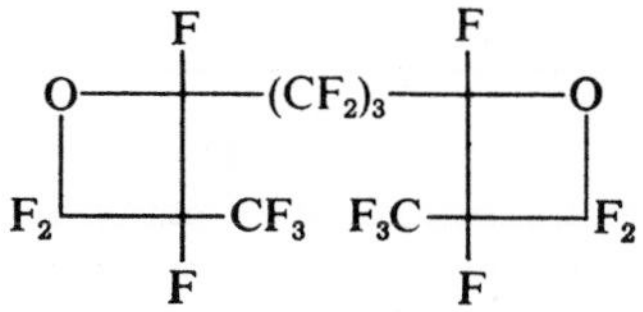 F ... F / O—$(CF_2)_3$—O / $F_2$—$CF_3$ $F_3C$—$F_2$ / F F | 31 | 153–155 | 51 |
| $CF_2ClCOCF_2Cl$ | $CHF_2CF_2CF{=}CF_2$ | 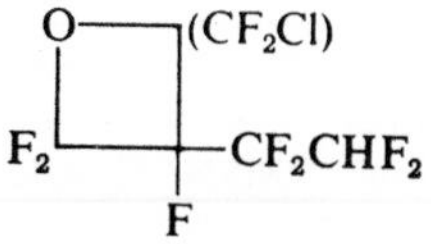 O—$(CF_2Cl)$ / $F_2$—$CF_2CHF_2$ / F | 30 | 144–146.5 | 50 |

**Table 3**

Preparation of Halogenated Oxetanes by Irradiation of
Acetaldehyde in Fluoroethylenes [14]

| Fluoroethylene | Oxetane | Yield (%) | Density (g/ml/°C) | NBP (°C) | Enthalpy (kcal/mole) |
|---|---|---|---|---|---|
| $CF_2{=}CF_2$ | 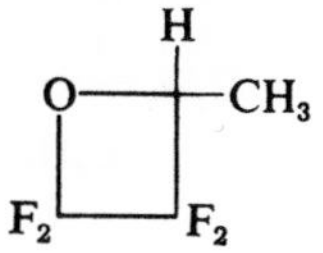 H / O—$CH_3$ / $F_2$—$F_2$ | 2.8 | 1.279/19 | 44 | — |

(*continued*)

**Table 3** (*continued*)

| Fluoroethylene | Oxetane | Yield (%) | Density (g/ml/°C) | NBP (°C) | Enthalpy (kcal/mole) |
|---|---|---|---|---|---|
| $CF_2{=}CFCl$ | 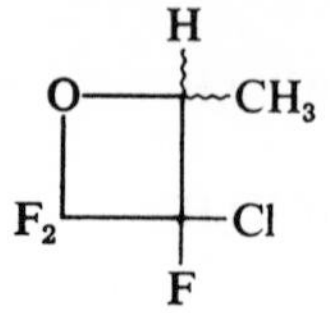 H ⋯CH$_3$ / F$_2$—Cl / F *cis* | 1.3 | 1.344/22 | 66.6 | 7.525 |
| | 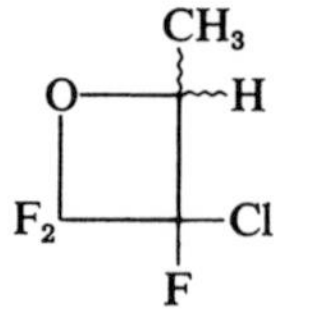 CH$_3$ ⋯H / F$_2$—Cl / F *trans* | 1.1 | 1.344/26 | 77.9 | 7.578 |
| $CF_2{=}CCl_2$ | 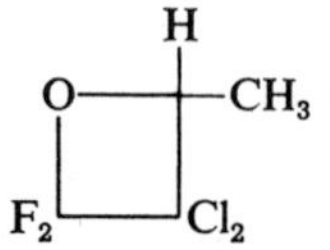 H—CH$_3$ / F$_2$—Cl$_2$ | 2.1 | 1.395/23 | 109.4 | 8.107 |

**Table 4**
Correlation of Photoreactions of Dimethyl-*N*-(2-cyano-2-propyl)
Ketenimine with the Photobehavior of Aromatic Aldehydes and
Ketones[82]

| Carbonyl compound | $E_{s-t}$[a] | Photo- reduc- tion[b] | Products from **37** TMSN[c] % Adducts | | Adduct structure |
|---|---|---|---|---|---|
| Cyclopropyl- phenyl ketone | ? | ? | 100 | 0 | 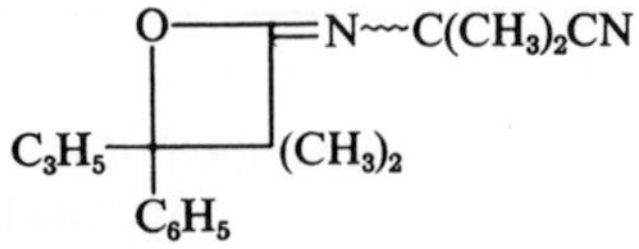 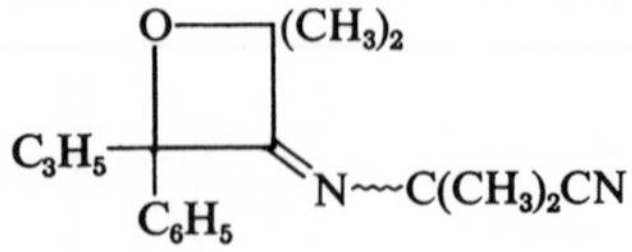 O═N⁓C(CH$_3$)$_2$CN / C$_3$H$_5$—(CH$_3$)$_2$ / C$_6$H$_5$   α |
| | | | | | O—(CH$_3$)$_2$ / C$_3$H$_5$— / C$_6$H$_5$ N⁓C(CH$_3$)$_2$CN   β |

(*continued*)

**Table 4** (*continued*)

| Carbonyl compound | $E_{s-t}{}^a$ | Photo-reduc-tion[b] | Products from **37** | | Adduct structure |
|---|---|---|---|---|---|
| | | | TMSN[c] % | Adducts | |
| Acetophenone | 74[d] | Yes[e] | 57 | 43 | |

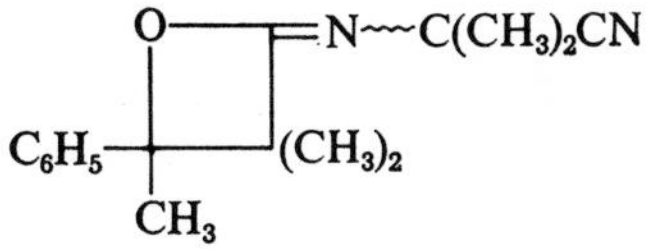

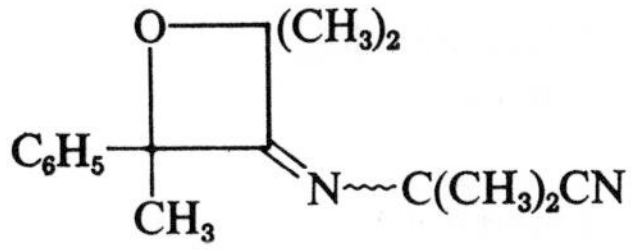

α

β

| *p*-Methoxy-benzaldehyde | ? | ? | 66 | 34 | |

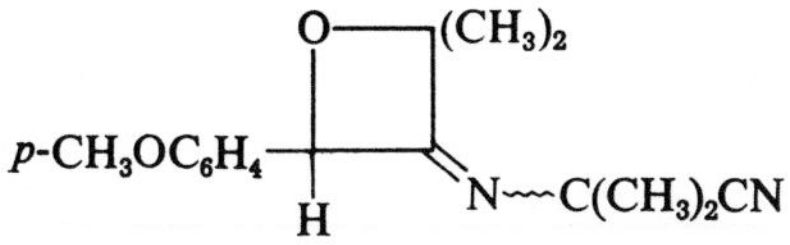

β

| *p*-Chlorobenzal-dehyde | ? | ? | 21[f] | 60[i] | |

β

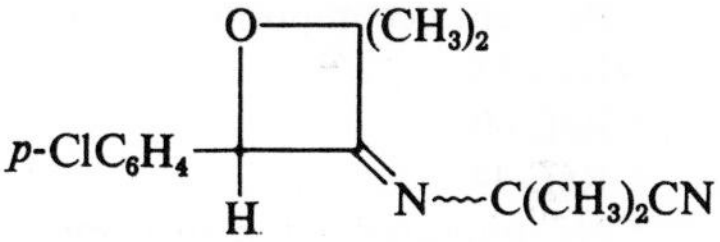

| Benzaldehyde | 72[d] | yes[e] | 10[i] | 50[i] | |

β

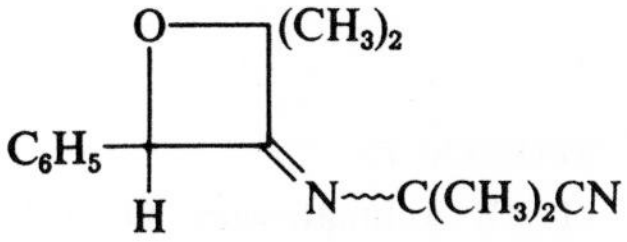

| Benzophenone | 70[d] | yes[e] | 5 | 95 | |

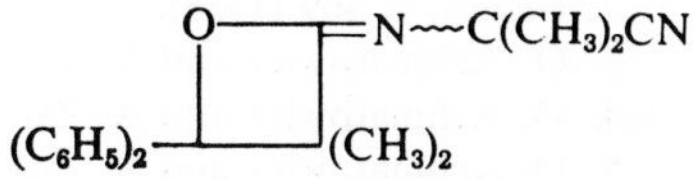

α

(*continued*)

**Table 4** (*continued*)

| Carbonyl compound | $E_{s-t}$[a] | Photo-reduc-tion[b] | TMSN[c] % | Products from **37** Adducts | Adduct structure |
|---|---|---|---|---|---|

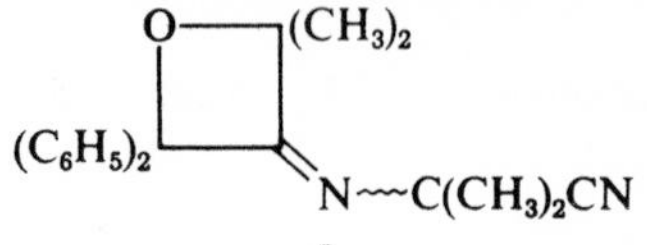

$$\beta$$

| 2-Acetonaphthone | 59[d] | no[f] | 0 | 0 | — |
| 1-Naphthalde-hyde | 57[d] | no[f] | 0 | 0 | — |
| Fluorenone | 53[g] | ?[h] | 20 | 80 | 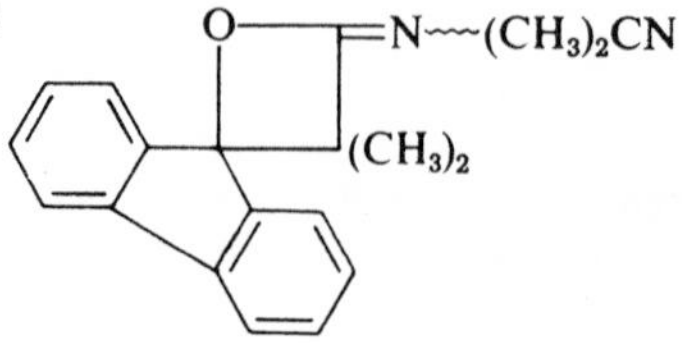 |

[a] Ground state–triplet excitation energy in kcal.
[b] Whether or not compound undergoes photoreduction to pinacol.
[c] Per cent decomposition to tetramethylsuccinonitrile.
[d] Ref. 58.
[e] Ref. 60.
[f] Ref. 44.
[g] No photoreduction in isopropyl alcohol[9]; however, fluorenopinacol photodecomposes to fluorenone.[76]
[h] Some unidentified products.

**REFERENCES**

1. O. Achmatowicz, O. Achmatowicz, Jr., K. Belniak, and J. Wrobel, *Roczniki Chem.*, **35**, 738 (1961).
2. O. Achmatowicz and M. Leplawy, *Bull. Acad. Polon. Sci., Ser. Sci. Chim., Geol. Geogr.*, **6**, 409 (1958).
3. O. Achmatowicz and M. Leplawy, *Roczniki Chem.*, **33**, 1349 (1959).
4. O. Achmatowicz and A. Zamojski, *Roczniki Chem.*, **35**, 799 (1961).
5. O. Achmatowicz and A. Zwierzak, *Roczniki Chem.*, **35**, 507 (1961).
6. P. W. Allen and L. E. Sutton, *Acta Cryst.*, **3**, 54 (1950).
7. D. R. Arnold, R. L. Hinman, and A. H. Glick, *Tetrahedron Letters*, **1964**, 1425.
8. J. G. Atkinson, D. E. Ayer, G. Büchi, and E. W. Robb, *J. Am. Chem. Soc.*, **85**, 2257 (1963).

9. W. E. Bachman, *J. Am. Chem. Soc.*, **55**, 394 (1933).

10. H. L. Bäckström and K. Sandros, *Acta Chim. Scand.*, **14**, 48 (1960).

11. G. M. Barrow and S. Searles, *J. Am. Chem. Soc.*, **75**, 1175 (1953).

12. A. Beckett and G. Porter, *Trans. Faraday Soc.*, **59**, 2038 (1963).

13. J. J. Beereboom and M. S. von Wittenau, *J. Org. Chem.*, **30**, 1231 (1965).

14. E. R. Bissell and D. B. Fields, *J. Org. Chem.*, **29**, 249 (1964).

15. N. K. Bridge and G. Porter, *Proc. Roy. Soc. (London)*, **244A**, 276 (1958).

16. W. A. Bryce and C. H. J. Wells, *Can. J. Chem.*, **41**, 2722 (1963).

17. D. Bryce-Smith, G. I. Fray, and A. Gilbert, *Tetrahedron Letters*, **1964**, 2137.

18. D. Bryce-Smith and A. Gilbert, *Proc. Chem. Soc.*, **1964**, 87.

19. D. Bryce-Smith and A. Gilbert, *Tetrahedron Letters*, **1964**, 3471.

20. G. Büchi, C. G. Inman, and E. S. Lipinsky, *J. Am. Chem. Soc.*, **76**, 4327 (1954).

21. G. Büchi, J. T. Kofron, E. Koller, and D. Rosenthal, *J. Am. Chem. Soc.*, **78**, 876 (1956).

22. T. W. Campbell, *J. Org. Chem.*, **22**, 1029 (1957).

23. S. I. Chen, J. Zinn, and W. D. Gwinn, *J. Chem. Phys.*, **33**, 3295 (1960).

24. D. D. Coffman and J. F. Harris, U.S. Pat. 3,125,581 (1964).

25. S. Cristol and R. F. Helmreich, *J. Am. Chem. Soc.*, **74**, 4083 (1952).

26. J. English, Jr. and F. V. Brutcher, Jr., *J. Am. Chem. Soc.*, **74**, 4279 (1952).

27. V. Ermolaev and A. Terenin, *J. Chim. Phys.*, **55**, 698 (1958).

28. V. Ermolaev, *Usp. Fiz. Nauk*, **80**, 3 (1963).

29. J. R. Fernandez, R. J. Meyer, and W. D. Gwinn, *J. Chem. Phys.*, **23**, 758 (1955).

30. G. Fleming, M. M. Anderson, A. J. Harrison, and L. W. Pickett, *J. Chem. Phys.*, **30**, 351 (1959).

31. R. Fonteyne, P. Cornand, and M. Ticket, *Natuurw. Tijdjschr. Ned. Indie*, **25**, 67 (1943); *Chem. Abstr.*, **38**, 5216 (1944).

32. R. Fonteyne and M. Ticket, *Natuurw. Tijdschr. Ned. Indie*, **25**, 49 (1943); *Chem. Zentr.*, **11**, 711 (1943).

33. H. Frey, *Chem. Ber.*, **28**, 2516 (1895).

34. E. J. Gallegos and R. W. Kiser, *J. Phys. Chem.*, **66**, 136 (1962).

35. E. J. Goldish, *J. Chem. Educ.*, **36**, 400 (1959).

36. F. D. Greene, *Bull. Soc. Chim. France*, **1960**, 1356.

37. F. D. Greene, S. L. Misrock, and J. R. Wolff, *J. Am. Chem. Soc.*, **77**, 3852 (1955).

38. F. D. Greene, S. R. Ocamp, and R. A. Kaminski, *J. Am. Chem. Soc.*, **79**, 5957 (1957).

39. G. W. Griffin, unpublished results.

40. R. Guepet, J. Seyden-Penne, P. Piganiol, and P. Chabrier, *Bull. Soc. Chim. France*, **1961**, 2081.

41. H. S. Gutowsky, R. L. Ruthdge, M. Tamres, and S. Searles, *J. Am. Chem. Soc.*, **76**, 4242 (1954).

42. W. D. Gwinn, *Discussions Faraday Soc.*, **19**, 50 (1955).

43. W. D. Gwinn, J. Zinn, and J. Fernandez, *Bull. Phys. Soc. II*, **4**, 153 (1959).

44. G. S. Hammond and P. A. Leermakers, *J. Am. Chem. Soc.*, **84**, 207 (1962).

45. G. S. Hammond and R. S. H. Liu, *J. Am. Chem. Soc.*, **85**, 477 (1963).

46. G. S. Hammond and J. Saltiel, *J. Am. Chem. Soc.*, **85**, 2516 (1963).

47. G. S. Hammond and N. J. Turro, *Science*, **142**, 1541 (1963).

48. G. S. Hammond, N. J. Turro, and A. Fischer, *J. Am. Chem. Soc.*, **83**, 4674 (1961).

49. G. S. Hammond, N. J. Turro, and P. A. Leermakers, *J. Phys. Chem.*, **66**, 1144 (1962).

50. J. F. Harris, U.S. Pat. 2,995,571 (1962).

51. J. F. Harris and D. D. Coffman, *J. Am. Chem. Soc.*, **84**, 1553 (1962).
52. A. L. Henne, *Intern. Symp. Fluorine Chemistry, Birmingham, England, July 14–17, 1959.*
53. L. M. Jackman, *Applications of Nuclear Magnetic Spectroscopy in Organic Chemistry*, Pergamon, London, 1959, p. 55.
54. M. Kasha, *Radiation Res. Suppl.*, **2**, 265 (1960).
55. M. Kasha, "Ultraviolet Radiation Effects: Molecular Photo-Chemistry," in *Comparative Effects of Radiation*, M. Burton, J. S. Kirby-Smith, and J. L. Magee, Eds., Wiley, New York, 1960, p. 72.
56. E. A. Kauck and J. H. Simons, U.S. Pat. 2,594,272 (1952).
57. M. S. Kharasch, W. H. Urry, and B. M. Kuderna, Jr., *J. Org. Chem.*, **14**, 248 (1949).
58. G. N. Lewis and M. Kasha, *J. Am. Chem. Soc.*, **66**, 2100 (1944).
59. J. D. Margerum, J. N. Pitts, Jr., J. G. Rutgers, and S. Searles, Jr., *J. Am. Chem. Soc.*, **81**, 1549 (1959).
60. C. R. Masson, V. Boekelheide, and W. A. Noyes, Jr., in *Catalytic, Photochemical, and Electrolytic Reactions*, 2nd ed., Vol. 2, A. Weissberger, Ed. (Interscience, New York, 1956), pp. 315 ff.
61. P. de Mayo, "Ultraviolet Photochemistry of Simple Unsaturated Systems," in *Advances in Organic Chemistry*, Vol. II, R. A. Raphael, E. C. Taylor, and H. Wynberg, Eds., Interscience, New York, 1960.
62. P. de Mayo, J. B. Strothers, and W. Templeton, *Can. J. Chem.*, **39**, 488 (1961).
63. W. J. Middleton, *J. Org. Chem.*, **30**, 1307 (1965).
64. C. W. Moore, G. S. Hammond, and R. P. Foss, *J. Am. Chem. Soc.*, **83**, 2789 (1961), and related papers by Hammond and co-workers.
65. D. S. McClure, *J. Chem. Phys.*, **17**, 905 (1949).
66. E. Paterno and G. Chieffi, *Gazz. Chim. Ital.*, **39**, 341 (1909); *Chem. Abstr.*, **5**, 681 (1911).
67. J. N. Pitts, Jr., H. W. Johnson, Jr., and T. Kuwana, *J. Phys. Chem.*, **66**, 2456 (1962).
68. G. Porter and T. Wilkinson, *Trans. Faraday Soc.*, **57**, 1686 (1961).
69. H. Primas, K. Frei, and H. H. Günthard, *Helv. Chim. Acta*, **41**, 35 (1958).
70. W. Reusch, *J. Org. Chem.*, **27**, 1882 (1962).
71. A. Rosowsky and D. S. Tarbell, *J. Org. Chem.*, **26**, 2255 (1961).
72. J. Saltiel and G. S. Hammond, *J. Am. Chem. Soc.*, **85**, 2515 (1963).
73. D. Scharf and F. Korte, *Tetrahedron Letters*, **1963**, 821.
74. G. O. Schenck, W. Hartmann, and R. Steinmetz, *Chem. Ber.*, **96**, 498 (1963).
75. A. Schönberg and A. Mustafa, *Chem. Rev.*, **40**, 181 (1947).
76. A. Schönberg and A. Mustafa, *J. Chem. Soc.*, **1944**, 67.
77. S. Searles, *J. Am. Chem. Soc.*, **73**, 124 (1951).
78. S. Searles, *J. Am. Chem. Soc.*, **73**, 4515 (1951).
79. S. Searles, Jr., in *Compounds with Three- and Four-Membered Rings (The Chemistry of Heterocyclic Compounds*, Vol. 19, A. Weissberger, Ed. (Interscience, New York, 1964), pp. 983 ff.
80. S. Searles, Jr. and H. E. Mortenson, *J. Org. Chem.*, **22**, 1979 (1957).
81. J. P. Simons, *Quart. Rev. (London)*, **13**, 3 (1959).
82. L. A. Singer and P. D. Bartlett, *Tetrahedron Letters*, **1964**, 1887.
83. L. A. Singer and P. D. Bartlett, unpublished work.
84. R. Srinivasan, *J. Am. Chem. Soc.*, **82**, 775 (1959).

85. T. S. Stevens, in *Chemistry of Carbon Compounds*, Vol. IVA, E. H. Rodd, Ed., Elsevier, New York, 1957, p. 20.
86. J. Thesing and D. Witzel, *Z. Angew. Chem.*, **86**, 425 (1950).
87. G. V. D. Tiers, NMR Summary, Minnesota Mining and Mfg. Co., 1959.
88. D. J. Trecker, R. L. Brandon, and J. P. Henry, *Chem. Ind. (London)*, **1963**, 625.
89. L. W. Trevoy and W. G. Brown, *J. Am. Chem. Soc.*, **71**, 1675 (1949).
90. H. Vieregge, H. J. T. Bos, and J. F. Arens, *Rec. Trav. Chim.*, **78**, 664 (1959).
91. C. Walling and W. Thaler, *J. Am. Chem. Soc.*, **83**, 3877 (1961).
92. S. Winstein and R. B. Henderson, in *Heterocyclic Compounds*, Vol. 1, R. C. Elderfield, Ed., Wiley, New York, 1950, p. 59.
93. N. C. Yang, M. Nussim, M. J. Jorgenson, and S. Murov, *Tetrahedron Letters*, **1964**, 3657.
94. R. F. Zürcher and H. H. Günthard, *Helv. Chim. Acta*, **38**, 849 (1955).
95. R. F. Zürcher and H. H. Günthard, *Helv. Chim. Acta*, **40**, 89 (1959).

### b. β-Lactones

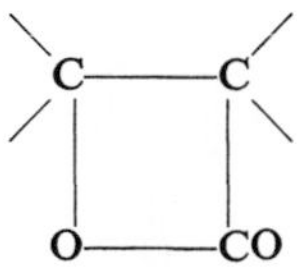

During his investigations of the reactions of ketenes, Staudinger reported[83,85,86,88-90,92,94,95] the cycloaddition of ketenes (1) to carbonyl compounds (2) resulting in the formation of unstable β-lactones* (3) which decomposed under the reaction conditions into carbon dioxide and olefins (4).[30,31] It had been previously reported[104] that the addition of

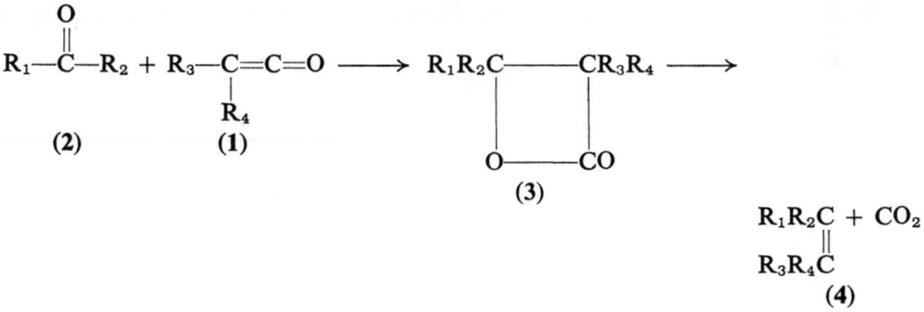

ketenes would not occur with all carbonyl compounds but only with α,β-unsaturated carbonyl compounds[3-5]; for example, an addition reaction was found to occur with benzoquinone and with dibenzalacetone, in contrast to Vorländer's report[107,108] that the reactivity of the carbon–oxygen double bond of carbonyl compounds was reduced by a double bond adjacent to it.

* For a review of the chemistry of β-lactones see Refs. 32, 68, 101, and 116.

Diphenylketene (6) reacted with benzoquinone (5) in ethereal solution at room temperature to give the mono-$\beta$-lactone (7a) in 72% yield.[86,92] With an excess of diphenylketene (6) the di-$\beta$-lactone (7b) is formed,[84,86] which

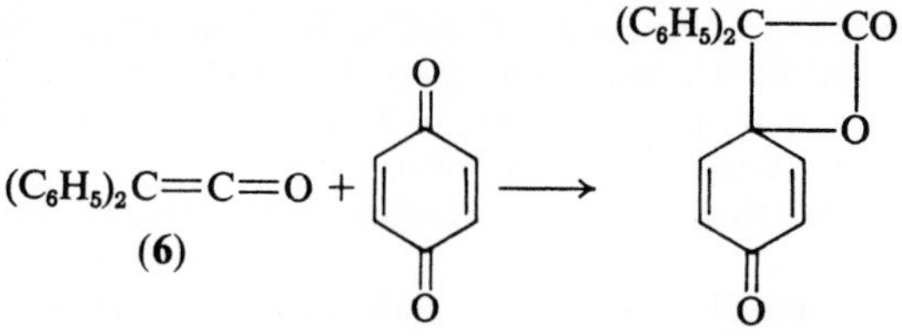

decomposed into the quinodimethane (8)[71,106] and carbon dioxide. Staudinger[92] found that a number of methylated and halogenated benzo-quinones, and even 1,4-naphthoquinone, react with diphenylketene to form the mono-$\beta$-lactones (Table 1). However, since the reaction is subject

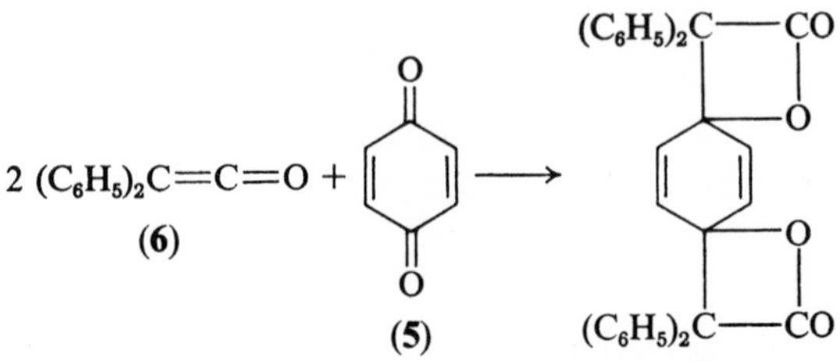

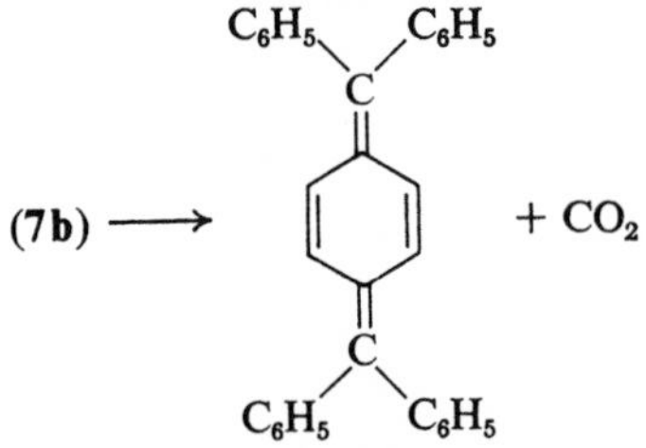

to steric hindrance, the m-xyloquinone, trichloroquinone, and 1,4-naph-thoquinone add to diphenylketene at room temperature while p-xylo-quinone, chloranil, and 9,10-anthraquinone do not add. If the reactions are run at elevated temperatures addition occurs, but the only isolable pro-ducts are the quinodimethanes (Table 3).[92]

A $\beta$-lactone (**10**) was obtained from dibenzalacetone (**9**) and diphenyl-ketene (**6**) which decomposed into an unsaturated hydrocarbon (**11**) referred to as an "open fulvene," which was an analog to the "fulvene" (**12**) prepared by Thiele.[105]

$$(C_6H_5CH=CH)_2C=O + (C_6H_5)_2C=C=O \longrightarrow$$
$$\quad\quad\quad (9) \quad\quad\quad\quad\quad\quad\quad (6)$$

$$
\begin{array}{ccc}
 & O\text{------}CO & \\
 & | \quad\quad\quad\quad | & \\
(C_6H_5CH=CH)_2C\text{------}C(C_6H_5)_2 &
\end{array}
$$
$$(10)$$

$$(10) \longrightarrow \quad \begin{array}{c} C_6H_5CH=CH \\ \diagdown \\ \quad\quad C=C(C_6H_5)_2 + CO_2 \\ \diagup \\ C_6H_5CH=CH \end{array}$$
$$(11)$$

$$\left( \begin{array}{c} CH=HC \\ | \quad\quad\quad \diagdown \\ \quad\quad\quad\quad C=CR_2 \\ | \quad\quad\quad \diagup \\ CH=HC \end{array} \right)$$
$$(12)$$

In the reaction of diphenylketene (**6**) and benzalacetophenone (**13**) and similar $\alpha,\beta$-unsaturated ketones—for example, methoxybenzalacetophenone (**15**)—Staudinger reported[93] that, in addition to the butadiene derivatives (**14**) formed according to equation a, there was still another reaction product which possessed a 1:1 mole ratio of ketene and ketone which was reported to be a $\delta$-lactone (**16**) (equation b).[94] Staudinger[91] also pointed

$$
\begin{array}{c} O \\ \| \end{array}
$$
$$C_6H_5CH=CHC\text{---}C_6H_5 + (C_6H_5)_2C=C=O \longrightarrow$$
$$\quad\quad (13) \quad\quad\quad\quad\quad\quad (6)$$

$$
\begin{array}{c}
C_6H_5 \\
| \\
C_6H_5CH=CHC\text{------}O \\
| \quad\quad\quad\quad | \\
(C_6H_5)_2C\text{------}CO
\end{array}
\longrightarrow
\begin{array}{c}
C_6H_5 \\
| \\
C_6H_5CH=CHC = C(C_6H_5)_2 + CO_2 \quad (a) \\
\\
(14)
\end{array}
$$

$$
\begin{array}{c} O \\ \| \end{array}
$$
$$CH_3OC_6H_4CH=CHC\text{---}C_6H_5 + (C_6H_5)_2C=C=O \longrightarrow$$
$$\quad\quad (15) \quad\quad\quad\quad\quad\quad (6)$$

$$
\begin{array}{c}
\quad\quad\quad\quad\quad\quad\quad\quad C_6H_5 \\
\quad\quad\quad\quad\quad\quad\quad\quad | \\
CH_3OC_6H_4CH\text{---}CH=C\text{---}O \\
\quad | \quad\quad\quad\quad\quad\quad\quad\quad | \quad\quad (b) \\
(C_6H_5)_2C\text{------------}
\end{array}
$$
$$(16)$$

out that with phenyl substitution the $\beta$-lactone rings as well as other heterocyclic four-membered compounds were less stable and decompose more easily than do the derivatives of dimethylketene. It was also pointed out that the starting material could be retained or an unsaturated compound could be obtained depending upon the direction of the cleavage,[76,87,91] as shown below:

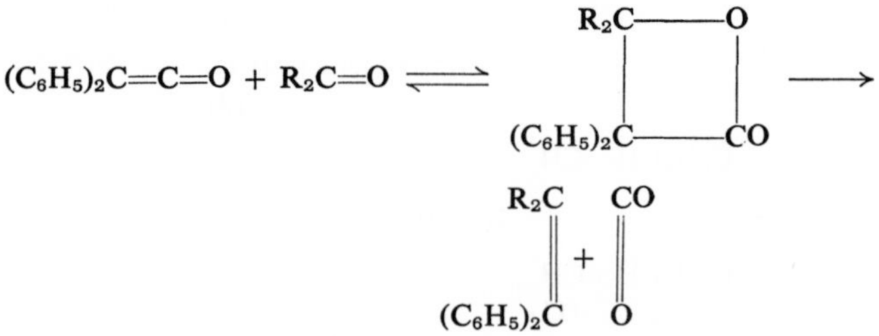

$$(C_6H_5)_2C=C=O + R_2C=O \rightleftharpoons$$

Quadbeck[77] has reported that when unsaturated ketones are formed from aldehydes and ketene, the primary diketene that results then reacts with the aldehyde to form a $\beta$-lactone (17), which loses carbon dioxide under the applied reaction conditions and then changes into an unsaturated ketone (18),[10] In contrast to previous reports,[30,31,76,83,85,87-92,94,95] Quadbeck states[77] that in the presence of suitable catalysts carbonyl com-

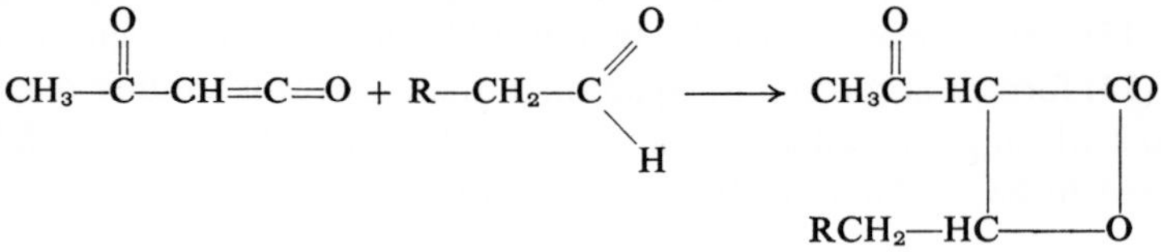

pounds form $\beta$-lactones with ketene, and these $\beta$-lactones can be isolated as such or can be changed into $\beta$-substituted propionic acid derivatives.

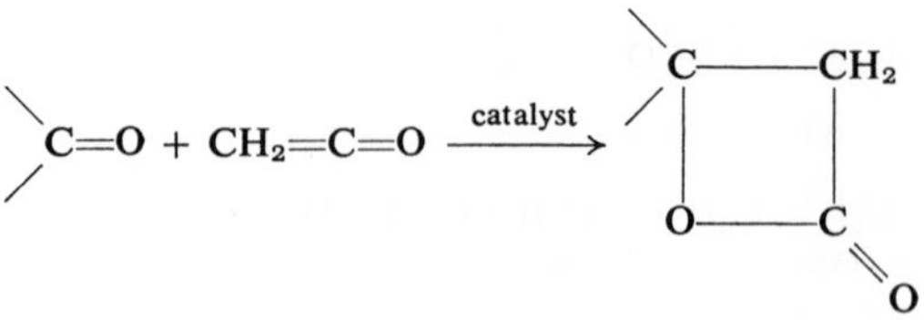

In a review on ketene, Lacey[68] also reported that in the presence of suitable catalysts ketene adds via a cycloaddition to the carbonyl group of aldehydes and ketones to give $\beta$-lactones. Künig[67] described the reaction of ketene with formaldehyde and acetaldehyde in the presence of a Friedel-Crafts type catalyst that resulted in propiolactone and $\beta$-butyrolactone, respectively. A similar reaction with ketene and furfural and with benzalde-

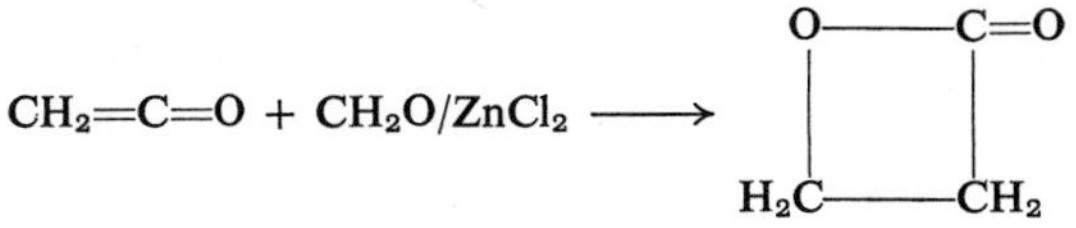

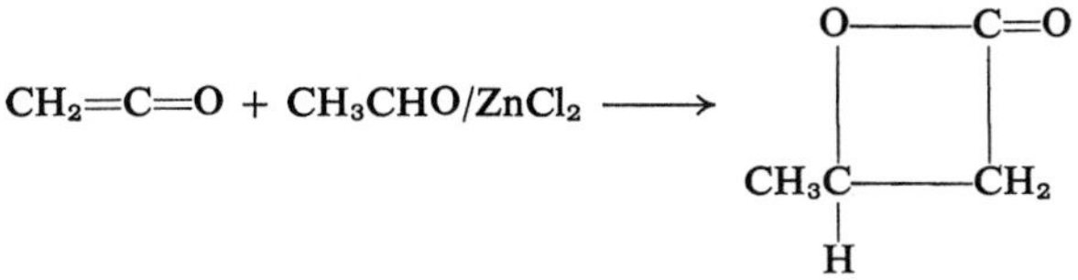

CH₂=C=O + CH₂O/ZnCl₂
O
C=O
H₂C
CH₂

CH₂=C=O + CH₃CHO/ZnCl₂
O
C=O
CH₃C
CH₂
H

hyde was reported by Hurd and Thomas[63] in which the $\beta$-lactone decarboxylation products $\alpha$-vinylfuran and styrene were isolated. The

CHO
+ CH₂=C=O
60°C
KOAc
H₂
CH=CH₂

C₆H₅CHO + CH₂=C=O
60°C
KOAc
H
C₆H₅
H₂
C₆H₅CH=CH₂

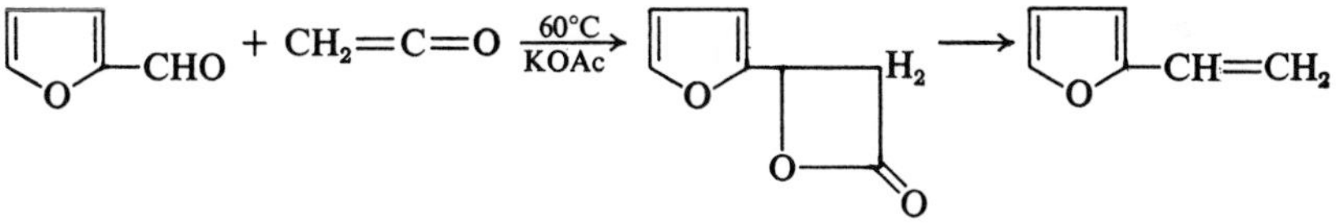

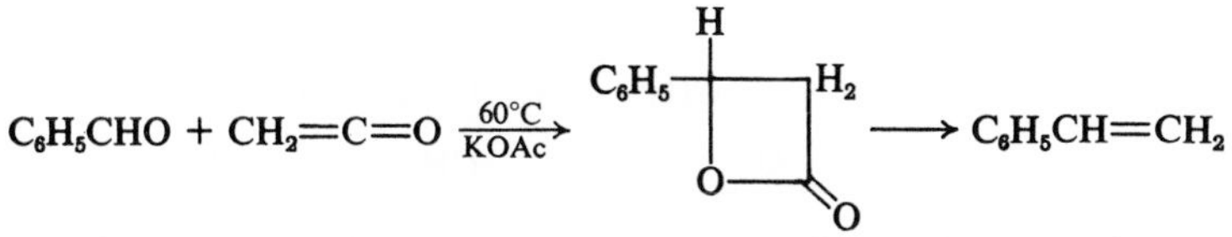

formation of $\beta$-propiolactone by the reaction of ketene and the appropriate carbonyl compounds has been reviewed by Zaugg[116] and by Hagemeyer,[39] who pointed out that suitable catalysts were generally salts which were strongly acid in aqueous solution[73] and were capable of forming coordination complexes with hydroxyl groups. For a list of those compounds that have been claimed effective in the reactions of ketene with carbonyl compounds, see Table 2.

For the reactions of ketene with aldehydes the less reactive catalysts (boric acid, zinc thiocyanate, zinc chloride) suffice; alkyl borates and *ortho*- and *meta*-phosphates are useful since it is not necessary to destroy them at the end of the reaction.[39,68,116] Since ketones are less reactive, a more active catalyst—for example, boron trifluoride etherate, zinc fluoroborate, zinc fluorophosphate or mercuric chloride—is required for the reaction with ketene. While reactions with aldehydes are generally carried out in ether, ketones or a medium of the $\beta$-lactone to be formed, reactions with ketones to form the $\beta$-lactone are generally done in the absence of a solvent (Table 3).* Reaction temperatures below 25°C are required since the $\beta$-lactones formed readily polymerize or are decarboxylated.[39, 68]

Both mono- and di-$\beta$-lactones were reported to have been formed in poor yields in the reactions of ketene (19) with diacetyl (24), acetylacetone, and acetonylacetone in the presence of boron trifluoride etherate.[39] The products were characterized by their thermal decarboxylation to unsaturated ketones (from the mono-$\beta$-lactone) and diene (from the di-$\beta$-lactone) (Table 3),* as is illustrated here.

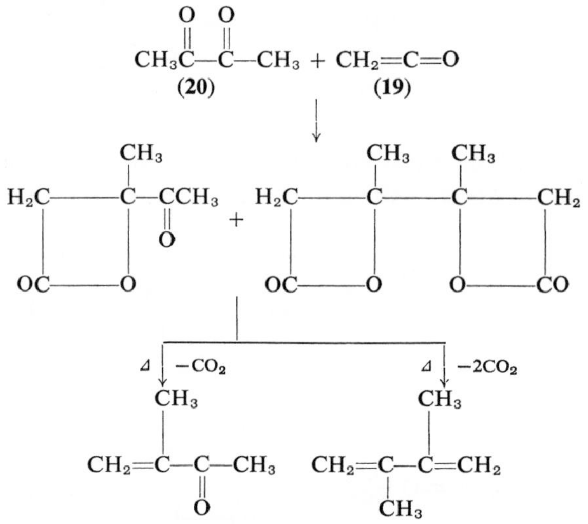

$\beta$-Alkyl vinyl ketones such as ethylidene acetone (21), mesityl oxide, and butylidene acetone did not react with ketene in the absence of a catalyst, but in the presence of boron trifluoride etherate gave $\beta,\gamma$-unsaturated $\delta$-lactones (23) in high yields* (Table 3)[114] via the formation of an un-

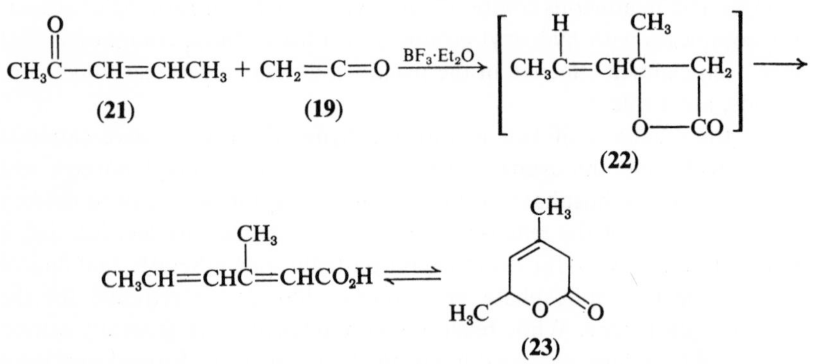

* See H. E. Zaugg[116] for a complete tabulation of these reactions.

stable $\beta$-lactone intermediate (**22**). Vinyl ketones such as methyl vinyl ketone (**24**) and methyl isopropyl ketone[39,49] reacted with ketene (**19**) in the presence of zinc chloride to give a mixture in the ratio 10:1 of a $\beta$-lactone (**25**) and a $\gamma,\delta$-unsaturated-$\delta$-lactone (**26**) (Table 3). In the absence of

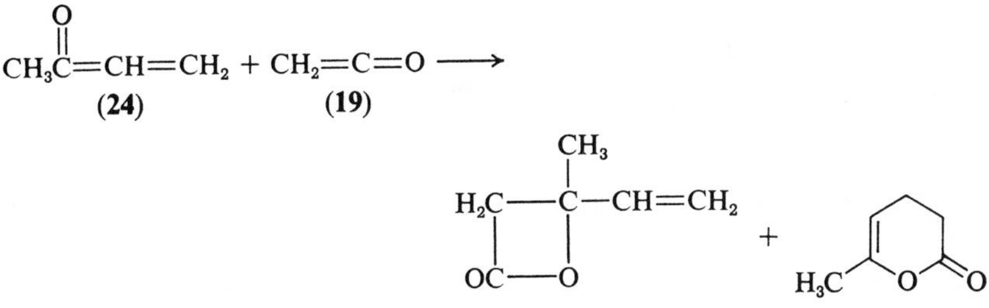

$$CH_3\overset{\overset{\textstyle O}{\|}}{C}{=}CH{=}CH_2 + CH_2{=}C{=}O \longrightarrow$$
$$\quad\text{(24)} \qquad\qquad \text{(19)}$$

$$\text{(25)} \qquad\qquad\qquad \text{(26)}$$

a catalyst, methyl vinyl ketone (**24**) reacts with ketene (**19**) to give **26** exclusively.[62,114]

Hagemeyer[39] found that benzaldehyde and acetophenone react with ketene in the presence of boric acid or zinc chloride at 0–10°C, and decarboxylation of the products gave a fair yield of styrene and $\alpha$-methylstyrene, respectively, indicating the presence of $\beta$-lactones in the product* (Table 3). For a tabulation of the products of the reactions of ketenes and carbonyl compounds, see Table 3 and the tables in the review by Zaugg.[116]

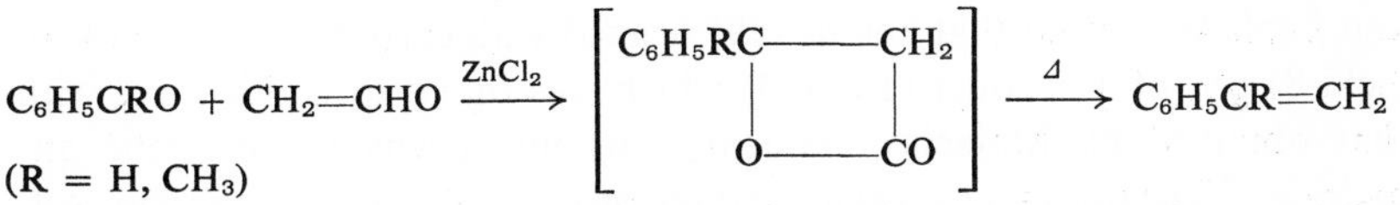

$$C_6H_5CRO + CH_2{=}CHO \xrightarrow{ZnCl_2}$$
$$\text{(R = H, CH}_3\text{)}$$

In applying the stereoselectivity in reactions of $\alpha$-chloroketones to the synthesis of optically active mevalonic acid (3,4-dihydro-3-methylpentanoic acid), Cornforth[27] found that the cycloaddition reaction of 3-chlorobutan-2-one (**27**) and ketene (**19**) in the presence of boron trifluoride yielded two stereoisomers of 4-chloro-3-methylpentane-3-lactone (**28**) in the ratio 2:3 which were isolated in 84% yield (Table 3).

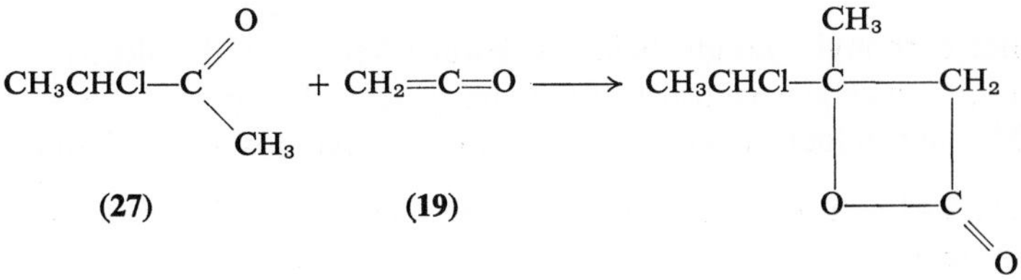

$$\text{(27)} \qquad\qquad \text{(19)} \qquad\qquad\qquad\qquad \text{(28)}$$

* See H. E. Zaugg[116] for a complete tabulation of these reactions.

Analogously, Schimmelschmidt and Mundlos[80] found that α-haloalde-
hydes or α-haloketones react with ketene in the presence of boron trifluoride forming the β-lactone via a cycloaddition reaction (Table 3). For
example, ketene (19) and α-chloroacetone (29) yield the β-lactone (30) in
80% yield.

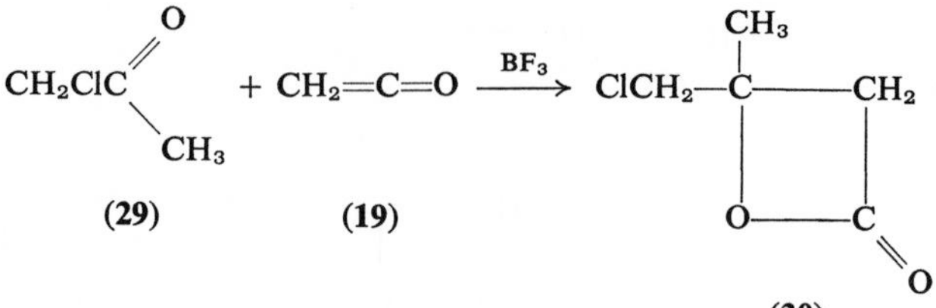

(29)                    (19)                                    (30)

Aldehydes were also found to react with ethylbutylketene resulting in a
β-lactone.[100]

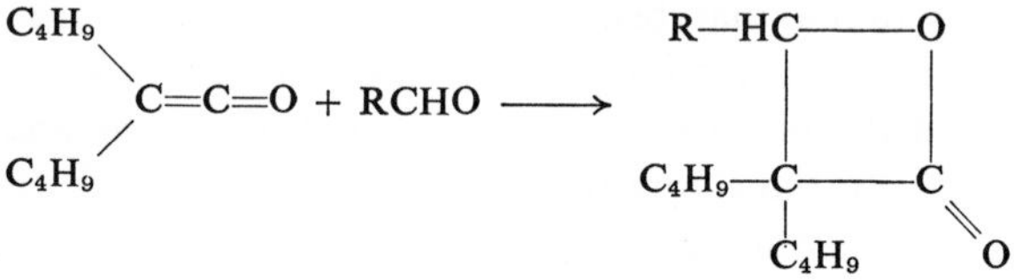

While investigating the chemistry of carbonyl cyanide, Achmatowicz
and Leplawy[1] found that ketene (19) reacted with carbonyl cyanide (3) to
yield 81.6% of a product (Table 3) which was found to be identical with
that obtained by Malachowski from carbonyl cyanide and acetic anhydride.[72] The product (32) exhibited the properties of a β-lactone, suggest-

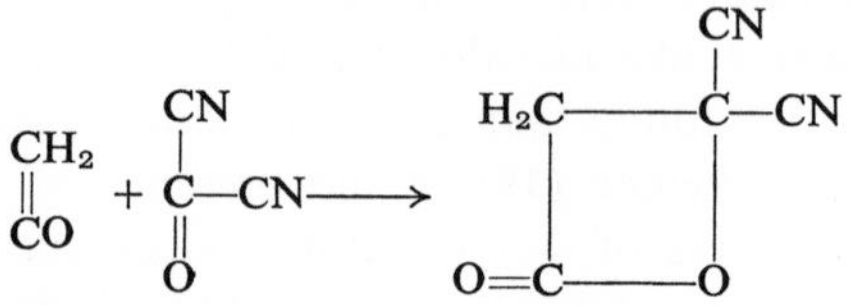

(30)        (31)                    (32)

ing that carbonyl cyanide behaves toward ketene as do aldehydes and
ketones,[67] which give lactones of β-hydroxy acids. In agreement with structure 32, the product showed the following infrared absorption bands:

1. At 4.41 μ, usually attributed to the CN group of a nonconjugated
   system.
2. At 5.34 μ, ascribed to C=O of a β-lactone ring, although it was somewhat less than the band (5.43 μ)[81] usually associated with that group

in this type of structure; the shift toward lower wavelengths was explained by the presence of electronegative substituents in the $\beta$-position.[1]

Studies of the ultraviolet[24,70] and infrared absorption[7,70,81] spectra of $\beta$-lactones have been reported. It was found that the vibration band of the carbonyl group of $\beta$-lactones appears generally at about 5.45 $\mu$ (1835 cm$^{-1}$) for most $\beta$-lactones.[7,8,19,61,74,75,79,81,111,112] It occurs at 5.49–5.53 $\mu$ (1820–1805 cm$^{-1}$)[14] when the $\alpha$-carbon is particularly crowded[14,78,82,102,103] and occasionally at 5.55 $\mu$ (1801 cm$^{-1}$)[29,64] or even at 5.74 $\mu$.[113] If the substituents on the $\alpha$-carbon are strongly electronegative, the absorption maximum is shifted to 5.39 $\mu$[1] or below.[66]

The nuclear magnetic resonance spectra of propiolactone[2,37] and other $\beta$-lactones[38] have been reported.

### Table 1

### $\beta$-Lactones from Quinones and Diphenylketene

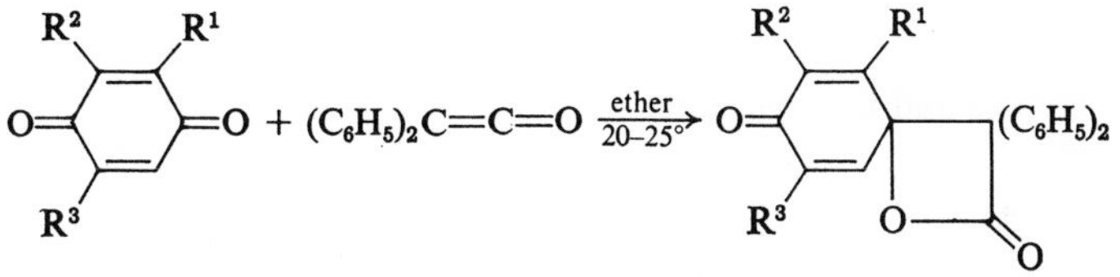

| R[1a] | R[2a] | R[3] | MP, °C | Yield, % | Ref. |
|---|---|---|---|---|---|
| H | H | H | 143 (dec) | — | 85 |
| | | | | 57 | 86 |
| | | | | 72 | 50, 92 |
| H | H | CH$_3$ | 123 (dec) | 28 | 92 |
| H | CH$_3$ | CH$_3$ | 123–124 | 36 | 92 |
| H | H | Cl | 129–130 | 74 | 92 |
| Cl | H | Cl | 143 | 56 | 92 |
| H | Cl | Cl | 180–192 (dec) | 70 | 92 |
| Cl | Cl | Cl | 220 (dec) | 61 | 92 |
| H | Br | Br | 141 (dec) | 78 | 92 |
| | | H | 127 | 43 | 92 |

[a] The quinone reactant was 1,4-naphthoquinone.

**Table 2**

Catalysts Used in the Cycloaddition Reactions between Ketene
and Carbonyl Compounds

| Types of catalysts | Ref. |
|---|---|
| Friedel-Crafts (complex) and other | 9, 11, 12, 19, 21, 25, 26, 27, 39, |
|     Halides | 40, 42, 44, 45, 47, 49, 50, 53, 54, |
|   Chlorides | 56, 58, 67, 78, 96, 97, 98, 109, 114 |
|     Aluminum | |
|     Mercury | |
|     Zinc | |
|     Tin | |
|     Titanium | |
|     Iron | |
|     Boron | |
|     Uranium | |
|   Fluorides | |
|     Boron | |
|   Bromides | |
|     Mercury | |
| | |
| Organic acids and salts | 22, 39, 42, 43, 46, 47, 48, 50, 51, |
|   Boric acid | 52, 54, 63 |
|   Triethyl borate | |
|   Fluoroborates and fluoroacetates | |
|     Nickel | |
|     Barium | |
|     Copper | |
|     Mercury | |
|     Zinc | |
|     Sodium | |
|     Boron | |
|     Potassium | |
| Thiocyanates | 17 |
|   Zinc | |
| Nitrates | 18, 21 |
|   Zinc | |
|   Uranium | |
| Phosphates | 20, 40 |
|   *Ortho-* and *meta-* phosphoric acid | |
|     Zinc | |
|     Cobalt | |
|     Lead | |
|     Iron | |
|     Cadmium | |

(*continued*)

**Table 2** (*continued*)

| Types of catalysts | Ref. |
|---|---|
| Peroxides | 6 |
|   Benzoyl peroxide | |
| Perchlorates | 16 |
|   Zinc | |
|   Tin | |
|   Mercury | |
|   Aluminum | |
|   Lithium | |
|   Boron | |
|   Iron | |
|   Manganese | |
|   Cobalt | |
| Oxides | 23, 46 |
|   Aluminum | |
|   Zirconium | |
|   Thorium | |
|   Silicon | |
| Activated clays | 36, 115 |

**Table 3**
β-Lactones from Carbonyl Compounds and Ketenes

| Carbonyl compounds | Ketene | Cycloadduct | MP, °C (BP, °C/mm) | Yield (%) | Ref. |
|---|---|---|---|---|---|
| $CH_3CHClCCH_3$ (=O) | $CH_2=C=O$ | 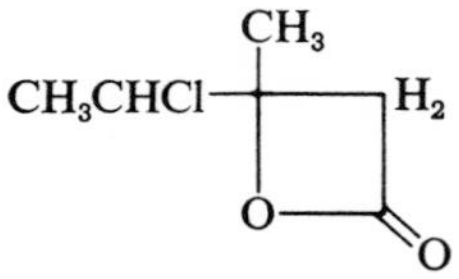 (CH₃CHCl, CH₃, H₂) | 36–38 / 56–57 / 71–72 (mixt.) | 84 | 27 |
| $(CN)_2C=O$ | $CH_2=C=O$ | 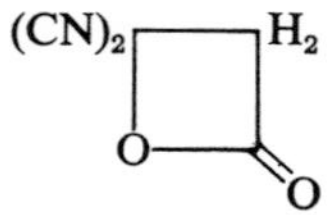 $(CN)_2$, H₂ | 182 | 81.6 | 1 |
| $CH_2ClCCH_3$ (=O) | $CH_2=C=O$ | 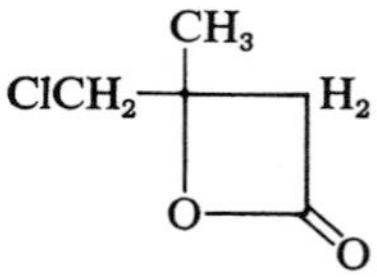 (ClCH₂, CH₃, H₂) | 20 (53/0.3) / 24–25 (36–42/0.003) | 80[a] | 80 27 |
| $CH_2ClCCH_2Cl$ (=O) | $CH_2=C=O$ | 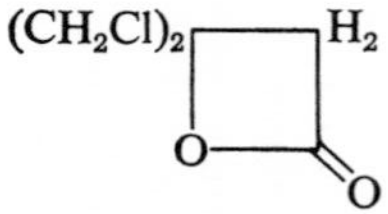 $(CH_2Cl)_2$, H₂ | (7.8/0.5) / 49 | 85[b] | 80 |

| | | | | | |
|---|---|---|---|---|---|
| CF$_3$CCH$_3$=O | CH$_2$=C=O | 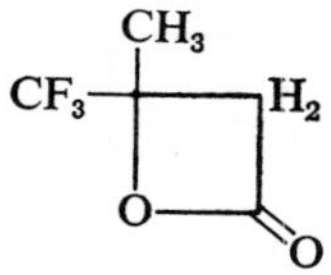 | (40/15) | 57[c] | 80 |
| CCl$_3$CH=O | CH$_2$=C=O | 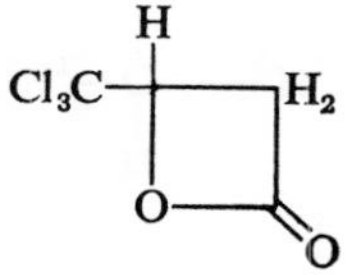 | (98/19) 32 | 70[d] | 80 |
| C$_2$H$_5$CHClCH=O | CH$_2$=C=O | 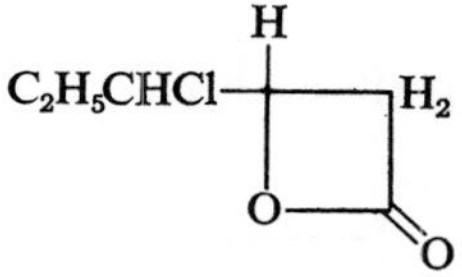 | (57/0.25) | 67[e] | 80 |
| CHBr$_2$CH=O | CH$_2$=C=O | 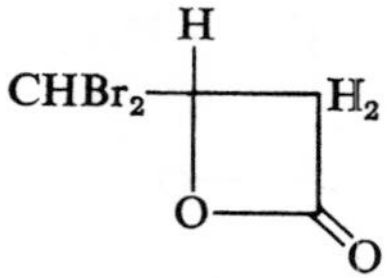 | (89/0.5) | 54[e] | 80 |
| CH$_2$O | CH$_2$=C=O | 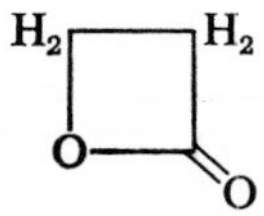 | (83/45–50) −33.6 | — | 32, 110 |

*(continued)*

Table 3 (*continued*)

| Carbonyl compounds | Ketene | Cycloadduct | MP, °C (BP, °C/mm) | Yield (%) | Ref. |
|---|---|---|---|---|---|
| $CH_3CH{=}O$ | $CH_2{=}C{=}O$ | 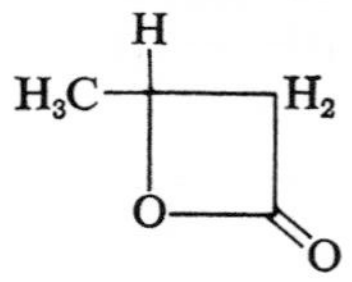 (β-lactone structure, $H_3C$, H, $H_2$, =O) | (72–74/29) | — | 39 |
| $(CH_3)_2C{=}O$ | $CH_2{=}C{=}O$ | 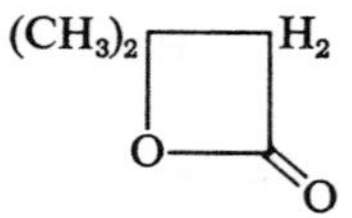 (β-lactone structure, $(CH_3)_2$, $H_2$, =O) | (58/12) −26.5 | — | 69 |
| $CH_2O$ | $(CH_3)_2C{=}C{=}O$ | 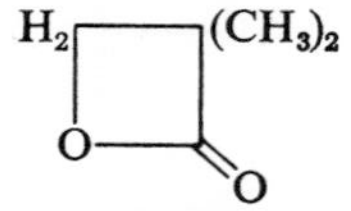 (β-lactone structure, $(CH_3)_2$, $H_2$, =O) | −13.0 (53.5/15) | — | 57, 60 |
| $n\text{-}C_3H_7CH{=}O$ | $CH_2{=}C{=}O$ | 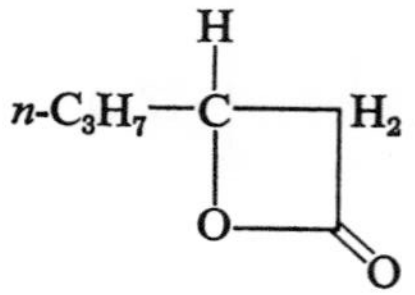 (β-lactone structure, $n\text{-}C_3H_7$, H, $H_2$, =O) | (62–63/5) | — | 39, 115 |
| $C_2H_5(CH_3)C{=}O$ | $CH_2{=}C{=}O$ | 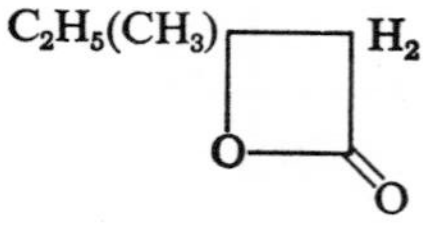 (β-lactone structure, $C_2H_5(CH_3)$, $H_2$, =O) | (60–61/10) | — | 39 |

| | | | | | |
|---|---|---|---|---|---|
| iso-C₃H₇CH=O | CH₂=C=O | | (110–113/10) | — | 21, 22 |
| CH₃CH=O | (CH₃)₂C=C=O | | (73/20) | 16 | 35 |
| C₂H₅CH=O | (CH₃)₂C=C=O | | (58/4.4) | 25 | 57 |
| CH₂O | CH₃(n-C₃H₇)C=C=O | | (64/5) | — | 57 |
| CH₂O | (C₂H₅)₂C=C=O | | (49/2) | — | 35, 57 |

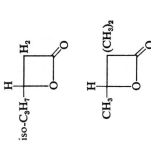
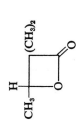

*(continued)*

**Table 3** (*continued*)

| Carbonyl compounds | Ketene | Cycloadduct | MP, °C (BP, °C/mm) | Yield (%) | Ref. |
|---|---|---|---|---|---|
| $n\text{-}C_3H_7CH{=}O$ | $(CH_3)_2C{=}C{=}O$ | 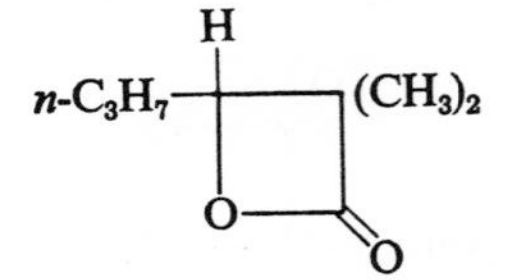 [β-lactone structure: H, $n\text{-}C_3H_7$, $(CH_3)_2$] | (68/5) (101/26) | — | 57 35 |
| $iso\text{-}C_3H_7CH{=}O$ | $(CH_3)_2C{=}C{=}O$ | 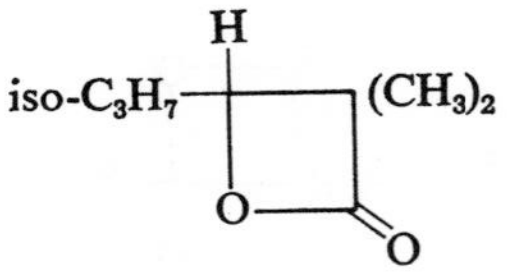 [β-lactone structure: H, $iso\text{-}C_3H_7$, $(CH_3)_2$] | (73–75/8) | 13.5 | 57, 35 |
| $CH_3CH{=}O$ | $(C_2H_5)_2C{=}C{=}O$ | 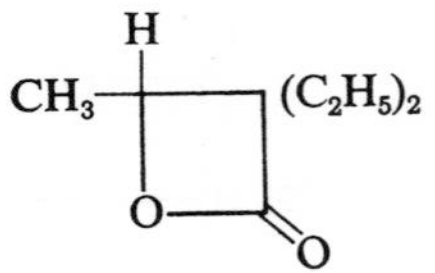 [β-lactone structure: H, $CH_3$, $(C_2H_5)_2$] | (47/0.9) | — | 57 |
| $n\text{-}C_6H_{13}CH{=}O$ | $CH_2{=}C{=}O$ | 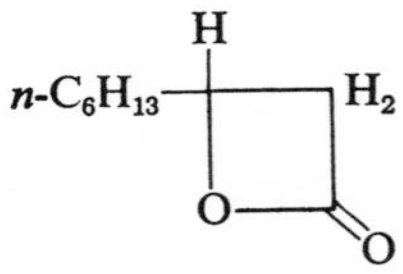 [β-lactone structure: H, $n\text{-}C_6H_{13}$, $H_2$] | — | — | 6 |

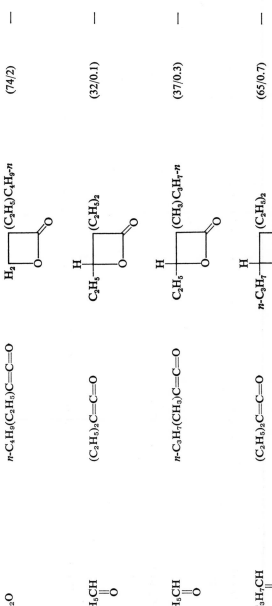

| | | | | |
|---|---|---|---|---|
| $n\text{-}C_5H_{11}(CH_3)C{=}O$ | $CH_2{=}C{=}O$ | | — | — | 11 |
| $CH_2O$ | $n\text{-}C_4H_9(C_2H_5)C{=}C{=}O$ | | (74/2) | — | 57 |
| $C_2H_5CH{=}O$ | $(C_2H_5)_2C{=}C{=}O$ | | (32/0.1) | — | 57 |
| $C_2H_5CH{=}O$ | $n\text{-}C_3H_7(CH_3)C{=}C{=}O$ | | (37/0.3) | — | 57 |
| $n\text{-}C_3H_7CH{=}O$ | $(C_2H_5)_2C{=}C{=}O$ | | (65/0.7) | — | 57 |

(continued)

**Table 3** (*continued*)

| Carbonyl compounds | Ketene | Cycloadduct | MP, °C (BP, °C/mm) | Yield (%) | Ref. |
|---|---|---|---|---|---|
| $n\text{-}C_3H_7CH{=}O$ | $CH_3(n\text{-}C_3H_7)C{=}C{=}O$ | 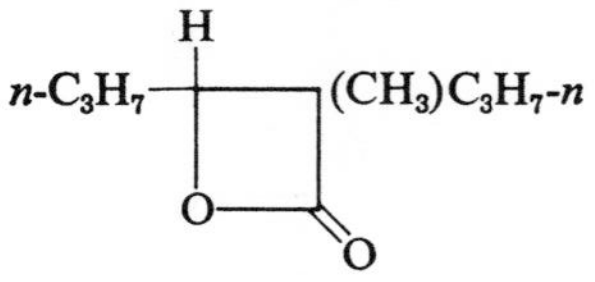 | (62/0.6) | — | 57 |
| $iso\text{-}C_3H_7CH{=}O$ | $(C_2H_5)_2C{=}C{=}O$ | 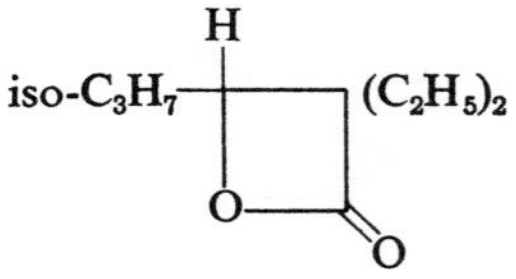 | (29/0.1) | — | 57 |
| $iso\text{-}C_3H_7CH{=}O$ | $n\text{-}C_3H_7(CH_3)C{=}C{=}O$ | 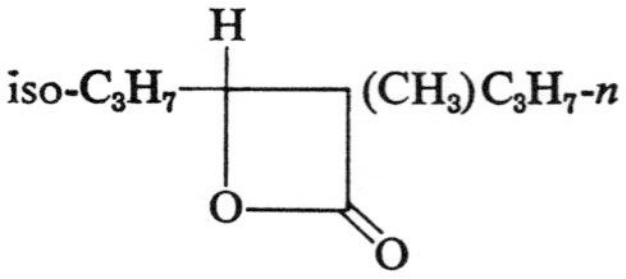 | (60/1) | — | 57 |
| $n\text{-}C_6H_{13}CH{=}O$ | $(CH_3)_2C{=}C{=}O$ | 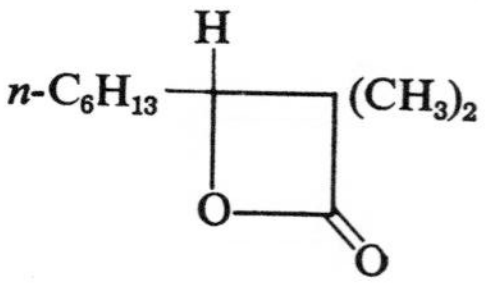 | (105–107/4) | — | 57 |

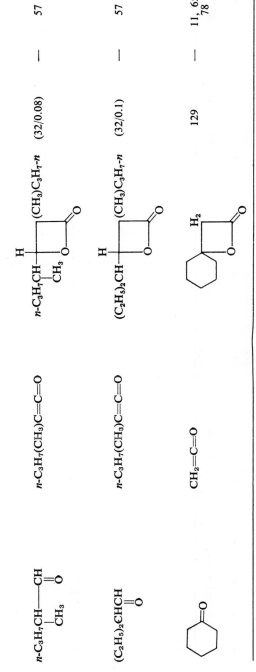

| | | | | | |
|---|---|---|---|---|---|
| $C_2H_5CH$—$CH$ ($CH_3$, =O) | $(C_2H_5)_2C$=C=O | | (31/0.1) | — | 57 |
| $(CH_3)_2CHCH_2(CH_2)_3CCH$=$CH_2$ (=O) | $CH_2$=C=O | | — | — | 11 |
| $n$-$C_3H_7CH$—$CH$ ($CH_3$, =O) | $n$-$C_3H_7(CH_3)C$=C=O | | (32/0.08) | — | 57 |
| $(C_2H_5)_2CHCH$ (=O) | $n$-$C_3H_7(CH_3)C$=C=O | | (32/0.1) | — | 57 |
| cyclohexanone | $CH_2$=C=O | | 129 | — | 11, 65, 78 |

(continued)

**Table 3** (*continued*)

| Carbonyl compounds | Ketene | Cycloadduct | MP, °C (BP, °C/mm) | Yield (%) | Ref. |
|---|---|---|---|---|---|
| 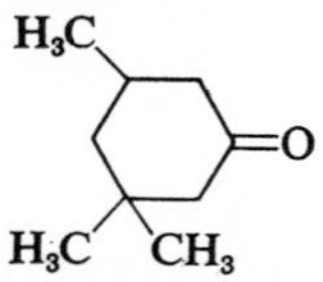 (3,5-dimethylcyclohexanone) | $CH_2=C=O$ | 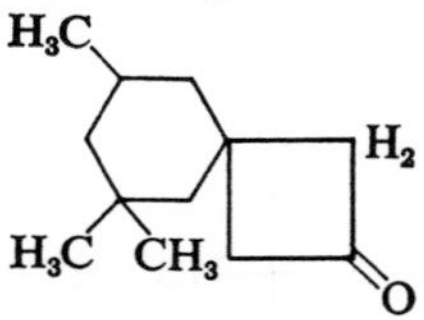 (spiro cyclobutanone adduct) | — | — | 11 |
| $CH_3CH=CHCH=O$ | $CH_2=C=O$ | 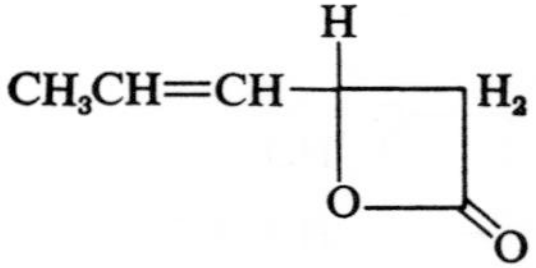 $CH_3CH=CH$ (β-lactone adduct) | — | — | 12, 15, 39, 55 |
| $CH_2=CHCCH_3$, $=O$ | $CH_2=C=O$ | $CH_2=CH$, $CH_3$ (β-lactone adduct) | — | — | 39 |
| $CH_2=C$—$CH=O$, $CH_3$ | $CH_2=C=O$ | $H_2C=C$—$CH_3$ (β-lactone adduct) | (64, 10) | — | 39, 49 |

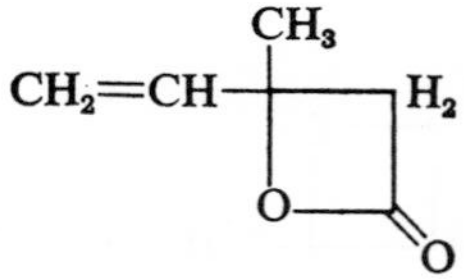

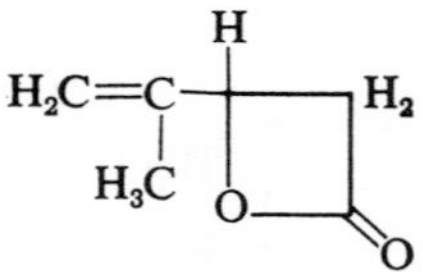

| | | | | | |
|---|---|---|---|---|---|
| $CH_2{=}C(C_2H_5){-}CH{=}O$ | $CH_2{=}C{=}O$ | 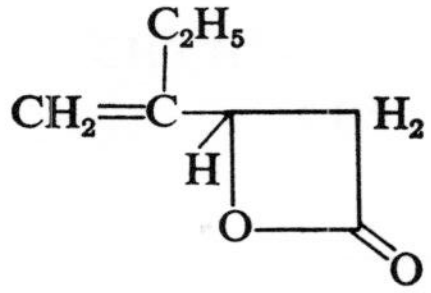 | — | — | 39 |
| $CH_2{=}C(CH_3){-}C(CH_3){=}O$ | $CH_2{=}C{=}O$ | 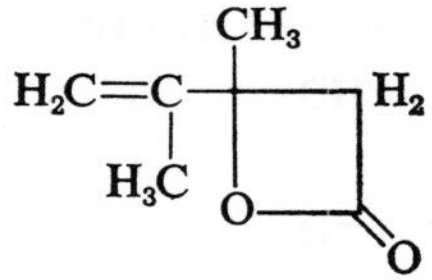 | — | — | 39, 49 |
| $CH_3CH{=}C(C_2H_5){-}CH{=}O$ | $CH_2{=}C{=}O$ | 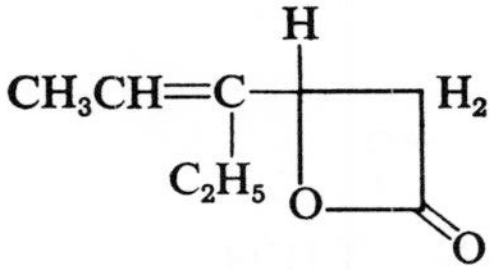 | — | — | 12 |
| $n\text{-}C_3H_7CH{=}C(C_2H_5){-}CH{=}O$ | $CH_2{=}C{=}O$ | 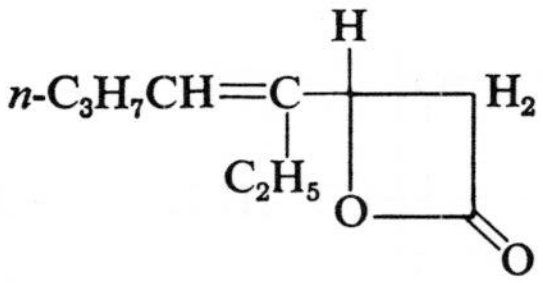 | — | — | 34 |

(*continued*)

Table 3 (*continued*)

| Carbonyl compounds | Ketene | Cycloadduct | MP, °C (BP, °C/mm) | Yield (%) | Ref. |
|---|---|---|---|---|---|
| $CH_3CH=CHCH=CHCH=O$ | $CH_2=C=O$ | 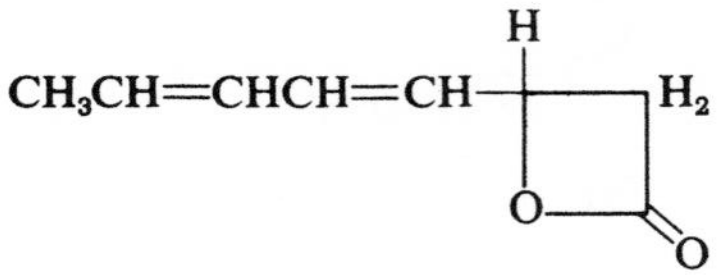 | — | — | 12 |
| $(FCH_2)_2C=O$ | $CH_2=C=O$ | 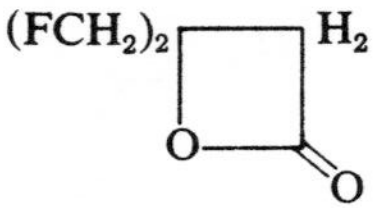 | (105–107/16) | — | 9 |
| $(CF_3)_2C=O$ | $CH_2=C=O$ | 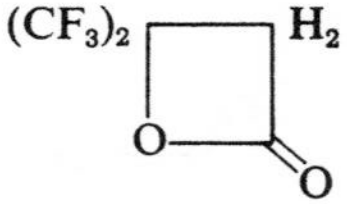 | (94.5–95/77.5) | — | 66 |
| $C_2H_5CHClCCH_3=O$ | $CH_3CH=C=O$ | 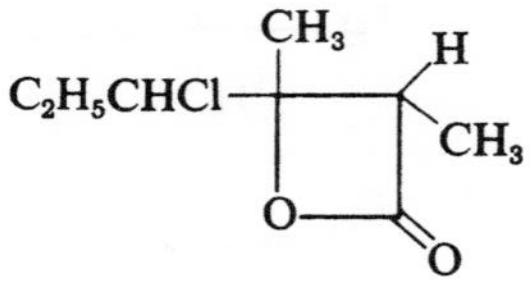 | (45–50/0.001) | — | 27 |
| $CH_3CO_2CH_2CH_2CCH_3=O$ | $CH_2=C=O$ | 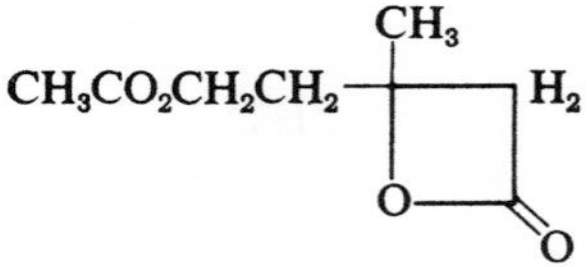 | unstable | — | 25, 26 |

| | | | | | |
|---|---|---|---|---|---|
| $CH_3C(=O)\!-\!C(=O)CH_3$ | $CH_2\!=\!C\!=\!O$ | 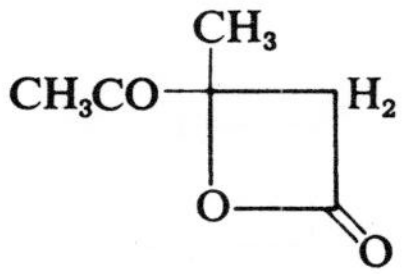 β-lactone ($CH_3CO$, $CH_3$ substituents) | — | — | 20, 39, 42 |
| $CH_3CCH_2CCH_3$ ($=O$, $=O$) | $CH_2\!=\!C\!=\!O$ | 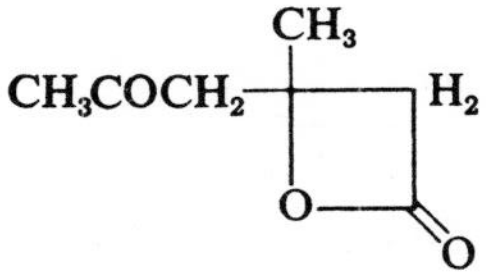 β-lactone ($CH_3COCH_2$, $CH_3$) | — | — | 16, 22, 39 |
| $CH_3CCH_2CH_2CCH_3$ ($=O$, $=O$) | $CH_2\!=\!C\!=\!O$ | 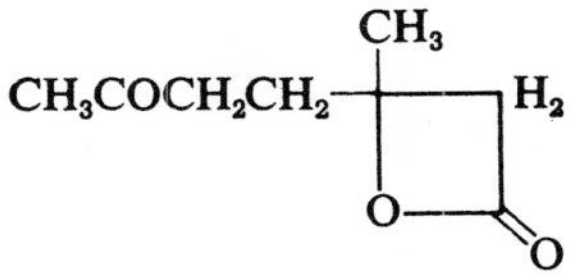 β-lactone ($CH_3COCH_2CH_2$, $CH_3$) | — | — | 39, 42 |
| $RO_2CCCH_3$ ($=O$) ($R = CH_3, C_2H_5$) | $CH_2\!=\!C\!=\!O$ | 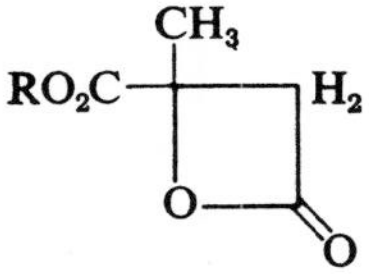 β-lactone ($RO_2C$, $CH_3$) | — | — | 39, 40, 45, 54 |
| $C_2H_5O_2CCCH_2CCH_3$ ($=O$) | $CH_2\!=\!C\!=\!O$ | 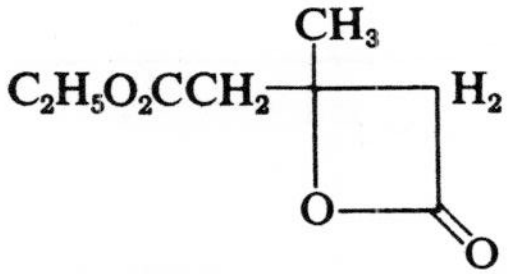 β-lactone ($C_2H_5O_2CCH_2$, $CH_3$) | — | — | 16, 39 |

*(continued)*

**Table 3** (*continued*)

| Carbonyl compounds | Ketene | Cycloadduct | MP, °C (BP, °C/mm) | Yield (%) | Ref. |
|---|---|---|---|---|---|
| $RO_2C(CH_2)_2CCH_3$, $C{=}O$ ($R = CH_3, C_2H_5$) | $CH_2{=}C{=}O$ | $RO_2C(CH_2)_2$, $CH_3$, $H_2$, $O$ (β-lactone) | — | — | 21, 39, 54 |
| $C_2H_5OCCHFCCH_3$, $C{=}O$, $C{=}O$ | $CH_2{=}C{=}O$ | $C_2H_5O_2CCHF$, $CH_3$, $H_2$, $O$ (β-lactone) | (108–110/0.2) | — | 9 |
| $(C_2H_5O_2C)_2CFCCH_2F$, $C{=}O$ | $CH_2{=}C{=}O$ | $(C_2H_5O_2C)_2CF$, $CH_2F$, $H_2$, $O$ (β-lactone) | (149–150/0.5) | — | 9 |
| $(C_2H_5O)_2POCCH_3$, $C{=}O$ | $CH_2{=}O{=}O$ | $(C_2H_5O)_2PO$, $CH_3$, $H_2$, $O$ (β-lactone) | (86–112/0.7) | — | 74 |

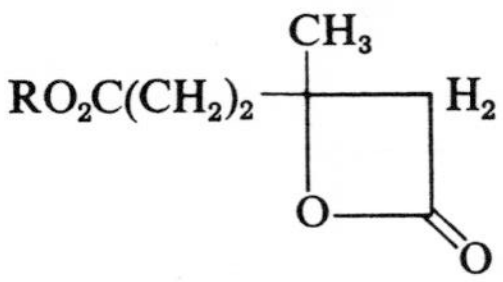

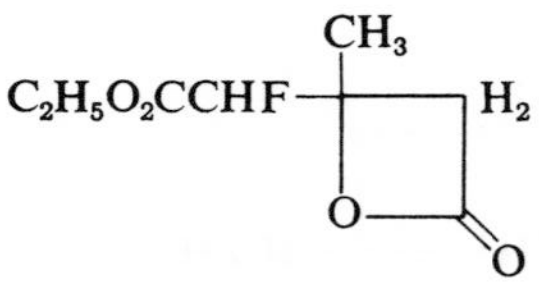

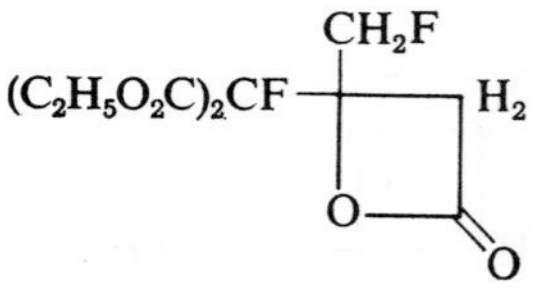

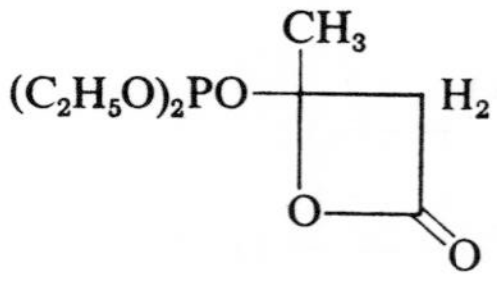

| | | | | | |
|---|---|---|---|---|---|
| $C_6H_5CH{=}O$ | $CH_2{=}C{=}O$ | 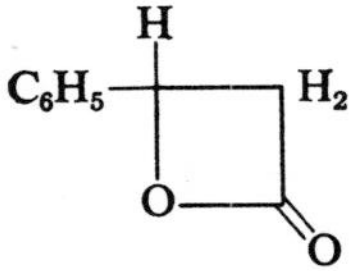 [β-lactone: $C_6H_5$, H, $H_2$] | — | — | 12, 47, 52 |
| $p\text{-}CH_3C_6H_4CH{=}O$ | $CH_2{=}C{=}O$ | 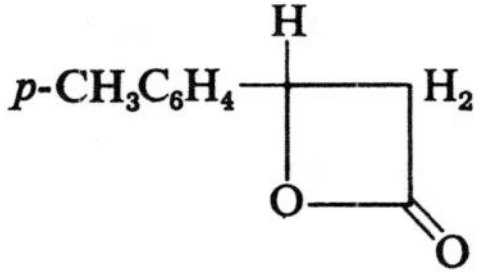 [β-lactone: $p\text{-}CH_3C_6H_4$, H, $H_2$] | — | — | 28 |
| $C_6H_5CCH_3{=}O$ | $CH_2{=}C{=}O$ | 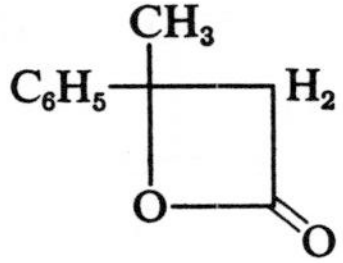 [β-lactone: $CH_3$, $C_6H_5$, $H_2$] | — | — | 11, 52 |
| $C_6H_5CH{=}CHCH{=}O$ | $CH_2{=}C{=}O$ | 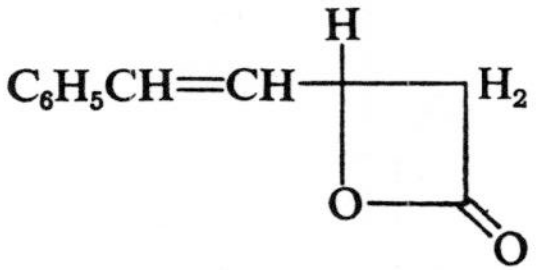 [β-lactone: $C_6H_5CH{=}CH$, H, $H_2$] | — | — | 12 |
| $CH_2{-}CH{-}CH{=}O$ (epoxide) | $CH_2{=}C{=}O$ | [β-lactone: $H_2C$, CH, O, H, $H_2$] | (84–86/1–2) | — | 111 |
| | | | (84–86/3) | — | 99 |

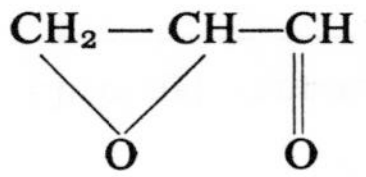

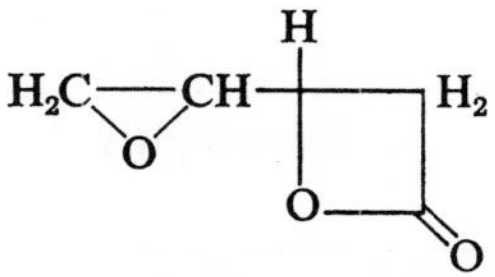

*(continued)*

**Table 3** (*continued*)

| Carbonyl compounds | Ketene | Cycloadduct | MP, °C (BP, °C/mm) | Yield (%) | Ref. |
|---|---|---|---|---|---|
| 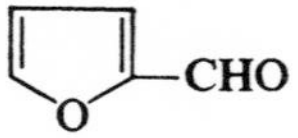 furyl-CHO | $CH_2{=}C{=}O$ | 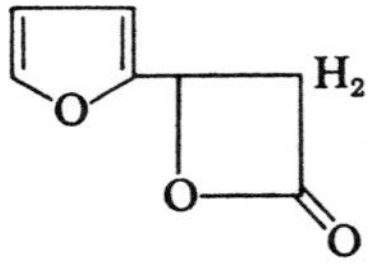 | — | — | 39, 47 |
| $CH_3C({=}O)CCH_3({=}O)$ | $CH_2{=}C{=}O$ | 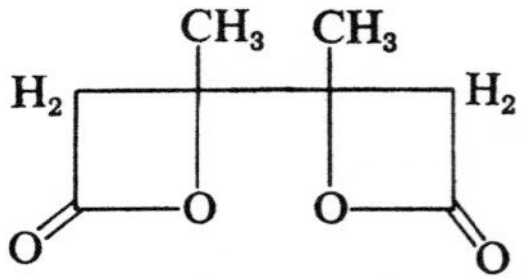 | — | — | 39, 42 |
| $CH_3CCH_2CCH_3({=}O)({=}O)$ | $CH_2{=}C{=}O$ | 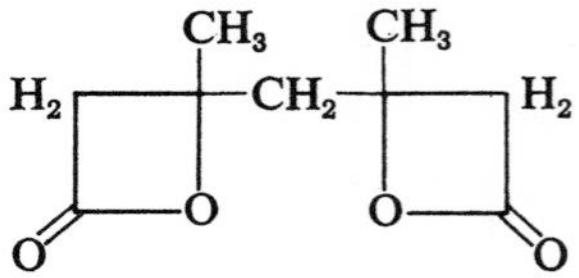 | — | — | 22, 23, 42 |
| $CH_3CCH_2CH_2CCH_3({=}O)({=}O)$ | $CH_2{=}C{=}O$ | 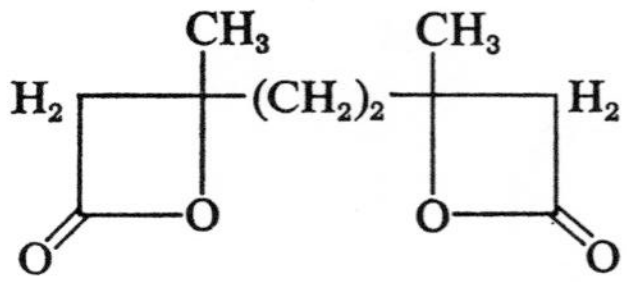 | — | — | 42 |

| | | | | | |
|---|---|---|---|---|---|
| 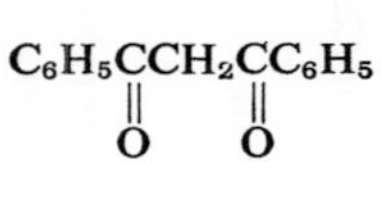 $C_6H_5CCH_2CC_6H_5$ (diketone) | $CH_2{=}C{=}O$ | 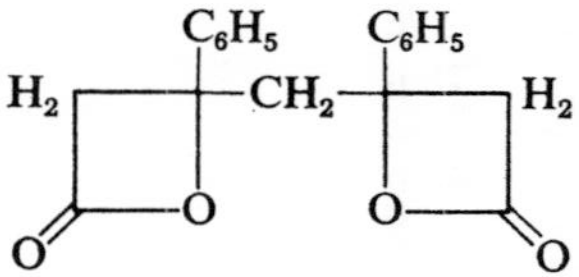 | — | — | 42 |
| 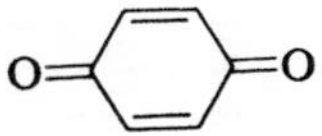 | $CH_2{=}C{=}O$ | 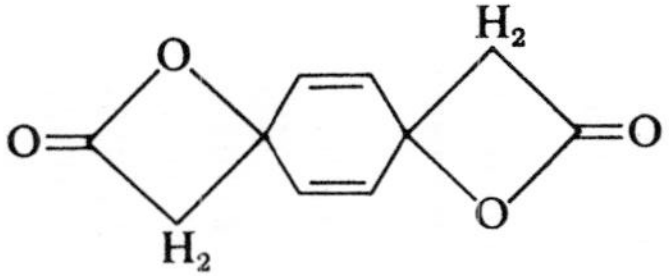 | — | — | 33, 50 |
| 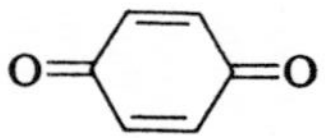 | $(C_6H_5)_2C{=}C{=}O$ | 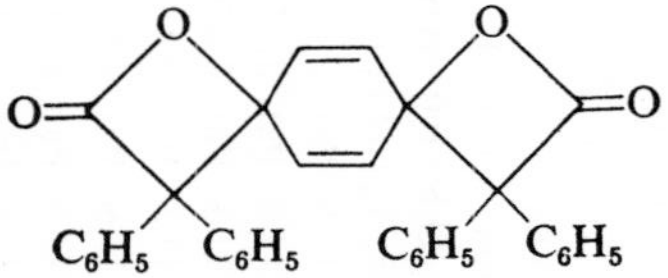 | — | — | 50, 92 |

IR absorption ($\gamma$ cm$^{-1}$): [a]—1830, [b]—1850, [c]—1843, [d]—1860, [e]—1840–1850.

REFERENCES

1. O. Achmatowicz and M. Leplawy, *Bull. Acad. Polon. Sci., Ser. Sci. Chim., Geol. Geogr.*, **6**, 417 (1958).
2. W. A. Anderson, *Phys. Rev.*, **102**, 151 (1956).
3. A. Baeyer, *Chem. Ber.*, **34**, 2682 (1901).
4. A. Baeyer and V. Villiger, *Chem. Ber.*, **35**, 1189 (1902).
5. A. Baeyer and V. Villiger, *Chem. Ber.*, **38**, 582 (1905).
6. B. Barnett, U.S. Pat. 2,513,615 (1950).
7. P. D. Bartlett and P. N. Rylander, *J. Am. Chem. Soc.*, **73**, 4275 (1951).
8. E. D. Bergmann, S. Cohen, E. Hoffman, and Z. Rand-Meir, *J. Chem. Soc.*, **1961**, 3452.
9. E. D. Bergmann, S. Cohen, E. Hoffman, and Z. Rand-Meir, *J. Chem. Soc.*, **1961**, 3456.
10. A. K. Boese, U.S. Pat. 2,108,427 (1938).
11. A. K. Boese, Jr., U.S. Pat. 2,382,464 (1945).
12. A. K. Boese, Jr., U.S. Pat. 2,484,067 (1949).
13. G. A. Boswell, W. G. Dauben, G. Ourisson, and T. Rull, *Bull. Soc. Chim France*, **1958**, 1598.
14. A. W. Burgstahler and D. E. Wetmore, *J. Org. Chem.*, **26**, 3516 (1961).
15. J. R. Caldwell, U.S. Pat. Appl. 252,194 (1951); *Official Gaz.* 673,839 (1953), *Chem. Abstr.*, **48**, 12169 (1954).
16. J. R. Caldwell, U.S. Pat. 2,450,116 (1948).
17. J. R. Caldwell, U.S. Pat. 2,450,117 (1948).
18. J. R. Caldwell, U.S. Pat. 2,450,118 (1948).
19. J. R. Caldwell, U.S. Pat. 2,484,486 (1949).
20. J. R. Caldwell, U.S. Pat. 2,518,662 (1950).
21. J. R. Caldwell, U.S. Pat. 2,585,223 (1952).
22. J. R. Caldwell, U.S. Pat. 2,739,158 (1956).
23. J. R. Caldwell and H. J. Hagemeyer, Jr., U.S. Pat. 2,462,357 (1949)
24. M. Calvin, T. T. Magel, and C. D. Hurd, *J. Am. Chem. Soc.*, **63**, 2174 (1941).
25. J. W. Cornforth, R. H. Cornforth, A. Pelter, M. G. Horning, and G. Popjak, *Endeavour*, **20**, 180 (1961).
26. J. W. Cornforth, R. H. Cornforth, A. Pelter, M. G. Horning, and G. Popjak, *Tetrahedron*, **5**, 311 (1959).
27. R. H. Cornforth, *J. Chem. Soc.*, **1959**, 4052.
28. B. N. Dashkevich, *Nauch. Zapiski Uzhgorodsk. Univ.*, **18**, 53 (1957); *Chem. Abstr.*, **54**, 12053 (1960).
29. P. A. Diassi and C. M. Dylion, *J. Am. Chem. Soc.*, **80**, 3746 (1958).
30. A. Einhorn, *Chem. Ber.*, **16**, 2208 (1883).
31. E. Erlenmeyer, *Chem. Ber.*, **13**, 305 (1880).
32. Y. Etienne and N. Fischer, in *Compounds with Three- and Four-Membered Rings* (*The Chemistry of Heterocyclic Compounds*, Vol. 19, A. Weissberger, Ed., Wiley, New York, 1964), pp. 729 ff.
33. H. von Euler and L. Ahlström, *Arkiv. Kemi, Mineral. Geol.*, **2a** (2), 1 (1932); *Chem. Abstr.*, **27**, 950 (1933).
34. G. K. Finch and C. D. Stringer, U.S. Pat. 2,947,767 (1960).
35. N. Fischer, *Thèse*, Paris (1959).
36. J. T. Fitzpatrick, U.S. Pat. 2,554,528 (1951).
37. D. M. Grant and H. S. Gutowsky, *J. Chem. Phys.*, **34**, 699 (1961).
38. H. S. Gutowsky, M. Karplus, and D. M. Grant, *J. Chem. Phys.*, **31**, 1278 (1959).

39. H. J. Hagemeyer, Jr., *Ind. Eng. Chem.*, **41**, 765 (1949).
40. H. J. Hagemeyer, Jr., U.S. Pat. 2,444,735 (1948).
41. H. J. Hagemeyer, Jr., U.S. Pat. 2,450,131 (1948).
42. H. J. Hagemeyer, Jr., U.S. Pat. 2,450,132 (1948).
43. H. J. Hagemeyer, Jr., U.S. Pat. 2,450,133 (1948).
44. H. J. Hagemeyer, Jr., U.S. Pat. 2,450,134 (1948).
45. H. J. Hagemeyer, Jr., U.S. Pat. 2,456,503 (1948).
46. H. J. Hagemeyer, Jr., U.S. Pat. 2,462,357 (1949).
47. H. J. Hagemeyer, Jr., U.S. Pat. 2,466,420 (1949).
48. H. J. Hagemeyer, Jr., U.S. Pat. 2,469,110 (1949).
49. H. J. Hagemeyer, Jr., U.S. Pat. 2,478,388 (1949).
50. H. J. Hagemeyer, Jr., U.S. Pat. 2,481,742 (1949).
51. H. J. Hagemeyer, Jr., U.S. Pat. 2,484,497 (1949).
52. H. J. Hagemeyer, Jr., U.S. Pat. 2,484,499 (1949).
53. H. J. Hagemeyer, Jr., U.S. Pat. 2,496,791 (1950).
54. H. J. Hagemeyer, Jr. and D. S. Cooper, U.S. Pat. 2,469,690 (1949).
55. K. Hamamoto, T. Isoshima, and M. Yoshioka, *J. Pharm. Soc. Japan*, **76**, 956 (1956); *Chem. Abstr.*, **51**, 2540 (1957).
56. R. Hart, *Bull. Soc. Chim. Belges*, **58**, 255 (1949); *Chem. Abstr.*, **45**, 6155 (1961).
57. R. H. Hasek and E. U. Elam, U.S. Pat. 3,004,989 (1961).
58. R. H. Hasek, E. U. Elam, and J. C. Martin, *J. Org. Chem.*, **26**, 4340 (1961).
60. R. H. Hasek and R. G. Nations, U.S. Pat. 3,000,906 (1960).
61. P. Hirsjärvi, *Ann. Acad. Sci. Fennicae Ser AI*, **45**, 7 (1952); *Chem. Abstr.*, **48**, 651 (1954).
62. H. Hopff and W. Rapp, U.S. Pat. 2,265,165 (1942).
63. C. D. Hurd and C. L. Thomas, *J. Am. Chem. Soc.*, **55**, 275 (1933).
64. H. B. Kagan and J. Jacques, *Bull. Soc. Chim. France*, **1958**, 1600.
65. A. Kandiah, *J. Chem. Soc.*, **1932**, 1215.
66. I. L. Knunyants and Y. A. Cheburkov, *Izv. Akad. Nauk SSSR, Otd. Khim Nauk*, **1960**, 678; *Chem. Abstr.*, **54**, 22349 (1960).
67. F. E. Künig, U.S. Pat. 2,356,459 (1944).
68. R. N. Lacey, in *Advances in Organic Chemistry*, Vol. 2, R. A. Raphael, E. C. Taylor, and H. Wynberg, Eds., Interscience, New York, 1960, pp. 226 ff.
69. H. T. Liang and P. D. Bartlett, *J. Am. Chem. Soc.*, **80**, 3585 (1958).
70. R. H. Linnell and W. A. Noyes, Jr., *J. Am. Chem. Soc.*, **72**, 3863 (1950).
71. Madelung, Inaugural Dissertation, Strassburg, 1905.
72. M. Malachowski, *Roczniki Chem.*, **24**, 229 (1950).
73. H. Meerwein, *Ann. Chem.*, **455**, 227 (1927).
74. R. L. McConnell and H. W. Coover, Jr., *J. Org. Chem.*, **23**, 830 (1958).
75. K. Noro and G. Morimoto, *Kogyo Kagaku Kyokaishi*, **65**, 399 (1962).
76. E. Ott, *Ann. Chem.*, **401**, 160 (1913).
77. G. Quadbeck, *Angew. Chem.*, **68**, 361 (1956).
78. A. Rosowsky and D. S. Tarbell, *J. Org. Chem.*, **26**, 2255 (1961).
79. T. Rull and G. Ourisson, *Bull. Soc. Chim. France*, **1958**, 1581.
80. K. Schimmelschmidt and E. Mundlos, Ger. Pat. 1,136,323 (1962).
81. S. Searles, M. Tamres, and G. M. Barrow, *J. Am. Chem. Soc.*, **75**, 71 (1953).
82. J. C. Sheehan, K. Hasspacher, and Y. L. Yeh, *J. Am. Chem. Soc.*, **81**, 6086 (1959).
83. H. Staudinger, *Ann. Chem.*, **356**, 51 (1907).
84. H. Staudinger, *Ann. Chem.*, **356**, 63 (1907).
85. H. Staudinger, *Chem. Ber.*, **40**, 1145 (1907).

86. H. Staudinger, *Chem. Ber.*, **41**, 1355 (1908).
87. H. Staudinger, *Chem. Ber.*, **41**, 1356 (1908).
88. H. Staudinger, *Chem. Ber.*, **41**, 1493 (1908).
89. H. Staudinger, *Chem. Ber.*, **42**, 4249 (1909).
90. H. Staudinger, *Chem. Ber.*, **44**, 521 (1911).
91. H. Staudinger, *Helv. Chim. Acta*, **5**, 103 (1923).
92. H. Staudinger and S. Bereza, *Ann. Chem.*, **380**, 243 (1911).
93. H. Staudinger and R. Endle, *Ann. Chem.*, **384**, 51 (1911).
94. H. Staudinger and R. Endle, *Ann. Chem.*, **401**, 263 (1913).
95. H. Staudinger and N. Kon, *Ann. Chem.*, **384**, 38 (1911).
96. T. R. Steadman, U.S. Pat. 2,424,589 (1947).
97. T. R. Steadman and P. L. Breyfogle, U.S. Pat. 2,424,590 (1947).
98. H. G. Stone, U.S. Pat. 2,469,704 (1949).
99. W. J. Sullivan, U.S. Pat. 2,940,982 (1960).
100. Tennessee Eastman Company, Technical Data on Butylethylketene, TDS NoX-163, unpublished results.
101. E. Testa, *Farmaco Pavia Ed. Sci.*, **17**, 168 (1962); *Chem. Abstr.*, **57**, 9772 (1962).
102. E. Testa, L. Fontanella, G. Cristiani, and F. Fava, *Ann. Chem.*, **619**, 47 (1958).
103. E. Testa, L. Fontanella, and L. Mariani, *J. Org. Chem.*, **25**, 1812 (1960).
104. J. Thiele, *Ann. Chem.*, **306**, 87 (1899).
105. J. Thiele, *Chem. Ber.*, **33**, 666 (1900).
106. J. Thiele and H. Balhorn, *Chem. Ber.*, **37**, 1463 (1904).
107. D. Vorländer, *Ann. Chem.*, **341**, 3 (1905).
108. D. Vorländer, *Chem. Ber.*, **36**, 1470 (1903).
109. Chemie Wacker, Fr. Pat. 1,164,860 (1958).
110. J. F. Walker, *Formaldehyde*, 3rd ed., Chapter 13, ACS Monograph No. 159, 1964.
111. P. H. Williams, G. B. Payne, W. J. Sullivan, and P. R. Van Ess, *J. Am. Chem. Soc.*, **82**, 4883 (1960).
112. H. E. Winberg, U.S. Pat. 2,744,130 (1956).
113. J. H. Wotz and J. S. Matthews, *J. Org. Chem.*, **26**, 2987 (1961).
114. F. G. Young, *J. Am. Chem. Soc.*, **71**, 1346 (1949).
115. F. G. Young and J. T. Fitzpatrick, U.S. Pat. 2,580,714 (1952).
116. H. E. Zaugg, *Organic Reactions*, Vol. 8, R. Adams, Ed., Wiley, New York, 1954, pp. 305 ff.

## 2. Nitrogen

### a. Azetidines*

Many addition reactions of tetracyanoethylene have been reported.[8,10,11] The majority of these reactions consist of nucleophilic additions to the carbon–carbon double bond,[8,10,11] or of cycloadditions to the carbon–carbon double bond.[11,21,22]

* For a review of azetidines see Ref. 12.

Trifluoromethanesulfenyl chloride (1) adds to tetracyanoethylene (2), resulting in 2-chloro-1-trifluoromethylthio-3,4,4-tricyano-1-aza-1,3-buta-diene (3), which undergoes cycloaddition reactions.[5] The structure of 3

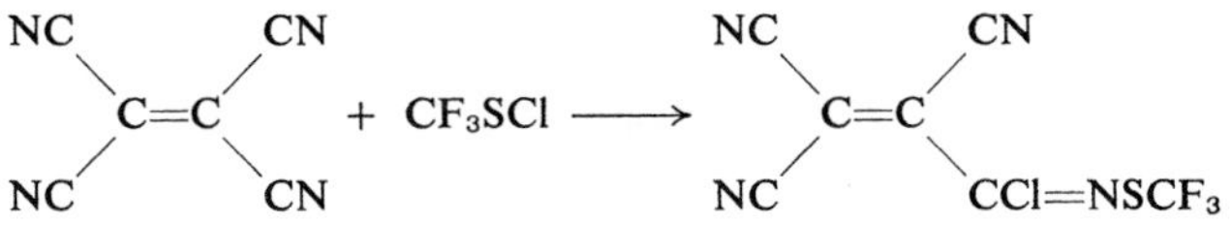

was established by ultraviolet absorption ($\lambda_{max}$ 335 m$\mu$ ($\varepsilon$ 8700)) and infra-red absorption (conjugated nitrile (4.48 $\mu$), tricyanovinyl double bond (6.35 $\mu$), carbon–nitrogen double bond (6.55 $\mu$), and carbon–fluorine (8 $\mu$)) spectra and analysis of the cycloaddition reaction products.[5]

Tetracyanoethylene reacts with electron-rich olefins to give tetracyano-cyclobutanes, while 3 reacts with vinyl ethers and styrenes at the carbon–nitrogen double bond to give substituted azetidines (4) (Table 1); these reactions occur more rapidly than do the reactions of tetracyanoethylene with the corresponding olefin.[5]

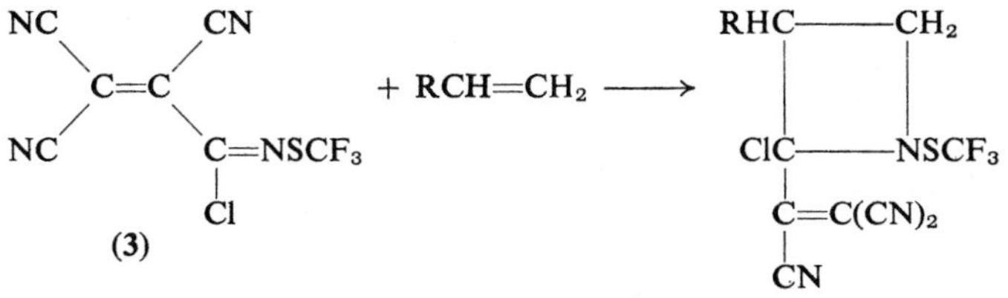

The structural assignments of the cycloadduct (4) were primarily estab-lished by spectral evidence (tricyanovinyl group is clearly indicated by infrared absorptions near 4.5 $\mu$ (conjugated nitrile) and 6.3 $\mu$ (tricyano-vinyl double bond) and ultraviolet absorption at 260–268 m$\mu$ with molar extinction coefficient around 16,000).[5] The nuclear magnetic resonance spectra of the azetidine (4) were in good agreement with the proposed structures; the ring hydrogens gave an ABX pattern common to all azeti-dines.[5] Thus, 4, R = $CH_3O$, has a proton spectrum with methoxy hydro-gens at $\tau$ 6.50, the methine hydrogen as four peaks centered at $\tau$ 4.80, and the methylene hydrogens as a weak, strong, strong, weak pattern with each split into doublets and centered at $\tau$ 7.25.

The rates of formation of the azetidines (4) are similar to those of tetracyanocyclobutanes, such as 5[22]; that is, they are markedly solvent dependent, although not to the extent of the tetracyanoethylene reactions.[5] The rate of dependence on solvents suggests that there is appreciable

$$\text{CH}_3\text{O} - \langle\text{C}_6\text{H}_4\rangle - \underset{\displaystyle \underset{\text{CN}}{|}}{\overset{\displaystyle |}{\text{HC}}} \!\!-\!\!\!-\!\! \overset{\displaystyle |}{\underset{\displaystyle \underset{\text{CN}}{|}}{\text{CH}_2}}$$

$$\text{NC}-\text{C}-\text{C}-\text{CN}$$

**(5)**

charge separation in the transition state. On this basis the transition state leading to **4** appears much more reasonable than one leading to the iso-

$$\text{RHC}\!-\!\!\!-\!\!\!-\!\text{CH}_2$$
$$\text{CF}_3\text{SN}\!-\!\!\!-\!\!\!-\!\underset{\text{Cl}}{\text{C}}-\text{C}=\underset{\text{CN}}{\text{C}}-\text{CN}$$

**(6)**

meric **6**. Thus, **7** allows a greater delocalization of charge than does **8**.[5] The transition state (**7**) leading to **6** has a charge distribution of the azo-

$$\overset{S^+}{\text{RHC}}\!-\!\!\!-\!\text{CH}_2$$
$$\text{Cl}-\overset{S^-}{\text{C}}\!-\!\!\!-\!\text{N}\!-\!\text{SCF}_3$$
$$\underset{\text{CN}}{\text{C}=\text{C(CN)}_2}$$

**(7)**

$$\overset{S^+}{\text{RHC}}\!-\!\!\!-\!\text{CH}_2$$
$$\text{CF}_3\text{SN}\!-\!\!\!-\!\overset{S^-}{\underset{\text{Cl}\ \text{CN}}{\text{C}}}-\text{C}=\text{C}\!\!\begin{smallmatrix}\text{CN}\\[2pt]\text{CN}\end{smallmatrix}$$

**(8)**

methine double bond which is opposite that of simpler azomethines in their cycloaddition reactions with ketenes.[13,14] The reversal in polarity is the result of the ability of the adjacent tricyanovinyl group to stabilize a negative charge.[5]

The addition of styrene to **3** is a reversible reaction, for when the resulting azetidine is dissolved in benzene, the red color of the $\pi$-complex[1,6,9] of **3** and styrene develops, indicating the ease of dissociation of the azetidine into its components.[5] This reversible reaction gives additional support to the postulation that there is considerable charge separation in the transition states of these cycloaddition reactions.

The reaction of **3** with $N$-vinylpyrrolidone (**9**) gave a compound (**10**) without a trifluoromethylthio group.[5] Ultraviolet, infrared, and nuclear magnetic resonance spectral evidence showed the presence of the tricyanovinyl group and the nitrogen–hydrogen bond. Conversion of the tri-

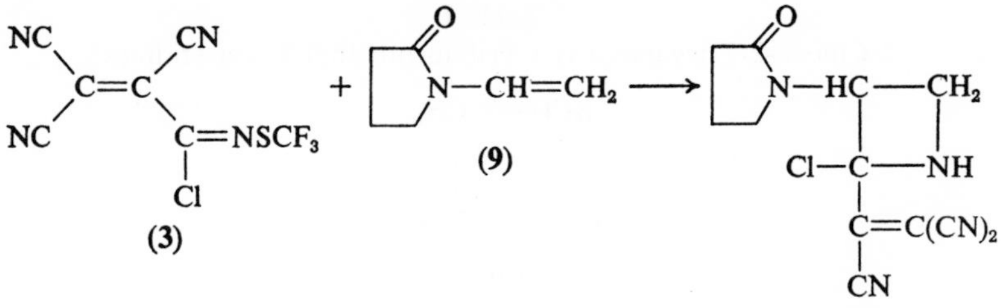

(3)          (9)          (10)

fluoromethylthioazetidines (4) to the azetidines (11) can be effected by heating with nucleophilic reagents such as alcohols or pyridine (Table 2).[5]

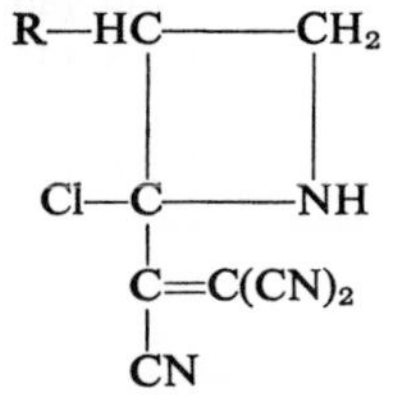

(11)

Other azetidine derivatives (12, 13, and 15) have been reported in the reactions of $N$-substituted $N'$-halosulfonylamidines,[4] in the reactions of

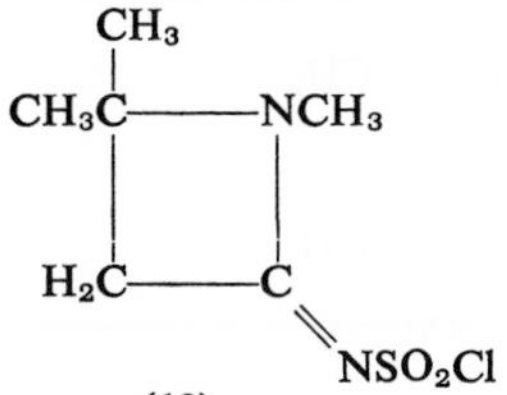

(12) 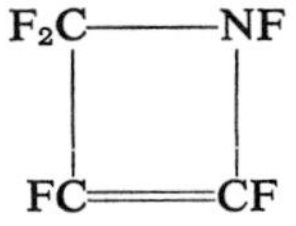          (13)

fluoroolefins with hydroazoic acid and rearrangements of perfluoroalkyl-azides[7] and treatment of the $\beta$-lactam azetididin-2-one (14) with lithium aluminum hydride.[2,3,15-20]

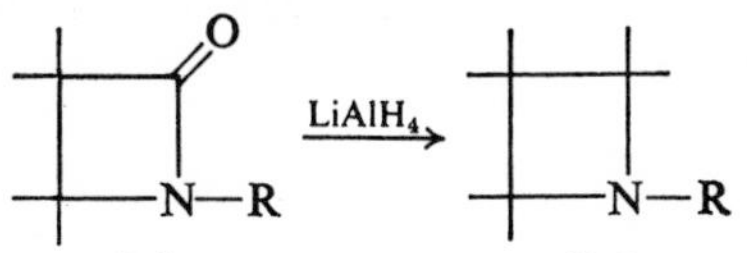

(14)          (15)

**Table 1**

2-Chloro-2-Tricyanovinyl-1-Trifluoromethyl Thioazetidines[5]

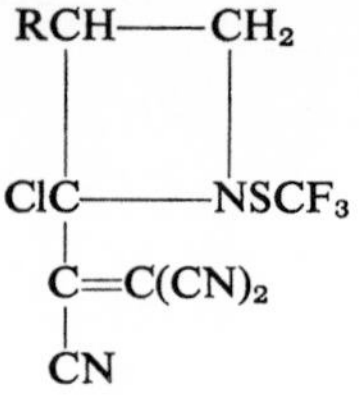

$$\begin{array}{ccc} RCH & \!\!\!\!-\!\!\!\! & CH_2 \\ | & & | \\ ClC & \!\!\!\!-\!\!\!\! & NSCF_3 \\ | & & \\ C\!\!=\!\!C(CN)_2 & & \\ | & & \\ CN & & \end{array}$$

| R | MP (°C) | Yield (%) |
|---|---|---|
| CH₃CH₂O | 112–112.4 | 76 |
| CH₃CH₂CH₂CH₂O | 106–106.6 | 89 |
| CH₃O | 139–140 | 82 |
| CH₂=CHO | 132.8–134 | 74 |
| C₆H₅ | 115–117 | 91 |
| 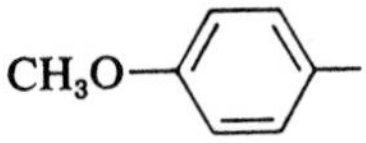 CH₃O—⟨benzene ring⟩— | 132.8–133.6 | 87 |

**Table 2**

2-Chloro-2-Tricyanovinylazetidines[5]

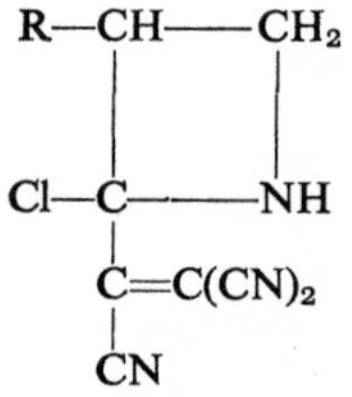

$$\begin{array}{ccc} R\!-\!CH & \!\!\!\!-\!\!\!\! & CH_2 \\ | & & | \\ Cl\!-\!C & \!\!\!\!-\!\!\!\! & NH \\ | & & \\ C\!\!=\!\!C(CN)_2 & & \\ | & & \\ CN & & \end{array}$$

| R | MP (°C) | Yield (%) |
|---|---|---|
| CH₃ | 262–263.5 | 70 |
| CH₃O— | 166–167.4 | 64 |
| CH₃CH₂O— | 154–155.5 | 60 |
| 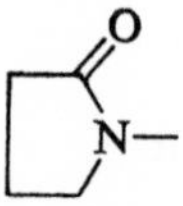 ⟨pyrrolidinone N—⟩ | 222–223 | 70 |

REFERENCES

1. L. J. Andrews and R. M. Keefer, *J. Am. Chem. Soc.*, **73**, 462 (1951).
2. Belg. Pat. 624,575 (1963).
3. A. Bonati, G. F. Cristiani, and E. Testa, *Ann. Chem.*, **647**, 813 (1961).
4. R. Graf, D. Guenther, H. Jensen, and K. Matterstock, Ger. Pat. 1,144,718 (1963).
5. H. D. Hartzler, *J. Org. Chem.*, **29**, 1194 (1964).
6. R. M. Keefer and L. J. Andrews, *J. Am. Chem. Soc.*, **72**, 4677 (1950).
7. I. L. Knunyants and E. G. Bykhovskaya, *Dokl. Akad. Nauk SSSR*, **131**, 1338 (1960); *Chem. Abstr.*, **54**, 20840 (1960).
8. B. C. McKusick, R. E. Heckert, T. L. Cairns, D. D. Coffman, and H. F. Mower, *J. Am. Chem. Soc.*, **80**, 2806 (1958).
9. R. E. Merrifield and W. D. Phillips, *J. Am. Chem. Soc.*, **80**, 2778 (1958).
10. W. J. Middleton and V. A. Englehardt, *J. Am. Chem. Soc.*, **80**, 2788 (1958).
11. W. J. Middleton, R. E. Heckert, E. L. Little, and C. G. Krespan, *J. Am. Chem. Soc.*, **80**, 2783 (1958).
12. J. A. Moore, in *Compounds with Three- and Four-Membered Rings* (*The Chemistry of Heterocyclic Compounds*, Vol. 19, A. Weissberger, Ed.) Interscience, New York, 1964, pp. 885 ff.
13. H. Staudinger, *Ann. Chem.*, **356**, 93 (1907).
14. H. Staudinger, *Chem. Ber.*, **40**, 1145 (1907).
15. E. Testa, *Farmaco Pavia Ed. Sci.*, **17**, 168 (1962); *Chem. Abstr.*, **57**, 9772 (1962).
16. E. Testa, A. Bonati, G. Pagani, and E. Gatti, *Ann. Chem.*, **647**, 92 (1961).
17. E. Testa, L. Fontanella, and G. F. Cristiani, *Ann. Chem.*, **626**, 114 (1959).
18. E. Testa, L. Fontanella, G. F. Cristiani, and L. Mariani, *Ann. Chem.*, **635**, 119 (1960).
19. E. Testa, L. Fontanella, L. Mariani, and G. F. Cristiani, *Ann. Chem.*, **633**, 56 (1960).
20. E. Testa, L. Fontanella, L. Mariani, and G. F. Cristiani, *Ann. Chem.*, **639**, 157 (1961).
21. J. K. Williams, *J. Am. Chem. Soc.*, **81**, 4013 (1959).
22. J. K. Williams, D. W. Wiley, and B. C. McKusick, *J. Am. Chem. Soc.*, **84**, 2210 (1962).

### *b. 2-Azetidinones*

The first β-lactams,* four-membered heterocyclic compounds,† containing nitrogen, were prepared by Staudinger and co-workers[100] using two novel methods.

---

* The term *β-lactam* will be used throughout this section interchangeably with the term *2-azetidinone*.
† For a review on four-membered heterocyclic compounds containing nitrogen see Refs. 51, 63, 117.

The cycloaddition reactions of ketenes* with imines (Schiff bases), phenylisocyanate, phenylisothiocyanate and carbodiphenylimide with formation of a four-membered ring were studied by Staudinger.[93]† It was found that diphenylketene (1) reacts readily with Schiff bases, such as benzylideneaniline (2) at room temperature to give the crystalline $\beta$-lactam (3), 1,3,3,4-tetraphenyl-2-azetidinone, in 72% yield.[93,96,102] This was

$$(C_6H_5)_2C{=}C{=}O + C_6H_5CH{=}NC_6H_5 \longrightarrow$$
$$\text{(1)} \qquad\qquad \text{(2)}$$

$$\begin{array}{cc} (C_6H_5)_2C & \!\!\!\!\!\!\!\!CO \\ | & | \\ C_6H_5CH & \!\!\!\!\!\!\!\!NC_6H_5 \\ & \text{(3)} \end{array}$$

the first representative of this class of compounds, although others had been reported.[28,62] The structure of the $\beta$-lactam (3) was determined by its cleavage to $\alpha,\alpha,\beta$-triphenyl-$\beta$-anilidopropionic acid (4), which decomposed into diphenylacetic acid (5) and benzylideneaniline (2). An analogous decomposition had been previously reported for the decomposition of another $\beta$-anilido acid.[2,31]

$$\begin{array}{cc} (C_6H_5)_2C & \!\!\!\!\!\!\!\!CO \\ | & | \\ C_6H_5CH & \!\!\!\!\!\!\!\!NC_6H_5 \\ & \text{(3)} \end{array} \longrightarrow \begin{array}{c} (C_6H_5)_2C{-}CO_2H \\ | \\ C_6H_5CH{-}NHC_6H_5 \\ \text{(4)} \end{array} \longrightarrow$$

$$(C_6H_5)_2CHCO_2H + C_6H_5CH{=}NC_6H_5$$
$$\text{(5)} \qquad\qquad \text{(2)}$$

It has been reported that the decomposition of $\beta$-lactams can occur in two directions; that is, the starting material can be retained,[98,101,113] or by cleavage in another direction new unsaturated compounds (isocyanates and ethylene derivatives)[57,98,101,102,113] form:

$$R_2C{=}NR + R_2C{=}C{=}O \rightleftharpoons \begin{array}{cc} R_2C & \!\!\!\!\!\!\!\!CO \\ | & | \\ R_2C & \!\!\!\!\!\!\!\!NR \end{array} \longrightarrow \begin{array}{cc} R_2C + CO \\ \| \quad \| \\ R_2C \quad NR \end{array}$$

Dimethylketene (6) was also reacted with benzylideneaniline (2) with the formation of the $\beta$-lactams 1,4-diphenyl-3,3-dimethyl-2-azetidinone (7).[100,104] Most of the $\beta$-lactams prepared by the above method have been

$$(CH_3)_2C{=}C{=}O + C_6H_5CH{=}NC_6H_5 \longrightarrow$$
$$\text{(6)} \qquad\qquad \text{(2)}$$

$$\begin{array}{cc} (CH_3)_2C & \!\!\!\!\!\!\!\!CO \\ | & | \\ C_6H_5CH & \!\!\!\!\!\!\!\!NC_6H_5 \\ & \text{(7)} \end{array}$$

* For reviews on ketenes see Refs. 52, 59, 73, 128.
† See Wedekind.[125-127]

made from dimethyl-[40,100,104,105] or diphenylketene,[93,96,100,102,109,113] which seem to react in general with imines derived from aromatic aldehydes or ketones and aromatic amines (Table 1). Other ketenes which have been used in this synthesis include diethylketene (8),[108] ethylcarbethoxyketene (9),[99,100] phenylcarbomethoxyketene (10),[99] methylphenylketene (11),[100,110] 2,2-biphenyleneketene (12),[100] dibenzylketene (13),[112] ethylphenoxyketene (14),[111] diphenoxyketene (15),[111] and ketene (16) it-

$$(C_2H_5)_2C\!=\!C\!=\!O$$
**(8)**

$$C_2H_5O_2C(C_2H_5)C\!=\!C\!=\!O$$
**(9)**

$$CH_3O_2C(C_6H_5)C\!=\!C\!=\!O$$
**(10)**

$$C_6H_5(CH_3)C\!=\!C\!=\!O$$
**(11)**

$$(C_6H_4)_2C\!=\!C\!=\!O$$
**(12)**

$$(C_6H_5CH_2)_2C\!=\!C\!=\!O$$
**(13)**

$$C_6H_5O(C_2H_5)C\!=\!C\!=\!O$$
**(14)**

$$(C_6H_5O)_2C\!=\!C\!=\!O$$
**(15)**

$$CH_2\!=\!C\!=\!O$$
**(16)**

self[99,107] (Table 1). Staudinger gave the following order of reactivity of the ketenes towards benzophenoneanil:

$$C\!=\!C\!=\!O > (C_6H_5)_2C\!=\!C\!=\!O > C_6H_5(CH_3)C\!=\!C\!=\!O \cong$$

**(3)**      **(1)**      **(11)**

$$(CH_3)_2C\!=\!C\!=\!O$$
**(6)**

Ketene (16) was found to be much less reactive than the substituted ketenes, for the reaction with benzophenoneanil only occurred at 200°C.[99] The scope of the ketene–imine reaction is limited by the availability of and the types of imines that can react to form the desired $\beta$-lactams. In most instances the imine has been one in which both the carbon atom and the nitrogen atom of the imino linkage are substituted by aryl groups. It has been found, however, when either or both the carbon and nitrogen atoms of the imino group are substituted with aliphatic groups or if the carbon–nitrogen double bond is part of an aromatic system as in pyridine (17) or quinoline, the expected $\beta$-lactam is not formed; the resulting product is a piperidinedione (18).[1,16,96,106] Cycloaddition reactions of diphenylketene (1) with 2-methylthiazoline (19) and benzothiazole (20) lead to the formation of a $\beta$-lactam and a pyridine-1,3-dione derivative (21 and 22, respectively).[14] Similar results were obtained by the cycloaddition of diphenylketene to certain oxazoles, thiazoles, and imidazoles, resulting in the respective piperidinediones.[50]

Staudinger[100] also pointed out that the reactivity of benzylidene-*p*-nitroaniline with diphenylketene is slight compared with that of benzylideneaniline; that *p*-dimethylamino substituents increase the reactivity of

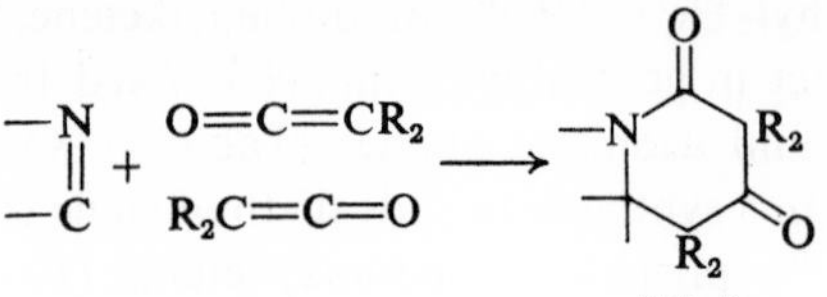

(18a)

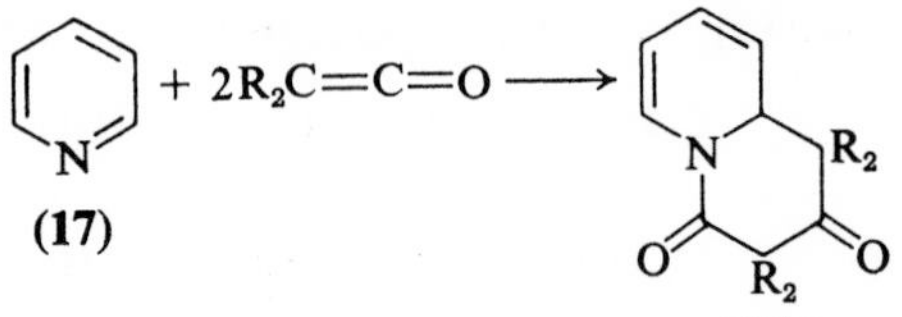

(17)

(18b)

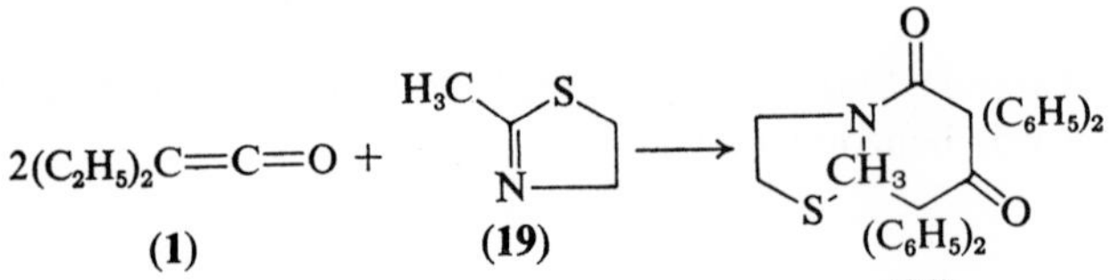

$2(C_2H_5)_2C=C=O$ +

(1)

(19)

(21)

$2(C_6H_5)_2C=C=O$ +

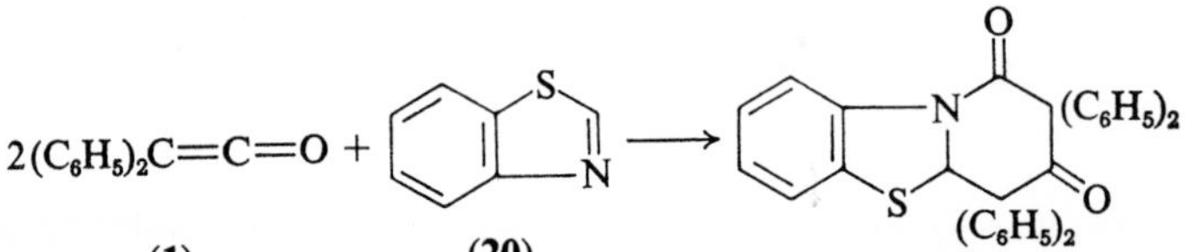

(1)

(20)

(22)

the Schiff base; and that acetophenoneanil is much less reactive to diphenyl-ketene than benzylideneaniline, although benzophenoneanil is much more reactive.

It was reported[69,93] that when diphenylketene (1) was reacted with cinnamylideneaniline (23) a β-lactam (24) (Table 1) was formed via a 1,2-cycloaddition instead of the δ-lactam (25) expected from a 1,4-cyclo-

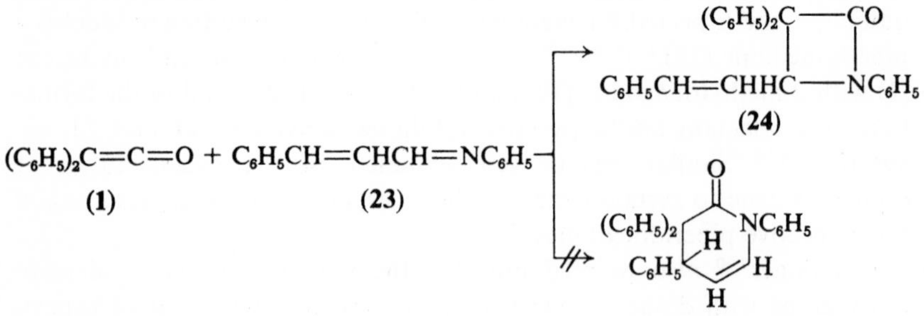

$(C_6H_5)_2C=C=O + C_6H_5CH=CHCH=NC_6H_5$

(1)                              (23)

$(C_6H_5)_2C$——$CO$

$C_6H_5CH=CHHC$——$NC_6H_5$

(24)

(25)

addition, demonstrating the increased ease of formation of highly substituted $\beta$-lactams. The reaction of ethylcarbethoxyketene (9) with benzylideneaniline (2) at $-10°C$ gave a 1:1 adduct which was not the $\beta$-lactam (26), but can be represented by the 3-azetidinone structure (27).[99,100] The

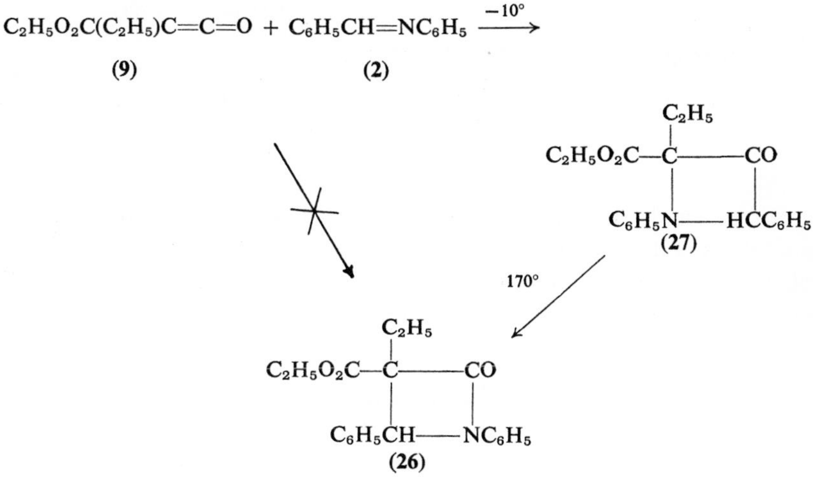

$$C_2H_5O_2C(C_2H_5)C{=}C{=}O + C_6H_5CH{=}NC_6H_5 \xrightarrow{-10°}$$

(9)                              (2)

$$
\begin{array}{c}
C_2H_5 \\
C_2H_5O_2C{-}C{-\!-\!-\!-}CO \\
C_6H_5N{-\!-\!-\!-}HCC_6H_5 \\
(27)
\end{array}
$$

170°

$$
\begin{array}{c}
C_2H_5 \\
C_2H_5O_2C{-}C{-\!-\!-\!-}CO \\
C_6H_5CH{-\!-\!-\!-}NC_6H_5 \\
(26)
\end{array}
$$

adduct, however, is unstable and decomposes at room temperature to a ketene and an imine. Upon heating of 27 at 170°C the compound forms the $\beta$-lactam (26). The $\beta$-lactam (26) can be obtained directly from the ketene and the imine at 180°C. Phenylcarbomethoxyketene (10) yields a $\beta$-lactam (28) directly with benzylideneaniline (2).

$$CH_3O_2C{-}C{=}C{=}O + C_6H_5CH{=}NC_6H_5 \longrightarrow
\begin{array}{c}
C_6H_5 \\
CH_3O_2C{-}C{-\!-\!-\!-}CO \\
C_6H_5CH{-\!-\!-\!-}NC_6H_5
\end{array}$$

C₆H₅ (under first structure)

(2)

(10)                                      (28)

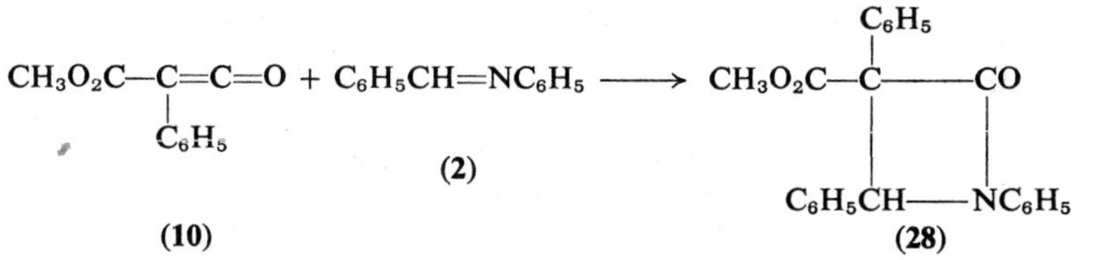

Staudinger and Meyer[109] also tried to react diphenylketene (1) with aminomethylene derivatives (29) in an analogous manner as Schiff bases, but all attempts failed to produce the aminomethylene derivatives (29).

$$R_3N{=}CR_2 + (C_6H_5)_2C{=}C{=}O \longrightarrow
\begin{array}{c}
R_3N{-\!-\!-\!-}CR_2 \\
OC{-\!-\!-\!-}C(C_6H_5)_2
\end{array}$$

(29)            (1)

$$RN{=}CR_2 + (1) \longrightarrow
\begin{array}{c}
RN{-\!-\!-\!-}CR_2 \\
OC{-\!-\!-\!-}C(C_6H_5)_2
\end{array}$$

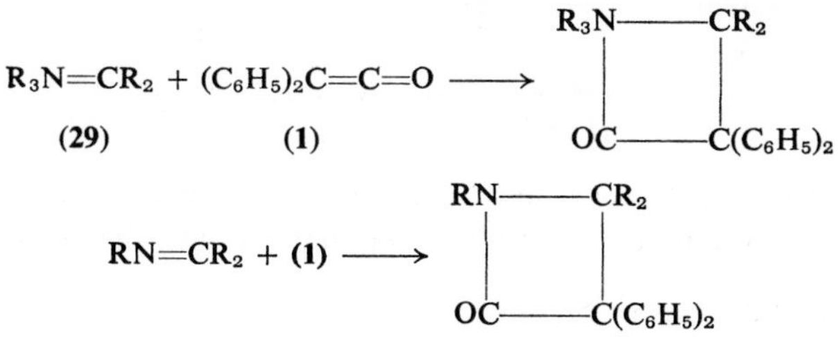

Holley and Holley[40] found that the presence of a sulfur substituent on the carbon of the imino group did not prevent the formation of the β-lactam (31) (in 60% yield) when the imino thioester (30) was added to dimethylketene (6) (Table 1).

$$(CH_3)_2C{=}C{=}O + C_6H_5C{=}NC_6H_5 \longrightarrow$$

(6)                          $\overset{|}{S}CH_3$

(30)

$$\begin{array}{ccc} (CH_3)_2C & \longrightarrow & CO \\ | & & | \\ C_6H_5C & \longrightarrow & NC_6H_5 \\ | & & \\ SCH_3 & & \end{array}$$

(31)

Kirmse and Horner[53] found that a β-lactam was formed by the photolysis of diazoketones* in the presence of Schiff bases (Table 2). The photolysis of diazoketones (32) had been reported[44-46] to give ketenes in good yield via a Wolff rearrangement, that is,

$$R{-}\overset{\overset{\displaystyle O}{\|}}{C}{-}CHN_2 \xrightarrow[-N_2]{h\nu} \left[ R{-}\overset{\overset{\displaystyle O}{\|}}{C}{-}\overset{-}{C}H \right] \longrightarrow R{-}CH{=}C{=}O$$

(32)

For example, if one irradiates benzoyldiazomethane (33) or azibenzil (34), forming the corresponding ketenes (35) and (1) respectively,[46] in the presence of imines (34) (Schiff bases) the corresponding β-lactams are formed (Table 2).[53]

$$R'{-}\overset{\overset{\displaystyle O}{\|}}{C}{-}\overset{\overset{\displaystyle}{|}}{\underset{N_2}{C}}{-}R'' \xrightarrow[-N_2]{h\nu} \left[ R'{-}\overset{\overset{\displaystyle O}{\|}}{C}{-}\overset{-}{C}{-}R'' \right] \longrightarrow R'{-}CR''O{=}C{=}O$$

(33)                                                    (35)

(33: R' = C_6H_5, R'' = H)
(34: R' = R'' = C_6H_5)

$$\begin{array}{c} R' \\ \phantom{x} \\ R'' \end{array}\!\!\!\!C{=}C{=}O + R^3R^4C{=}NR^5 \longrightarrow$$

(35)              (36)

$$\begin{array}{ccc} & R^1 & \\ & | & \\ R^2{-}C & \longrightarrow & CO \\ | & & | \\ R^3C & \longrightarrow & NR^5 \\ | & & \\ R^4 & & \end{array}$$

(35: R' = C_6H_5, R'' = H)
(1: R' = R'' = C_6H_5)

Analogously, the diazocarbonyl compound (37) undergoes cleavage of nitrogen under the influence of ultraviolet light to give the corresponding

*For a review of diazoketones see Ref. 128.

$$\underset{(37)}{R'-\overset{\overset{\textstyle O}{\|}}{C}-\underset{\underset{\textstyle N_2}{|}}{C}-CO_2R''} \quad \xrightarrow[-N_2]{h\nu} \quad \underset{(38)}{O=C=\overset{\overset{\textstyle R'}{|}}{C}-CO_2R''}$$

$(R' = CH_3, C_2H_5)$      $(R' = CH_3, C_2H_5)$
$(R'' = CH_3, C_2H_5)$      $(R'' = CH_3, C_2H_5)$

ketenecarboxylic esters (38),[44] which in the presence of imines (36) form the respective $\beta$-lactams (39) (Table 2).[53]

$$(38) + \underset{(36)}{R^3R^4C=NR^5} \longrightarrow$$

$$\begin{array}{ccc} R^2O_2C-\overset{\overset{\textstyle R^1}{|}}{C} & ---- & CO \\ | & & | \\ R^3-\underset{\underset{\textstyle R^4}{|}}{C} & ---- & N-R^5 \\ & (39) & \end{array}$$

The formation of $\beta$-lactams by the thermal decomposition of diazo-ketones in the presence of imines was reported by Pfleger and Jäger[71]; for example, benzoyldiazomethane (33), upon heating in the presence of ben-zylideneaniline (2), forms the $\beta$-lactam (40). Pfleger and Jäger found the

$$\underset{(33)}{C_6H_5-\overset{\overset{\textstyle O}{\|}}{C}-CHN_2} \xrightarrow[-N_2]{\varDelta} \left[ \underset{(35)}{C_6H_5-\overset{\overset{\textstyle H}{|}}{C}=C=O} \right] \xrightarrow{2} \begin{array}{cc} C_6H_5\overset{\overset{\textstyle H}{|}}{C} & ---- CO \\ | & | \\ C_6H_5CH & ---- NC_6H_5 \\ & (40) \end{array}$$

additions were hindered by *ortho*-, *para*-chloro or *ortho*-, *meta*-, or *para*-nitro groups in either ring of the benzalaniline, while being favored by *meta-chloro* or *para*-dimethylamino groups (Table 2).

Staudinger and Jelagin[94,102] found that diphenylketene (1) and nitroso-benzene (41) gave a 63–65% yield of a product (42) (Table 3-A), while a 2:1 molar ratio of diphenylketene (1) and nitrosobenzene (41) gave a mix-ture of the $\beta$-lactam (43), which can be prepared from (1) and benzo-phenoneanil (45), and the 1,2-oxazetidinone-3 (42) (see Section III-B-2a). The $\beta$-lactam formation was explained by the decarboxylation of the 1,2-oxazetidinone-4 (44) to a Schiff base (45) and carbon dioxide[94,101,102] which reacted with an excess of diphenylketene (1).

Analogously, *p*-dimethylaminonitrosobenzene, more reactive than nitrosobenzene, gave 65% of the $\beta$-lactam when treated with 2 moles of

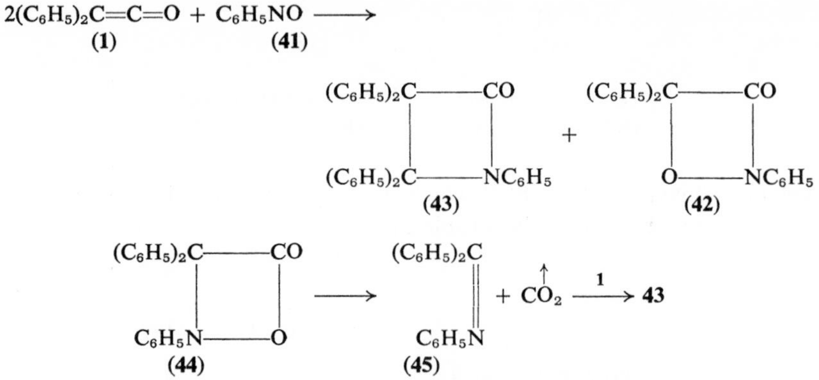

$$2(C_6H_5)_2C=C=O + C_6H_5NO \longrightarrow$$
$$\quad\;\; (1) \qquad\qquad\qquad (41)$$

diphenylketene, but not with 35. This work was also repeated by Kresze and Trede,[58] confirming Staudinger's work (see Section III-B-2a).

$\beta$-Lactams have also been formed by the reaction of diazomethane and isocyanates (Table 3-B)[86, 87]; for example, phenylisocyanate (46) and diazomethane (47) form 1-phenyl-2-azetidinone (48) in a 20% yield. The reaction of (46) and (47) had been reported by Pechman,[68] but the oily product

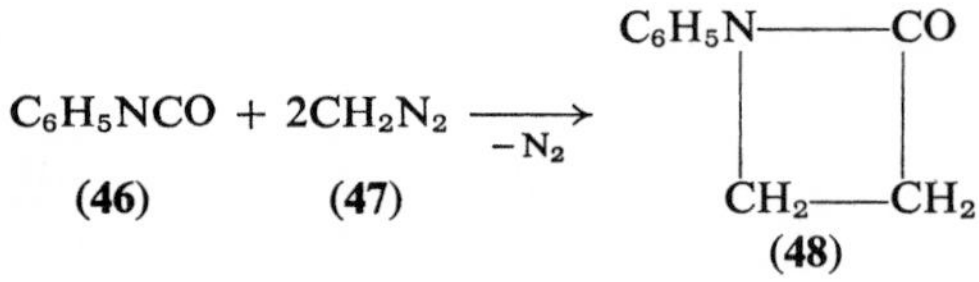

$$C_6H_5NCO + 2CH_2N_2 \xrightarrow[-N_2]{}$$
$$\quad (46) \qquad\qquad (47)$$

was not characterized. *p*-Bromophenylisocyanate (49) was also converted into the $\beta$-lactam (50) under similar conditions. The reaction, however, is not a general method of preparation, for no $\beta$-lactam was formed by the

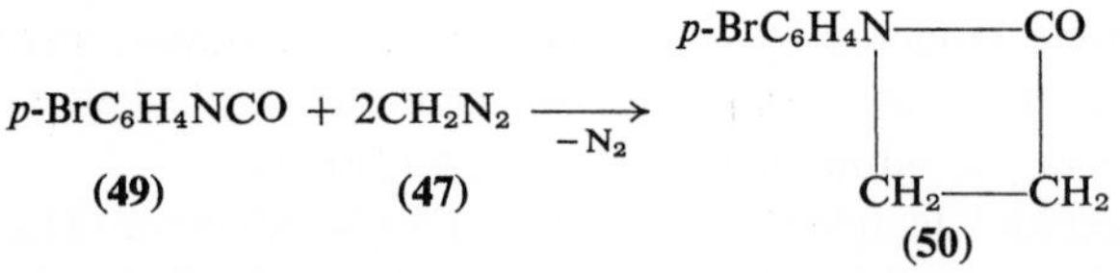

$$p\text{-BrC}_6H_4NCO + 2CH_2N_2 \xrightarrow[-N_2]{}$$
$$\quad (49) \qquad\qquad\quad (47)$$

reaction of diazomethane with $\alpha$-naphthyl-, *p*-nitrophenyl-, benzyl-, benzoyl-, or methyl-isocyanates.[86, 87]

The reaction of phenylisocyanate (46) and certain ketene acetals, such as phenylketene dimethylacetal (51) and dimethylketene dimethylacetal (52), has been reported to result in the formation of a $\beta$-lactam derivative (53 and 54, respectively).[75, 76] (See Table 3-C.)

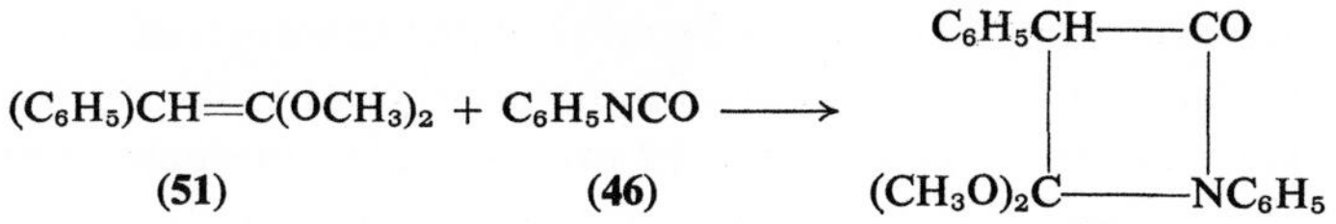

$$(C_6H_5)CH=C(OCH_3)_2 + C_6H_5NCO \longrightarrow$$

**(51)**                          **(46)**

$$\begin{array}{c} C_6H_5CH\!\!-\!\!-\!\!-\!\!CO \\ |\qquad\qquad| \\ (CH_3O)_2C\!\!-\!\!-\!\!-\!\!NC_6H_5 \\ \textbf{(53)} \end{array}$$

$$(CH_3)_2C=C(OCH_3)_2 + \textbf{(46)} \longrightarrow$$

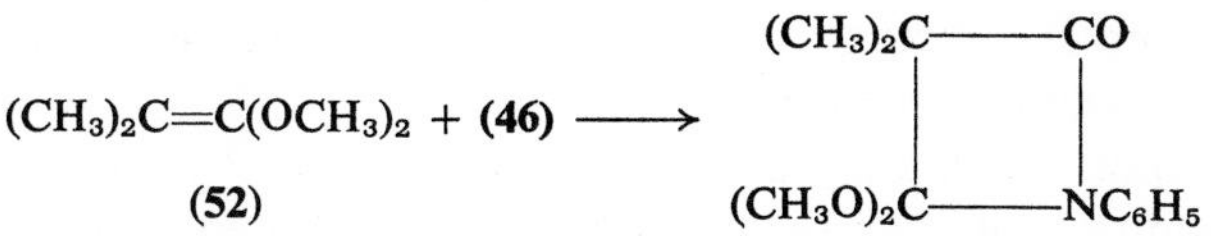

**(52)**

$$\begin{array}{c} (CH_3)_2C\!\!-\!\!-\!\!-\!\!CO \\ |\qquad\qquad| \\ (CH_3O)_2C\!\!-\!\!-\!\!-\!\!NC_6H_5 \\ \textbf{(54)} \end{array}$$

Hoffmann and Häuser[38] found that tetramethoxyethylene **(55)** generated by the thermal decomposition of 7,7-dimethoxybicyclo[2.2.1]heptadiene derivatives **(56)**[29,39,60] and phenylisocyanate **(46)** form a β-lactam

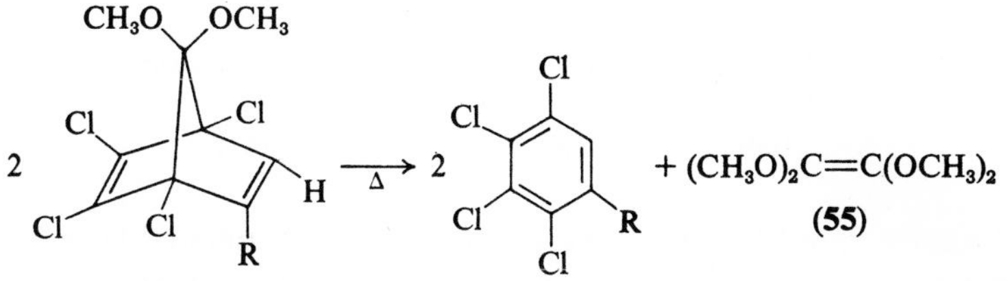

$$(R = C_6H_5, Br)$$

**(57)**, 3,3,4,4-tetramethoxy-1-phenyl-2-azetidinone, in 76% yield (Table 3-C).

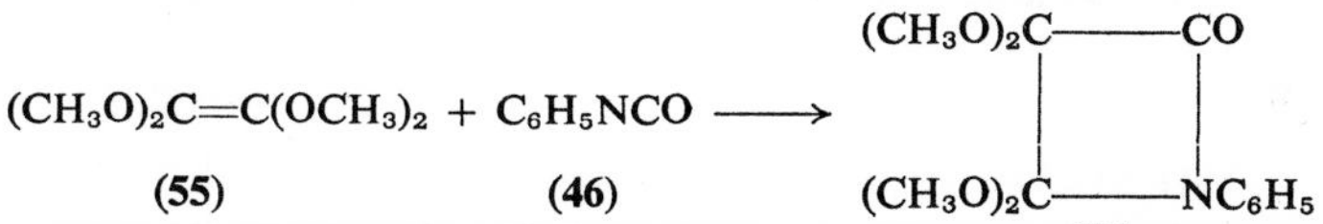

$$(CH_3O)_2C=C(OCH_3)_2 + C_6H_5NCO \longrightarrow$$

**(55)**                          **(46)**

$$\begin{array}{c} (CH_3O)_2C\!\!-\!\!-\!\!-\!\!CO \\ |\qquad\qquad| \\ (CH_3O)_2C\!\!-\!\!-\!\!-\!\!NC_6H_5 \\ \textbf{(57)} \end{array}$$

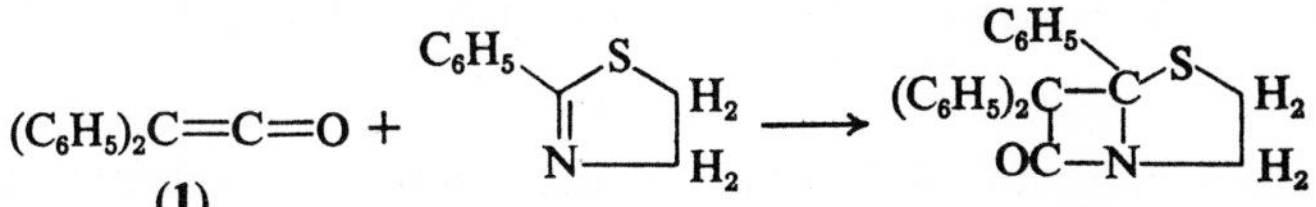

Penicillin's importance in medicine led to a series of investigations of its chemistry.[14,18] It was found that penicillin was a β-lactam-thiazolidine derivative. Prior to 1950 there was only a single instance in which a fused β-lactam-thiazolidine **(59)** had been prepared from 2-phenyl-2-thiazoline **(58)** and diphenylketene **(1)** via a cycloaddition reaction[17] which was used as the model compound in infrared studies on the structures of penicillin.[15] The substitution of dimethylketene for diphenylketene in the reaction with **58** leads to a piperidinedione, not the expected $\beta$-lactam-thiazolidine. Recently, Kirmse and Horner[53] and Pfleger and Jäger[71] reported the formation of $\beta$-lactam-thiazolidine derivatives by ketenes or ketene derivatives generated from diazoketones photolytically[44–46,53] and thermally[71] in the presence of thiazolidines (Table 4).

Recent reports mention $\beta$-amino-$\beta$-lactams[3,4,8,66,67,70] resulting from the cycloaddition of isocyanates with $\beta,\beta$-disubstituted vinylamines; for example, 1-pyrrolidinoisobutene-1 (**60**) and phenylisocyanate (**46**) produced the $\beta$-amino-$\beta$-lactam (**61**), 1-phenyl-3,3-dimethyl-4-pyrrolidino-

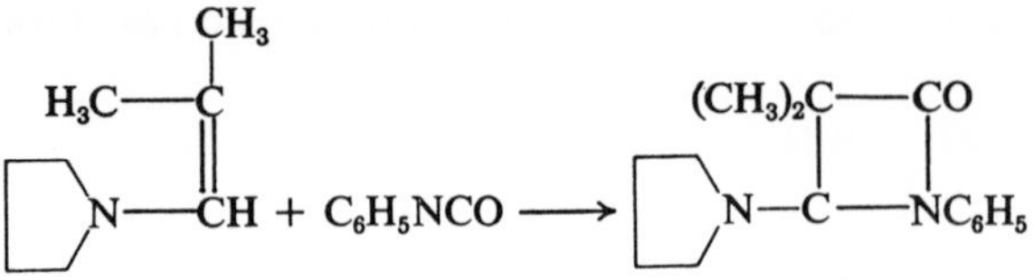

azetidinone-2, in 84% yield. The structures of the $\beta$-amino-$\beta$-lactams produced in this manner were determined by chemical evidence and infrared and nuclear magnetic resonance (the characteristic band for $\beta$-lactams at 1730–1750 cm$^{-1}$) analysis (Table 3-D).

Recently, Scheinbaum[77] reported the isolation of the $\beta$-lactam 1,3,3,4,4-pentaphenyl-2-azetidinone (**43**) during the irradiation of a mixture of nitrobenzene (**62**) and tolane (**63**) in 1.8% yield (Table 3-A). The reaction

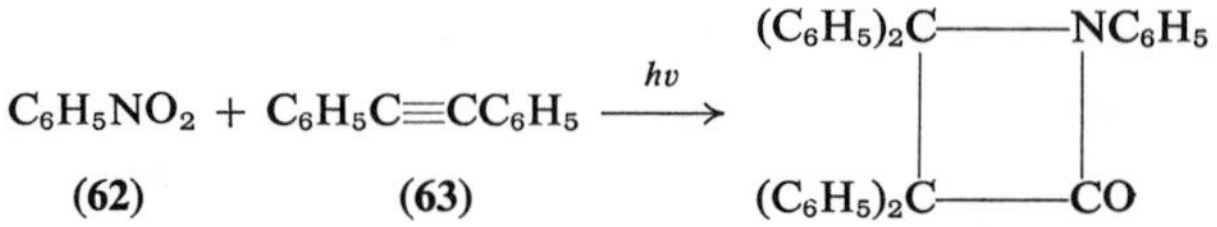

was assumed to proceed through a diphenylketene (**1**) intermediate formed by the transfer of an oxygen atom from nitrogen to the acetylenic carbon followed by cleavage of nitrosobenzene (**41**) and migration of a phenyl group. The $\beta$-lactam (**43**) was formed by the reaction of diphenylketene (**1**)

$$C_6H_5NO_2 + C_6H_5C{\equiv}CC_6H_5 \xrightarrow{h\upsilon} C_6H_5NO + (C_6H_5)_2C{=}C{=}O$$
$$\text{(62)} \qquad\qquad \text{(63)} \qquad\qquad \text{(41)} \qquad\qquad \text{(1)}$$

and benzophenoneanil (**45**) formed by the reaction of diphenylketene (**1**) and nitrosobenzene (**41**), first observed by Staudinger and Jelagin.[103]

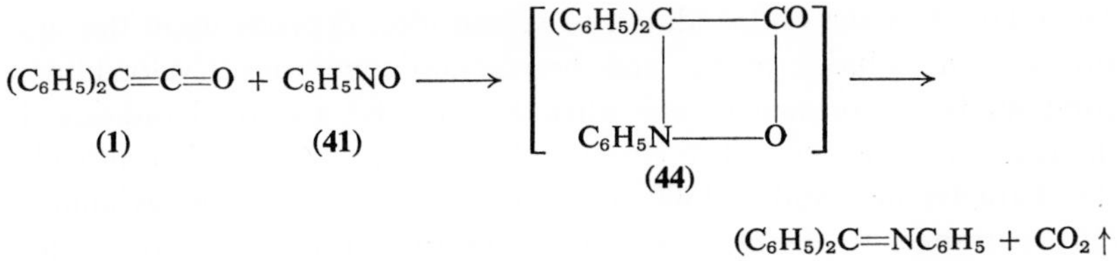

$$(C_6H_5)_2C=C=O + C_6H_5NO \longrightarrow \begin{bmatrix} (C_6H_5)_2C\text{------}CO \\ | \qquad\qquad | \\ C_6H_5N\text{------}O \end{bmatrix} \longrightarrow$$

$$\text{(1)} \qquad\qquad \text{(41)} \qquad\qquad\qquad \text{(44)}$$

$$(C_6H_5)_2C=NC_6H_5 + CO_2 \uparrow$$
$$\text{(45)}$$

$$\text{(1)} + \text{(45)} \longrightarrow \begin{matrix} (C_6H_5)_2C\text{------}NC_6H_5 \\ | \qquad\qquad\quad | \\ (C_6H_5)_2C\text{------}CO \end{matrix}$$
$$\text{(43)}$$

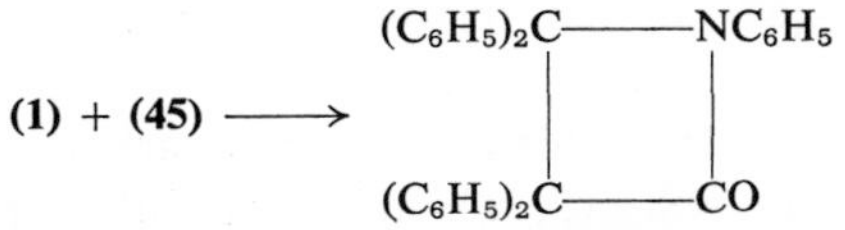

Enol ethers (64) with sulfonylisocyanate (65) were found to produce 4-alkoxy-2-azetidinones (66) via a cycloaddition reaction or 3-alkoxy-acrylamides (67), depending on the reaction conditions (Table 5).[20-22] Aliphatic and aromatic isocyanate such as benzoylisocyanate do not react

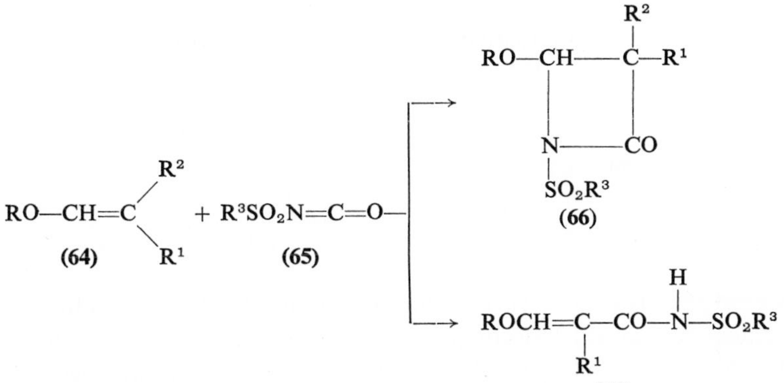

$$RO\text{---}CH=C\underset{R^1}{\overset{R^2}{<}} + R^3SO_2N=C=O \longrightarrow$$

$$\text{(64)} \qquad\qquad\qquad \text{(65)}$$

$$\begin{matrix} & R^2 \\ & | \\ RO\text{---}CH\text{------}C\text{---}R^1 \\ | \qquad\qquad\quad | \\ N\text{------}CO \\ | \\ SO_2R^3 \\ \text{(66)} \end{matrix}$$

$$\begin{matrix} & & H \\ & & | \\ ROCH=C\text{---}CO\text{---}N\text{---}SO_2R^3 \\ & | \\ & R^1 \\ & \text{(67)} \end{matrix}$$

with enol ethers.[22] The cycloaddition products (66) rearrange in hot benzene to the corresponding acrylamides (67), as is shown here.

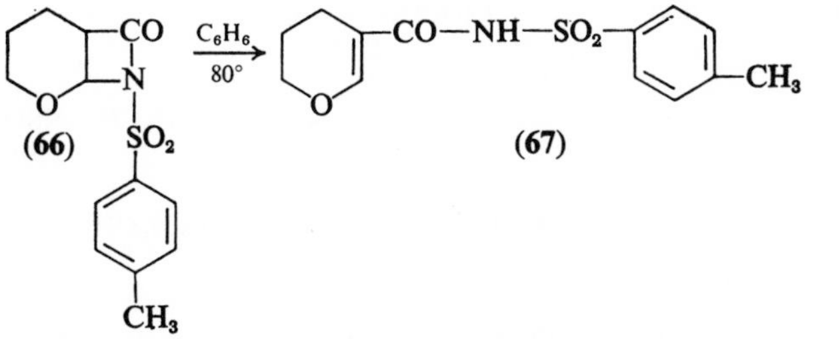

$$(R = \text{---}(CH_2)_3\text{---}, \quad R^3 = p\text{---}CH_3C_6H_4\text{---})$$

The relation of the cycloaddition to substitution depends upon the substituents, the solution media, and the reaction conditions. Cycloaddition compounds are formed except when $R^1$ and $R^2$ are alkyl radicals. If the reaction is carried out in strong polar solvents, as dimethylsulfoxide, the characteristic band at 1800 cm$^{-1}$ disappears; that is, the azetidinone (66) rearranges to the $\beta$-alkoxy-acrylamide (67). The quantitative determination of the proportion of the cycloaddition product (66) and the $\beta$-alkoxyacrylamide (67) in the mixture was determined by infrared spectroscopy.[11, 22]

In conclusion, treatment of aldehydes with $N$-carbonylsulfamoyl chlorides (68) forms $RCH{=}NSO_2Cl$, which reacts with ketene to give the corresponding $\beta$-lactam-$N$-sulfonyl chlorides (Table 4-A).[32, 35] For example, benzaldehyde (69) reacts with $N$-carbonylsulfamoyl chloride (68) with cleavage of the carbon dioxide to give the $N$-benzalsulfamic acid chloride (70), which reacts with ketene (16) to form the $\beta$-lactam-$N$-sulfonyl chloride (71). The preparation of $N$-benzalsulfamic acid chloride (70)

$$C_6H_5CHO + OCNSO_2Cl \xrightarrow{-CO_2} C_6H_5CH{=}NSO_2Cl$$
$$\text{(69)} \qquad \text{(68)} \qquad\qquad \text{(70)}$$

$$\begin{array}{cc} & C_6H_5CH\text{----}CH_2 \\ 70 + CH_2{=}C{=}O \longrightarrow & | \qquad\quad | \\ \text{(16)} & ClO_2SN\text{----}CO \\ & \text{(71)} \end{array}$$

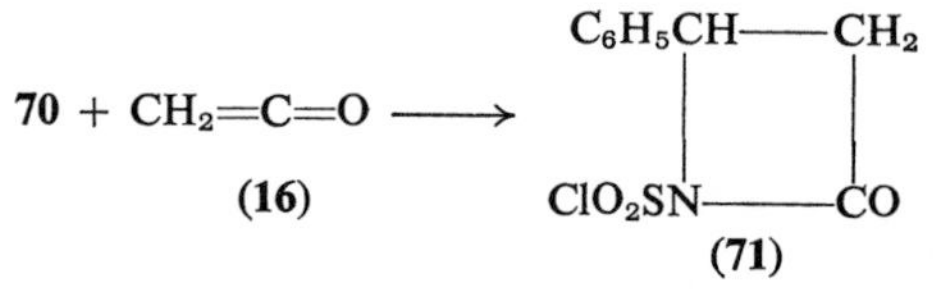

has been postulated as occurring through an unstable 1,3-oxazetidinone-4-intermediate (72) which decomposes into carbon dioxide and the chloride (70).[32] $N$-Carbonylsulfamoyl fluoride (73) was found to react analogously,[32] as is shown here.

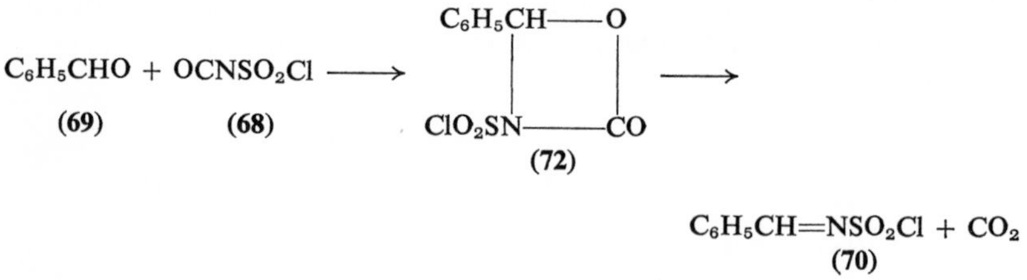

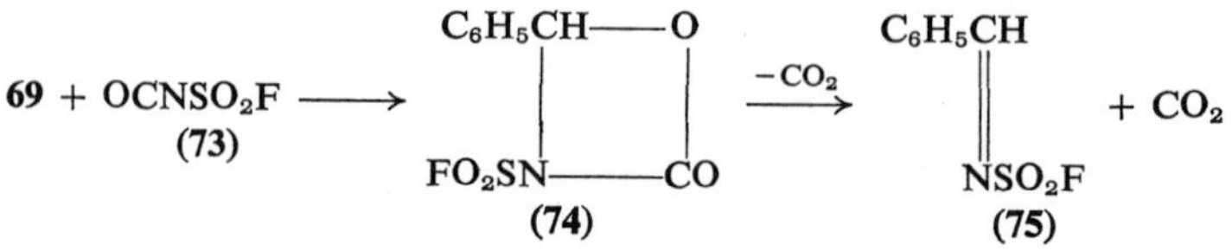

$$\begin{array}{cc} & C_6H_5CH\text{----}O \\ C_6H_5CHO + OCNSO_2Cl \longrightarrow & | \qquad\quad | \longrightarrow \\ \text{(69)} \qquad\quad \text{(68)} & ClO_2SN\text{----}CO \\ & \text{(72)} \end{array}$$

$$C_6H_5CH{=}NSO_2Cl + CO_2$$
$$\text{(70)}$$

$$\begin{array}{ccc} & C_6H_5CH\text{----}O & C_6H_5CH \\ 69 + OCNSO_2F \longrightarrow & | \qquad\quad | \xrightarrow{-CO_2} & \| \qquad + CO_2 \\ \text{(73)} & FO_2SN\text{----}CO & NSO_2F \\ & \text{(74)} & \text{(75)} \end{array}$$

$$C_6H_5CH\text{---}CH_2$$

$$\textbf{75} + CH_2\text{=}C\text{=}O \longrightarrow$$

$$(\textbf{16}) \qquad\qquad FO_2SN\text{----}CO$$
$$(\textbf{76})$$

The reactions of *N*-carbonsulfamoyl halides with olefins were reported to have occurred in two directions[32-34]; for example, the reaction of iso-butylene (**77**) with (**68**) forms the *N*-sulfonyl chloride (**78**) of a β-amino-carboxylic acid lactam via a cycloaddition reaction in a 70% yield (Table 6-B) and the *N*-sulfonyl chloride (**79**) of an unsaturated carboxylic acid amide in a 30% yield. Reactions of *N*-carbonylsulfamoyl fluoride (**73**) and

$$CH_3$$
$$\overset{|}{CH_3C}\text{-----}CH_2$$
$$70\%$$
$$N\text{-----}CO$$
$$\overset{|}{SO_2Cl}$$
$$(\textbf{78})$$

$$CH_3 \qquad N\text{=}C\text{=}O$$
$$\overset{|}{CH_3\text{---}C\text{=}CH_2} \quad \overset{|}{SO_2Cl}$$
$$(\textbf{77}) \qquad\qquad (\textbf{68})$$

$$30\% \qquad CH_3 \qquad O$$
$$\overset{|}{CH_2\text{=}C\text{---}CH_2\text{---}}\overset{\|}{C}\text{---}NHSO_2Cl}$$
$$(\textbf{79})$$

olefins are analogous. These cycloaddition reactions are very similar to those involving enol ethers and sulfonylisocyanates[20-22] previously mentioned.

In general, aliphatic olefins of the types isobutylene (**77**), trimethyl-ethylenes (**81**), and tetramethylenes (**82**), react smoothly and rapidly with *N*-carbonylsulfamoyl halides. It was also found that the alkyl radical can

$$R_2C\text{=}CH_2 \qquad R_2C\text{=}CHR \qquad R_2C\text{=}CR_2$$
$$(\textbf{76}) \qquad\qquad (\textbf{81}) \qquad\qquad (\textbf{83})$$

be bound to a ring system as in biscyclohexylidene, pinene, camphene, dipentene, and similar hydrocarbons. In most cases, it was found[32] that in the cycloaddition of *N*-carbonylsulfamoyl chloride (**68**) to the olefin with formation of a β-lactam-*N*-sulfonyl chloride, the *N*-sulfonyl chloride group adds to the more highly branched carbon.

Electrophilic substituents diminish the reactivity of the olefin in contrast to the *N*-carbonylsulfamoyl chloride. Methallyl chlorides and methallyl cyanide do not react with *N*-carbonylsulfamoyl halides. Methallylalkyl-and aryl esters slowly react with **68** to give the corresponding β-lactam-*N*-sulfonyl chloride (**83** and **84**, respectively). β,β-Dimethylacrylic acid

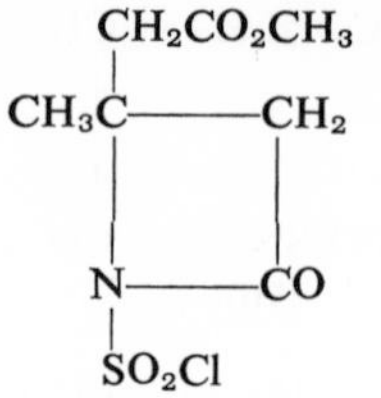

$$
\begin{array}{cc}
\text{CH}_2\text{CO}_2\text{CH}_3 & \text{CH}_2\text{OR} \\
\mid & \mid \\
\text{CH}_3\text{C}\!\!-\!\!\!-\!\!\!-\!\!\text{CH}_2 & \text{CH}_3\text{C}\!\!-\!\!\!-\!\!\!-\!\!\text{CH}_2 \\
\mid \quad\quad \mid & \mid \quad\quad \mid \\
\text{N}\!\!-\!\!\!-\!\!\!-\!\!\text{CO} & \text{N}\!\!-\!\!\!-\!\!\!-\!\!\text{CO} \\
\mid & \mid \\
\text{SO}_2\text{Cl} & \text{SO}_2\text{Cl} \\
(83) & (84,\ \text{R} = \text{CH}_3,\ \text{C}_6\text{H}_5)
\end{array}
$$

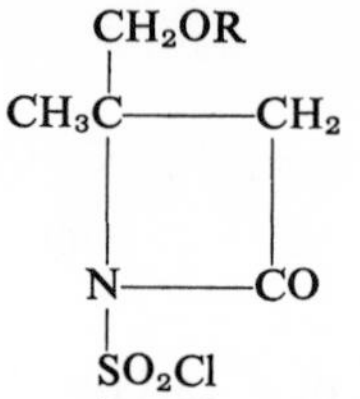

ester and methacrylic acid ester do not react with $N$-carbonylsulfamoyl chloride.[32]

Various aromatic olefins such as styrene (85) were found to react much slower than isobutylene (77) with $N$-carbonylsulfamoyl chloride (68), giving the $\beta$-lactam-$N$-sulfonyl chloride (71). Analogously, 4-chlorostyrene

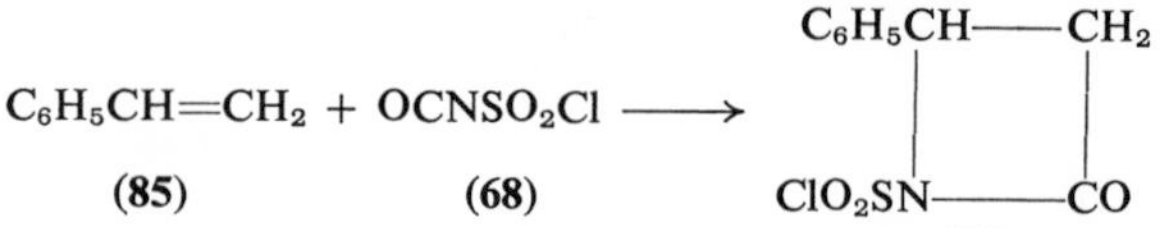

$$
\begin{array}{c}
\text{C}_6\text{H}_5\text{CH}\!\!=\!\!\text{CH}_2 + \text{OCNSO}_2\text{Cl} \longrightarrow
\quad
\begin{array}{c}
\text{C}_6\text{H}_5\text{CH}\!\!-\!\!\!-\!\!\!-\!\!\text{CH}_2 \\
\mid \quad\quad\quad \mid \\
\text{ClO}_2\text{SN}\!\!-\!\!\!-\!\!\!-\!\!\text{CO}
\end{array}
\\
\quad (85) \quad\quad\quad\quad (68) \quad\quad\quad\quad\quad (71)
\end{array}
$$

and $\beta$-methylstyrene react with $N$-carbonylsulfamoyl chloride, while 4-nitrostyrene and 2,4-dichlorostyrene do not react (Table 6-B).[32]

The free $\beta$-lactams (87) were obtained by reduction of the $\beta$-lactam-$N$-sulfonyl halides in the presence of thiophenol (86) and pyridine (17) (Table 7),[32] as is shown here.

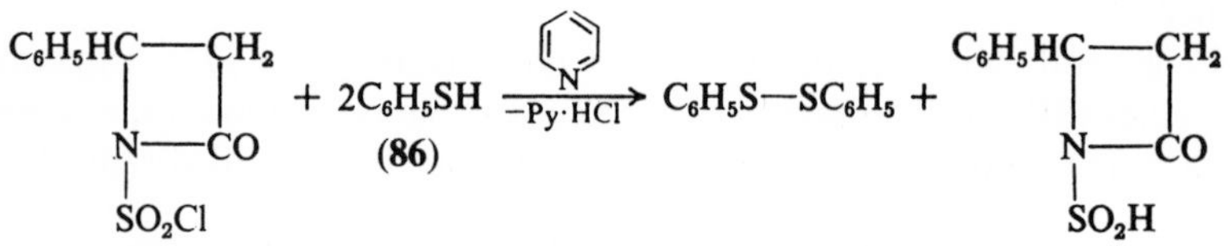

$$
\begin{array}{c}
\text{C}_6\text{H}_5\text{HC}\!\!-\!\!\!-\!\!\!-\!\!\text{CH}_2 \\
\mid \quad\quad\quad \mid \\
\text{N}\!\!-\!\!\!-\!\!\text{CO} \\
\mid \\
\text{SO}_2\text{Cl} \\
(71)
\end{array}
+ 2\text{C}_6\text{H}_5\text{SH} \xrightarrow[-\text{Py}\cdot\text{HCl}]{} \text{C}_6\text{H}_5\text{S}\!\!-\!\!\text{SC}_6\text{H}_5 +
\begin{array}{c}
\text{C}_6\text{H}_5\text{HC}\!\!-\!\!\!-\!\!\!-\!\!\text{CH}_2 \\
\mid \quad\quad\quad \mid \\
\text{N}\!\!-\!\!\text{CO} \\
\mid \\
\text{SO}_2\text{H}
\end{array}
$$

$$
\begin{array}{ccc}
\text{C}_6\text{H}_5\text{CH}\!\!-\!\!\!-\!\!\!-\!\!\text{CH}_2 & & \text{C}_6\text{H}_5\text{CH}\!\!-\!\!\!-\!\!\!-\!\!\text{CH}_2 \\
\mid \quad\quad\quad \mid & \longrightarrow & \mid \quad\quad\quad \mid \\
\text{N}\!\!-\!\!\!-\!\!\text{CO} & & \text{NH}\!\!-\!\!\!-\!\!\text{CO} \\
\mid & & (87) \\
\text{SO}_2\text{H} & &
\end{array}
$$

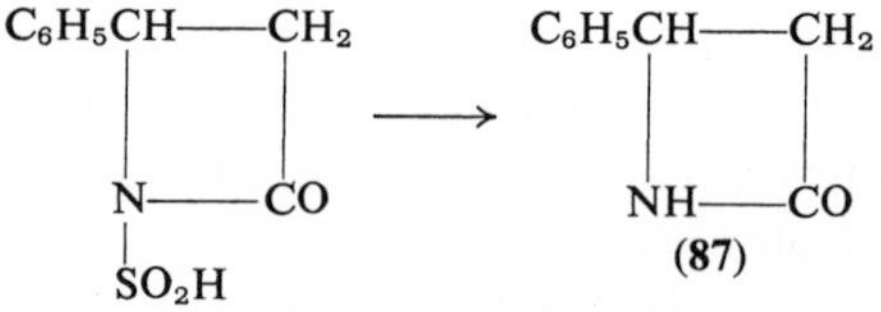

In a study of the reaction of $N$-carbonylsulfamoyl chloride (68) on dienes, such as 1-methylbutadiene (88), Hoffmann and Diehr[37] found that the only identified product was the $N$-carbonylsulfamoyl chloride (89).

$$CH_3CH{=}CHCH{=}CH_2 + OCNSO_2Cl \longrightarrow$$
$$\text{(88)} \qquad\qquad \text{(68)}$$

$$CH_3CH{=}CHCH{=}CHC\overset{\overset{O}{\|}}{{}}{-}NHSO_2Cl$$
$$\text{(89)}$$

Isoprene and 1,3- and 2,3-dimethylbutadiene were found to react similarly. If the reactions were run at 0°C, however, $\beta$-lactam-$N$-sulfonyl chlorides (Table 6-B) were formed, the yields being extremely dependent on the concentration and the reaction time. Addition of $N$-carbonylsulfamoyl chloride (68) to 1,4-dimethylbutadiene (90) leads to either of two cycloaddition products (91 or 92).[36, 37]

$$\begin{array}{cc}
C_3H_5CH{-}{-}CHCH_3 & C_3H_5CH{-}{-}CHCH_3 \\
| \qquad\qquad | & | \qquad\qquad | \\
N{-}{-}{-}CO & OC{-}{-}{-}NSO_2Cl \\
| & \\
SO_2Cl & \text{(92)} \\
\text{(91)} &
\end{array}$$

In conclusion, Nieuwenhuis and Arens[65] reported that ethylene was eliminated from 1-ethoxy-1-alkynes (93) by heating at 130°, producing ketenes (94) which were not isolable but which readily reacted with the unchanged ethoxyalkyne forming cyclobutenone ethers (95). The formation

$$RC{\equiv}COC_2H_5 \xrightarrow{130°} C_2H_4 + [RCH{=}C{=}O]$$
$$\text{(93)} \qquad\qquad\qquad \text{(94)}$$

$$94 + 93 \longrightarrow \begin{array}{c} RCH{-}{-}CO \\ | \qquad\quad | \\ C_2H_5OC{=\!=\!=}CR \\ \text{(95)} \end{array}$$

of anilides (97) by heating aniline (96) with ethoxyalkynes (93)[25, 65, 72] had previously indicated that the intermediate ketene (94) could be trapped by aniline before it reacted with unchanged ethoxyalkyne, as above. Leusen

$$RC{\equiv}COC_2H_5 \xrightarrow{130°} [RCH{=}C{=}O] \xrightarrow{C_6H_5NH_2} RCH_2CONHC_6H_5$$
$$\text{(93)} \qquad\qquad\quad \text{(94)} \qquad\qquad\qquad \text{(97)}$$

and Arens[61] found that the intermediate ketene (94) could also be trapped by heating the ethoxyalkyne (93) in the presence of an imine (98) resulting in the formation of a $\beta$-lactam (99) (Table 8).

$$RC{\equiv}COC_2H_5 \xrightarrow{130°} [RCH{=}C{=}O]$$
$$\text{(93)} \qquad\qquad\quad \text{(94)}$$

$$\textbf{(94)} + R'C_6H_5C{=}NC_6H_5 \longrightarrow \begin{array}{ccc} RCH\!\!&\!\!\!\!\!\!\!\!\!\!\!\!C(C_6H_5)R' \\ | & | \\ OC\!\!&\!\!\!\!\!\!\!\!\!\!\!\!NC_6H_5 \end{array}$$

$$\textbf{(98)} \qquad\qquad\qquad \textbf{(99)}$$

$$(R = CH_3,\ Am)\quad (R' = H,\ C_6H_5)\quad \textbf{(99)}$$

The reactions with imines (98) were promoted by working at low concentrations of ethoxyalkyne (93) by adding a xylene solution of the latter dropwise into a boiling solution of the imine in xylene. At this temperature a ready elimination of ethylene occurred and the ketene (94) was trapped as soon as it was formed.[61] The $\beta$-lactam structures were determined by the infrared absorption spectra showing strong carbonyl absorption bands at 1775 and 1750 cm$^{-1}$ characteristic of $\beta$-lactams.[83,124]

Pyrolysis of the $\beta$-lactams (99) led to phenylisocyanate (46) and an unsaturated compound (100); such decompositions are characteristic of $\beta$-lactams.[98]

$$\begin{array}{ccc} R\!\!\searrow \\ \quad C\!\!&\!\!\!\!\!\!\!\!\!\!CO \\ H\!\!\nearrow & \\ R'\!\!-\!\!C\!\!&\!\!\!\!\!\!\!\!\!\!N\!\!-\!\!C_6H_5 \\ |\\ C_6H_5 \end{array} \xrightarrow{\Delta} C_6H_5N{=}C{=}O + RCH{=}C(C_6H_5)R'$$

$$\textbf{(99)} \qquad\qquad\qquad \textbf{(46)} \qquad\qquad \textbf{(100)}$$

Recently, 2-azetidinethiones (102) were reported to have been prepared by treating the $\beta$-lactam (101) with diphosphorus pentasulfide.[92]

$$\begin{array}{cc} R^1 & O \\ R^2\!\!-\!\!\rlap{\phantom{x}}& \\ R^3\!\!-\!\!\rlap{\phantom{x}}&\!\!-\!\!NR \\ H \end{array} + P_2S_5 \longrightarrow \begin{array}{cc} R^1 & S \\ R^2\!\!-\!\!\rlap{\phantom{x}}& \\ R^3\!\!-\!\!\rlap{\phantom{x}}&\!\!-\!\!NR \\ H \end{array}$$

$\beta$-Lactam syntheses have been reviewed by Sheehan and Corey.[82] See also the further tabulations of $\beta$-lactams according to methods of preparation other than cycloaddition reactions:

I. Cyclization of $\beta$-amino acid derivatives.[9,10,12,14,26,41,42,54,55,84,105,116,118-123]

II. Imines with $\alpha$-bromoesters and zinc.[30,43,49]

III. Imines, acid chlorides and tertiary amines.[5,6,7,19,23,27,48,64,80,81,85,88-91,114,115,118]

IV. Dehydration of $N$-$\alpha$-haloacylaminomalonic esters.[78,79]

## Table 1

Preparation of $\beta$-Lactams from Ketenes and Imines

$$\underset{R^2}{\overset{R^1}{\diagdown}}C=C=O + \underset{R^4}{\overset{R^3}{\diagdown}}C=N-R^5 \longrightarrow \text{(β-lactam)}$$

| $R^1$ | $R^2$ | $R^3$ | $R^4$ | $R^5$ | MP (°C) | Yield (%) | Ref. |
|---|---|---|---|---|---|---|---|
| H | H | $C_6H_5$ | H | $C_6H_5$ | 153–154 155 | 39 | 99 |
| $CH_3$ | $CH_3$ | $C_6H_5$ | H | $C_6H_5CH_2$ | 36 | 10 | 105 |
| $CH_3$ | $CH_3$ | $C_6H_5$ | H | $C_6H_5$ | 148–149 | — | 104 |
| $C_2H_5$ | $C_2H_5$ | $C_6H_5$ | H | $C_6H_5$ | 72–73 | 82 | 108 |
| $C_2H_5O_2C$ | $C_2H_5$ | $C_6H_5$ | H | $C_6H_5$ | 109–110 | 1 | 99 |
| $CH_3O_2C$ | $C_6H_5$ | $C_6H_5$ | H | $C_6H_5$ | 158–159 | 15 | 99 |
| $C_6H_5$ | $C_6H_5$ | $C_6H_5$ | H | $C_6H_5$ | 159–160 | 72 | 96, 104 |
| $C_6H_5$ | $C_6H_5$ | $C_6H_5CH{=}CH$ | H | $C_6H_5$ | 172 | 70 | 93 |
| $C_6H_5$ | $CH_3$ | $C_6H_5$ | H | $C_6H_5$ | 125–126 | — | 110 |
| $C_6H_5CH_2$ | $C_6H_5CH_2$ | $C_6H_5$ | H | $C_6H_5$ | 121 | — | 112 |
| $C_6H_5O$ | $C_2H_5$ | $C_6H_5$ | $C_6H_5$ | $C_6H_5$ | 164 | — | 111 |
| $C_6H_5O$ | $C_6H_5O$ | $C_6H_5$ | H | $C_6H_5$ | 165 | — | 111 |
| $C_6H_5O$ | $C_6H_5O$ | $CH_3OC_6H_4$ | H | $C_6H_5$ | 143 | — | 111 |
| $C_6H_5$ | $C_6H_5$ | $C_6H_5$ | $C_6H_5$ | $p\text{-}(CH_3)_2NC_6H_4$ | > 200 | 100 | 97 |
| $CH_3$ | $CH_3$ | $p\text{-}(CH_3)_2NC_6H_4$ | H | $C_6H_5$ | — | — | 100 |
| $CH_3$ | $CH_3$ | $C_6H_5$ | H | $C_6H_5(C_6H_5CH_2)CH$ | — | — | 100 |
| $CH_3$ | $CH_3$ | $C_6H_5CH{=}CH$ | H | $C_6H_5$ | — | — | 100 |
| $CH_3$ | $CH_3$ | $C_6H_5$ | H | $p\text{-}NO_2C_6H_4$ | — | — | 100 |
| $C_6H_5$ | $C_6H_5$ | $C_6H_5$ | $C_6H_5$ | $C_6H_5$ | 191 | 84 | 100 |
| $CH_3$ | $CH_3$ | $C_6H_5$ | $C_6H_5$ | $C_6H_5$ | — | — | 100 |
| $CH_3$ | $CH_3$ | $CH_3$ | $C_6H_5$ | $C_6H_5$ | — | — | 100 |
| $CH_3$ | $C_6H_5$ | $C_6H_5$ | $C_6H_5$ | $C_6H_5$ | — | — | 100 |
| $O{-}(C_6H_4)_2$ | | $C_6H_5$ | $C_6H_5$ | $C_6H_5$ | — | — | 100 |
| $CH_3$ | $CH_3$ | $C_6H_5$ | $CH_3S$ | $C_6H_5$ | 78–80 | 60 | 40 |
| $C_6H_5$ | $C_6H_5$ | $C_6H_5$ | H | $p\text{-}NO_2C_6H_4CH_2$ | 133–134 | — | 47 |
| $C_6H_5$ | $C_6H_5$ | $C_6H_5$ | $C_6H_5$ | $(C_6H_5)_2CH$ | 188–190 | 80 | 74 |
| $C_6H_5$ | $C_6H_5$ | $C_6H_5$ | (fluorenyl, O / $NCOC_6H_5$) | | — | — | 24 |

**Table 2**

Preparation of $\beta$-Lactams from Diazocarbonyl Compounds and Imines

| R¹ | R² | R³ | R⁴ | R⁵ | MP (°C) | Yield (%) | Ref. |
|---|---|---|---|---|---|---|---|
| $C_6H_5$ | $C_6H_5$ | $C_6H_5$ | $C_6H_5$ | $C_6H_5$ | 190–191 | 72 | 103 |
| H | H | H | H | H | 162 | 71 | 53 |
| $C_6H_5$ | $C_6H_5$ | $C_6H_5$ | H | $C_6H_5$ | 161–162 | 71 | 53, 93 |
| $C_6H_5$ | $C_6H_5$ | $C_6H_5$ | H | $C_6H_5CH_2$ | 85–86 | 46 | 53 |
| $C_6H_5$ | $C_6H_5$ | $o\text{-}CH_3C_6H_4$ | H | $C_6H_5$ | 168 | 52 | 71 |
| $C_6H_5$ | $C_6H_5$ | $m\text{-}CH_3C_6H_4$ | H | $C_6H_5$ | 107.5–108 | 63 | 71 |
| $C_6H_5$ | $C_6H_5$ | $p\text{-}CH_3C_6H_4$ | H | $C_6H_5$ | 171 | 72 | 71 |
| $C_6H_5$ | $C_6H_5$ | $o\text{-}CH_3OC_6H_4$ | H | $C_6H_5$ | 236 | 30 | 71 |
| $C_6H_5$ | $C_6H_5$ | $m\text{-}CH_3OC_6H_4$ | H | $C_6H_5$ | 204 | 21 | 71 |
| $C_6H_5$ | $C_6H_5$ | $m\text{-}ClC_6H_4$ | H | $C_6H_5$ | 176.5–177 | 71 | 71 |
| $C_6H_5$ | $C_6H_5$ | $p\text{-}(CH_3)_2NC_6H_4$ | H | $C_6H_5$ | 173.5–174 | 67 | 71 |
| $C_6H_5$ | $C_6H_5$ | $C_6H_5$ | H | $o\text{-}CH_3C_6H_4$ | 165 | 72 | 71 |
| $C_6H_5$ | $C_6H_5$ | $C_6H_5$ | H | $m\text{-}CH_3C_6H_4$ | 166.5 | 69 | 71 |
| $C_6H_5$ | $C_6H_5$ | $C_6H_5$ | H | $p\text{-}CH_3C_6H_4$ | 169 | 21 | 71 |
| $C_6H_5$ | $C_6H_5$ | $C_6H_5$ | H | $o\text{-}CH_3OC_6H_4$ | 150 | 55 | 71 |
| $C_6H_5$ | $C_6H_5$ | $C_6H_5$ | H | $p\text{-}CH_3OC_6H_4$ | 204 | 16 | 71 |
| $C_6H_5$ | $C_6H_5$ | $C_6H_5$ | H | $m\text{-}ClC_6H_4$ | 183 | 98 | 71 |
| $C_6H_5$ | H | $C_6H_5$ | $C_6H_5$ | $C_6H_5$ | 146–147 | 76 | 53 |
|  |  |  |  |  | 153 | 42 | 71 |
| $C_6H_5$ | H | $C_6H_5$ | H | $C_6H_5$ | 134 | 74 | 53 |
|  |  |  |  |  | 133 | 35 | 71 |
| $C_6H_5$ | H | $p\text{-}NO_2C_6H_4$ | H | $C_6H_5$ | 148–149 | 78 | 53 |
| $C_6H_5$ | H | $p\text{-}(CH_3)_2NC_6H_4$ | H | $C_6H_5$ | 153 | 90 | 71 |
|  |  |  |  |  | 157–158 | 79 | 53 |
| $C_6H_5$ | H | $C_6H_5$ | H | $p\text{-}(CH_3)_2NC_6H_4$ | 176–177 | 70 | 53 |
| $C_6H_5$ | H | $p\text{-}NO_2C_6H_4$ | H | $C_6H_5CH_2$ | 140–141 | 65 | 53 |
| $C_6H_5$ | H | $\alpha\text{-}(C_5H_4N)$ | H | $C_6H_5$ | 162–163 | 56 | 53 |
| $C_6H_5$ | H | $o\text{-}CH_3C_6H_4$ | H | $C_6H_5$ | 138 | 21 | 71 |
| $C_6H_5$ | H | $m\text{-}CH_3C_6H_4$ | H | $C_6H_5$ | 129 | 20 | 71 |
| $C_6H_5$ | H | $p\text{-}CH_3C_6H_4$ | H | $C_6H_5$ | 117.5–118 | 14 | 71 |
| $C_6H_5$ | H | $o\text{-}CH_3OC_6H_4$ | H | $C_6H_5$ | 124 | 25 | 71 |
| $C_6H_5$ | H | $m\text{-}CH_3OC_6H_4$ | H | $C_6H_5$ | 136 | 29 | 71 |
| $C_6H_5$ | H | $m\text{-}ClC_6H_4$ | H | $C_6H_5$ | 131 | 13.5 | 71 |
| $C_6H_5$ | H | $C_6H_5$ | H | $o\text{-}CH_3C_6H_4$ | 143 | 12 | 71 |
| $C_6H_5$ | H | $C_6H_5$ | H | $m\text{-}CH_3C_6H_4$ | 133 | 15 | 71 |

*(continued)*

**Table 2** (*continued*)

| R$^1$ | R$^2$ | R$^3$ | R$^4$ | R$^5$ | MP (°C) | Yield (%) | Ref. |
|---|---|---|---|---|---|---|---|
| C$_6$H$_5$ | H | C$_6$H$_5$ | H | $p$-CH$_3$C$_6$H$_4$ | 180 | 15 | 71 |
| C$_6$H$_5$ | H | C$_6$H$_5$ | H | $o$-CH$_3$OC$_6$H$_4$ | 139 | 5 | 71 |
| C$_6$H$_5$ | H | C$_6$H$_5$ | H | $p$-CH$_3$OC$_6$H$_4$ | 156 | 19 | 71 |
| C$_6$H$_5$ | H | C$_6$H$_5$ | H | $m$-ClC$_6$H$_4$ | 123 | 28 | 71 |
| H | H | $o$-CH$_3$C$_6$H$_4$ | H | C$_6$H$_5$ | 134 | 11.5 | 71 |
| H | H | $m$-CH$_3$C$_6$H$_4$ | H | C$_6$H$_5$ | 87 | 12 | 71 |
| H | H | $p$-CH$_3$C$_6$H$_4$ | H | C$_6$H$_5$ | 109 | 22 | 71 |
| H | H | $o$-CH$_3$OC$_6$H$_4$ | H | C$_6$H$_5$ | 108 | 39 | 71 |
| H | H | $m$-CH$_3$OC$_6$H$_4$ | H | C$_6$H$_5$ | 96 | 16 | 71 |
| H | H | $m$-ClC$_6$H$_4$ | H | C$_6$H$_5$ | 148 | 32 | 71 |
| H | H | $p$-(CH$_3$)$_2$NC$_6$H$_4$ | H | C$_6$H$_5$ | 155.5 | 62 | 71 |
| H | H | C$_6$H$_5$ | H | $o$-CH$_3$C$_6$H$_4$ | 107 | 7 | 71 |
| H | H | C$_6$H$_5$ | H | $m$-CH$_3$C$_6$H$_4$ | 91 | 18 | 71 |
| H | H | C$_6$H$_5$ | H | $p$-CH$_3$C$_6$H$_4$ | 126 | 13 | 71 |
| H | H | C$_6$H$_5$ | H | $p$-CH$_3$OC$_6$H$_4$ | 86 | 19 | 71 |
| H | H | C$_6$H$_5$ | H | $m$-ClC$_6$H$_4$ | 97 | 34 | 71 |
| $p$-CH$_3$OC$_6$H$_4$ | H | C$_6$H$_5$ | H | C$_6$H$_5$ | 199 | 65 | 53 |
| $p$-CH$_3$OC$_6$H$_4$ | H | C$_6$H$_5$ | H | C$_6$H$_5$CH$_2$ | 75–76 | 36 | 53 |
| $p$-ClC$_6$H$_4$ | H | C$_6$H$_5$ | H | C$_6$H$_5$ | 175–176 | 54 | 53 |
| CH$_3$ | H | C$_6$H$_5$ | C$_6$H$_5$ | C$_6$H$_5$ | 122–123 | 48 | 53 |
| CH$_3$ | H | C$_6$H$_5$ | H | C$_6$H$_5$ | 113 | 47 | 30, 53 |
| C$_2$H$_5$ | H | C$_6$H$_5$ | H | C$_6$H$_5$ | 122–123 | 24 | 53 |
| C$_6$H$_5$ | CH$_3$O$_2$C C$_6$H$_5$ | C$_6$H$_5$ | C$_6$H$_5$ | C$_6$H$_5$ | 194–195 | 35 | 53 |
| C$_6$H$_5$ | CH$_3$O$_2$C C$_6$H$_5$ | C$_6$H$_5$ | H | C$_6$H$_5$ | 158–159 | 5 | 95 |
|  |  |  |  |  | 159 | 14 | 53 |

**Table 3**

Miscellaneous Preparations of $\beta$-Lactams via Cycloaddition Reactions

A. Nitroso Compounds and Diphenylketene

| Nitroso compound | Cycloadduct | MP (°C) | Yield (%) | Ref. |
|---|---|---|---|---|
| $p$-NOC$_6$H$_4$N(CH$_3$)$_2$ | (C$_6$H$_5$)$_2$ ⎤O / (C$_6$H$_5$)$_2$⎦—NC$_6$H$_4$N(CH$_3$)$_2$-$p$ | 196 | 65 | 97 |

(*continued*)

**Table 3** (*continued*)

### A. Nitroso Compounds and Diphenylketene

| Nitroso compound | Cycloadduct | MP (°C) | Yield (%) | Ref. |
|---|---|---|---|---|
| $C_6H_5NO$ | 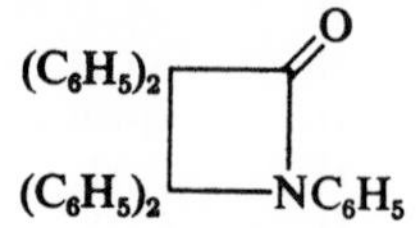 | 191 | —<br>1.8[a] | 97<br>77 |
| $p\text{-}CH_3OC_6H_4NO$ | 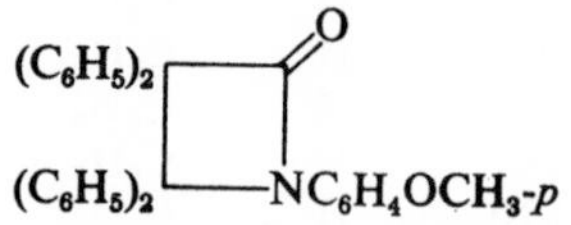 | 222–225 (dec) | — | 58 |

[a] The irradiation of nitrobenzene and tolane to form the $\beta$-lactam was postulated to have occurred by the addition of the intermediate, diphenylketene, and phenylisocyanate formed during the reaction.

### B. Diazomethane and Isocyanates

| Isocyanate | Cycloadduct | MP (°C) | Yield (%) | Ref. |
|---|---|---|---|---|
| $C_6H_5NCO$ | 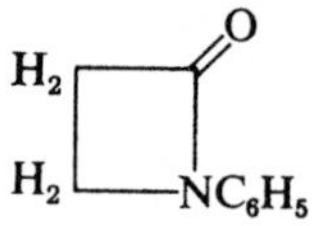 | 74–79 | 20 | 86 |
| $p\text{-}BrC_6H_4NCO$ | 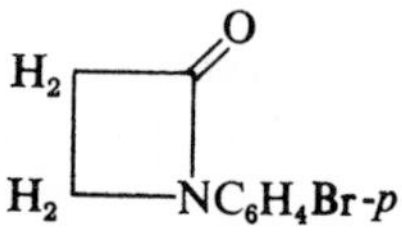 | 126–127 | 12 | 87 |

### C. Ketene Acetals or Diacetals and Phenylisocyanate

| Ketene acetal | Cycloadduct | MP, °C (BP, °C/mm) | Yield (%) | Ref. |
|---|---|---|---|---|
| $C_6H_5CH{=}C(OCH_3)_2$ | 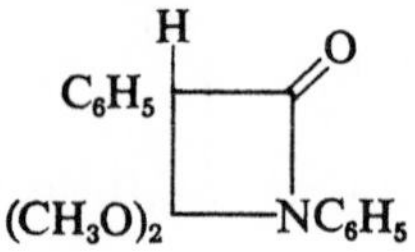 | 133–138 | — | 75 |

(*continued*)

**Table 3** (*continued*)

---

### C. Ketene Acetals or Diacetals and Phenylisocyanate

| Ketene acetal | Cycloadduct | MP, °C (BP, °C/mm) | Yield (%) | Ref. |
|---|---|---|---|---|
| $(CH_3)_2C=C(OCH_3)_2$ | 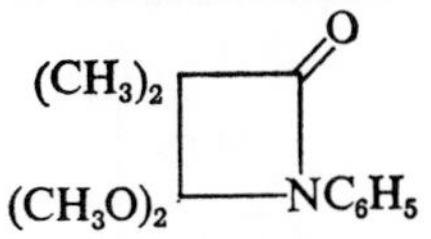 | 42–45 | 68 | 76 |
| $(CH_3O)_2C=C(OCH_3)_2$ | 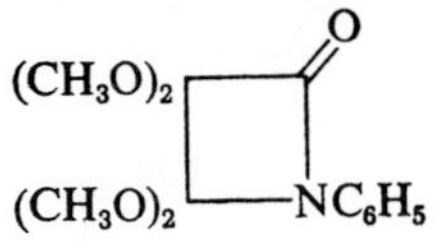 | 132/0.01 | 76 | 36 |

---

### D. Amino-Olefins and Isocyanates

| Amino-olefin | Isocyanate | Cycloadduct | MP (°C) | Yield (%) | Ref. |
|---|---|---|---|---|---|
| 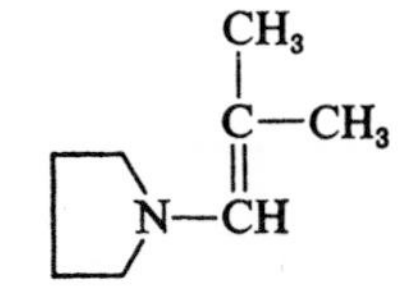 | $C_6H_5NCO$ | 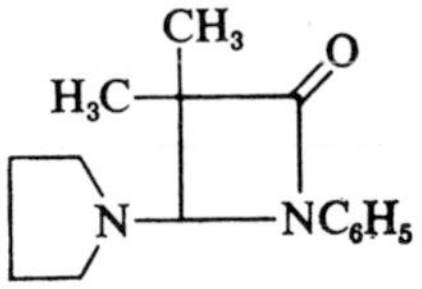 | 54 | 84 | 67 |
| 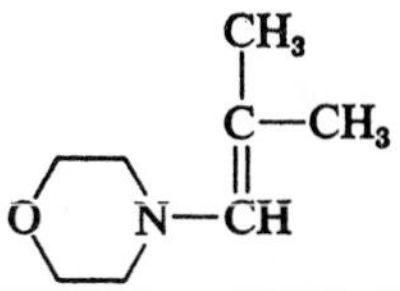 | $C_6H_5NCO$ | 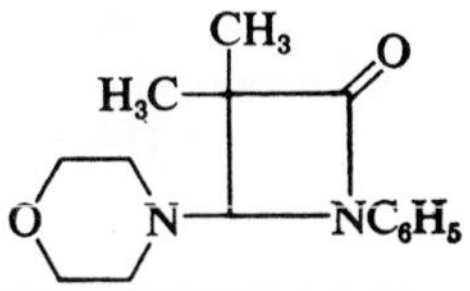 | 98–99 | 95 | 67 |
| 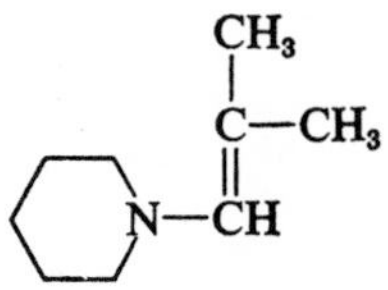 | $C_6H_5NCO$ | 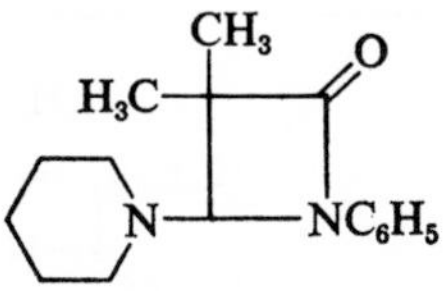 | 56 | 92 | 67 |
| 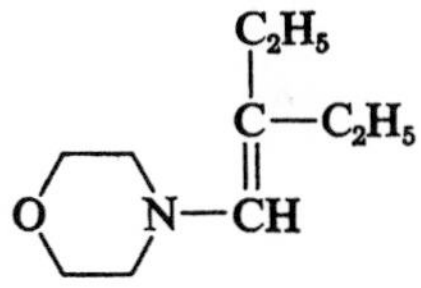 | $C_6H_5NCO$ | 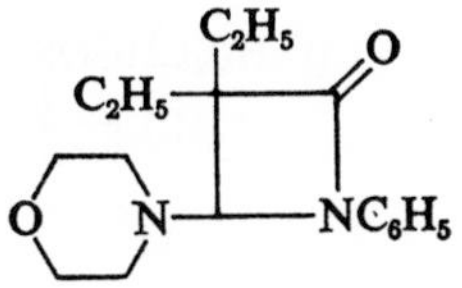 | 103–104 | 94 | 67 |

---

(*continued*)

**Table 3** (*continued*)

### D. Amino-Olefins and Isocyanates

| Amino-olefin | Isocyanate | Cycloadduct | MP (°C) | Yield (%) | Ref. |
|---|---|---|---|---|---|
| 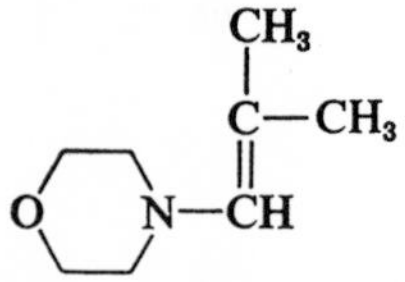 | $\alpha\text{-}C_{10}H_7NCO$ | 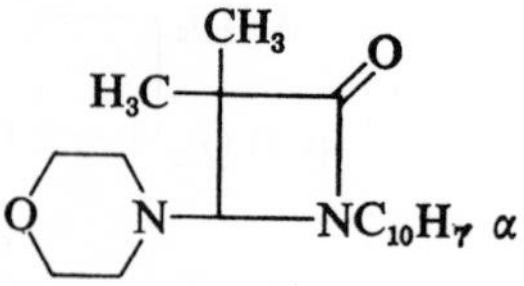 | 96 | 85 | 67 |
| $(CH_3)_2C=C-$ $N(CH_3)_2$ | $C_6H_5NCO$ | 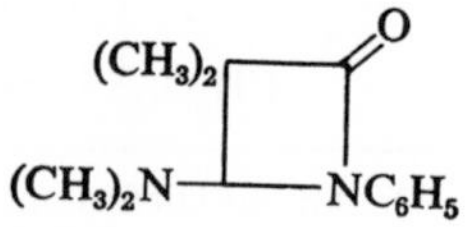 | — | 95 | 70 |
| $(CH_3)_2C=C-$ $N(C_6H_5)CH_3$ | $C_6H_5NCO$ | 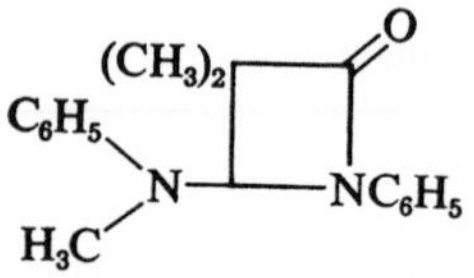 | 113–115 | 60–90 | 70 |

**Table 4**

Preparation of $\beta$-Lactam-Thiazolines from Diphenylketene and Thiazolines

| Thiazoline | Cycloadduct | MP (°C) | Yield (%) | Ref. |
|---|---|---|---|---|
| 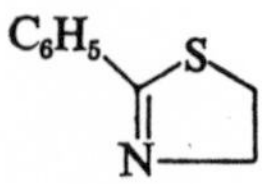 | 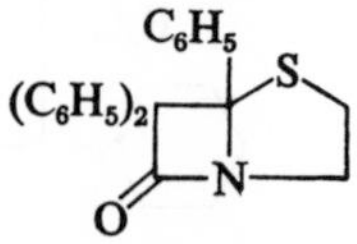 | 140–143 156–157 | 63 23 | 14 14 |
|  | 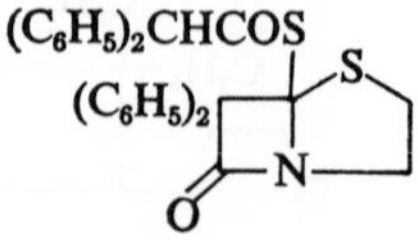 | 182 | 68 | 71 |

(*continued*)

**Table 4** (*continued*)

| Thiazoline | Cycloadduct | MP (°C) | Yield (%) | Ref. |
|---|---|---|---|---|
| 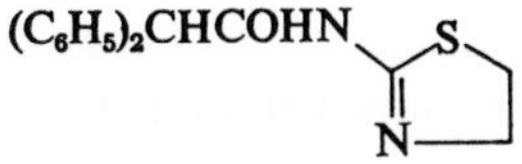 (C$_6$H$_5$)$_2$CHCOHN — thiazoline ring | 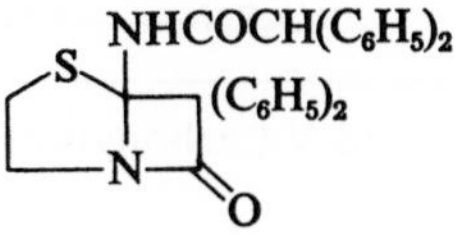 S NHCOCH(C$_6$H$_5$)$_2$ (C$_6$H$_5$)$_2$ bicyclic | 147 | 54 | 71 |
| 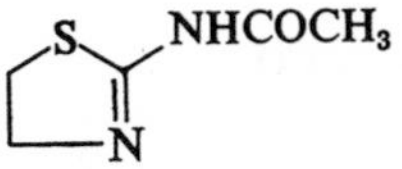 thiazoline NHCOCH$_3$ | 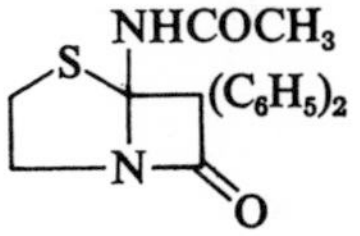 S NHCOCH$_3$ (C$_6$H$_5$)$_2$ bicyclic | 125 | 44 | 71 |

**Table 5**

4-Alkoxy-2-Azetidinones from the Cycloaddition of Enol Ethers and Sulfonylisocyanates [20-22]

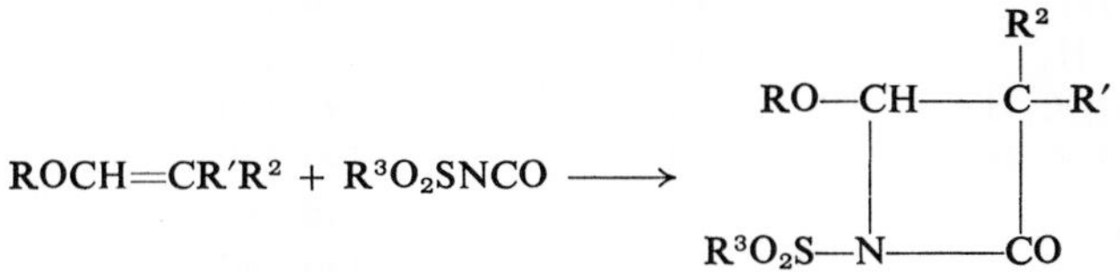

$$ROCH{=}CR'R^2 + R^3O_2SNCO \longrightarrow$$

$$
\begin{array}{c}
R^2 \\
| \\
RO{-}CH{-\!-\!-}C{-}R' \\
| \qquad\quad | \\
R^3O_2S{-}N{-\!-\!-\!-}CO
\end{array}
$$

| Enol ether | | Isocyanate | | MP (°C) | Yield (%) | CO-frequency (cm$^{-1}$) | |
|---|---|---|---|---|---|---|---|
| R | R' | R$^2$ | R$^3$ | | | | |
| C$_2$H$_5$ | H | H | p-CH$_3$C$_6$H$_4$ | 56–63 | quant. | 1725 | 1792 |
| i-C$_4$H$_9$ | H | H | | 68–72 | 84.2 | 1730 | 1800 |
| C$_2$H$_5$ | CH$_3$ | H | | 55–60 | 67.2 | 1720 | 1800 |
| C$_2$H$_5$ | C$_2$H$_5$ | H | | 76–78 | quant. | — | 1790 |
| C$_2$H$_5$ | CH$_3$ | CH$_3$ | | 54–56 | quant. | — | 1790 |
| —[CH$_2$]$_3$— | H | | | 65–70 | quant. | 1685 | 1790 |
| C$_2$H$_5$ | C$_2$H$_5$ | H | p-ClC$_6$H$_4$ | — | quant. | 1732 | 1806 |
| C$_2$H$_5$ | CH$_3$ | CH$_3$ | | — | quant. | — | 1800 |
| —[CH$_2$]$_3$— | H | | | 65–68 | 76.6 | 1720 | 1800 |

**Table 6**

Preparation of β-Lactam-N-Sulfonyl Halides

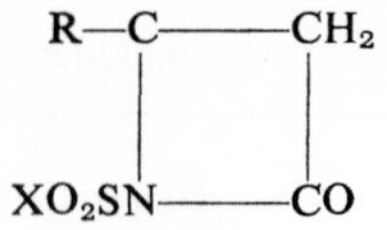

$$R-C\underline{\hspace{1cm}}CH_2$$

$$XO_2SN\underline{\hspace{1cm}}CO$$

A.  Reaction of Aldehydes and N-Carbonylsulfamoyl Halides with Ketene[32, 35]

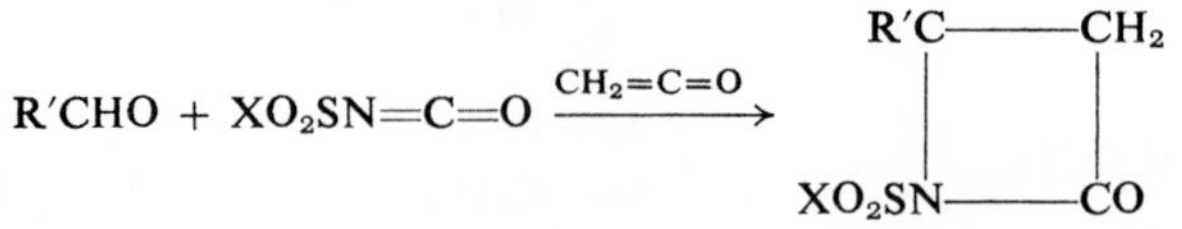

$$R'CHO + XO_2SN{=}C{=}O \xrightarrow{CH_2{=}C{=}O} \begin{array}{c} R'C\underline{\hspace{1cm}}CH_2 \\ \\ XO_2SN\underline{\hspace{1cm}}CO \end{array}$$

| $R^1$ | X | MP (°C) | Yield (%) |
|---|---|---|---|
| 2,4-Cl$_2$C$_6$H$_3$ | Cl | 105–106 | 80 |
| C$_6$H$_5$ | Cl | 90 | 50 |
|  |  | 97–98 |  |
| C$_6$H$_5$CH=CH | Cl | 117–118 | — |
| C$_6$H$_5$ | F | 59 | 80 |
| 2-NO$_2$C$_6$H$_4$ | Cl | 117–122 | — |
| 4-NO$_2$C$_6$H$_4$ | Cl | 115–117 | — |
| 3-BrC$_6$H$_4$ | Cl | 79–80 | — |
| 2,6-Cl$_2$C$_6$H$_3$ | Cl | 116–117 | — |
| 3-CH$_3$OC$_6$H$_4$ | Cl | 85–87 | — |
| 4,3-Cl(NO$_2$)C$_6$H$_3$ | Cl | 96–100 | — |
| 2,5-Cl(NO$_2$)C$_6$H$_3$ | Cl | 140–148 (dec) | — |
|  |  | 130–140 (dec) |  |
| 3,6-Cl(NO$_2$)C$_6$H$_3$ | Cl | 130–140 (dec) | — |
| a | Cl | 160–180 (dec) | — |
| 3-NO$_2$C$_6$H$_4$ | Cl | 136–137 (dec) | — |

*(continued)*

a The aldehyde is p-C$_6$H$_4$(CHO)$_2$ which forms the β-lactam-N-sulfonyl halide:

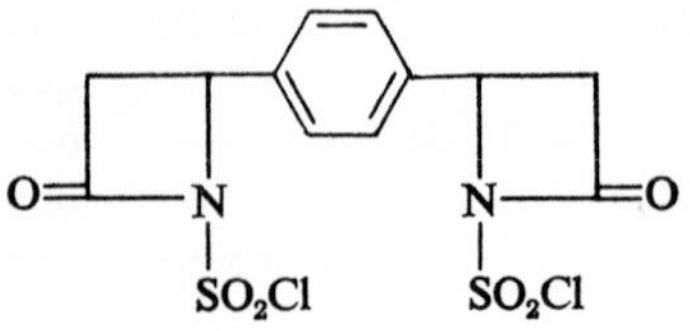

**Table 6** (*continued*)

B. Reactions of Olefins with *N*-Carbonylsulfamoyl Halides

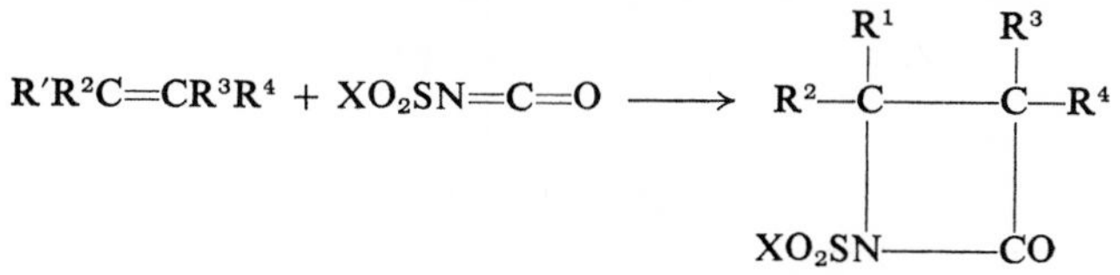

$$R'R^2C{=}CR^3R^4 + XO_2SN{=}C{=}O \longrightarrow \begin{array}{cc} R^1 & R^3 \\ R^2{-}C{-\!\!\!-\!\!\!-\!\!\!-}C{-}R^4 \\ \\ XO_2SN{-\!\!\!-\!\!\!-\!\!\!-}CO \end{array}$$

| $R^1$ | $R^2$ | $R^3$ | $R^4$ | X | MP (°C) | Yield (%) | Ref. |
|---|---|---|---|---|---|---|---|
| CH$_3$ | CH$_3$ | H | H | Cl | 77–78 | 70 | 32 |
|  |  |  |  |  | 75–76 |  | 33 |
| CH$_3$ | CH$_3$ | H | H | F | 40 | — | 32, 34 |
| CH$_3$ | CH$_3$ | H | C(CH$_3$)$_3$ | Cl[a] | 71–72 | 50 | 32–34 |
|  |  |  |  |  | 65–66 | — |  |
| C$_6$H$_5$ | H | H | H | Cl | 89–90 (dec) | 80–85 | 32 |
|  |  |  |  |  | 90–91 | 90 | 33 |
| CH$_3$ | CH$_3$ | H | CH$_3$ | Cl | 45–46 | 80 | 32 |
| CH$_3$ | CH$_3$ | CH$_3$ | CH$_3$ | Cl | 66–67 | 100 | 32, 34 |
| CH$_3$ | CH$_3$ | CH$_3$ | CH$_3$ | F | 54–55 | — | 32 |
| C$_3$H$_7$ | CH$_3$ | H | H | Cl | 53–54 | 65 | 32 |
|  |  |  |  |  | 52 | — | 33 |
| bis(cyclohexylidene) |  |  |  | Cl | 90–91 | 100 | 32 |
| *p*-CH$_3$C$_6$H$_7$ | CH$_3$ | H | H | Cl | 125–127 (dec) | — | 32 |
| 4-ClC$_6$H$_4$ | H | H | H | Cl | 82–84 | — | 32 |
| CH$_3$CO$_2$CH$_2$ | CH$_3$ | H | H | Cl | — | — | 32 |
| C$_2$H$_5$ | C$_2$H$_5$ | H | H | Cl | — | 65 | 32 |
| CH$_3$CH=CH | H | H | H | Cl | — | — | 36, 37 |
| CH$_2$=CH | CH$_3$ | H | H | Cl | — | — | 36, 37 |
| CH$_3$CH=CH | H | H | CH$_3$ | Cl[a] | — | — | 11, 36, 37 |
| C$_4$H$_9$ | C$_2$H$_5$ | H | H | Cl | oil | — | 33 |

[a] Two isomers.

**Table 7**

Desulfonation of $\beta$-Lactam-$N$-Sulfonyl Halides to $\beta$-Lactams[32]

$$R^1-\underset{\underset{HN}{\overset{\overset{R^2}{|}}{C}}}{}\text{———}\underset{\underset{CO}{\overset{\overset{R^3}{|}}{C}}}{}-R^4$$

| $R^1$ | $R^2$ | $R^3$ | $R^4$ | MP (BP) | $n_D^{20}$ | $d_0^{20}$ |
|---|---|---|---|---|---|---|
| **A. From Olefinic Compounds** | | | | | | |
| $CH_3$ | $C_2H_5$ | H | H | 78/0.2 | 1.4570 | — |
| $CH_3$ | $CH_3$ | $CH_3$ | H | 74–75/0.5 | 1.4515 | 0.956 |
| $C_2H_5$ | $C_2H_5$ | H | H | 95/0.7 | — | — |
| $CH_3$ | $n$-$C_3H_7$ | H | H | 80/0.3 | 1.4565 | — |
| $CH_3$ | $(CH_3)_2CH$ | H | H | 77/0.3 | 1.4590 | — |
| $CH_3$ | $CH_3$ | $CH_3$ | $CH_3$ | 104 | — | — |
| $C_2H_5$ | $n$-$C_4H_9$ | H | H | 108/0.8 | 1.4625 | — |
| $CH_3$ | $(CH_3)_3CCH_2$ | H | H | 108/0.1 | 1.4639 | — |
| $CH_3$ | $CH_3$ | $(CH_3)_3C$ | H | 76 (subl.) | — | — |
| $CH_3OCH_2$ | $CH_3$ | H | H | 76–77/0.3 | 1.4601 | — |
| $C_6H_5OCH_2$ | $CH_3$ | H | H | 86 | — | — |
| $4$-$ClC_6H_4$ | H | H | H | 98–99 | — | — |
| Bis-$\beta$-lactam from dipentene | | | | 220–221 | — | — |
| $R^1$—$R^2$ or $R^3$—$R^4$ = —$[CH_2]_5$— from bis(cyclohexylidene) | | | | 221–222 | — | — |
| **B. From Aldehydes** | | | | | | |
| $CH_3$ | H | H | H | 50/0.1 | 1.4585 | — |
| $CH_3$ | H | $CH_3$ | $CH_3$ | 75/0.1 | 1.4520 | — |
| $(CH_3)_2CH$ | H | $CH_3$ | $CH_3$ | 90–91 | — | — |
| $3$-$BrC_6H_4$ | H | H | H | 101–102 | — | — |
| $2,4$-$Cl_2C_6H_3$ | H | H | H | 139–140 | — | — |
| $2,6$-$Cl_2C_6H_3$ | H | H | H | 143 | — | — |
| $3$-$CH_3OC_6H_4$ | H | H | H | 69–70 | — | — |
| $2$-$NO_2C_6H_4$ | H | H | H | 152–153 | — | — |
| $3$-$NO_2C_6H_4$ | H | H | H | 129 | — | — |
| $4$-$NO_2C_6H_4$ | H | H | H | 153–154 | — | — |
| $3,4$-$NO_2(Cl)C_6H_3$ | H | H | H | 125–126 | — | — |
| $3,6$-$NO_2(Cl)C_6H_3$ | H | H | H | 194–195 | — | — |
| $2,5$-$NO_2(Cl)C_6H_3$ | H | H | H | 190–191 | — | — |
| $C_6H_5$ | H | $CH_3$ | $CH_3$ | 104–105 | — | — |
| $1,4$-$C_6H_4$[a] | H | H | H | > 300 | — | — |

[a] Bis-$\beta$-lactam from terephthaldialdehyde.

## Table 8
### Preparation of β-Lactams from Acetylenic Ethers and Imines[61]

$$R^1C{\equiv}CR^2 + R^3R^4C{=}NR^5 \longrightarrow$$

| Ether | | Imine | | | | | |
|-------|-------|-------|-------|-------|---------|-------|-------|
| $R^1$ | $R^2$ | $R^3$ | $R^4$ | $R^5$ | MP (°C) | Yield (%) | IR (C=O) |
| $C_5H_{11}$ | $C_2H_5O$ | $C_6H_5$ | H | $C_6H_5$ | 107.5–108.5 | 47 | 1730 |
| $C_5H_{11}$ | $C_2H_5O$ | $C_6H_5$ | $C_6H_5$ | $C_6H_5$ | 80.5–81.5 | 81 | 1748 |
| $CH_3$ | $C_2H_5O$ | $C_6H_5$ | $C_6H_5$ | $C_6H_5$ | 126.5–127.5 | 55 | 1727 |
| $CH_3$ | $C_2H_5O$ | $C_6H_5$ | H | $C_6H_5$ | 112–112.5 | 27 | 1724 |

REFERENCES

1. J. A. Berson and W. M. Jones, *J. Am. Chem. Soc.*, **78**, 1625 (1956).
2. R. Blank, *Chem. Ber.*, **28**, 145 (1895).
3. A. K. Boese and S. Garratt, *Tetrahedron*, **19**, 85 (1963).
4. A. K. Boese, S. Garratt, and J. J. Pelosi, *J. Org. Chem.*, **28**, 730 (1963).
5. A. K. Boese, B. N. Ghosh-Mazumdar, and B. G. Chatterjee, *J. Am. Chem. Soc.*, **82**, 2382 (1960).
6. A. K. Boese and M. S. Manhas, *J. Org. Chem.*, **27**, 1244 (1962).
7. A. K. Boese, M. S. Manhas, and B. N. Ghosh-Mazumdar, *J. Org. Chem.*, **27**, 1458 (1962).
8. A. K. Boese and G. Mina, *J. Org. Chem.*, **30**, 812 (1965).
9. R. Breckpot, *Bull. Soc. Chim. Belg.*, **32**, 412 (1923); *Chem. Abstr.*, **18**, 1113 (1924).
10. Brit. Pat. 924,589 (1963).
11. W. Bruegel, *Einfuehrung in die Ultrarotspektroskopie*, 3rd ed., Dr. Dietrich Steinkopff, Darmstadt, 1962.
12. B. G. Chatterjee, P. N. Moza, and S. K. Roy, *J. Org. Chem.*, **28**, 1418 (1963).
13. G. Cignarella, G. F. Cristiani, and E. Testa, *Ann. Chem.*, **661**, 1817 (1963).
14. H. T. Clarke, J. R. Johnson, and R. Robinson, Eds., *The Chemistry of Penicillin*, Princeton University Press, Princeton, N.J., 1949.
15. H. T. Clarke, J. R. Johnson, and R. Robinson, *The Chemistry of Penicillin*, Princeton University Press, Princeton, N.J., 1949, p. 405.
16. H. T. Clarke, J. R. Johnson, and R. Robinson, *The Chemistry of Penicillin*, Princeton University Press, Princeton, N.J., 1949, pp. 975 ff.
17. H. T. Clarke, J. R. Johnson, and R. Robinson, *The Chemistry of Penicillin*, Princeton University Press, Princeton, N.J., 1949, p. 996.
18. A. H. Cook, *Quart. Rev.* (*London*), **2**, 203 (1948).
19. E. J. Corey, Ph.D. Thesis, Massachusetts Institute of Technology, 1951.
20. F. Effenberger and R. Gleiter, *Angew. Chem.*, **75**, 450 (1963).
21. F. Effenberger and R. Gleiter, *Angew. Chem. Intern. Ed. Engl.*, **3**, 142 (1964).

22. F. Effenberger and R. Gleiter, *Chem. Ber.*, **97**, 1576 (1964).
23. J. A. Erickson, Ph.D. Thesis, Massachusetts Institute of Technology, 1953.
24. E. Fahr, K. Doeppert, and E. Scheckenbach, *Angew. Chem.*, **75**, 670 (1963).
25. J. Ficini, *Bull. Soc. Chim. France*, **1954**, 1367.
26. L. Fontanella and E. Testa, *Ann. Chem.*, **616**, 148 (1958).
27. L. Fontanella and E. Testa, *Ann. Chem.*, **622**, 117 (1959).
28. P. Friedländer and S. Wleügel, *Chem. Ber.*, **16**, 2227 (1883).
29. P. G. Gassman and W. M. Hooker, *J. Am. Chem. Soc.*, **87**, 1079 (1965).
30. H. Gilman and M. Speeter, *J. Am. Chem. Soc.*, **65**, 2255 (1943).
31. I. Goldstern, *Chem. Ber.*, **28**, 1454 (1895).
32. R. Graf, *Ann. Chem.*, **661**, 111 (1963).
33. R. Graf, Ger. Pat. 941,847 (1956).
34. R. Graf, Ger. Pat. 1,119,277 (1961).
35. R. Graf, Ger. Pat. 1,134,993 (1962).
36. H. Hoffmann and H. J. Diehr, *Angew. Chem. Intern. Ed. Engl.*, **3**, 142 (1964).
37. H. Hoffmann and H. J. Diehr, *Tetrahedron Letters*, **1963**, 1875.
38. R. W. Hoffmann and H. Häuser, *Angew. Chem.*, **76**, 346 (1964); *Angew. Chem. Int. Ed. Engl.*, **3**, 380 (1964).
39. R. W. Hoffmann and H. Häuser, *Tetrahedron Letters*, **1964**, 197.
40. A. D. Holley and R. W. Holley, *J. Am. Chem. Soc.*, **73**, 3172 (1951).
41. R. W. Holley and A. D. Holley, *J. Am. Chem. Soc.*, **71**, 2124 (1949).
42. R. W. Holley and A. D. Holley, *J. Am. Chem. Soc.*, **71**, 2129 (1949).
43. A. Horeau, J. Jacques, H. B. Kagan, and Y-Heng Hsuan, *Compt. Rend.*, **255**, 717 (1962).
44. L. Horner and E. Spietschka, *Chem. Ber.*, **85**, 225 (1952).
45. L. Horner and E. Spietschka, *Chem. Ber.*, **89**, 2765 (1956).
46. L. Horner, E. Spietschka, and A. Gross, *Ann. Chem.*, **573**, 17 (1951).
47. C. K. Ingold and S. D. Weaver, *J. Chem. Soc.*, **127**, 378 (1925).
48. D. A. Johnson, Ph.D. Thesis, Massachusetts Institute of Technology, 1952.
49. H. B. Kagan, J. J. Basselier, and J. L. Luche, *Tetrahedron Letters*, **1964**, 941.
50. R. D. Kimbrough, Jr., *J. Org. Chem.*, **29**, 1242 (1964).
51. F. E. King, *J. Chem. Soc.*, **1949**, 1318.
52. W. Kirmse, *Angew. Chem.*, **71**, 537 (1959).
53. W. Kirmse and L. Horner, *Chem. Ber.*, **89**, 2759 (1956).
54. I. L. Knunyants and N. P. Gambaryan, *Izv. Akad. Nauk SSSR, Otd. Khim. Nauk*, **1955**, 1037; *Chem. Abstr.*, **50**, 11277 (1956).
55. I. L. Knunyants, E. E. Rytslin, and N. P. Gambaryan, *Izv. Akad. Nauk SSSR, Otd. Khim. Nauk*, **1960**, 527; *Chem. Abstr.*, **54**, 22467 (1960).
56. I. L. Knunyants, E. E. Rytslin, and N. P. Gambaryan, *Izv. Akad. Nauk SSSR, Otd. Khim. Nauk*, **1961**, 83; *Chem. Abstr.*, **55**, 18696 (1961).
57. P. Köber, Ph.D. Dissertation, Strassburg, 1909.
58. G. Kresze and A. Trede, *Tetrahedron*, **19**, 133 (1963).
59. R. N. Lacey, in *Advances in Organic Chemistry*, Vol. 2, R. A. Raphael, E. C. Taylor, and H. Wynberg, Eds., Interscience, New York, 1960, pp. 226 ff.
60. D. M. Lemal, E. P. Gosselink, and A. Ault, *Tetrahedron Letters*, **1964**, 579.
61. A. M. van Leusen and J. F. Arens, *Rec. Trav. Chim.*, **78**, 551 (1959).
62. H. Meyer, *Monatsh. Chem.*, **1900**, 965.
63. J. A. Moore, in *Compounds with Three- and Four-Membered Rings* (*The Chemistry of Heterocyclic Compounds*, Vol. 19, A. Weissberger, Ed.), Wiley, New York, 1964, pp. 885 ff.

64. B. J. R. Nicholaus, E. Bellasio, G. Pagani, and E. Testa, *Gazz. Chim. Ital.*, **93**, 618 (1963); *Chem. Abstr.*, **59**, 12735 (1963).

65. J. Nieuwenhuis and J. F. Arens, *Rec. Trav. Chim.*, **77**, 761 (1958).

66. G. Opitz, *Angew. Chem.*, **76**, 724 (1964); *Angew. Chem. Intern. Ed. Engl.*, **3**, 708 (1964).

67. G. Opitz and J. Köch, *Angew. Chem.*, **75**, 167 (1963).

68. H. v. Pechmann, *Chem. Ber.*, **28**, 861 (1895).

69. Penicillin Program Report, *Shell*, **14**, 215.

70. M. Perelman and S. A. Mizsak, *J. Am. Chem. Soc.*, **84**, 4988 (1962).

71. R. Pfleger and A. Jäger, *Chem. Ber.*, **90**, 2460 (1957).

72. J. C. W. Postma and J. F. Arens, *Rec. Trav. Chim.*, **75**, 1377 (1956).

73. G. Quadbeck, *Angew. Chem.*, **68**, 361 (1956).

74. A. Rahman, M. S. Khan, and M. C. Cabaleiro, *Chem. Ind. (London)*, **1962**, 1423.

75. R. Scarpati, *Rend. Accad. Sci. Fis. Mat., Soc. Nazl. Sci. Napoli*, **1958**, 25; *Chem. Abstr.*, **55**, 11423 (1961).

76. R. Scarpati, G. D. Re, and T. Maone, *Rend. Accad. Sci. Fis. Mat., Soc. Nazl. Sci. Napoli*, **1959**, 26; *Chem. Abstr.*, **55**, 11423 (1961).

77. M. L. Scheinbaum, *J. Org. Chem.*, **29**, 2200 (1964).

78. J. C. Sheehan and A. K. Boese, *J. Am. Chem. Soc.*, **72**, 5158 (1950).

79. J. C. Sheehan and A. K. Boese, *J. Am. Chem. Soc.*, **73**, 1761 (1951).

80. J. C. Sheehan, E. L. Buhle, E. J. Corey, G. D. Laubach, and J. J. Ryan, *J. Am. Chem. Soc.*, **72**, 3828 (1950).

81. J. C. Sheehan and E. J. Corey, *J. Am. Chem. Soc.*, **73**, 4756 (1951).

82. J. C. Sheehan and E. J. Corey, in *Organic Reactions*, Vol. 9, F. R. Adams, Ed., Wiley, New York, 1957, pp. 395 ff.

83. J. C. Sheehan and V. S. Frank, *J. Am. Chem. Soc.*, **71**, 1855 (1949).

84. J. C. Sheehan, K. R. Henery-Logan, and D. A. Johnson, *J. Am. Chem. Soc.*, **75**, 3292 (1953).

85. J. C. Sheehan, H. W. Hill, Jr., and E. L. Buhle, *J. Am. Chem. Soc.*, **73**, 4373 (1951).

86. J. C. Sheehan and P. T. Izzo, *J. Am. Chem. Soc.*, **70**, 1985 (1948).

87. J. C. Sheehan and P. T. Izzo, *J. Am. Chem. Soc.*, **71**, 4059 (1949).

88. J. C. Sheehan and G. D. Laubach, *J. Am. Chem. Soc.*, **73**, 4376 (1951).

89. J. C. Sheehan and G. D. Laubach, *J. Am. Chem. Soc.*, **73**, 4752 (1951).

90. J. C. Sheehan and J. J. Ryan, *J. Am. Chem. Soc.*, **73**, 1204 (1951).

91. J. C. Sheehan and J. J. Ryan, *J. Am. Chem. Soc.*, **73**, 4367 (1951).

92. A. Spasov, B. Panaiotova, and E. Golovinskii, *Dokl. Akad. Nauk SSSR*, **158**, 429 (1964).

93. H. Staudinger, *Ann. Chem.*, **356**, 51 (1907).

94. H. Staudinger, *Ann. Chem.*, **356**, 61 (1907).

94a. H. Staudinger, *Ann. Chem.*, **356**, 95 (1907).

95. H. Staudinger, *Chem. Ber.*, **40**, 1040 (1907).

96. H. Staudinger, *Chem. Ber.*, **40**, 1145 (1907).

97. H. Staudinger, *Chem. Ber.*, **44**, 375 (1911).

98. H. Staudinger, *Chem. Ber.*, **44**, 521 (1911).

99. H. Staudinger, *Chem. Ber.*, **50**, 1035 (1917).

100. H. Staudinger, *Die Ketene*, F. Enke, Stuttgart, 1912.

101. H. Staudinger, *Helv. Chim. Acta*, **5**, 103 (1922).

102. H. Staudinger and S. Jelagin, *Chem. Ber.*, **44**, 365 (1911).

103. H. Staudinger and S. Jelagin, *Chem. Ber.*, **44**, 373 (1911).

104. H. Staudinger and H. W. Klever, *Chem. Ber.*, **40**, 1149 (1907).
105. H. Staudinger, H. W. Klever, and P. Köber, *Ann. Chem.*, **374**, 1 (1910).
106. H. Staudinger, H. W. Klever, and P. Köber, *Ann. Chem.*, **374**, 13 (1910).
107. H. Staudinger and O. Kupfer, *Chem. Ber.*, **45**, 501 (1912).
108. H. Staudinger and J. Maier, *Ann. Chem.*, **401**, 292 (1913).
109. H. Staudinger and J. Meyer, *Helv. Chim. Acta*, **2**, 608 (1919).
110. H. Staudinger and L. Ruzicka, *Ann. Chem.*, **380**, 278 (1911).
111. H. Staudinger and H. Schneider, *Helv. Chim. Acta*, **6**, 304 (1923).
112. H. Staudinger, H. Schneider, P. Schotz, and P. M. Strong, *Helv. Chim. Acta*, **6**, 291 (1923).
113. H. Staudinger and E. Suter, *Chem. Ber.*, **53**, 1092 (1920).
114. G. Sunagawa and N. Yoshida, *Yakugaku Zasshi*, **82**, 826 (1962); *Chem. Abstr.*, **58**, 5649 (1963).
115. G. Sunagawa and N. Yoshida, Japan. Pat. 3580 (1960).
116. O. Süs, *Ann. Chem.*, **571**, 201 (1951).
117. E. Testa, *Farmaco Pavia Ed. Sci.*, **17**, 168 (1962); *Chem. Abstr.*, **57**, 9772 (1962).
118. E. Testa, F. Fava, and L. Fontanella, *Ann. Chem.*, **614**, 167 (1958).
119. E. Testa and L. Fontanella, *Ann. Chem.*, **625**, 95 (1959).
120. E. Testa and L. Fontanella, *Ann. Chem.*, **661**, 187 (1963).
121. E. Testa, L. Fontanella, and G. F. Cristiani, *Ann. Chem.*, **626**, 114 (1959).
122. E. Testa, L. Fontanella, G. F. Cristiani, and F. Fava, *Ann. Chem.*, **614**, 158 (1958).
123. E. Testa, L. Fontanella, G. F. Cristiani, and F. Fava, *Ann. Chem.*, **619**, 47 (1958).
124. H. W. Thompson, R. R. Brattain, H. M. Randall, and R. S. Rasmussen, in *The Chemistry of Penicillin*, H. T. Clarke, J. R. Johnson, and R. Robinson, Eds., Princeton University Press, Princeton, New Jersey, 1949, p. 391.
125. E. Wedekind, *Chem. Ber.*, **39**, 1631 (1906).
126. E. Wedekind and W. Weisswange, *Chem. Ber.*, **39**, 1636 (1906).
127. E. Wedekind and W. Weisswange, *Chem. Ber.*, **39**, 1644 (1906).
128. F. Weygand and H. J. Bestmann, *Angew. Chem.*, **72**, 548 (1960).

### c. 2,-4-Azetidinediones*

$$
\begin{array}{ccc}
-\text{C} & \longrightarrow & \text{CO} \\
| & & | \\
\text{OC} & \longrightarrow & \text{N}-
\end{array}
$$

Staudinger and co-workers[21] were the first to report the formation of the 2,4-azetidinedione, 1,3,3-triphenyl-2,4-azetidinedione (**3**), via the cycloaddition reaction of diphenylketene (**1**) and phenylisocyanate (**2**). More recently, in a series of articles, King[13–16] has reported that many of the

$$
(C_6H_5)_2C{=}C{=}O + C_6H_5N{=}C{=}O \longrightarrow
$$
(1)                           (2)

(3)

* For a review of 2,4-azetidinediones see Moore.[18]

previously reported[1] 2,4-azetidinediones were incorrectly characterized as such. This four-membered ring (3) was unusually stable in comparison to malonic acid anhydrides, $\beta$-lactams, and $\beta$-lactones.[20, 22] It decomposes at very high temperatures with formation of the starting materials (equation a) undergoing a decomposition similar to that of the malonic acid anhydride (4) (equation b).[22]

$$(C_6H_5)_2C\text{------}CO$$
$$\big| \qquad\qquad \big| \qquad \xrightarrow{\Delta} \quad (C_6H_5)_2C{=}C{=}O + C_6H_5N{=}C{=}O \qquad (a)$$
$$OC\text{------}NC_6H_5 \qquad\qquad (1) \qquad\qquad\qquad (2)$$
$$(3)$$

$$(C_6H_5)_2C\text{------}CO$$
$$\big| \qquad\qquad \big| \qquad \xrightarrow{\Delta} \quad (1) + CO_2\uparrow \qquad\qquad\qquad (b)$$
$$OC\text{------}O$$
$$(4)$$

In a study of various preparations of 2,4-azetidinediones, Ebnöther and co-workers[3] also confirmed Staudinger's findings that diphenylketene (1) reacts with isocyanates (5) via a cycloaddition reaction to form the corresponding 2,4-azetidinediones (6) (Table 1), which were characterized by infrared analysis (Table 2).

$$(C_6H_5)_2C{=}C{=}O + R\text{---}N{=}C{=}O \longrightarrow$$
$$(5)$$
$$(1) \qquad\qquad (R = CH_3, C_6H_{11})$$

$$(C_6H_5)_2C\text{------}CO$$
$$\big| \qquad\qquad \big|$$
$$OC\text{------}N\text{---}R$$
$$(6)$$

Mundlos and Graf[19] found that ketenes do not react readily below 200°C with isocyanates, but since greater reactivity was expected from sulfonyl isocyanates, they reacted the sulfonyl isocyanates (7a–d) with ketene (8). The resulting products were the very reactive cycloadducts (9a–d) (Table 7) and some polymeric substances. The arylsulfonyl isocyanates (7a, b) were obtained from arylsulfonamides and phosgene,[17]

$$R\text{---}SO_2\text{---}N{=}C{=}O + CH_2{=}C{=}O \longrightarrow$$
$$(7a\text{--}d) \qquad\qquad (8)$$

$$R\text{---}SO_2N\text{------}CO$$
$$\big| \qquad\qquad \big|$$
$$OC\text{------}CH_2$$
$$(9a\text{--}d)$$

$$\begin{pmatrix} 7, 9\ \text{a: } R = C_6H_4CH_3\text{-}p \\ \text{b: } R = C_6H_4Cl\text{-}p \\ \text{c: } R = Cl \\ \text{d: } R = F \end{pmatrix}$$

while the N-carbonylsulfamoyl chloride (7c) was obtained from cyanogen chloride and sulfur trioxide.[4]

The 1-halogensulfonylazetidinediones-2,4 (**9c, d**) are more unstable than the 1-arylsulfonylazetidinediones-2,4 (**9a, b**), decomposing at room temperature.

From $N,N'$-dicarbonylsulfurylamide (**10**)[6] and ketene (**8**) the crystalline product (**11**) is formed, which decomposes when exposed to moist air.

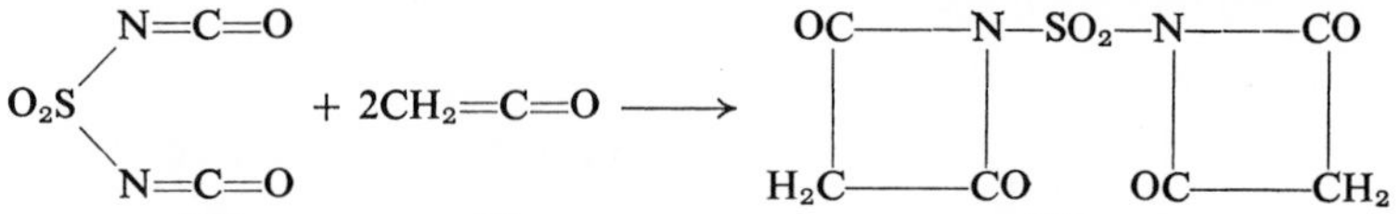

$$O_2S \overset{N=C=O}{\underset{N=C=O}{\diagdown\diagup}} \quad + 2CH_2=C=O \longrightarrow \begin{array}{c} OC\text{——}N\text{—}SO_2\text{—}N\text{——}CO \\ | \quad\quad | \quad\quad | \quad\quad | \\ H_2C\text{——}CO \quad\quad OC\text{——}CH_2 \end{array}$$

$$\text{(10)} \qquad\qquad \text{(8)} \qquad\qquad\qquad\qquad \text{(11)}$$

Another 2,4-azetidinedione (**12**) resulting from a cycloaddition reaction is that prepared by Graf[5] from ethyl-$n$-butylketene (**13**) and $p$-toluene-sulfonyl isocyanate (**14**).

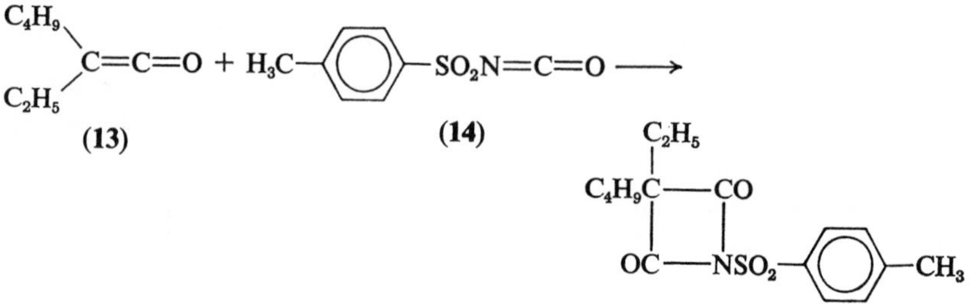

$$\overset{C_4H_9}{\underset{C_2H_5}{\diagdown\diagup}}C=C=O + H_3C-\!\!\!\bigcirc\!\!\!-SO_2N=C=O \longrightarrow$$

$$\text{(13)} \qquad\qquad\qquad \text{(14)}$$

$$\begin{array}{c} \quad\quad C_2H_5 \\ \quad\quad | \\ C_4H_9C\text{——}CO \\ | \quad\quad | \\ OC\text{——}NSO_2-\!\!\!\bigcirc\!\!\!-CH_3 \end{array}$$

$$\text{(12)}$$

2,4-Azetidinediones prepared by various cyclization reactions and the characteristic infrared bands have been summarized.[2,3,8-12,21,23-25]

**Table 1**

Preparation of 2,4-Azetidinediones via Cycloaddition of Ketenes and Isocyanates

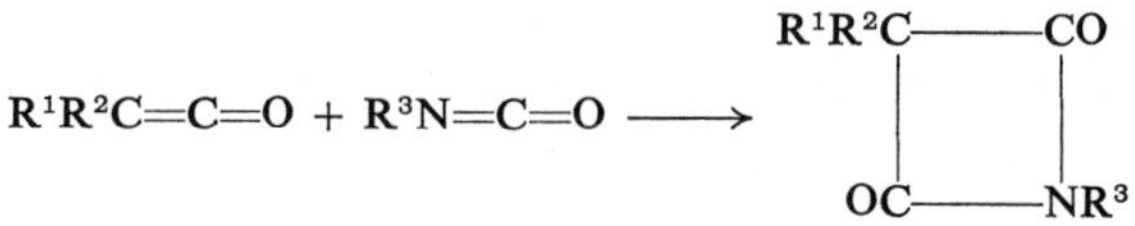

$$R^1R^2C=C=O + R^3N=C=O \longrightarrow \begin{array}{c} R^1R^2C\text{——}CO \\ | \quad\quad | \\ OC\text{——}NR^3 \end{array}$$

| $R^1$ | $R^2$ | $R^3$ | MP (°C) | Yield (%) | Ref. |
|-------|-------|-------|---------|-----------|------|
| $C_6H_5$ | $C_6H_5$ | $C_6H_5$ | 125–126 | — | 21 |
| $C_6H_5$ | $C_6H_5$ | $CH_3$ | 100–101 | 18 | 3 |
| $C_6H_5$ | $C_6H_5$ | $C_6H_{11}$ | 78 | 26 | 3 |
| $C_4H_9$ | $C_2H_5$ | $p$-$CH_3C_6H_4SO_2$ | — | — | 5 |

(continued)

**Table 1** (*continued*)

| $R^1$ | $R^2$ | $R^3$ | MP (°C) | Yield (%) | Ref. |
|-------|-------|-------|---------|-----------|------|
| H | H | $p$-$CH_3C_6H_4SO_2$ | 125 (dec) | 5 | 19 |
| H | H | $p$-$ClC_6H_4SO_2$ | 101 (dec) | — | 19 |
| H | H | $ClSO_2$ | room temp. (dec) | — | 19 |
| H | H | $FSO_2$ | room temp. (dec) | — | 19 |
| H | H | —$SO_2$— | (dec) | — | 19 |

**Table 2**

Characteristic Infrared Bands of 2,4-Azetidinediones[3]

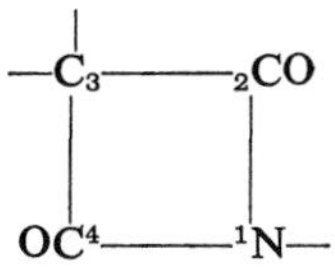

$$-\overset{|}{C_3}\quad\underset{2}{\quad}CO$$
$$O\overset{4}{C}\quad\quad{}^1N-$$

| 2,4-Azetidinediones | IR bands 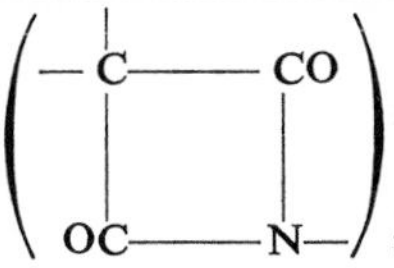 | $\left(\begin{array}{cc}-\overset{|}{C}&CO\\O C&N-\end{array}\right)\nu$ | | |
|---------------------|----------|--------|------|------|
| 1-Methyl-3,3-diphenyl- | 1735 | 1810 | 1890 cm$^{-1}$ | |
| 1-Cyclohexyl-3,3-diphenyl- | 1730 | 1820 | 1885 cm$^{-1}$ | |

REFERENCES

1. S. A. Ballard and D. S. Melstrom, in *Heterocyclic Compounds*, Vol. 1, R. C. Elderfield, Ed., Wiley, New York, 1950, p. 78.
2. Brit. Pat. 890,725 (1962).
3. A. Ebnöther, E. Jucker, E. Rissi, J. Rutschmann, E. Schreier, R. Steiner, R. Süess, and A. Vogel, *Helv. Chim. Acta*, **42**, 918 (1959).
4. R. Graf, *Chem. Ber.*, **89**, 1071 (1956).
5. R. Graf, Can. Pat. 657,615 (1963).
6. R. Graf, Ger. Pat. 940,351 (1954).
7. R. Graf and E. Mundlos, Ger. Pat. 1,098,515 (1958).
8. E. Jucker, *Angew. Chem.*, **71**, 321 (1959).
9. E. Jucker, A. Ebnöther, E. Rissi, A. Vogel, and R. Steiner, Swiss Pat. 360,393 (1962).
10. E. Jucker, A. Ebnöther, E. Rissi, A. Vogel, and R. Steiner, Swiss Pat. 367,174 (1963).
11. E. Jucker, A. Ebnöther, E. Rissi, A. Vogel, and R. Steiner, US Pat. 2,955,112 (1960).

12. E. Jucker, A. Ebnöther, E. Rissi, A. Vogel, and R. Steiner, US Pat. 3,036,065 (1962).
13. F. E. King, *J. Chem. Soc.*, **1949**, 1318.
14. F. E. King and J. W. Clark-Lewis, *J. Chem. Soc.*, **1951**, 3077.
15. F. E. King and J. W. Clark-Lewis, *J. Chem. Soc.*, **1951**, 3080.
16. F. E. King, J. W. Clark-Lewis, and C. R. P. Morgan, *J. Chem. Soc.*, **1951**, 3074
17. H. Krizkalla, Ger. Pat. 817,602 (1949).
18. J. A. Moore, in *Compounds with Three- and Four-Membered Rings* (*The Chemistry of Heterocyclic Compounds*, Vol. 19, A. Weissberger, Ed.), Interscience, New York, 1964, pp. 885 ff.
19. E. Mundlos and R. Graf, *Ann. Chem.*, **677**, 108 (1964).
20. H. Staudinger, *Chem. Ber.*, **44**, 525 (1911).
21. H. Staudinger, D. Göhring, and M. Schöller, *Chem. Ber.*, **47**, 40 (1914).
22. H. Staudinger and E. Ott, *Chem. Ber.*, **41**, 2208 (1908).
23. E. Testa, *Farmaco Pavia Ed. Sci.*, **17**, 168 (1962); *Chem. Abstr.*, **57**, 9772 (1962).
24. E. Testa and L. Fontanella, *Ann. Chem.*, **660**, 118 (1962).
25. E. Testa, L. Fontanella, G. F. Cristiani, and L. Mariani, *Helv. Chim. Acta*, **42**, 2370 (1959).

## 3. Sulfur

### a. Thietanes, Thietane 1,1-Dioxides, Thietanone Dioxides, and Thiete 1,1-Dioxides

The chemistry of four-membered heterocyclic compounds containing a sulfur atom—i.e., thietanes—has been recently reviewed.[11] In this review, the formation of thietane derivatives or thietane itself (with the exception of the 1,1-dioxides) via a cycloaddition reaction was not described. However, Staudinger[44] found that thioketones and ketenes react via a cycloaddition, analogously to the reaction between carbonyl compounds and ketenes, forming the β-thiolactone or thietan-2-one. These compounds decomposed at high temperatures (about 180°C) into carbon oxysulfide and unsaturated compounds. In this manner, 4,4'-bis(dimethylamino)thiobenzophenone (**1**) reacts with diphenylketene (**2**) resulting in the formation of the β-thiolactone    3,3-diphenyl-4,4'-bis(*N,N'*-dimethylanilino)-thietan-2-one (**3**). The β-thiolactone was not isolated; at high temperatures the cleavage product, 3,3-diphenyl-4,4'-bis(*N,N'*-dimethylanilino)ethylene (**4**) and carbon oxysulfide (**5**) were detected. Similar reactions were repeated using thiobenzophenone or dimethoxythiobenzophenone and diphenylketene. Here again the β-thiolactone was not isolated; only the corresponding unsaturated compounds were isolated.[44]

$$[(CH_3)_2NC_6H_4]_2C=S + (C_6H_5)_2C=C=O \longrightarrow$$

$$\mathbf{(1)} \qquad\qquad \mathbf{(2)}$$

$$\begin{array}{ccc} [(CH_3)_2NC_6H_4]_2C & \!\!\!\!-\!\!\!\! & S \\ | & & | \\ (C_6H_5)_2C & \!\!\!\!-\!\!\!\! & CO \end{array}$$

$$\mathbf{(3)}$$

$$\mathbf{(3)} \longrightarrow \begin{array}{c} [(CH_3)_2NC_6H_4]_2C \\ \| \\ (C_6H_5)_2C \end{array} + \begin{array}{c} SCO \\ \mathbf{(5)} \end{array}$$

$$\mathbf{(4)}$$

Recently, Middleton[30] found that hexafluorothioacetone, $(CF_3)_2C=S$, would form cycloadducts with certain electron-rich olefins, even though they possess no allylic hydrogens (Table 1). For example, methyl vinyl ether and methyl vinyl sulfide form $1:1$ cyclic adducts with hexafluorothio-

$$(CF_3)_2C=S + CH_3OCH=CH_2 \longrightarrow \begin{array}{ccc} CH_3OCH & \!\!\!\!-\!\!\!\! & CH_2 \\ | & & | \\ S & \!\!\!\!-\!\!\!\! & C(CF_3)_2 \end{array}$$

$$(CF_3)_2C=S + CH_3SCH=CH_2 \longrightarrow \begin{array}{ccc} CH_3SCH & \!\!\!\!-\!\!\!\! & CH_2 \\ | & & | \\ S & \!\!\!\!-\!\!\!\! & C(CF_3)_2 \end{array}$$

acetone at $-78°C$. Other adducts were formed with dihydropyran, dioxene, ethyl vinyl ether, and $t$-butyl vinyl sulfide.

The structures of these vinyl ether and sulfide adducts have not been conclusively proved, but Middleton believes them to be 2-alkoxy-(or 2-alkylthio-)thietanes rather than 3-alkoxy-(or 3-alkylthio-)thietanes on the basis of their mass spectrometer patterns. Major peaks in the patterns of these adducts correspond to the charged fragments that would result by cleaving the thietane ring in all possible ways. That is, the most abundant peak for the hexafluorothioacetone–methyl vinyl ether adduct is $m/e$ 76, $(C_2H_4SO)\oplus$, which is most probably $[HC(S)OCH_3]\oplus$. However, thermal pyrolysis of these adducts proceeds unilaterally to give the starting materials as the only isolated products.

Several recent references have been made to the preparation of thietane 1,1-dioxides (**8**) via the cycloaddition of sulfenes (**6**) to enamines (**7**). Since at this time there has been no compilation of the chemistry of sulfenes, it

$$RCH=SO_2 + R^1-N-CH=CR^2R^3 \longrightarrow \begin{array}{ccc} R-CH & \!\!\!\!-\!\!\!\! & SO_2 \\ | & & | \\ R^1-N-CH & \!\!\!\!-\!\!\!\! & CR^2R^3 \end{array}$$

$$\mathbf{(6)} \qquad\qquad \mathbf{(7)} \qquad\qquad\qquad \mathbf{(8)}$$

seems appropriate and necessary that a brief review of sulfenes follows as an explanatory introduction to the above-mentioned cycloaddition reactions.

The interest in sulfenes ($RR^1C{=}SO_2$) has been recently revived since their discovery as intermediates in newly developed reactions.[4,16,23,32,34-36,38,46,52-54] In 1908 Zincke and Brune[63] reported that if 2,6-dibromophenol-4-sulfonic acid chloride (9) was treated with a sodium acetate solution, hydrogen chloride was released, resulting in the formation of the sulfene (10) which could not be isolated. Wedekind and Schenk[60] have

been cited, however, as the earliest source for the preparation of a sulfene intermediate. They reported that benzylsulfonyl chloride (11) upon treatment with triethylamine gave *trans*-stilbene (12), sulfur dioxide, and triethylamine hydrochloride. The formation of *trans*-stilbene was assumed to have proceeded according to the following mechanism:

$$2C_6H_5CH_2SO_2Cl \xrightarrow{Et_3N} 2C_6H_5CH{=}SO_2 \longrightarrow 2C_6H_5CH: + SO_2$$
(11)

$$2C_6H_5CH: \longrightarrow C_6H_5CH{=}CHC_6H_5$$
(12)

Wedekind and co-workers extended their work to camphor-10-sulfonyl chloride[61] and camphor-8-sulfonyl chloride.[62] Analogous reactions were carried out on 3-bromocamphor-8-sulfonyl chloride[5] and camphor-8-sulfonyl bromide.[15] These reactions were reinvestigated by King and Durst,[22] and the findings were in accord with those reported by Wedekind and Schenk. In addition to the stilbene formed in the reaction of benzenesulfonyl chloride, an oxythio compound (13) was isolated. Structure 13 was confirmed by spectral ($\lambda_{max}$ 234 m$\mu$ ($\epsilon$ 7750) and 323 m$\mu$ ($\epsilon$ 8800), $\lambda_{max}$ 1145 cm$^{-1}$ and 1030 cm$^{-1}$, and in the nuclear magnetic resonance spectrum only a complex band around 7.5 ppm) and chemical evidence. King and Durst[22] and Strating[48] also prepared the "camphorchlorosulfoxide" (14) from camphor-10-sulfonyl chloride (15); this was in agreement with Wedekind's observations and left no doubt that Wedekind's structure (14) was correct. The mechanism given by Strating for the formation of camphorchlorosulfoxide involved elimination of hydrogen chloride from

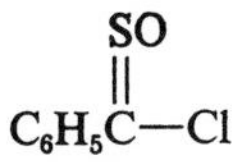

$$\overset{\displaystyle SO}{\underset{\displaystyle C_6H_5\overset{\|}{C}-Cl}{}}$$

**(13)**

$$\overset{\displaystyle SO}{\underset{\displaystyle \overset{\|}{C}-Cl}{}}$$

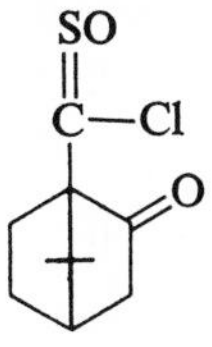

**(14)**

camphor sulfonyl chloride **(15)** giving the sulfene **(16)** which extracts a molecule of water from another molecule of camphor-10-sulfonyl chloride **(15)**, giving D-camphor-10-sulfonic acid **(17)** and the D-10-chlorosulfoxide-camphor **(14)**. The mechanism given by King and Durst for the formation

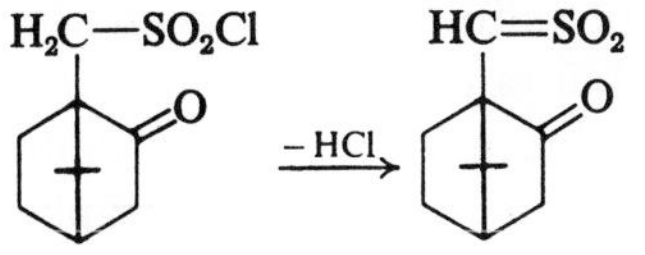

$$H_2C-SO_2Cl \qquad\qquad HC=SO_2$$

**(15)**        $\xrightarrow{-HCl}$        **(16)**

$$H_2C-SO_2Cl \qquad HC=SO_2 \qquad H_2C-SO_3H \quad Cl-C=SO$$

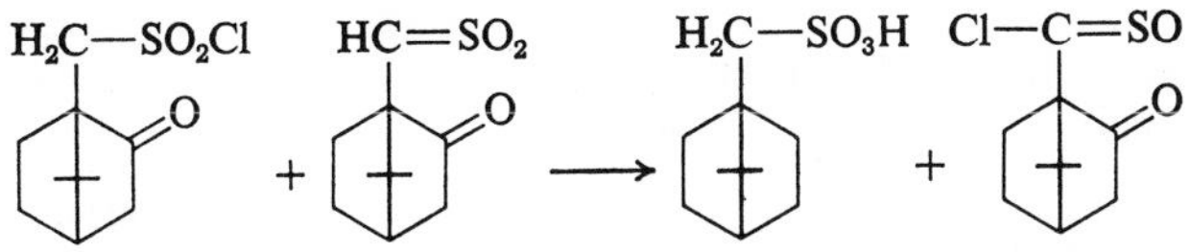

**(15)**   +   **(16)**   $\longrightarrow$   **(17)**   +   **(14)**

of stilbene **(12)** and oxythiobenzoyl chloride **(13)** is depicted as proceeding via a sulfene intermediate **(18)**. The oxythiobenzoyl chloride **(13)** has been

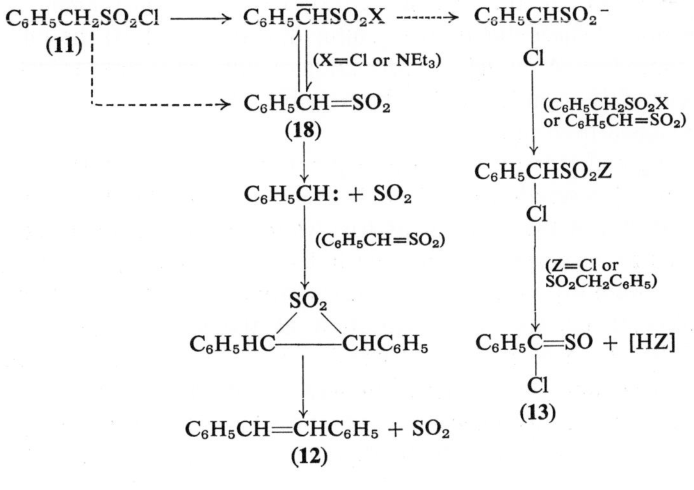

$$C_6H_5CH_2SO_2Cl \longrightarrow C_6H_5\overline{C}HSO_2X \dashrightarrow C_6H_5CHSO_2^-$$
**(11)**

$(X=Cl\ or\ NEt_3)$                      $\underset{Cl}{|}$

$C_6H_5CH=SO_2$                      $(C_6H_5CH_2SO_2X$
**(18)**                              $or\ C_6H_5CH=SO_2)$

$C_6H_5CH: + SO_2$                   $C_6H_5CHSO_2Z$

$(C_6H_5CH=SO_2)$                    $\underset{Cl}{|}$

$(Z=Cl\ or$
$SO_2CH_2C_6H_5)$

$$\overset{SO_2}{C_6H_5HC\overset{\triangle}{\underline{\qquad}}CHC_6H_5} \qquad C_6H_5C=SO + [HZ]$$

$\underset{Cl}{|}$

$C_6H_5CH=CHC_6H_5 + SO_2$        **(13)**
**(12)**

reinvestigated[20] and was found to be a mixture of the geometrical isomers, *cis*- and *trans*-oxythiobenzoyl chloride (**13a** and **b**).

(**13a**)                          (**13b**)

Recently, Opitz and Fischer[36] reported that sulfenes ($R'$—$CH$=$SO_2$) were produced by dehydrochlorination of primary alkanesulfonyl chlorides in the presence of triethylamine. Additional evidence for the formation of sulfenes from aliphatic sulfonyl chlorides and triethylamine was offered by Fusco, Rossi, and Maiorano.[12]

Staudinger and Pfenninger[45] found that diphenyldiazomethane (**19**) readily reacted with sulfur dioxide giving tetraphenylthiirane 1,1-dioxide (**21**) (see Section II-3-a). The mechanism involved a diphenylsulfene intermediate (**20**). More recently, others have studied the reactions of substi-

$$(C_6H_5)_2CN_2 + SO_2 \xrightarrow{-N_2} [(C_6H_5)_2C=SO_2] \longrightarrow (C_6H_5)_2C\underset{\underset{(21)}{SO_2}}{\diagdown \diagup}C(C_6H_5)_2$$

(**19**)                          (**20**)

tuted diazoalkanes and sulfur dioxide that possibly form the corresponding sulfenes (see Section II-3-a).[1,17,18,24-26,31,59]

The intermediacy of a sulfene ($RR'C$=$SO_2$) has been proposed to rationalize the course of three general reactions: (*1*) the reaction of sulfonyl halides of the type $RR'CHSO_2Cl$ with tertiary amines,[60] (*2*) the reaction of diazoalkanes with sulfur dioxide,[45] and (*3*) the photolysis of sulfones.[16,23] Although the formation of sulfenes in these transformations is currently regarded as highly probable,[4,13,16,22,23,34,36,46,52-54] in no case has it been proved.

King and Durst[21] described experiments which show that sulfenes are produced in reaction (*1*) above. Benzenesulfonyl chloride was treated with an alcohol in the presence of triethylamine and was quantitatively converted to the corresponding ester in less than 1 min at room temperature. There were two possible mechanisms proposed for this reaction: (*a*) a bimolecular nucleophilic substitution at the sulfur atom by the alcohol[19,42,51] (or its conjugate base) or (*b*) initial formation of phenylsulfene by an elimination reaction, followed by addition of the alcohol. In an experiment to distinguish between possible mechanisms, benzylsulfonyl chloride was treated with triethylamine in isopropyl alcohol-*d* with an estimated deuterium content of 92 ± 2% of the active hydrogen. The mixture of esters formed contained 90% of the monodeuterated ester, $PhCHDSO_3CH(CH_3)_2$, the remainder being the nondeuterated ester with very little or none of the di-deuterated ester $PhCD_2SO_3CH(CH_3)_2$. Since formation of the last product would require that the deuterium be incorporated in an irreversible step, it was concluded that mechanism (b) uniquely fulfilled the requirements for at least the major portion of the products. In reactions (2) and (3) above, sulfene formation could not be tested by deuteration experiments as readily as it was in reaction (1). Though the comparison is somewhat limited, reactions (1), (2), and (3) apparently yield similar products under similar conditions, providing circumstantial evidence that these reactions all proceed through a common sulfene intermediate.

To date, there has been only one report of the isolation of a crystalline sulfene[28] which was reinvestigated and found to be inaccurate.

Recently, there have been two reports of the isolation of a stable sulfine (RR′C=S=O) which draw attention to the remarkable difference in the stability of sulfenes (RR′C=SO_2) and sulfines (RR′C=S=O).[43,49] Strating and co-workers[49] treated the sulfinic acid (22) with thionyl chloride (23), and then treated the resultant sulfinyl chloride (24) with triethylamine to obtain the sulfine (25), which was isolated. Sheppard and Diekmann[43] reported the isolation of fluorenylidene sulfine (27) by reacting

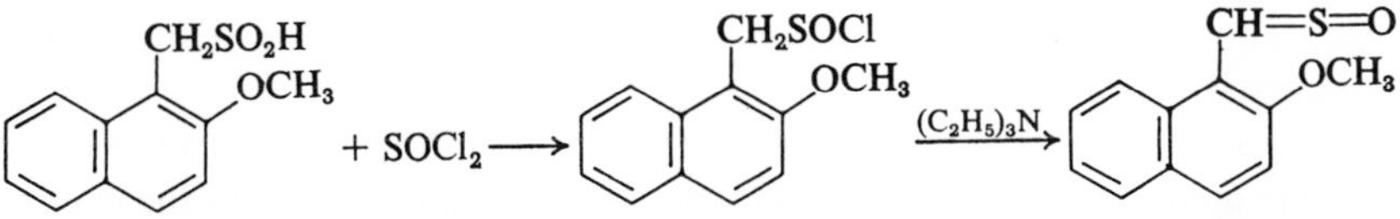

(22)    (23)    (24)    (25)

fluorenylidene sulfinyl chloride (26) with triethylamine. The structure of the sulfine (27) was confirmed by molecular weight determination, proton

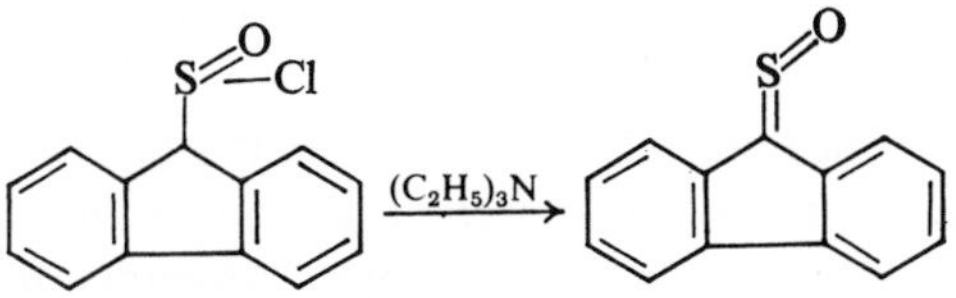

(26)    (27)

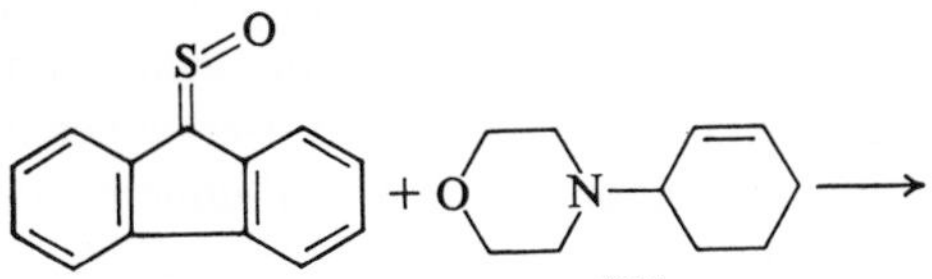

(27)    (28)    (29)

nuclear magnetic resonance, and infrared and ultraviolet absorption spectra.

The sulfine (27) was added to a stoichiometric amount of 3-morpholino-cyclohexene (28) in tetrahydrofuran to give a white crystalline solid. Two structures, 29a and b, were proposed for the adduct, although 29b is pre-

or

(29a)                (29b)

ferred because of the strong absorption band at 1710 cm$^{-1}$ in the infrared spectrum. Further work is now being done to elucidate the structure of the adduct.

Aliphatic analogs of sulfines were also prepared[43] but were too unstable for isolation at room temperature. Efforts to isolate these sulfines by trapping with reactive olefins or dienes have not been successful.

Having established the existence of sulfenes as intermediates, the various cycloaddition reactions of sulfenes forming thietane derivatives will be discussed.

It was reported[4,52,54] that methanesulfonyl chloride (30) reacted with ketene diethylacetal (31) in the presence of triethylamine to give the cyclo-addition product 3,3-diethoxythietane 1,1-dioxide (32) via the formation

$$CH_2=C(OC_2H_5)_2 + CH_3SO_2Cl \xrightarrow{(C_2H_5)_3N} \begin{array}{c} CH_2\!\!-\!\!C(OC_2H_5)_2 \\ | \qquad\qquad | \\ O_2S\!\!-\!\!-\!\!CH_2 \end{array}$$
$$\quad (31) \qquad\qquad (30) \qquad\qquad\qquad (32)$$

of the sulfene intermediate, $(CH_2=SO_2)$. The structure of 32 was confirmed by elemental analysis, molecular weight determination, and infrared and nuclear magnetic resonance spectroscopy. Attempts to isolate similar products from methanesulfonyl chloride and the following unsaturated systems have been unsuccessful: ethyl vinyl ether, $p$-tolylmercaptoethene, ethoxyacetylene, diphenylketene, ketene-diethylmercaptan, vinylidene chloride and cyclopentadiene,[52] 1-ethoxy-1-ethylmercaptoethene, 1,1-bis(4,4'-dimethoxyphenyl)-ethene, 1,1-bis(4,4'-dimethylaminophenyl)-eth-ene, diethylimino carbonate, acrolein, benzalaniline, methyl acrylate, trifluorochloroethylene, and hexachlorobutadiene.[54] The reaction of sulfonyl chloride and ketene diethylacetal in the presence of triethylamine was extended[54]; the results are shown in Table 2. The structures assigned were supported by nuclear magnetic resonance (Table 3) and infrared spectra data (asymmetric stretching of the sulfone, 7.4–7.5 $\mu$.; symmetric stretching of the sulfone, 8.7 $\mu$; weak absorbance at 8.4–8.6 $\mu$, and strong absorbance at 9.0–9.2 $\mu$). It was concluded[54] that, for four-membered ring formation to occur, a highly polarizable double bond is required, the polarization being induced by strongly electron-donating substituents. That is, the

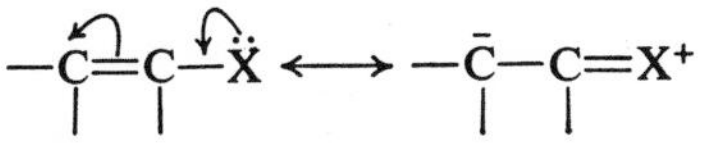

$$-\overset{|}{\underset{|}{C}}=\overset{|}{\underset{|}{C}}-\ddot{X} \longleftrightarrow -\overset{|}{\underset{|}{\bar{C}}}-\overset{|}{\underset{|}{C}}=X^+$$

double bonds, which form a cyclic product, are those which are readily attacked by electrophilic moieties or show appreciable nucleophilicity, such as ketene acetals[29] and enamines.[47]

The reactions of 3,3-diethoxythietane 1,1-dioxide (32) and 2-phenyl-3,3-diethoxythietane 1,1-dioxide (33) were reported.[55,56] The acid hydrolysis of 32 resulted in the formation of the ketosulfone 34, 3-thietanone 1,1-dioxide, whose structural assignment was supported by elemental analysis, molecular weight determination, and nuclear magnetic resonance and infrared spectroscopy. Formation of other thietan-3-one 1,1-dioxides have

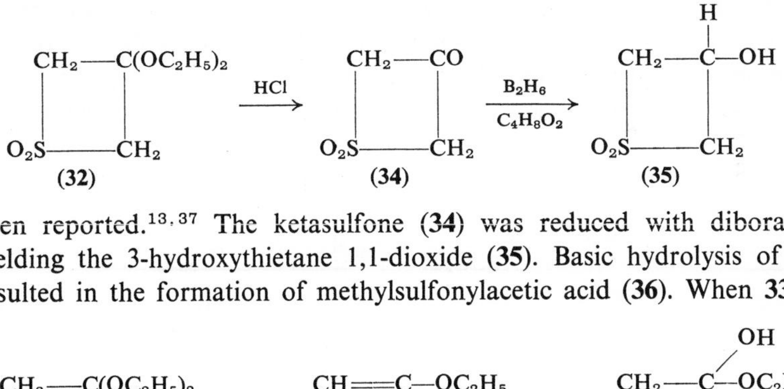

been reported.[13,37] The ketasulfone (34) was reduced with diborane, yielding the 3-hydroxythietane 1,1-dioxide (35). Basic hydrolysis of 32 resulted in the formation of methylsulfonylacetic acid (36). When 33 is

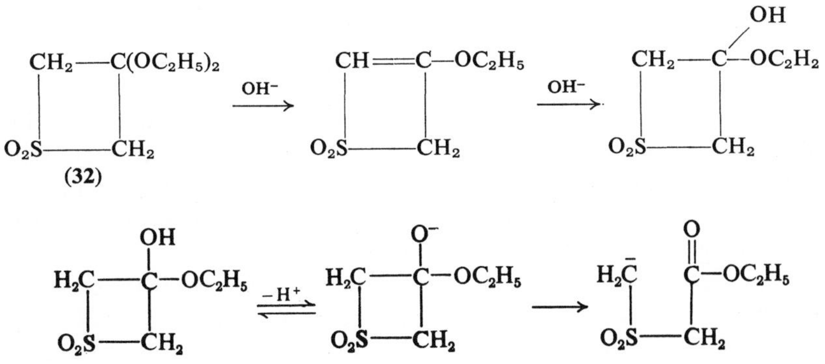

$$\begin{array}{c} \bar{C}H_2 \quad \overset{\displaystyle O}{\overset{\displaystyle \|}{C}}-OC_2H_5 \\ | \qquad | \\ O_2S\!-\!\!-\!\!-\!CH_2 \end{array} \xrightarrow{H_2O} CH_3SO_2CH_2CO_2C_2H_5 \xrightarrow{OH^-} \xrightarrow{HCl}$$

$$CH_3SO_2CH_2CO_2H$$
(36)

treated with sodium ethoxide in ethanol, the thiete sulfone derivative, 3-ethoxy-4-phenylthiete 1,1-dioxide (37), is obtained in 40% yield. If 33

$$\begin{array}{cc} C_6H_5\!-\!CH\!\!-\!\!-\!\!C(OC_2H_5)_2 & \xrightarrow[\text{EtOH}]{\text{NaOEt}} & C_6H_5\!-\!C\!=\!\!=\!C\!-\!OC_2H_5 \\ | \qquad\qquad | & & | \qquad\quad | \\ OS_2\!\!-\!\!-\!\!CH_2 & & O_2S\!\!-\!\!-\!\!CH_2 \\ \quad\text{(33)} & & \quad\text{(37)} \end{array}$$

$$\text{(33)} \quad\Bigg\downarrow \begin{array}{c}\text{NaOH}\\ \text{H}_2\text{O}\end{array}$$

$$\longrightarrow C_6H_5CH_2SO_2CH_2CO_2H$$
(38)

is treated with sodium hydroxide, a ring opening occurs and benzyl-sulfonylacetic acid (38) is formed. Identification of 37 and 38 was based on elemental analysis, molecular weight determination, and nuclear magnetic resonance and infrared spectroscopy.

Stork and Borowitz[4,46] found that in the presence of triethylamine—a proton acceptor—methanesulfonyl chloride reacted with a variety of morpholine enamines to give aminothietane 1,1-dioxides (Table 4). For example, 1-N-morpholinocyclohexene (39) and methanesulfonyl chloride (30) gave the aminothietane 1,1-dioxide (40). The structural assignment of

(39)                                    (40)

40 was confirmed by its nuclear magnetic resonance spectrum and by its reduction[3] to the aminosulfide (41). Similar reactions were repeated with 1-N-morpholinocyclopentene and 1-N-morpholinopropene (Table 4). The mechanism postulated was the initial formation of the sulfene (42), which then undergoes cycloaddition reactions with the enamines, forming the corresponding thietane 1,1-dioxides. No adduct was formed in the presence of cyclohexene, ethoxyacetylene, or anthracene,[4] further substantiating the conclusion by Truce and Norell[54] that thietane 1,1-dioxide formation

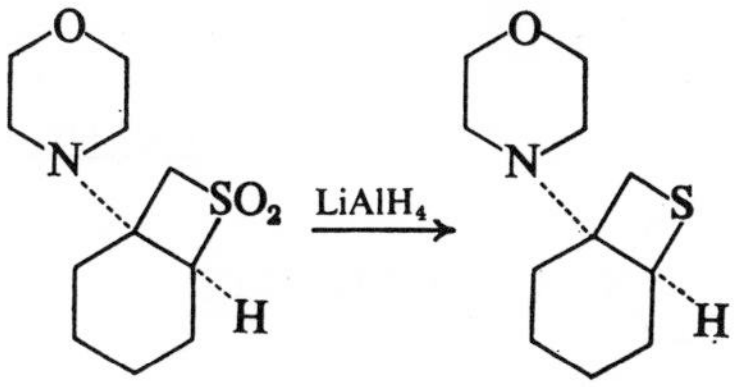

$$CH_3SO_2Cl + (C_2H_5)_3N \longrightarrow CH_2{=}SO_2 + HCl \cdot N(C_2H_5)_3$$
$$(30) \hspace{4.5cm} (42)$$

$$(42) + R{-}N{-}CH{=}CR^1R^2 \longrightarrow$$
$$(7)$$

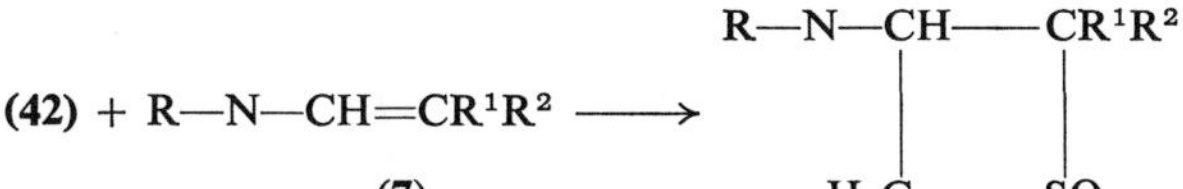

occurs only in the presence of olefins with strongly electron-donating substituents.

Opitz and co-workers [33,34,36,38] also reported that sulfenes from aliphatic sulfonyl chlorides and triethylamine form thietane 1,1-dioxides with enamines (Table 4). For example, 1-pyrrolidinoisobutylene (43) reacts with the sulfene (42) produced by the dehydrochlorination of methanesulfonyl chloride (30) with triethylamine via a cycloaddition reaction, producing the thietane 1,1-dioxide, 3-pyrrolidino-2,2-dimethylthietane 1,1-dioxide

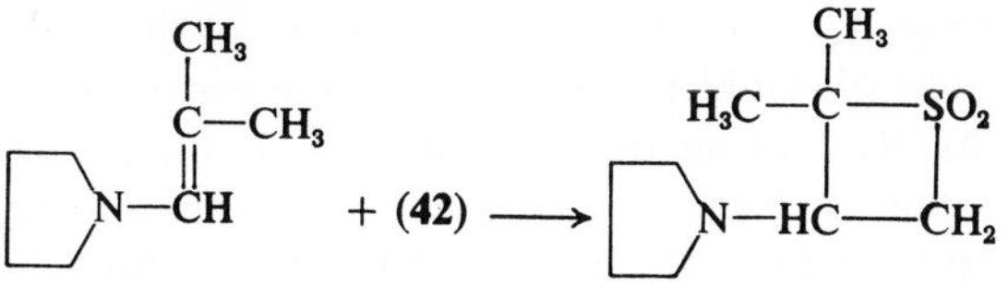

(44) in an 80% yield. The structural assignment of 44 was in agreement with chemical and spectral evidence.

The reactions of enamines with electrophilic sulfur compounds have recently been discussed.[27,50] The cycloaddition of sulfenes to bicyclic enamines has been reported recently by Paquette.[39,40] He studied the stereoselectivity of the reactions of various enamines derived from 5-norbornene-2-carboxaldehyde with methanesulfonyl chloride and triethylamine[39]; for example, the enamine (45) and triethylamine were treated with methanesulfonyl chloride (30), and upon completion of the addition the thietane dioxide, 3'-(4-methyl-1-piperazinyl)spiro[5-norbornene-2,2'-thietane]1',1'-dioxide (46), was obtained (Table 6). It was found that for the bicyclic enamines (47) two possible isomeric structures existed—the transoid form (47a) and the cisoid counterpart (47b). However, the nuclear

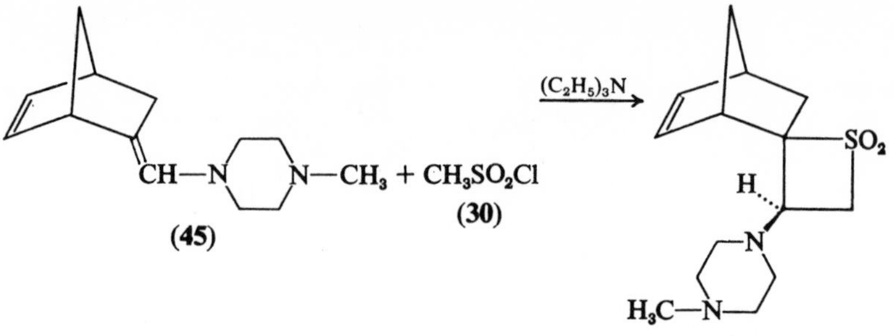

$$(C_2H_5)_3N$$

(45) $\overset{|}{C}H-N\overset{\frown}{\phantom{xx}}N-CH_3 + CH_3SO_2Cl$ (30)

(46)

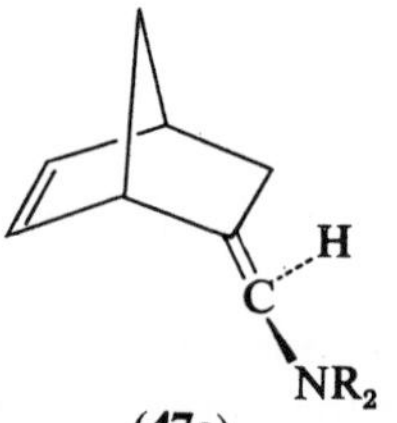

(47a) 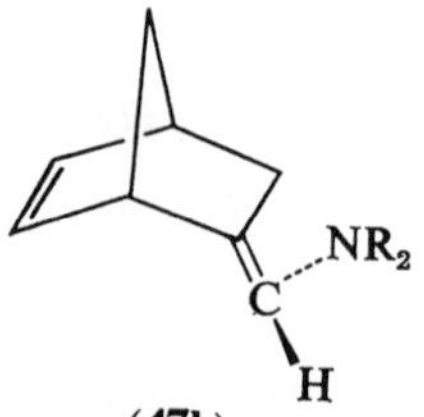    (47b)

magnetic resonance spectra revealed that the transoid form (47b) pre-dominated to the extent of 80–90% depending on the amine substituent.

Examination of the nuclear magnetic resonance spectra of the 5-norbor-nene-2,2'-thietane 1',1'-dioxides revealed that the olefinic region consisted solely of two sets of doublets, as in the *endo* aldehyde, and the transoid enamines (47b). By making the assumption that the sulfene reagent of necessity must approach the bicyclic system from the *exo* side,[2] the result-ing spiro compound must be represented by 48a or 48b. Examination of molecular models of the isomeric structure (47b) revealed that the amine

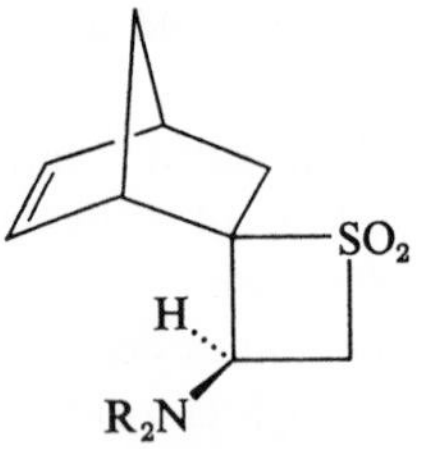

(48a) 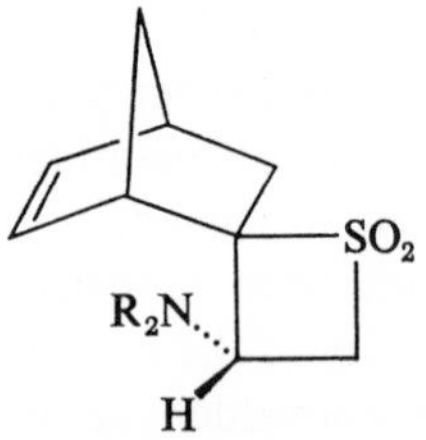    (48b)

substituent is located at a point roughly equidistant to the two vinyl pro-tons—an arrangement that would not be expected to give rise to the un-symmetrical perturbation that was in evidence.[39] Also, structure 48b, with the bulky heterocyclic moiety embedded under the bicyclic superstructure,

would be extremely sterically resistant to formation; Paquette thus
assigned the stereochemistry indicated by structure **48a** to the thietane 1,1-
dioxides (Table 6).

The 3′-substituted spiro[5-norbornene-2,2′-thietane]1′,1′-dioxides (**48a**)
were readily catalytically hydrogenated to their dihydroderivatives (**49**).

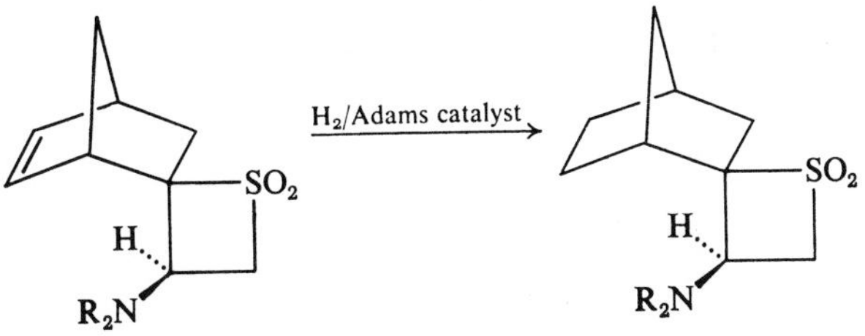

**(48a)**                                          **(49)**

The cycloaddition of chlorosulfene to various morpholine enamines was
reported by Paquette.[40] Addition of chloromethanesulfonyl chloride (**50**)
to an equimolar mixture of triethylamine and the morpholine enamines of
cyclopentanone (**51**), cyclohexanone, or cycloheptanone in dioxane solution resulted in the formation of the corresponding chloro morpholino-
thietane dioxides (**52**) (Table 7). A similar reaction with 1-methyl-4-

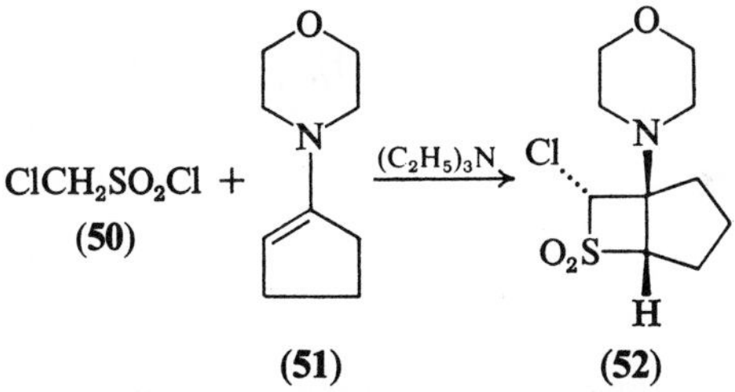

$ClCH_2SO_2Cl$ +
**(50)**

**(51)**                                          **(52)**

morpholino-1,2,5,6-tetrahydropyridine (**53**), however, gave both of the
possible isomeric cycloadducts (**54** and **55**).

Analogously, treatment of the morpholine enamine of 5-norbornene-2-
carboxaldehyde (**56**) with chlorosulfene (obtained from chloromethanesulfonyl chloride (**56**) and triethylamine (**57**)) gave a mixture of the two
isomers (**58** and **59**). The structural assignments were confirmed by nuclear
magnetic resonance (Table 7).

It has been shown that various sulfonyl chlorides react with ketene diethylacetal to give thietane dioxides.[54] Under similar conditions ketene
aminals yield either a cycloadduct, thiete dioxide, or a substitution product
depending on the nature of the reactants and the reaction media (Table
8).[13,33,36,58] For example, when methanesulfonyl chloride (**30**) was added

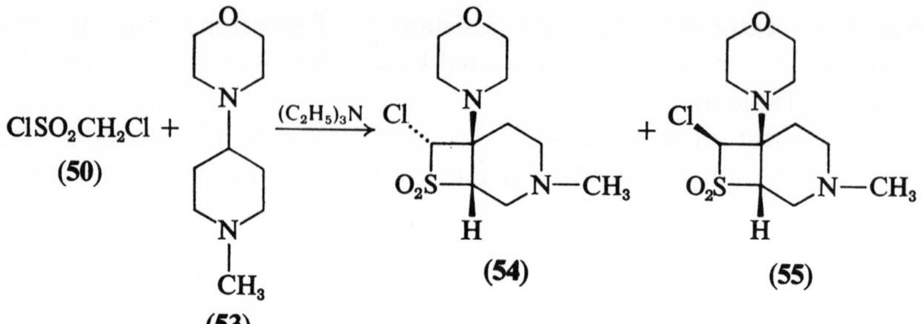

$$ClSO_2CH_2Cl + \mathbf{(50)}$$

$$\mathbf{(53)}$$

$$\xrightarrow{(C_2H_5)_3N}$$

$$\mathbf{(54)} \qquad + \qquad \mathbf{(55)}$$

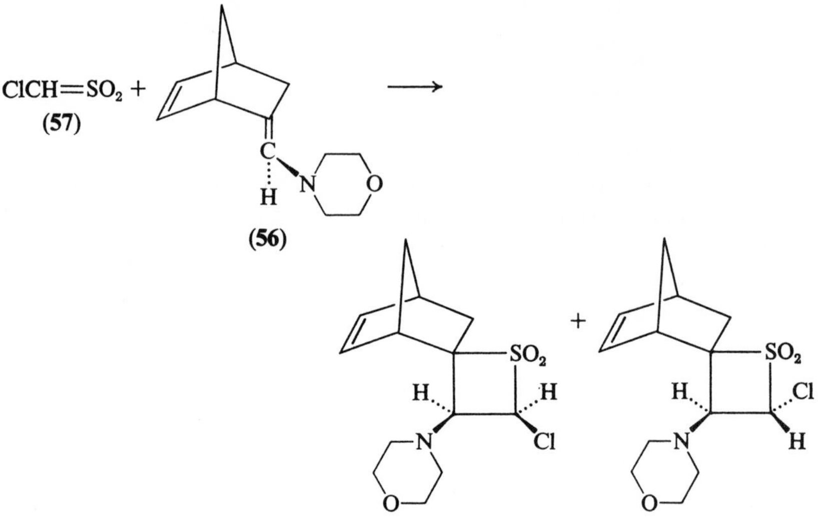

$$ClCH{=}SO_2 + \mathbf{(57)}$$

$$\mathbf{(56)}$$

$$\longrightarrow$$

$$\mathbf{(58)} \qquad + \qquad \mathbf{(59)}$$

to a solution of 1-ethoxy-$N,N$-dimethylvinylamine (**60**) and triethylamine in tetrahydrofuran at 0°C, the 3-dimethylaminothiete 1,1-dioxide (**61**) was obtained.[13]

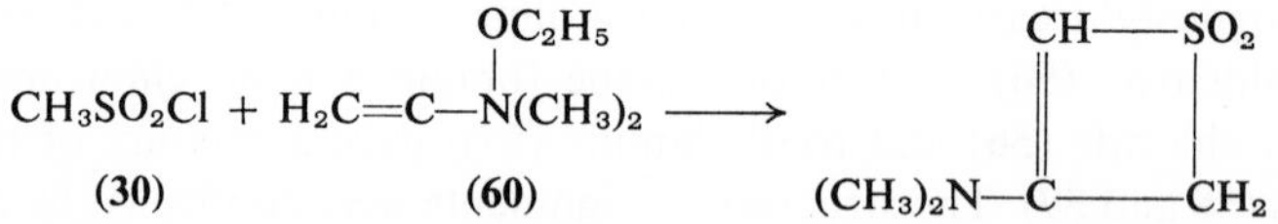

$$CH_3SO_2Cl + H_2C{=}\underset{\underset{\textstyle\mathbf{(60)}}{|}}{\overset{\overset{\textstyle OC_2H_5}{|}}{C}}{-}N(CH_3)_2 \longrightarrow$$

$$\mathbf{(30)}$$

$$(CH_3)_2N{-}\underset{\underset{\textstyle\mathbf{(61)}}{\textstyle CH_2}}{\overset{\overset{\textstyle CH{-\!\!-}SO_2}{|}}{C}}$$

Truce and Son[58] found that in tetrahydrofuran, 1,1-bis(diethylamino)-ethene (**62**) reacted with phenylmethanesulfonyl chloride (**11**) in the presence of triethylamine, to produce a substitution product, 1,1-bis(di-ethylamino)2-(phenylmethane sulfonyl)ethene (**63**) in 67% yield; none of the cycloadduct (**64**) was found. The reason for the formation of **63** and not the cycloadduct (64) may be due to an electronic as well as a steric

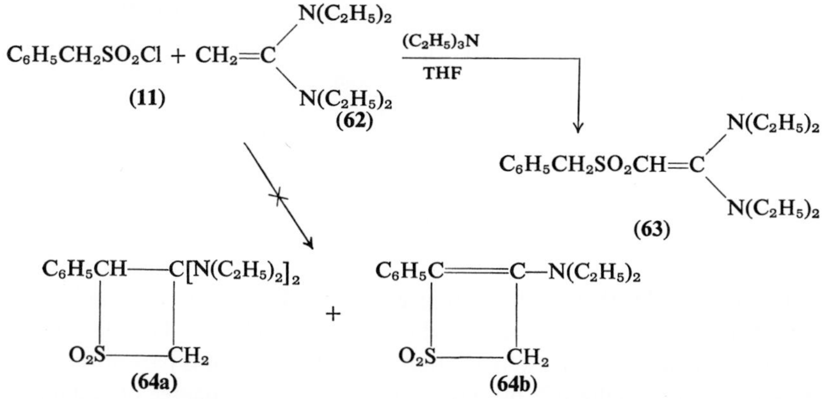

$$C_6H_5CH_2SO_2Cl + CH_2=C\begin{smallmatrix}N(C_2H_5)_2\\\\N(C_2H_5)_2\end{smallmatrix}$$

(11)                    (62)

$$\xrightarrow[THF]{(C_2H_5)_3N}$$

$$C_6H_5CH_2SO_2CH=C\begin{smallmatrix}N(C_2H_5)_2\\\\N(C_2H_5)_2\end{smallmatrix}$$

(63)

$$C_6H_5CH\!-\!C[N(C_2H_5)_2]_2$$
$$O_2S\!-\!CH_2$$
(64a)

+

$$C_6H_5C\!=\!C\!-\!N(C_2H_5)_2$$
$$O_2S\!-\!CH_2$$
(64b)

factor. The assigned structure was verified on the basis of elemental analysis, molecular weight determination, and infrared and nuclear magnetic resonance spectra. Structure 64b is preferred over the cyclic structure 64a, for in interactions of "sulfenes" with ketene aminals, no cycloadducts—without an elimination of one of the two amino groups—have been observed.[13,37] The same is true for the less hindered ketene $O,N$-acetal[13] (the alkoxyl group is eliminated). In contrast to these results, Opitz and Schempp[37] and Hasek et al.[13] found that 1,1-bis(dimorpholino)ethene (65) reacted with methanesulfonyl chloride (30) in ether and tetrahydrofuran to give 3-morpholinothietene 1,1-dioxide (66), whereas in chloroform only the substitution product, 1,1-bis(dimorpholino)-2-methanesulfonylethene (67) resulted.

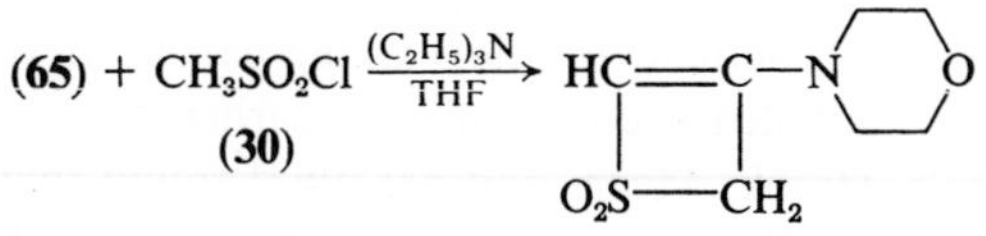

$$(65) + CH_3SO_2Cl \xrightarrow[THF]{(C_2H_5)_3N} HC\!=\!C\!-\!N\!\!\bigcirc\!\!O$$

(30)

$$O_2S\!-\!CH_2$$

(66)

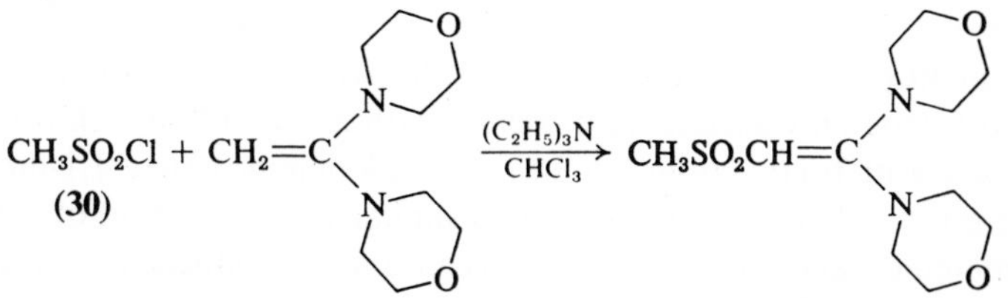

$$CH_3SO_2Cl + CH_2=C\begin{smallmatrix}N-\bigcirc O\\\\N-\bigcirc O\end{smallmatrix} \xrightarrow[CHCl_3]{(C_2H_5)_3N} CH_3SO_2CH=C\begin{smallmatrix}N-\bigcirc O\\\\N-\bigcirc O\end{smallmatrix}$$

(30)                    (65)                                                    (67)

It appears that the solvent is a major factor in determining the nature of the product. Chloroform, unlike the ethers, readily dissolves the triethylamine hydrochloride, produced by the dehydrochlorination of methane-

$$C_6H_5CH_2SO_2Cl + CH_2{=}C\overset{OC_2H_5}{\underset{OC_2H_5}{\diagdown}} \xrightarrow[\text{Et}_2\text{O}]{(C_2H_5)_3N} \quad \begin{array}{c} OC_2H_5 \\ | \\ C_6H_5CH\!-\!\!-\!\!-\!C\!-\!OC_2H_5 \\ | \qquad\qquad | \\ O_2S\!-\!\!-\!\!-\!\!-\!CH_2 \end{array}$$

$$\xrightarrow[\text{CHCl}_3]{(C_2H_5)_3N}$$

sulfonyl chloride, thereby liberating a source of protons. By employing ketene diethylacetal, no solvent effect was observed.[58] The difference between ketene acetal and ketene aminal (where nitrogen is part of the ring system) was rationalized[58] by assuming a difference in degree of stabilization of positive charge being developed at the carbon atom which is substituted either by alkoxyl or amino groups. Since the latter is more effective in stabilization of positive charge, the postulated zwitterion (probably formed by the addition of sulfene) would have a longer lifetime for picking up protons producing the substitution product. There is currently additional work being conducted on determining whether there is actually a

$$R\bar{C}HSO_2CH_2C^+\overset{X^-}{\underset{X_-}{\diagup}}$$

(X = O or N) (R = alkyl or aryl)

zwitterion produced by the sulfene addition taking part in these reactions.

Recently, in a more detailed account of their earlier work with ketene O,N- and N,N-acetals, Hasek, Meen, and Martin[14] found that methanesulfonyl chloride reacted with ketene N,N- and O,N-acetals in the presence of triethylamine in a nonpolar solvent to give 3-(dialkylamino)-thiete 1,1-dioxides; however, if polar solvents were used with N,N-acetals the predominant products were the acyclic sulfonylketene N,N-acetals.

When ketene O,N-acetals were treated with alkanesulfonyl chlorides in the presence of triethylamine (TEA), 3-(dialkylamino)thiete 1,1-dioxides (68) were formed. This cycloaddition is similar to the reaction of sulfenes with enamines and ketene acetals because the products are thietanes formed via 1,2-cycloaddition of a sulfene with a compound containing an electron-rich double bond. The products, thiete 1,1-dioxides (68), may have arisen from β-elimination of an alcohol from the intermediate thietane structure.

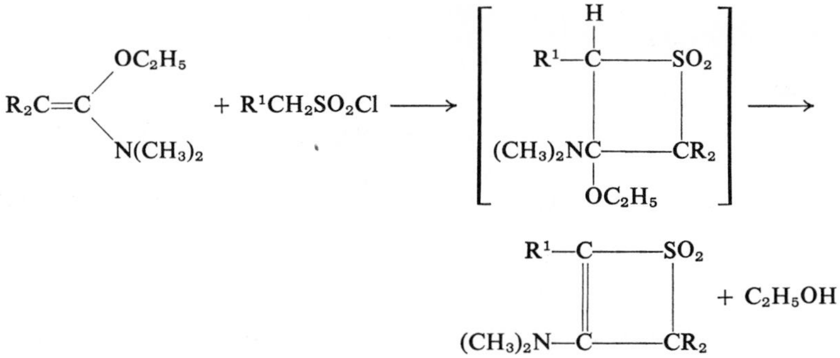

$$R_2C=C\begin{smallmatrix}OC_2H_5\\N(CH_3)_2\end{smallmatrix} + R^1CH_2SO_2Cl \longrightarrow \left[\begin{array}{c} H \\ R^1-C\!\!-\!\!-\!\!-SO_2 \\ \\ (CH_3)_2NC\!\!-\!\!-\!\!-CR_2 \\ OC_2H_5 \end{array}\right] \longrightarrow$$

$$\begin{array}{c} R^1-C\!\!-\!\!-\!\!-SO_2 \\ \\ (CH_3)_2N-C\!\!-\!\!-\!\!-CR_2 \end{array} + C_2H_5OH$$

(68)

$$\begin{pmatrix} 63a, R = H; R^1 = H \\ 63b, R = CH_3; R^1 = H \\ 63c, R = CH_3; R^1 = C_3H_7 \end{pmatrix}$$

Ketene $N,N$-acetals were found to react with alkanesulfonyl chlorides in the presence of triethylamine to give 3-(dialkylamino)thiete 1,1-dioxides and 2-alkylsulfonyl-1,1-bis(dialkylamino)ethylenes; the amounts of both products depend upon the solvent and the nature of the alkane group of the sulfonyl chloride. Nonpolar solvents such as tetrahydrofuran and benzene favored the formation of the cyclic derivatives (66) (79% and 69% yields, respectively), whereas in polar solvents such as acetonitrile and $N,N$-dimethylformamide, the acyclic derivative (67) was formed in 48–58% yields, respectively. The cyclic compounds exhibited characteristic

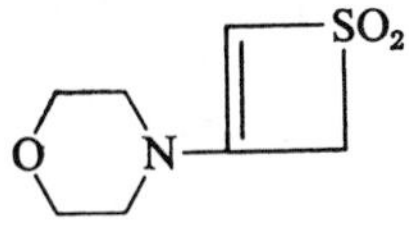

(66) 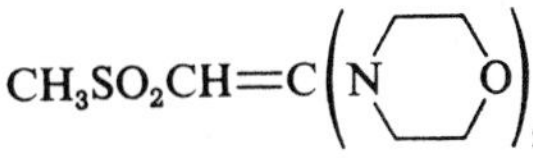                              (67)

strong infrared absorption bands at 6.1–6.2 $\mu$ (olefinic function) and 7.9–8.0 and 9.1 $\mu$ (sulfon function), and the cyclic materials showed bands at 6.5 $\mu$.

The reaction of methanesulfonyl chloride (30) with 4,4′-propenylidenedimorpholine (69) in the presence of triethylamine using tetrahydrofuran as solvent gave 52% yield of a mixture of 4-methyl-3-morpholinothiete 1,1-dioxide (70) and 2-methyl-3-morpholinothiete 1,1-dioxide (71) in the ratio of 3:1. The structures and amounts of 70 and 71 were determined by nuclear magnetic resonance spectra. The nuclear magnetic resonance spectrum of 71 showed an unusual long-range splitting; the methylene group appeared as a quartet at 4.12 ppm ($J = 2.1$ cps) and the methyl group as a triplet at 2.00 ppm ($J = 2.1$ cps).

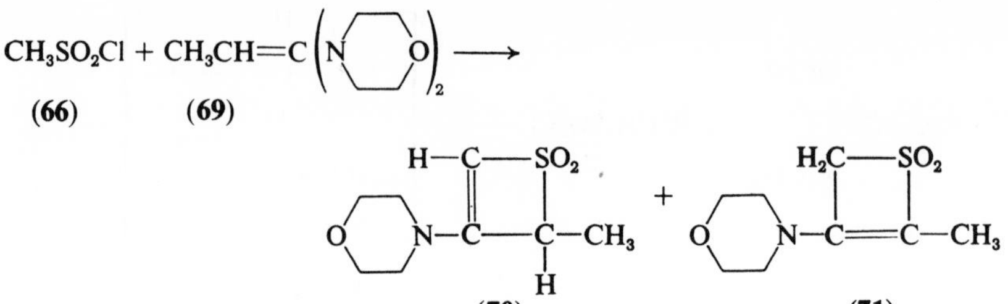

$$CH_3SO_2Cl + CH_3CH=C\left(N\overbrace{\phantom{xx}}O\right)_2 \longrightarrow$$

**(66)**          **(69)**

$$\text{(70)} \quad + \quad \text{(71)}$$

(70): structure with H—C—SO$_2$ / O-morpholine N—C—C—CH$_3$ with H

(71): structure H$_2$C—SO$_2$ / O-morpholine N—C=C—CH$_3$

The path of these reactions cannot be stated with certainty, but a postulated mechanism is shown below.

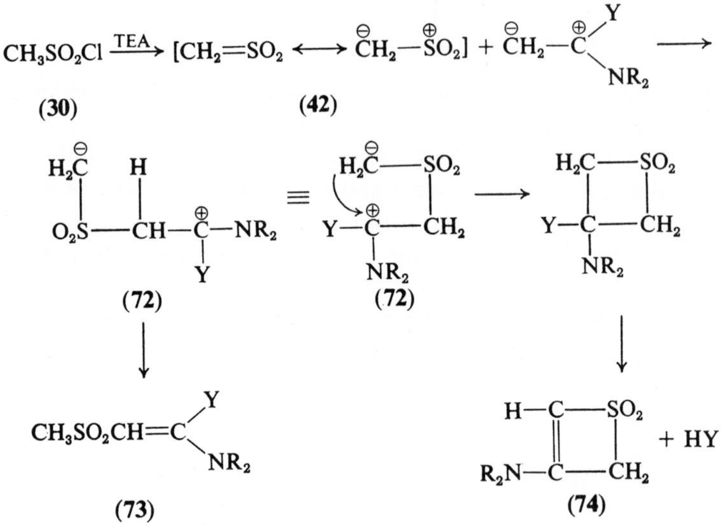

$$CH_3SO_2Cl \xrightarrow{\text{TEA}} [CH_2=SO_2 \longleftrightarrow \overset{\ominus}{C}H_2-\overset{\oplus}{S}O_2] + \overset{\ominus}{C}H_2-\overset{\oplus}{C}\overset{Y}{\underset{NR_2}{\diagdown}} \longrightarrow$$

**(30)**                              **(42)**

Structure (72):
$$\underset{O_2S}{\overset{\ominus}{H_2C}}\!-\!\overset{H}{\underset{Y}{C}}H\!-\!\overset{\oplus}{C}\!-\!NR_2 \equiv \begin{matrix} H_2\overset{\ominus}{C}\!-\!SO_2 \\ Y\!-\!\overset{\oplus}{C}\!-\!CH_2 \\ NR_2 \end{matrix} \longrightarrow \begin{matrix} H_2C\!-\!SO_2 \\ Y\!-\!C\!-\!CH_2 \\ NR_2 \end{matrix}$$

**(72)**                **(72)**

$$\downarrow \qquad\qquad\qquad\qquad \downarrow$$

$$CH_3SO_2CH=C\overset{Y}{\underset{NR_2}{\diagdown}} \qquad\qquad \begin{matrix} H\!-\!C\!-\!SO_2 \\ R_2N\!-\!C\!-\!CH_2 \end{matrix} + HY$$

**(73)**                **(74)**

(Y = OR or NR$_2$)

This mechanism assumes that triethylamine dehydrohalogenates methanesulfonyl chloride (**30**) producing the sulfene (**42**). The sulfene then adds to the electron-rich double bond of the ketene O,N- or N,N-acetal, forming the intermediate zwitterion (**72**). The path of collapse of **72** determines whether the ultimate product is **73** or **74**.

Other reports of thiete 1,1-dioxides are found in the literature[6-10,41,55,57]; however, the thiete 1,1-dioxides were not the product of a cycloaddition reaction. Thiete 1,1-dioxides are prepared by dehydrochlorination of a halothietane 1,1-dioxide (equation a),[6,7] by the Hofmann elimination of the ammonium salt of the thietane 1,1-dioxide (equation b),[9,57] and by the hydrolysis of a dialkoxythietane 1,1-dioxide (equation c).[55]

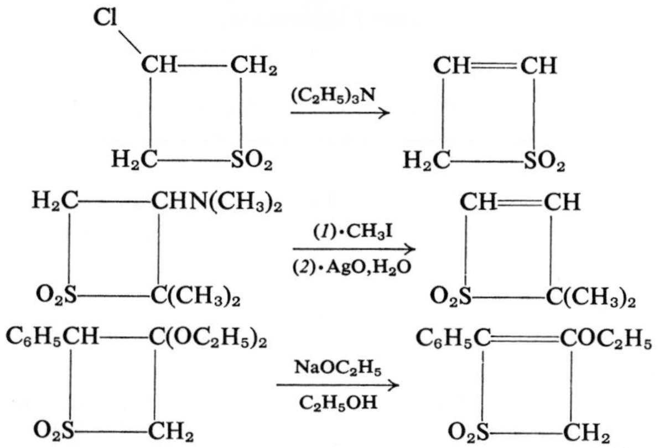

$$\text{(a)}$$

$$\text{(b)}$$

$$\text{(c)}$$

In conclusion, the dienophilic character of the thiete 1,1-dioxides has been recently discussed.[6,10,41] For example, thiete 1,1-dioxide or substituted thiete 1,1-dioxides react with dienes such as anthracene and 1,4-diphenyl-2,3-benzofuran to give the corresponding 1,4-cycloadducts.

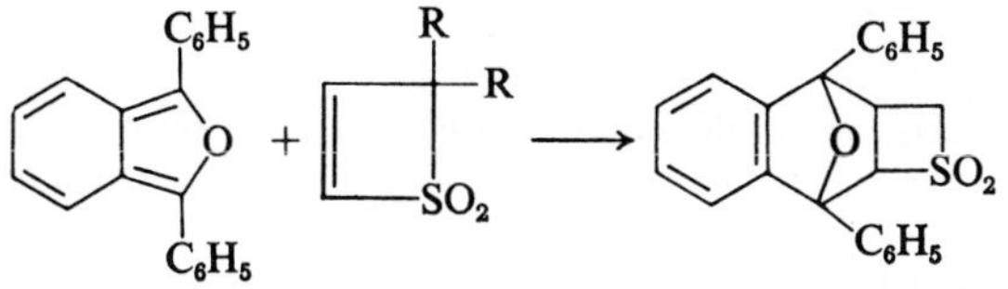

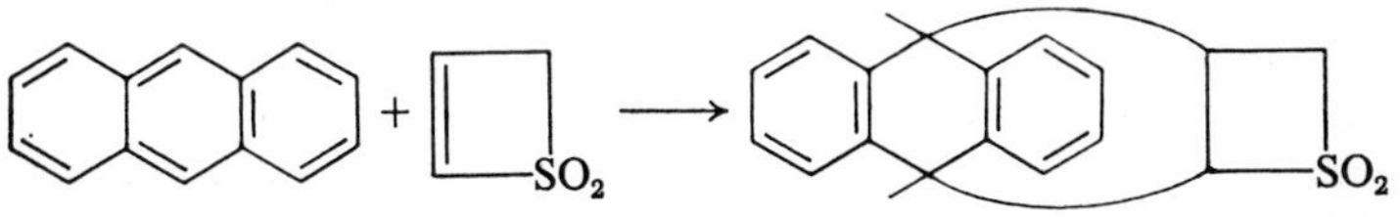

**Table 1**

Adducts of Hexafluorothioacetone with Vinyl Ethers or Sulfides [30]

| Adduct | BP (°C/mm) | $n_D^{25}$ | IR(CH) | $F_1^{19}$ NMR | Proton NMR (ppm) |
|---|---|---|---|---|---|
| $CH_3OCH$—$CH_2$[f] $S$—$C(CF_3)_2$ | 43/18 | 1.3750 | 3.35 3.45 | Single unsplit resonance band | 5.28[a] 3.30[b] 3.33[c] |
| $C_2H_5OCH$—$CH_2$ $S$—$C(CF_3)_2$ | 43/10 | 1.3793 | | Single unsplit resonance band | |

*(continued)*

**Table 1** (*continued*)

| Adduct | BP (°C/mm) | $n_D^{25}$ | IR(CH) | $F_1^{19}$ NMR | Proton NMR (ppm) |
|---|---|---|---|---|---|
| 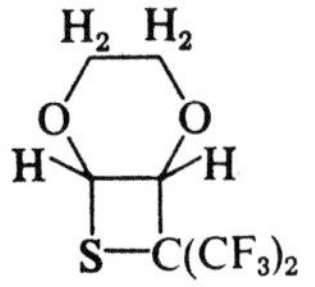 | 72–73/10 | 1.4068 | | Pair of quadruplets | 5.13[d] 3.87[d] 3.50–4.43[e] |
| 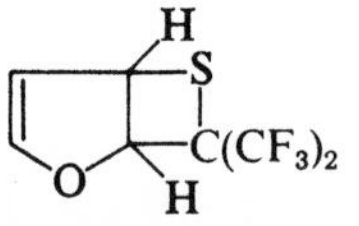 | 57/4.7 | | | Two quadruplets of equal area | |
| $t$-$C_4H_9S$—CH——CH$_2$ <br> S———C(CF$_3$)$_2$ | 38/0.6 | 1.4252 | | $A_3B_3$ pattern | |
| CH$_3$S—CH——CH$_2$ <br> S———C(CF$_3$)$_2$ | 40–41/3.6 | 1.4268 | | Two quadruplets of equal area | |

[a] Triplet ($J = 6$ cps).
[b] Doublet ($J = 6$ cps).
[c] Singlet.
[d] AB pattern of area 1.
[e] Multiplet of area 2.
[f] Mass spectrometer pattern ($m/e$): $C_2H_4OS^+$, 76; $C_6H_6F_6OS^+$, 240; $C_4H_2F_5^+$, 145; $C_3H_2F_3^+$, 95; $C_4H_2F_6^+$, 164.


**Table 2**
Thietane 1,1-Dioxides via Cycloaddition of Sulfonyl Chlorides to
Ketene Diethylacetal in the Presence of Triethylamine

| Sulfonyl chloride | Adduct | MP (°C) | Yield (%) | Ref. |
|---|---|---|---|---|
| CH$_3$SO$_2$Cl | H$_2$C—C(OC$_2$H$_5$)$_2$ <br> O$_2$S—CH$_2$ | 49–50 | 79 | 52 |
| | | | 65 | 54 |
| | | | 35 | 4 |

(*continued*)

**Table 2** (*continued*)

| Sulfonyl chloride | Adduct | MP (°C) | Yield (%) | Ref. |
|---|---|---|---|---|
| $C_6H_5CH_2SO_2Cl$ | $H_2C-C(OC_2H_5)_2$ <br> $O_2S-CHC_6H_5$ | 89–90 <br> 91–92 | 70 <br> 70 | 54 <br> 58 |
| $p\text{-}NO_2C_6H_4CH_2SO_2Cl$ | $H_2C-C(OC_2H_5)_2$ <br> $O_2S-CHC_6H_4NO_2\text{-}p$ | 113–114 | 54 | 54 |
| $p\text{-}CH_3C_6H_4CH_2SO_2Cl$ | $H_2C-C(OC_2H_5)_2$ <br> $O_2S-CHC_6H_4CH_3\text{-}p$ | 72–73.5 | 55 | 54 |
| $p\text{-}ClC_6H_4CH_2SO_2Cl$ | $H_2C-C(OC_2H_5)_2$ <br> $O_2S-CHC_6H_4Cl\text{-}p$ | 82–83 | — | 54 |
| $ClCH_2SO_2Cl$ | $H_2C-C(OC_2H_5)_2$ <br> $O_2S-CHCl$ | 72–74 | 31 | 54 |
| $CF_3CH_2SO_2Cl$ | $H_2C-C(OC_2H_5)_2$ <br> $O_2S-CHCF_3$ | 103–105 | 61 | 54 |
| $CH_2{=}CHCH_2SO_2Cl$ | $H_2C-C(OC_2H_5)_2$ <br> $O_2S-CHCH{=}CH_2$ | 46–48 | 46 | 54 |
| $CH_3CH{=}CHSO_2Cl$ | $H_2C-C(OC_2H_5)_2$ <br> $O_2S-C{=}CHCH_3$ | 49–50 | 51 | 54 |

**Table 3**

Nuclear Magnetic Resonance Values ($\delta$) for Thietane 1,1-Dioxides[a,54]

| R | a | b | c | d | e | Relative areas, a:b:c:d:e |
|---|---|---|---|---|---|---|
| H | 1.25 (3) | 3.48 (4) | 4.19 (1) | — | — | 3:2:2 |
| $C_6H_5$ | 1.10 (3) | 3.45 (4) | 4.12 (1) | 5.37 (1) | 7.34 (c) | 6:4:2:1:5 |
| $p\text{-}NO_2C_6H_4$ | 1.18 (3d) | 3.42 (4) | 4.31 (1) | 5.55 (1) | 7.98 (c) | 6:4:2:1:4 |
| $p\text{-}ClC_6H_4$ | 1.16 (3) | 3.38 (4) | 4.12 (1) | 5.35 (1) | 7.35 (4) | 6:4:2:1:4 |
| $p\text{-}CH_3C_6H_4$[b] | 1.18 (3) | 3.38 (4) | 4.09 (1) | 5.29 (1) | 7.22 (4) | 6:4:2:1:4 |
| Cl | 1.28 (3) | 3.60 (4) | 4.11 (1) | 5.45 (1) | — | 6:4:2:1 |

(*continued*)

**Table 3** (*continued*)

| R | a | b | c | d | e | Relative areas, a:b:c:d:e |
|---|---|---|---|---|---|---|
| CH$_2$=CH | 1.23 (*3*) | 3.48 (*4*) | 4.00 (*c*) | 5.48 (*c*) | 5.25 and 4.78 (*c*) | 6:2:3:7:4[c] |
| CF$_3$ | 1.23 (*3*) | 3.52 (*c*) | 4.26 (*c*) | 4.71 (*c*) | — | 6:4:2:8 |

[a] The multiplicity is expressed as: (*1*) singlet; (*3*) triplet; (*3d*) double triplet; (*4*) quartet; (*c*) complex or multiplet.

[b] For the *p*-CH$_3$ group the shift is 2.35δ, which appears as a singlet in a relative ratio of 3.

[c] The c, d, and e hydrogens do not exhibit first order splitting and appear as a complex multipet; however, the total integrated relative area is 4.

**Table 4**

Thietane 1,1-Dioxides via Cycloaddition of Sulfonyl Halides to Enamines

| Sulfonyl halide | Enamine | Cycloadduct | MP (BP) | Yield (%) | Ref. |
|---|---|---|---|---|---|
| CH$_3$SO$_2$Cl | 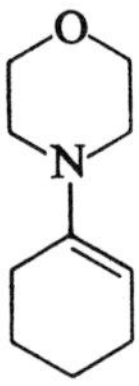 | 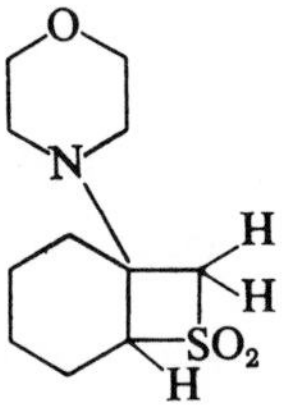 | 139–140 136 | 54 | 46 4 12 |
| CH$_3$SO$_2$Cl | 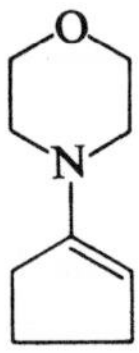 | 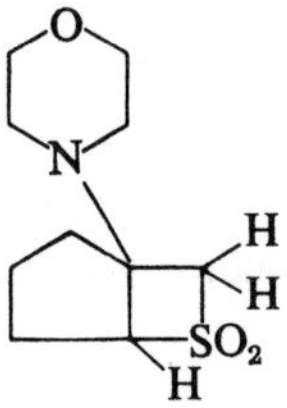 | 117–120 | 77 | 46 4 |
| CH$_3$SO$_2$Cl | 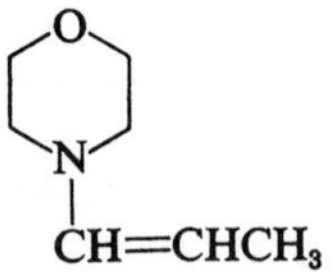 | 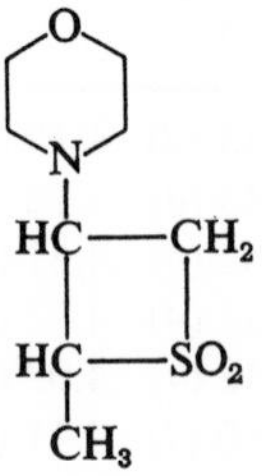 | 64–65 | 71 | 4 46 |

(*continued*)

**Table 4** (*continued*)

| ılfonyl halide | Enamine | Cycloadduct | MP (BP) | Yield (%) | Ref. |
|---|---|---|---|---|---|
| H$_3$SO$_2$Cl | C(CH$_3$)$_2$ on N–CH (pyrrolidine) | (CH$_3$)$_2$C—SO$_2$ / N—HC—CH$_2$ | 68 | 80 | 34 |
| | | | 67–68 | 80 | 36 |
| ₆H$_5$CH$_2$SO$_2$Cl | 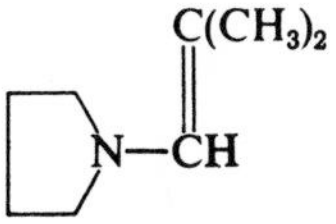 C(CH$_3$)$_2$ on N–CH (pyrrolidine) | 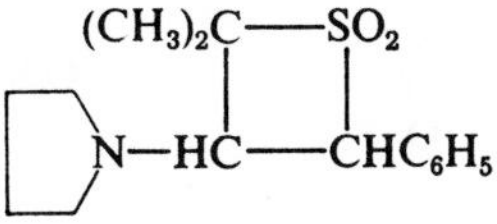 (CH$_3$)$_2$C—SO$_2$ / N—HC—CHC$_6$H$_5$ | 161 | 70 | 34 |
| H$_3$SO$_2$Cl | 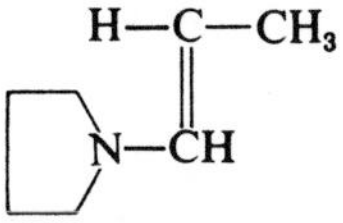 H–C—CH$_3$ on N–CH (pyrrolidine) | 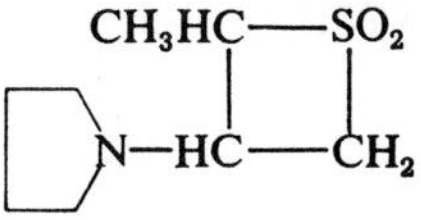 CH$_3$HC—SO$_2$ / N—HC—CH$_2$ | (121/10$^{-3}$) | 90 | 34 |
| H$_3$SO$_2$Cl | 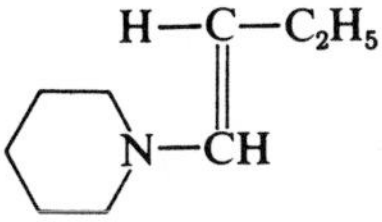 H—C—C$_2$H$_5$ on N—CH (piperidine) | 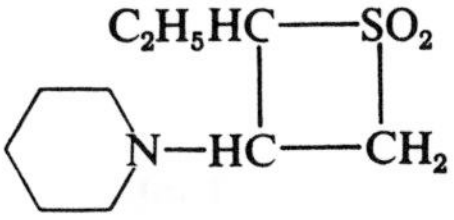 C$_2$H$_5$HC—SO$_2$ / N—HC—CH$_2$ | 114 | 83 | 34 |
| ₆H$_5$CH$_2$SO$_2$Cl | 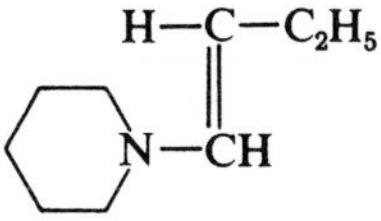 H—C—C$_2$H$_5$ on N—CH (piperidine) | 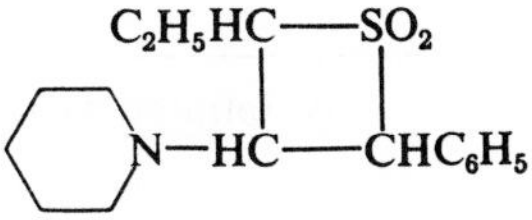 C$_2$H$_5$HC—SO$_2$ / N—HC—CHC$_6$H$_5$ | 170 | 65 | 34 |
| H$_3$CH$_2$CH$_2$SO$_2$Cl | 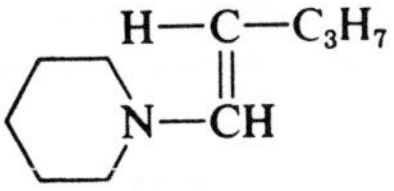 H—C—C$_3$H$_7$ on N—CH (piperidine) | 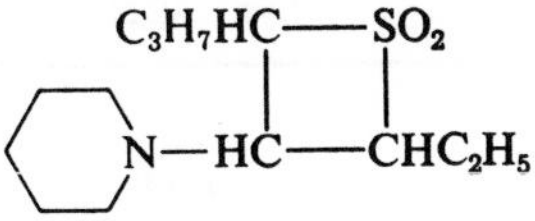 C$_3$H$_7$HC—SO$_2$ / N—HC—CHC$_2$H$_5$ | — | 88 | 34 |
| H$_3$SO$_2$Cl | 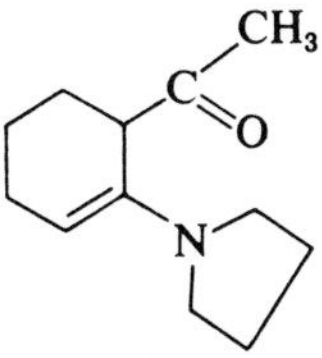 cyclohexene enamine with COCH$_3$ and pyrrolidine N | 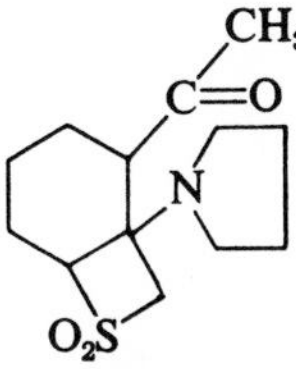 bicyclic cycloadduct with COCH$_3$, N-pyrrolidine, O$_2$S | 80–82 | 80 | 38 |
| H$_3$SO$_2$Cl | 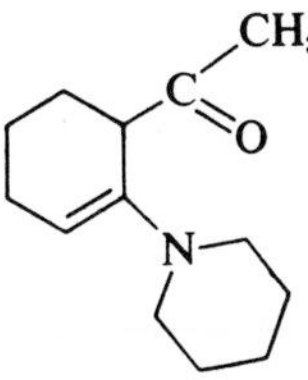 cyclohexene enamine with COCH$_3$ and piperidine N | 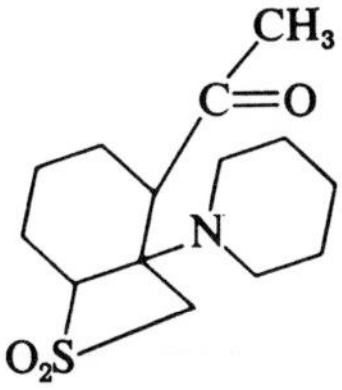 bicyclic cycloadduct with COCH$_3$, N-piperidine, O$_2$S | 118–119 | 57 | 38 |

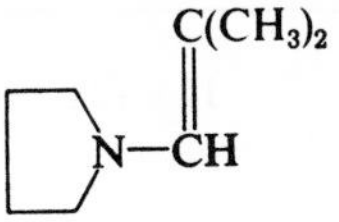

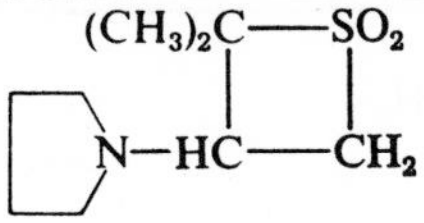

(*continued*)

**Table 4** (*continued*)

| Sulfonyl halide | Enamine | Cycloadduct | MP (BP) | Yield (%) | Ref. |
|---|---|---|---|---|---|
| CH$_3$SO$_2$Cl | 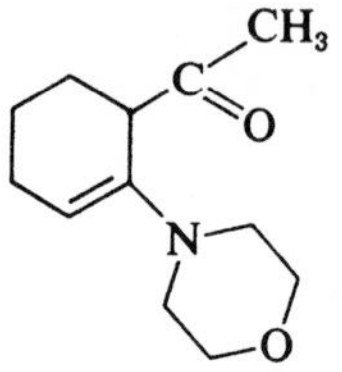 | 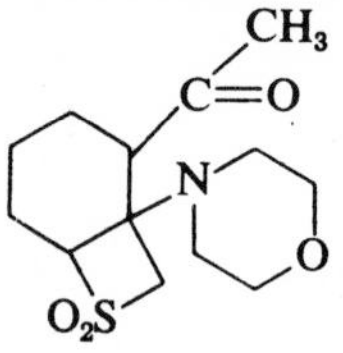 | 123–124 | 66 | 38 |
| CH$_3$SO$_2$Cl | (CH$_3$)$_2$NCH=C(CH$_3$)$_2$ | 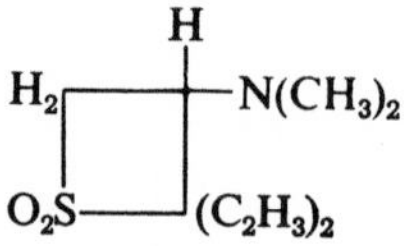 | (80–81/0.3) | 75–80 | 57 |

**Table 5**

Nuclear Magnetic Resonance and Infrared Data on Thietane 1,1-Dioxides[4]

| | A. Infrared data, $\mu$ | | |
|---|---|---|---|
| | Sulfone | | |
| Adduct | Sym. stretch | Asym. stretch | Ether |
| 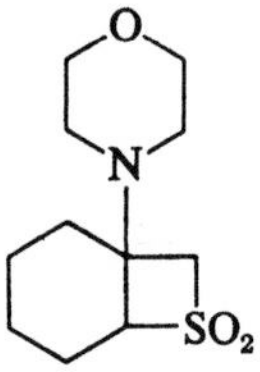 | 7.60 | 8.58 | 8.97 |
| 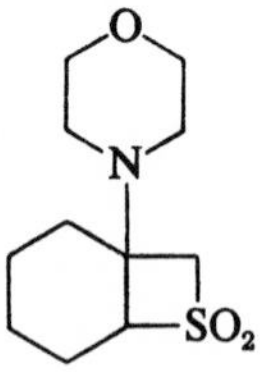 | 7.64 | 8.40 8.51 | 8.96 |

(*continued*)

**Table 5** (*continued*)

### A. Infrared data, $\mu$

| Adduct | Sulfone | | Ether |
|---|---|---|---|
| | Sym. stretch | Asym. stretch | |
| | 7.5<br>7.65 | 8.67 | 9.00 |
| | 7.6 | 8.4 | |

### B. Nuclear Magnetic Resonance Data (ppm)

| Adduct | NMR ($CHCl_3$) | | | | | NMR (HCl)[6] | | | | | | |
|---|---|---|---|---|---|---|---|---|---|---|---|---|
| | a | b | c | d | e | f | g | a | b | c | d | e |
| | 6.1[1] | 5.6[2] | 7.45[3] | 6.3[4] | 8.25[5] | — | — | 5.1 | 4.5 | 5.5 | 6.2 | 6.85<br>7.10<br>7.30<br>7.50<br>7.90[7] |
| | — | — | — | — | — | — | — | — | — | — | — | — |

(*continued*)

**Table 5** (*continued*)

|  | B. Nuclear Magnetic Resonance Data (ppm) | | | | | | | | | | | |
|  | NMR (CHCl$_3$) | | | | | | NMR (HCl)[6] | | | | | |
| Adduct | a | b | c | d | e | f | g | a | b | c | d | e |
| 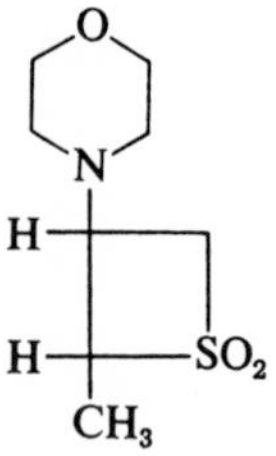 | 5.63[8] 5.76[8] 5.97[8] 6.02[8] 6.10[8] | — | 7.60[3] 7.15[9] 7.28[9] 7.42[9] | 6.32[4] | — | 8.5[10] | — | — | — | — | — | — |
| | 5.95[11] | — | — | — | — | — | 8.80[12] | 6.6[13] | — | — | — | — |

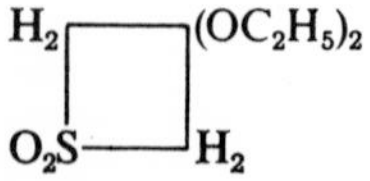

[1] Center of AB quartet with $J = 12.5$ cps for two nonequivalent H of —CH$_2$SO$_2$—.
[2] Broad multiplet for tertiary H of CH—SO$_2$—.
[3] Center of triplet for 4H of —CH$_2$NCH$_2$—
[4] Center of triplet for 4H of —CH$_2$OCH$_2$—.
[5] Center of broad peak for 8H of cyclohexane ring.
[6] In acid the sulfone hydrogens shift down-field from 6.1 and 5.6τ to 5.1 and 4.5τ and are now seen separately from the hydrogens next to the morpholine oxygen. The hydrogens next to morpholine nitrogen overlap some cyclohexane ring methylene hydrogen absorption but are distinct in acid solution since they are shifted from 7.45τ to 5.5τ.
[7] Main peak.

[8] Multiplet for 3H of —CH$_2$—SO$_2$—$\overset{\text{H}}{\underset{|}{\text{C}}}$—.

[9] Triplet for ring H next to nitrogen.
[10] Doublet for 3H of CH$_3$—C—.
[11] Singlet, 4H of —CH$_2$—SO$_2$—CH$_2$—.
[12] Triplet, 6H from methyl of ethyl group.
[13] Quartet, 4H from methylenes of ethyl group.

**Table 6**

3'-Substituted Spiro[5-Norbornene-2,2'-Thietane]1',1'-Dioxides [39]

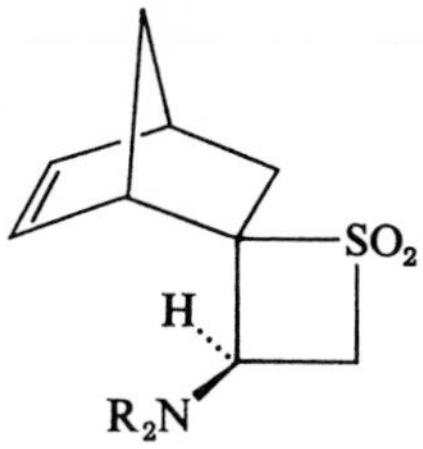

| $R_2N$ | MP (°C) | Yield (%) |
|---|---|---|
| 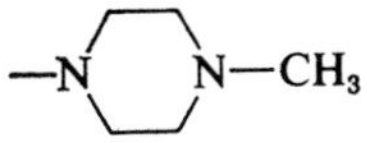 —N\_\_\_N—CH₃ | 162–164 | 45.2 |
| 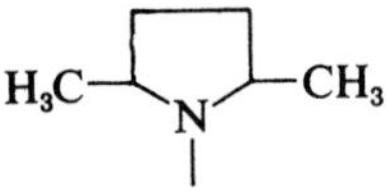 H₃C—\_\_\_—CH₃ (N) | 102–104 | 47.5 |
| 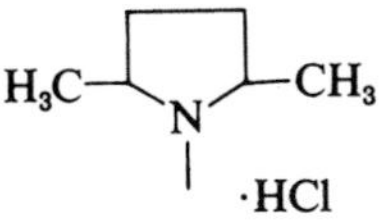 H₃C—\_\_\_—CH₃ (N) ·HCl | 207–209 (dec.) | — |
| 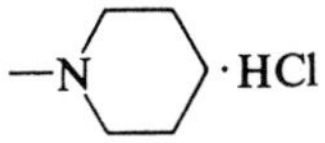 —N\_\_\_·HCl | 243 (dec.) | 44.5 |
| 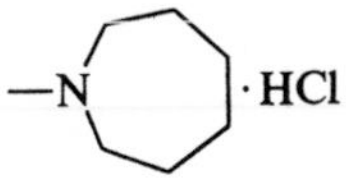 —N\_\_\_·HCl | 221 (dec.) | 69.0 |
| 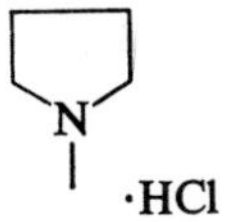 N ·HCl | 238 (dec.) | 63.5 |
| 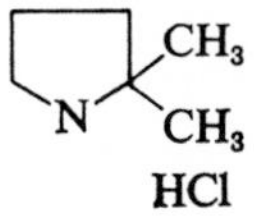 N—CH₃ / CH₃ HCl | 234 (dec.) | 59.8 |

(*continued*)

**Table 6** (*continued*)

| R$_2$N | MP (°C) | Yield (%) |
|---|---|---|
| 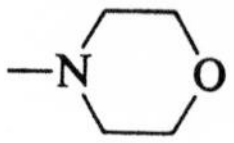 —N⟨   ⟩O | 128–129 | 76.6 |
| 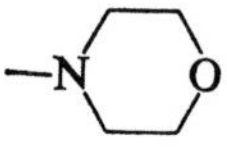 —N⟨   ⟩O·HCl | 225–226 (dec.) | — |

**Table 7**

α-Halothietane Dioxides[40]

| Cycloadduct | MP (°C) | Yield (%) | $SO_2$ (cm$^{-1}$) | NMR parameters δ-units CDCl₃ | | |
|---|---|---|---|---|---|---|
| | | | | | | |
| 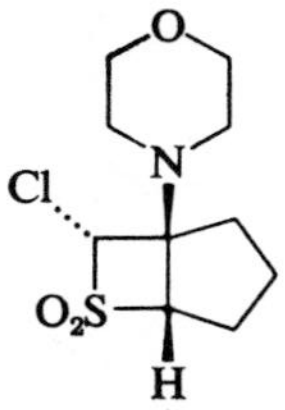 | 131–133 | 37.2 | 1321 1110 | 5.71 ($J = 2.5$)[a] | 4.54[b] | — |
| 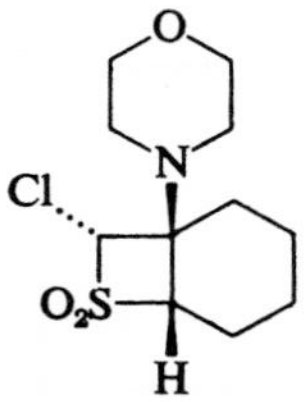 | 155–157 | 40.8 | 1323 1141 | 5.49 ($J = 1.5$)[a] | 4.27[b] | — |

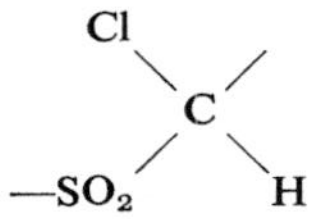

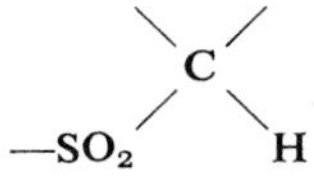

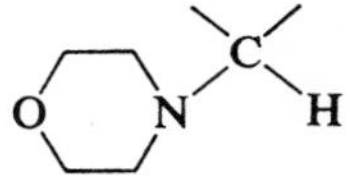

(continued)

**Table 7** (*continued*)

| Cycloadduct | MP (°C) | Yield (%) | $SO_2$ (cm$^{-1}$) | NMR parameters δ-units CDCl$_3$ | | |
|---|---|---|---|---|---|---|
| | | | | 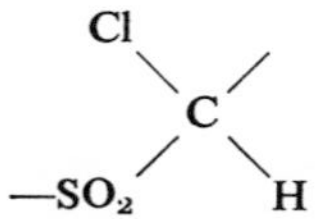 Cl, H / —SO$_2$ | 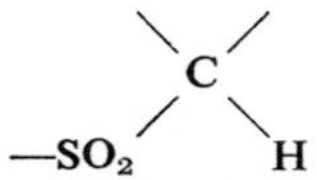 H / —SO$_2$ | 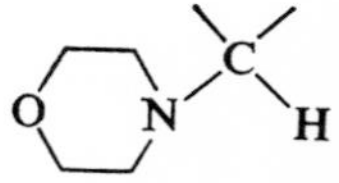 morpholine CH |
| 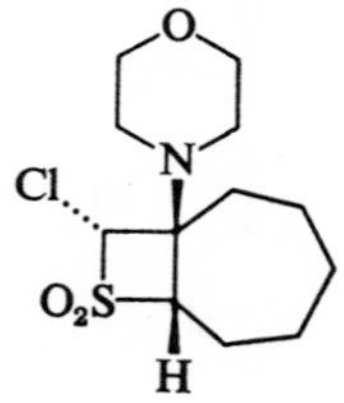 | 131–133 | 35.6 | 1319 1165 | c | | |
| 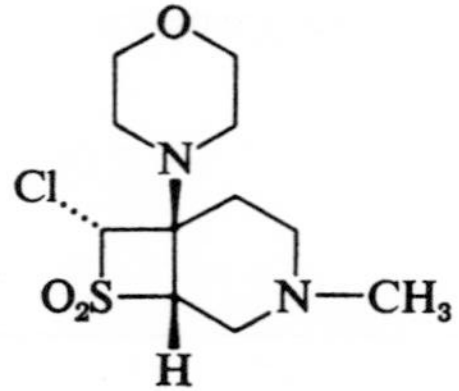 | 149 | 39.2 | 1325 1192 | 5.58 (J = 2.0)[a] | 4.35[b] | |

| | | | | |
|---|---|---|---|---|
| 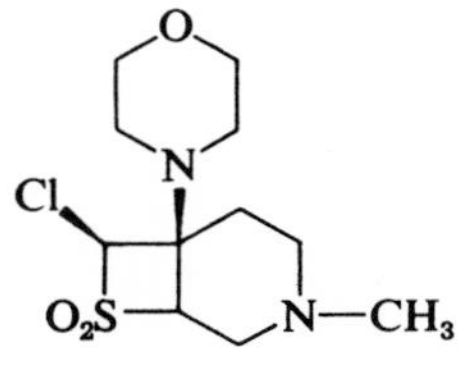 153–155 (dec) | — | 1328<br>1160 | 5.22 ($J$ = 2.0)a | 4.50b |
| 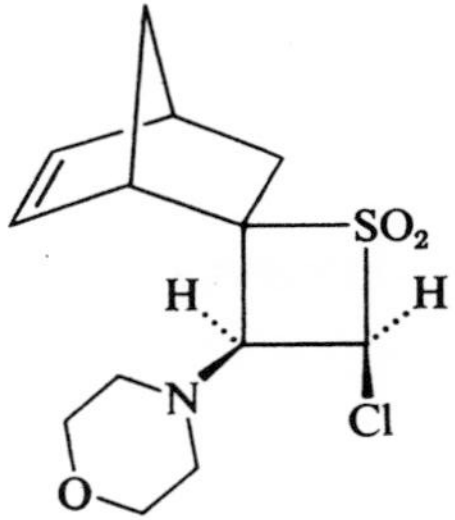 162–164 | 48.7 | — | 5.80 ($J$ = 9)d | 3.42 ($J$ = 9)d |
| 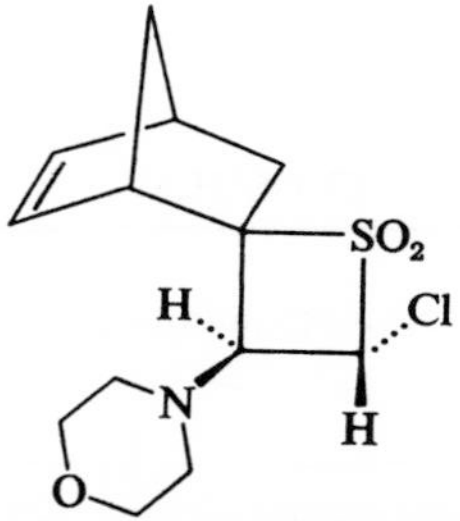 125–126 | — | — | 5.50 ($J$ = 5)d | 3.04 ($J$ = 5)d |

a Triplet.   b Broad doublet with small additional splitting.   c Spectrum could only be obtained in dimethyl sulfoxide.   d Doublet.

**Table 8**

Thiete 1,1-Dioxides via Cycloaddition Reaction of Sulfonyl Chlorides and Ketene Aminals

A. Physical Data

| No. | Sulfonyl chloride | Ketene aminal | Cycloadduct | MP (°C) | Yield (%) | Ref. |
|---|---|---|---|---|---|---|
| I | $CH_3SO_2Cl$ | 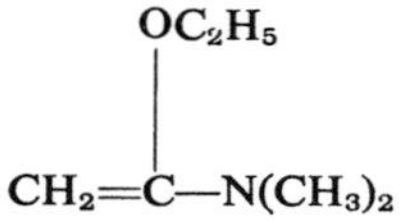 $OC_2H_5$, $CH_2{=}C{-}N(CH_3)_2$ | 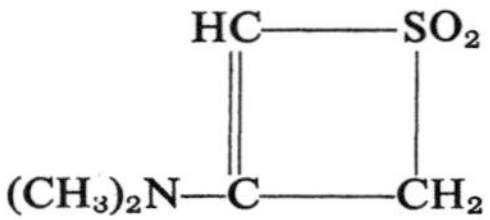 $HC{=}C({-}N(CH_3)_2){-}C({-}OC_2H_5){-}SO_2{-}CH_2$ (thiete 1,1-dioxide) | 121–123 | 34 | 13 |
| II | $CH_3SO_2Cl$ | $OC_2H_5$, $(CH_3)_2C{=}C{-}N(CH_3)_2$ | $HC{=}C({-}N(CH_3)_2){-}C({-}OC_2H_5){-}SO_2{-}C(CH_3)_2$ (thiete 1,1-dioxide) | 120–123 | 33 | 14 |
| | | | | 135–136 | 62 | 13 |
| III | $CH_3SO_2Cl$ | $CH_2{=}C({-}N\text{-morpholino})_2$ | $HC{=}C({-}N\text{-morpholino}){-}C{-}SO_2{-}CH_2$ (thiete 1,1-dioxide) | 135–136 | 69 | 14 |
| | | | | 140–142 | 84 | 13 |
| IV | $CH_3SO_2Cl$ | $CH_3CH{=}C({-}N\text{-morpholino})_2$ | $HC{=}C({-}N\text{-morpholino}){-}C{-}SO_2{-}CHCH_3$ (thiete 1,1-dioxide) | 140–141 | 79 | 14 |
| | | | | 144 | 72 | 37 |
| | | 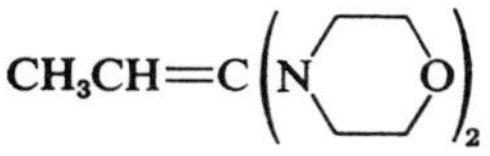 | 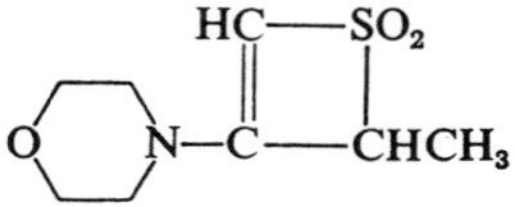 | 136–138[a] | 34[a] | 37 |
| | | | 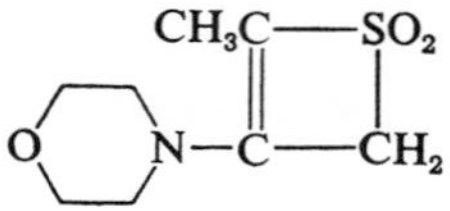 $CH_3C{=}C({-}N\text{-morpholino}){-}C{-}SO_2{-}CH_2$ (thiete 1,1-dioxide) | 136–138[a] | 52[a] | 14 |

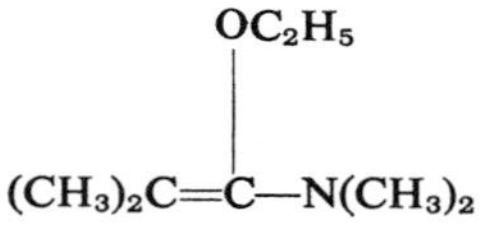

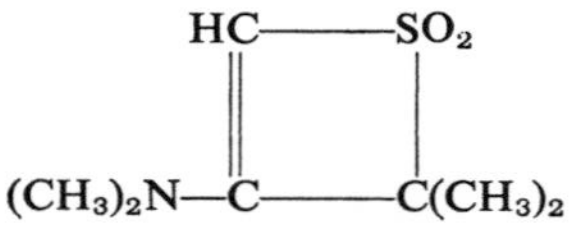

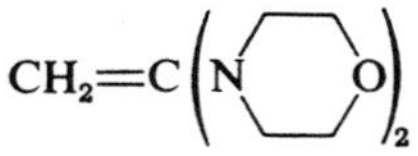

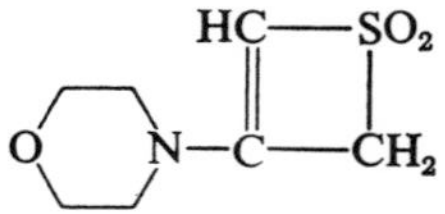

| | | | | | |
|---|---|---|---|---|---|
| V | $C_6H_5CH_2CH_2SO_2Cl$ | 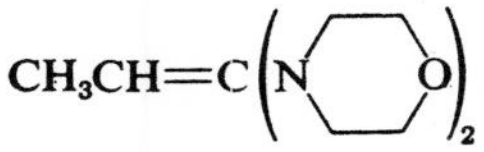 $CH_3CH=C(N\overset{O}{\underset{}{)}_2}$ | 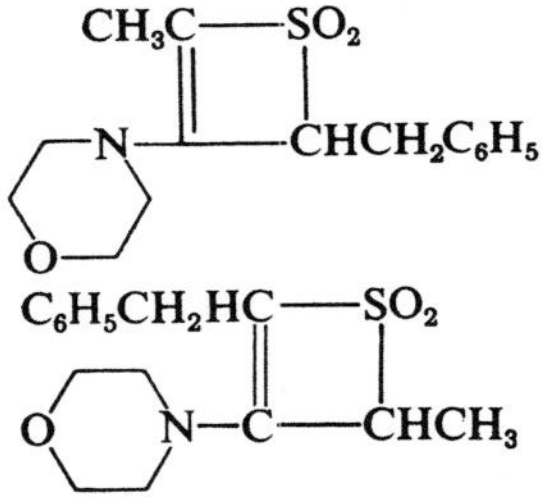 | 139–142[a] | 33[a] 37 |
| VI | $C_3H_7CH_2SO_2Cl$ | 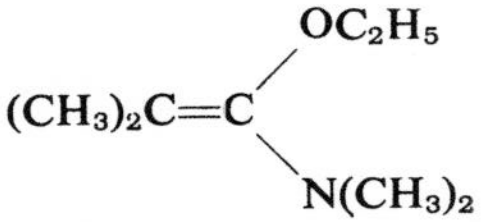 $(CH_3)_2C=C\overset{OC_2H_5}{\underset{N(CH_3)_2}{}}$ | 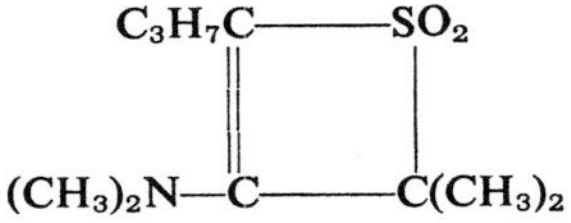 | 59–60.5 | 22 14 |

[a] Mixture.

(*continued*)

**Table 8** (*continued*)

B. Spectral Data, NMR (ppm)[13, 14, 37]

| Thiete 1,1-dioxide | IR ($\mu$) | CH | N(CH$_3$)$_2$ | CH$_2$ | CH=CH | C—CH$_3$ | CH$_3$CH$_2$CH$_2$ | (CH$_3$)$_2$ | —CH$_2$C≡C | |
|---|---|---|---|---|---|---|---|---|---|---|
| I | 6.10<br>7.95<br>9.15 | — | 2.90[a] | 4.35[a] | 5.23[a] | — | — | — | — | — |
| II | 6.20<br>(6.21)<br>8.00<br>9.20 | — | 2.88[a]<br>(2.92) | (4.45)<br>— | (5.22)<br>5.03[a]<br>(5.05) | 1.68[a] | — | (1.67) | — | — |
| III | (6.19)<br>6.20<br>7.90<br>8.85<br>9.05 | — | | 4.38[a]<br>(4.40) | 5.30[a] | | | | | 3.19[b]<br>(3.20)<br>(3.75)<br>3.76[b] |
| IV | 6.2<br>7.9<br>9.1 | 4.82[e] | | | 5.49[a] | 1.19[d] | | | | 3.34[c]<br>3.94 |
| VI | 6.15<br>8.00<br>9.10 | | 2.95[a] | 1.62[c] | | | 0.97[b] | 1.57[a] | 2.31[b] | |

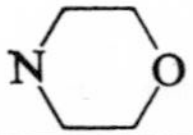

[a] Singlet.    [b] Triplet.    [c] Multiplet.    [d] Doublet.    [e] Quartet.

REFERENCES

1. H. J. Backer and H. Kloosterziel, *Proc. Koninkl. Ned. Akad. Wetenschap*, **53**, 1507 (1950).
2. J. A. Berson, "Carbonium Ion Rearrangements In Bridged Bicyclic Systems," in *Molecular Rearrangements*, P. de Mayo, Ed., Interscience, New York, 1963.
3. F. G. Bordwell and W. H. McKellin, *J. Am. Chem. Soc.*, **73**, 2251 (1951).
4. I. Borowitz, *J. Am. Chem. Soc.*, **86**, 1146 (1964).
5. H. Burgess and T. M. Lowry, *J. Chem. Soc.*, **127**, 271 (1925).
6. D. C. Dittmer and M. E. Christy, *J. Am. Chem. Soc.*, **84**, 399 (1962).
7. D. C. Dittmer and M. E. Christy, *J. Org. Chem.*, **26**, 1324 (1961).
8. D. C. Dittmer and F. A. Davis, *J. Am. Chem. Soc.*, **87**, 2064 (1965).
9. D. C. Dittmer and F. A. Davis, *J. Org. Chem.*, **29**, 3131 (1964).
10. D. C. Dittmer and N. Taskashina, *Tetrahedron Letters*, **1964**, 3809.
11. Y. Etienne, R. Soulas, and H. Lumbroso, *Compounds with Three- and Four-Membered Rings* (*The Chemistry of Heterocyclic Compounds*, Vol. 19, A. Weissberger, Ed.), Interscience, New York, 1964, p. 647.
12. R. Fusco, S. Rossi, and S. Maiorano, *Chim. Ind.* (*Milan*), **44**, 873 (1962); *Chem. Abstr.*, **60**, 13240 (1964).
13. R. H. Hasek, P. G. Gott, R. H. Meen, and J. C. Martin, *J. Org. Chem.*, **28**, 2496 (1963).
14. R. H. Hasek, R. H. Meen, and J. C. Martin, *J. Org. Chem.*, **30**, 1495 (1965).
15. T. Hasselström, *Acta Acad. Sci. Fennicae*, **A30** (12) (1930).
16. E. Henmo, P. de Mayo, A. B. M. A. Sattar, and A. Stoessl, *Proc. Chem. Soc.*, **1961**, 238.
17. G. Hesse and S. Majmudar, *Chem. Ber.*, **93**, 1129 (1960).
18. G. Hesse, E. Reichold, and S. Majmudar, *Chem. Ber.*, **90**, 2106 (1957).
19. P. Hirsjärvi and E. Tommila, *Acta Chem. Scand.*, **5**, 1097 (1951).
20. J. F. King and T. Durst, *J. Am. Chem. Soc.*, **85**, 2676 (1963).
21. J. F. King and T. Durst, *J. Am. Chem. Soc.*, **86**, 287 (1964).
22. J. F. King and T. Durst, *Tetrahedron Letters*, **1963**, 585.
23. J. F. King, P. de Mayo, E. Morkved, A. B. M. A. Sattar, and A. Stoessl, *Can. J. Chem.*, **41**, 100 (1963).
24. H. Kloosterziel and H. J. Backer, *Rec. Trav. Chim.*, **71**, 1235 (1952).
25. H. Kloosterziel, J. S. Boerema, and H. J. Backer, *Rec. Trav. Chim.* **72**, 612 (1953).
26. H. Kloosterziel, M. H. Deinema, and H. J. Backer, *Rec. Trav. Chim.*, **71**, 1228 (1952).
27. M. E. Kuehne, *J. Org. Chem.*, **28**, 2124 (1963).
28. A. Locher and H. E. Fierz, *Helv. Chim. Acta*, **10**, 642 (1927).
29. S. M. McElvain, *Chem. Rev.*, **45**, 453 (1949).
30. W. J. Middleton, *J. Org. Chem.*, **30**, 1395 (1965).
31. N. P. Neureiter and F. G. Bordwell, *J. Am. Chem. Soc.*, **85**, 1209 (1963).
32. J. R. Norell, "Cycloaddition by 'Sulfene' Intermediates. I. The Synthesis and Chemistry of Thietane Dioxides," Ph.D. Thesis, Purdue University, Lafayette, Indiana, 1964.
33. G. Opitz, *Angew. Chem.*, **76**, 724 (1964); *Angew. Chem. Intern. Ed. Engl.*, **3**, 708 (1964).
34. G. Opitz and H. Adolph, *Angew. Chem.*, **74**, 77 (1962); *Angew. Chem. Intern. Ed. Engl.*, **1**, 113 (1962).
5. G. Opitz and K. Fischer, *Angew. Chem.*, **77**, 41 (1965); *Angew. Chem. Intern. Ed. Engl.*, **4**, 70 (1965).

36. G. Opitz and K. Fischer, *Z. Naturforsch.*, **18B**, 775 (1963).
37. G. Opitz and H. Schempp, *Z. Naturforsch.*, **19B**, 78 (1964).
38. G. Opitz and E. Tempel, *Angew. Chem. Intern. Ed. Engl.*, 3, 754 (1964).
39. L. A. Paquette, *J. Org. Chem.*, **29**, 2851 (1964).
40. L. A. Paquette, *J. Org. Chem.*, **29**, 2854 (1964).
41. L. A. Paquette, *J. Org. Chem.*, **30**, 629 (1965).
42. R. B. Scott, Jr., and R. E. Lutz, *J. Org. Chem.*, **19**, 830 (1954).
43. W. A. Sheppard and J. Diekmann, *J. Am. Chem. Soc.*, **86**, 1891 (1964).
44. H. Staudinger, *Helv. Chim. Acta*, 3, 862 (1920).
45. H. Staudinger and F. Pfenninger, *Chem. Ber.*, **49**, 1941 (1916).
46. G. Stork and I. J. Borowitz, *J. Am. Chem. Soc.*, **84**, 313 (1962).
47. G. Stork, A. Brizzolara, H. Landesman, J. Szmuskovicz, and R. Terrell, *J. Am. Chem. Soc.*, **85**, 207 (1963).
48. J. Strating, *Rec. Trav. Chim.*, **83**, 94 (1964).
49. J. Strating, L. Thijs, and B. Zwanenburg, *Rec. Trav. Chim.*, **83**, 631 (1964).
50. J. Szmuskovicz, in *Advances in Organic Chemistry*, Vol. 4, R. Raphael, E. C. Taylor, and H. Wynberg, Eds., Interscience, New York, 1964, p. 69.
51. E. Tommila and P. Hirsjärvi, *Acta Chem. Scand.*, 5, 659 (1951).
52. W. E. Truce, J. J. Breiter, D. J. Abraham, and J. R. Norell, *J. Am. Chem. Soc.*, **84**, 3030 (1962).
53. W. E. Truce, R. W. Campbell, and J. R. Norell, *J. Am. Chem. Soc.*, **86**, 288 (1964).
54. W. E. Truce and J. R. Norell, *J. Am. Chem. Soc.*, **85**, 3231 (1963).
55. W. E. Truce and J. R. Norell, *J. Am. Chem. Soc.*, **85**, 3236 (1963).
56. W. E. Truce and J. R. Norell, *Tetrahedron Letters*, **1963**, 1297.
57. W. E. Truce, J. R. Norell, J. E. Richman, and J. P. Walsh, *Tetrahedron Letters*, **1963**, 1677.
58. W. E. Truce and P. N. Son, *J. Org. Chem.*, **30**, 71 (1965).
59. L. v. Vargha and E. Kovacs, *Chem. Ber.*, **75**, 794 (1942).
60. E. Wedekind and D. Schenk, *Chem. Ber.*, **44**, 198 (1911).
61. E. Wedekind, D. Schenk, and R. Stüsser, *Chem. Ber.*, **56**, 633 (1923).
62. E. Wedekind and R. Stüsser, *Chem. Ber.*, **56**, 1557 (1923).
63. Th. Zincke and R. Brune, *Chem. Ber.*, **41**, 902 (1908).

## B. TWO HETEROATOMS

### 1. Nitrogen Only

#### a. Diazetidines*

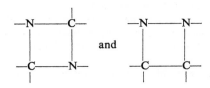

In an investigation of equilibrium systems resembling those of the dimerization of nitroso compounds (1)[11] (at that particular time nitroso

* See J. A. Moore.[10]

compounds were believed to dimerize as in the reaction shown below) and reversible reactions with ketenes (2)[12] Ingold and Piggott[7] examined the

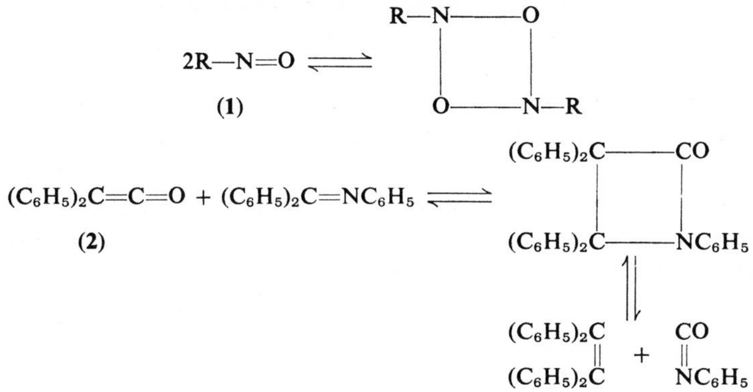

$$2R—N{=}O \;\rightleftharpoons\; \begin{array}{cc} R—N & \!\!\!—O \\ | & | \\ O & \!\!\!—N—R \end{array}$$

(1)

$$(C_6H_5)_2C{=}C{=}O + (C_6H_5)_2C{=}NC_6H_5 \;\rightleftharpoons\;$$

(2)

$$\begin{array}{cc} (C_6H_5)_2C & \!\!\!—CO \\ | & | \\ (C_6H_5)_2C & \!\!\!—NC_6H_5 \end{array}$$

$$\Updownarrow$$

$$\begin{array}{cc} (C_6H_5)_2C & CO \\ \| & + \quad \| \\ (C_6H_5)_2C & NC_6H_5 \end{array}$$

conditions of the formation and the stability of 1,3-diazetidines (originally termed 1,3-dimethindiazidines) via the following reaction:

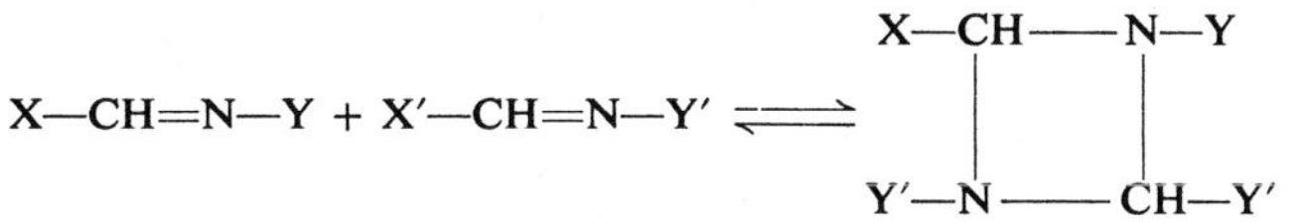

$$X—CH{=}N—Y + X'—CH{=}N—Y' \;\rightleftharpoons\; \begin{array}{cc} X—CH & \!\!\!—N—Y \\ | & | \\ Y'—N & \!\!\!—CH—Y' \end{array}$$

They reported[7] that the reaction of the substituted imines (Schiff bases) was an equilibrium reaction in which the four-membered heterocyclic compound decomposes into the starting material or into new substituted imines; for example, *p*-hydroxybenzylideneaniline (3) reacted with benzylidene-*p*-bromoaniline (4) yielding the cycloadduct, 3-*p*-bromophenyl-2-*p*-hydroxyphenyl-1,4-diphenyl-1,3-diazetidine (5), which decomposed upon heating into *p*-hydroxybenzylidene-*p*-bromoaniline (6) and benzylidene-aniline (7). Numerous substituted imines were reacted with one another,

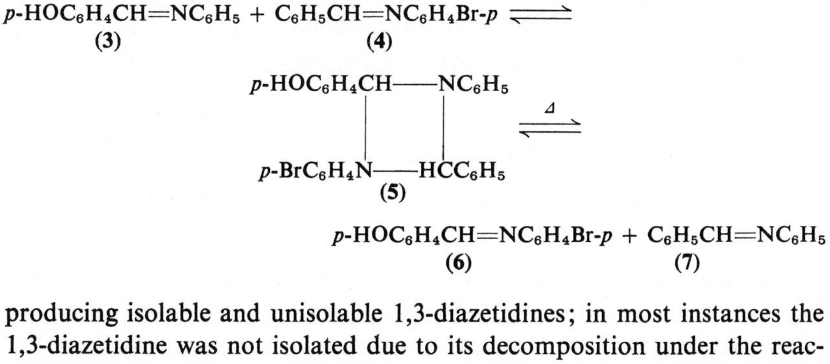

$$p\text{-HOC}_6H_4CH{=}NC_6H_5 + C_6H_5CH{=}NC_6H_4Br\text{-}p \;\rightleftharpoons\;$$
(3)                                     (4)

$$\begin{array}{cc} p\text{-HOC}_6H_4CH & \!\!\!—NC_6H_5 \\ | & | \\ p\text{-BrC}_6H_4N & \!\!\!—HCC_6H_5 \end{array} \quad \overset{\Delta}{\rightleftharpoons}$$
(5)

$$p\text{-HOC}_6H_4CH{=}NC_6H_4Br\text{-}p + C_6H_5CH{=}NC_6H_5$$
(6)                                     (7)

producing isolable and unisolable 1,3-diazetidines; in most instances the 1,3-diazetidine was not isolated due to its decomposition under the reaction conditions (Tables 1 and 2).[7] It was assumed that the instability of the

1,3-diazetidines was due to the four ring substituents, which were all phenyl- and benzyl- or substituted phenyl- or benzyl-groups.[8] To increase the stability of the 1,3-diazetidines, Ingold and Piggott[8] diminished the number of bulk of the substituents; for example, the di-$p$-tolyl derivative was found to have the desired stability.

Hoffmann and Häuser[5] found that tetramethoxylene (9), obtained from the thermal decomposition of 7,7-dimethoxybicyclo[2.2.1]heptadiene derivatives (8),[3,6,9] is a ketene diacetal exhibiting high reactivity. It was found to add to the azodicarboxylic acid ester (10) resulting in the quantitative formation of the cycloadduct (11),[5] 3,3,4,4-tetramethoxy-1,2-carbethoxy-1,2-diazetidine (Table 3).

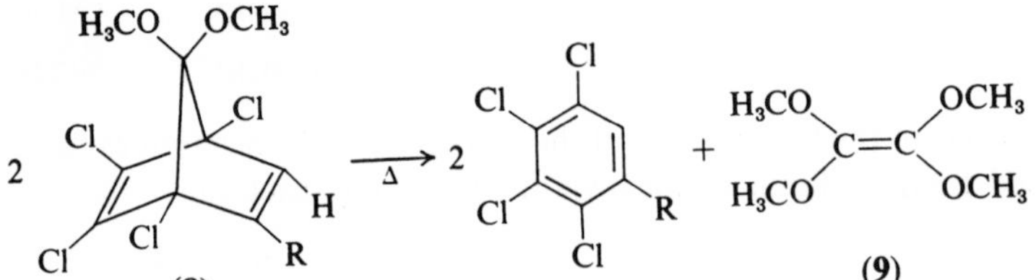

$$2 \quad (8) \quad \xrightarrow{\Delta} \quad 2 \quad + \quad (9)$$

(8)

(R = $C_6H_5$, Br)

(9)

$$9 + C_2H_5OCN{=}NCOC_2H_5 \longrightarrow$$

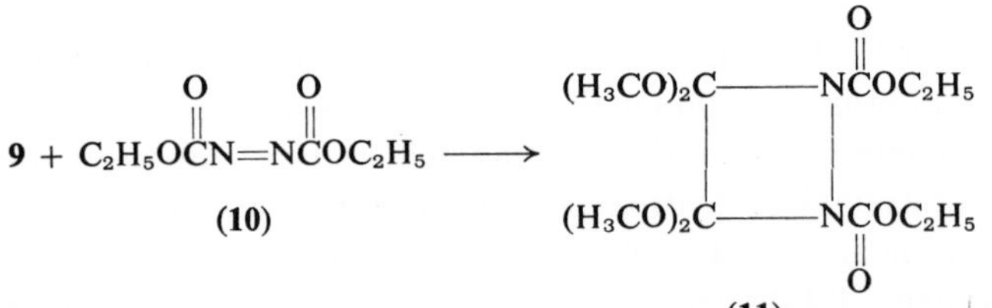

(10)

(11)

Earlier, Cramer[1] had reported the synthesis of a 1,2-diazetidine, 3,3,4,4-tetrafluoro-1,2-carbethoxy-1,2-diazetidine (13), during the reaction of azidocarboxylic acid ester (10) and tetrafluoroethylene (12) at 150°C. Trifluoro- and chlorotrifluoroethylene yield analogous products.

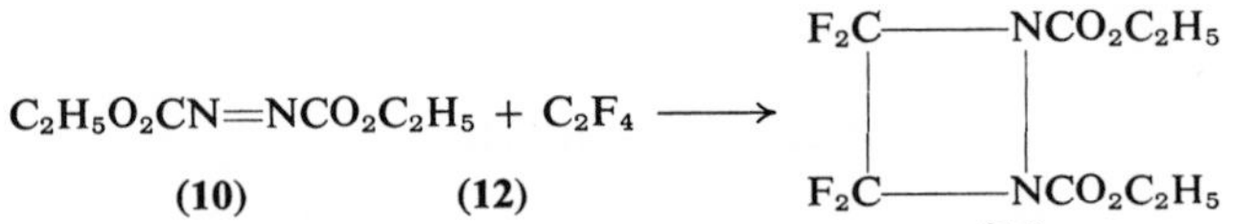

$$C_2H_5O_2CN{=}NCO_2C_2H_5 + C_2F_4 \longrightarrow$$

(10)       (12)

(13)

Ginsburg and co-workers[4] found that trifluoronitrosomethane (14) formed a 2:1 cycloadduct with perfluoroolefins; for example, with perfluorostyrene (15) the 1,2-diazetidine derivative, 1,2-bis(trifluoromethyl)-3,3,4-trifluoro-4-phenyl-1,2-diazetidine-1,2-dioxide (16), was formed (Table

3). The 1,2-diazetidine (16) was reported to have a dipole moment of 5.5 D.[4]

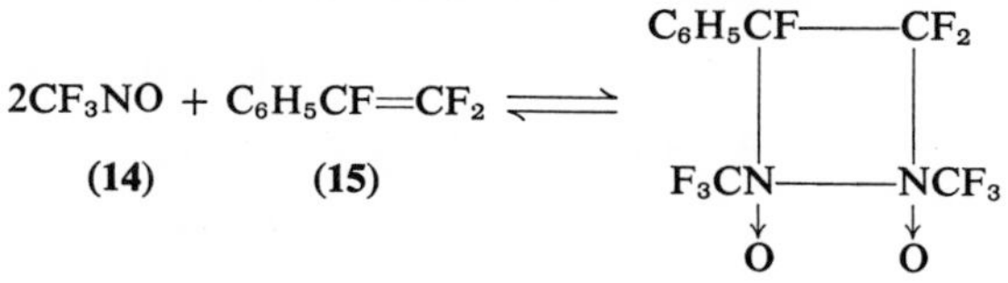

$$2CF_3NO + C_6H_5CF=CF_2 \rightleftharpoons$$

(14)  (15)

$$\begin{array}{ccc} C_6H_5CF & \text{---} & CF_2 \\ | & & | \\ F_3CN & \text{---} & NCF_3 \\ \downarrow & & \downarrow \\ O & & O \end{array}$$

(16)

In conclusion, Thaler and Franzus[13] reported two possible structures (17 and 18) that were consistent with the nuclear magnetic resonance analysis of the adduct of norbornene and ethyl azodicarboxylate (10). A cycloaddition product such as 18 would be compatible with the observed

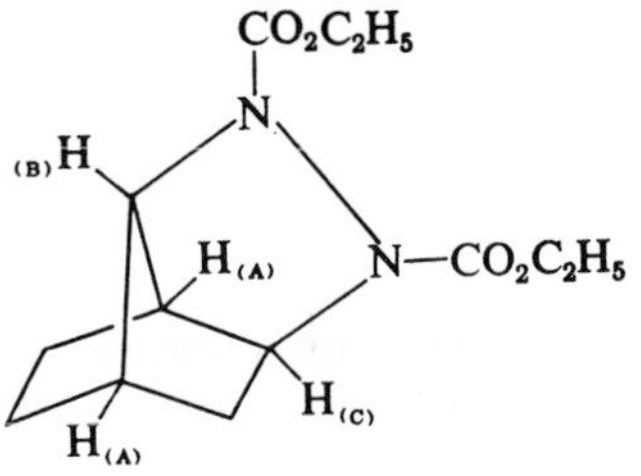

(17)

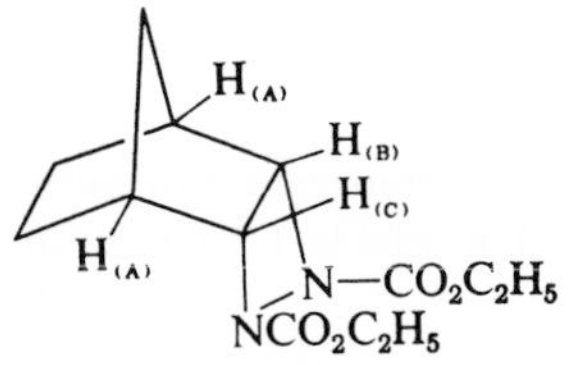

(18)

nuclear magnetic resonance spectrum if inversion of the carbethoxy group were restricted. It is likely, however, that the inversion of these groups would be sufficiently easy for the bridgehead hydrogens to be equivalent and give a different nuclear magnetic resonance spectrum from that observed (Table 4).[13] In other monoolefin systems investigated, no cycloadduct was found to result from the reaction with ethyl azodi-carboxylate.[13]

Only one representative of an unsaturated diazetidine, a diazete (19), was found in the literature. The diazete, the four-membered ring structure (19), was considered in an early paper[2] for the high-melting condensation product of biacetyl and hydrazine. The preparation was repeated[14] and the product was clearly shown to be the expected condensation polymer (20), which gave the bishydrazone on further treatment with hydrazine.

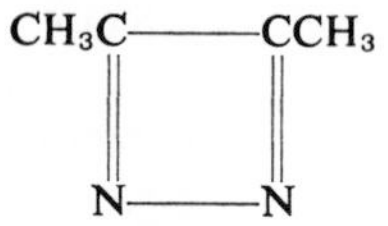

$$\begin{array}{ccc} CH_3C & \text{---} & CCH_3 \\ \| & & \| \\ N & \text{---} & N \end{array}$$

(19)

$$CH_3O \left[ \begin{array}{cc} CH_3 & CH_3 \\ | & | \\ C=N-N=C \end{array} \right] \begin{array}{c} CH_3 \\ | \\ C=NNH_2 \end{array}$$

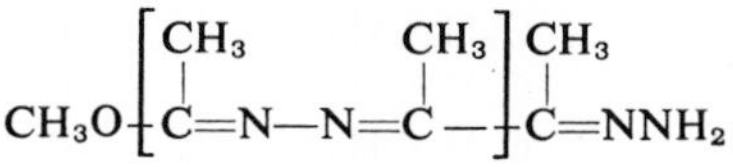

(20)

**Table 1**

Preparation of Isolable 1,3-Diazetidines by the Cycloaddition
Reaction of Substituted Imines[7]

$$R-CH=N-R' + R^2-CH=N-R^3 \rightleftharpoons \begin{array}{c} R-CH\!-\!\!-\!N-R^1 \\ | \qquad\qquad | \\ R^3-N\!-\!\!-\!\!-\!CH-R^2 \end{array}$$

| R | $R^1$ | $R^2$ | $R^3$ | MP (°C) |
|---|---|---|---|---|
| $p$-OHC$_6$H$_4$ | C$_6$H$_5$ | C$_6$H$_5$ | $p$-BrC$_6$H$_4$ | 165–167 |
| $p$-OHC$_6$H$_4$ | C$_6$H$_5$ | C$_6$H$_5$ | $p$-NO$_2$C$_6$H$_4$ | 178 |
| $p$-NO$_2$C$_6$H$_4$ | C$_6$H$_5$ | C$_6$H$_5$ | $o$-NO$_2$C$_6$H$_4$ | 163–165 |

**Table 2**

Preparation of Substituted Imines by the Decomposition of
Unisolable 1,3-Diazetidines Formed by the Cycloaddition Reaction
of Substituted Imines[7,8]

$$R-CH=N-R^1 + R^2-CH=N-R^3 \rightleftharpoons \begin{array}{c} R-CH\!-\!\!-\!N-R^1 \\ | \qquad\qquad | \\ R^3-N\!-\!\!-\!\!-\!CHR^2 \end{array}$$
$$\rightleftharpoons R-CH=NR^3 + R^2CH=NR^1$$

| R | $R^1$ | $R^2$ | $R^3$ |
|---|---|---|---|
| $m$-NO$_2$C$_6$H$_4$ | C$_6$H$_5$ | C$_6$H$_5$ | $p$-BrC$_6$H$_4$ |
| $m$-NO$_2$C$_6$H$_4$ | $p$-NO$_2$C$_6$H$_4$CH$_2$ | $p$-NO$_2$C$_6$H$_4$ | $m$-NO$_2$C$_6$H$_4$CH$_2$ |
| $m$-NO$_2$C$_6$H$_4$ | $m$-NO$_2$C$_6$H$_4$CH$_2$ | $p$-NO$_2$C$_6$H$_4$ | $p$-NO$_2$C$_6$H$_4$CH$_2$ |
| $m$-NO$_2$C$_6$H$_4$ | C$_6$H$_5$ | C$_6$H$_5$ | $o$-NO$_2$C$_6$H$_4$ |
| $m$-NO$_2$C$_6$H$_4$ | C$_6$H$_5$ | C$_6$H$_5$ | $m$-NO$_2$C$_6$H$_4$ |
| $m$-NO$_2$C$_6$H$_4$ | C$_6$H$_5$ | C$_6$H$_5$ | $p$-NO$_2$C$_6$H$_4$ |
| $p$-NO$_2$C$_6$H$_4$ | C$_6$H$_5$ | C$_6$H$_5$ | $m$-NO$_2$C$_6$H$_4$ |
| $p$-NO$_2$C$_6$H$_4$ | C$_6$H$_5$ | C$_6$H$_5$ | $p$-NO$_2$C$_6$H$_4$ |
| $p$-NO$_2$C$_6$H$_4$ | C$_6$H$_5$ | C$_6$H$_5$ | $p$-BrC$_6$H$_4$ |
| $p$-NO$_2$C$_6$H$_4$ | C$_6$H$_5$CH$_2$ | C$_6$H$_5$ | $p$-NO$_2$C$_6$H$_4$CH$_2$ |
| $m$-NO$_2$C$_6$H$_4$ | C$_6$H$_5$CH$_2$ | C$_6$H$_5$ | $m$-NO$_2$C$_6$H$_4$CH$_2$ |
| $p$-NO$_2$C$_6$H$_4$ | C$_6$H$_5$CH$_2$ | C$_6$H$_5$ | $m$-NO$_2$C$_6$H$_4$CH$_2$ |
| $m$-NO$_2$C$_6$H$_4$ | C$_6$H$_5$CH$_2$ | C$_6$H$_5$ | $p$-NO$_2$C$_6$H$_4$CH$_2$ |

**Table 3**

Preparation of 1,2-Diazetidines via Cycloaddition Reactions

| Reactants | Cycloadduct | MP, °C (BP, °C) | Yield (%) | Ref. |
|---|---|---|---|---|
| $(CH_3O)_2C{=}C(OCH_3)_2$ <br><br> $+$ <br><br> $C_2H_5CO_2N{=}NCO_2C_2H_5$ | $(CH_3O)_2C{-\!-\!-\!-}NCO_2C_2H_5$ <br> | <br> $(CH_3O)_2C{-\!-\!-\!-}NCO_2C_2H_5$ | 111 | quant. | 5 |
| $C_2H_5CF{=}CF_2$ <br><br> $+$ <br><br> $CF_3NO$ | 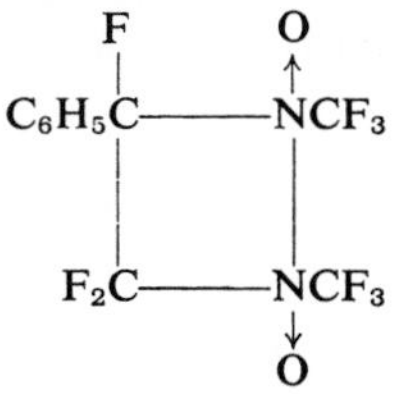 $\overset{F}{\underset{}{C_6H_5C}}{-\!-\!-\!-}\overset{O\uparrow}{NCF_3}$ <br> $F_2C{-\!-\!-\!-}\underset{O\downarrow}{NCF_3}$ | 76 | — | 4 |
| $C_2F_4$ <br><br> $+$ <br><br> $(C_2H_5O_2CN{=})_2$ | 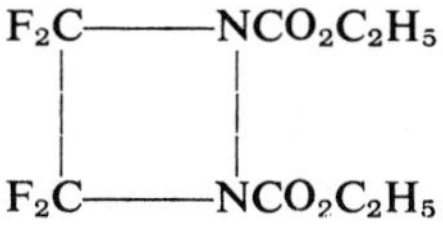 $F_2C{-\!-\!-\!-}NCO_2C_2H_5$ <br> $F_2C{-\!-\!-\!-}NCO_2C_2H_5$ | (66) | — | 1 |

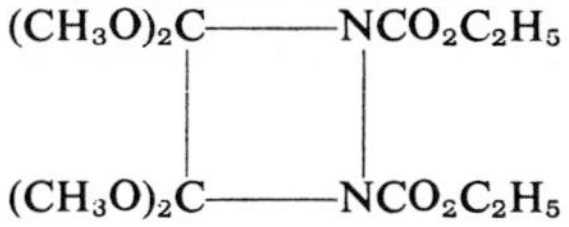

**Table 4**

Nuclear Magnetic Resonance of Norbornene Ethyl
Azidocarboxylate Adduct[13]

| | Analysis | | |
|---|---|---|---|
| | Calc. | Found | ppm from TMS |
| $CH_3$ + ring hydrogens | 12 | 12 | 1.28 (center line) |
| $H_A$ | 2 | 2.3 | 2.45 |
| $H_B$ or $H_C$ | 1 | 0.9 | 3.66 or 4.35 |
| $CH_2O$ + $H_B$ or $H_C$ | 5 | 4.8 | 4.09 or 4.13 |

REFERENCES

1. R. D. Cramer, U.S. Pat. 2,456,176 (1948).
2. T. Curtius and J. Thun, *J. Prakt. Chem.*, 2 (44), 175 (1891).
3. P. G. Gassman and W. M. Hooker, *J. Am. Chem. Soc.*, 87, 1079 (1965).
4. V. A. Ginsburg, S. S. Dubov, A. N. Medvedev, L. L. Martynova, B. I. Tetel'baum, M. N. Vasil'eva, and A. Ya. Yakubovich, *Dokl. Akad. Nauk SSSR*, 152, 1104 (1963); *Chem. Abstr.*, 60, 1570 (1964).

5. R. W. Hoffmann and H. Häuser, *Angew. Chem.*, **76**, 346 (1964); *Angew. Chem. Intern. Ed. Engl.*, **3**, 380 (1964).
6. R. W. Hoffmann and H. Häuser, *Tetrahedron Letters*, **1964**, 197.
7. C. K. Ingold and H. A. Piggott, *J. Chem. Soc.*, **121**, 2793 (1922).
8. C. K. Ingold and H. A. Piggott, *J. Chem. Soc.*, **123**, 2745 (1923).
9. D. M. Lemal, E. P. Gosselink, and A. Ault, *Tetrahedron Letters*, **1964**, 579.
10. J. A. Moore, in *Compounds with Three- and Four-Membered Rings* (*The Chemistry of Heterocyclic Compounds*, Vol. 19, A. Weissberger, Ed.), Interscience, New York, 1964, pp. 885 ff.
11. C. N. Rüber, *Chem. Ber.*, **35**, 2908 (1902).
12. H. Staudinger, *Chem. Ber.*, **44**, 532 (1911).
13. W. A. Thaler and B. Franzus, *J. Org. Chem.*, **29**, 2226 (1964).
14. B. G. Zimmerman and H. L. Lochte, *J. Am. Chem. Soc.*, **58**, 948 (1936).

### b. Diazetidinones

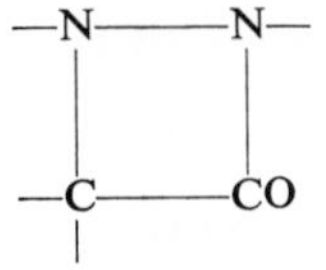

From ketenes, especially diphenylketene, and unsaturated compounds containing a heteroatom a large series of four-membered heterocyclic systems was obtained which decompose either into the starting material or in another direction to form different unsaturated compounds.[28] For example, the diazetidinone (**3**) formed by the cycloaddition of diphenyl-ketene (**1**) and an azo compound (**2**) R—N=N—R,[26-28] decomposes into the isocyanate (**4**) and the imine (**5**).

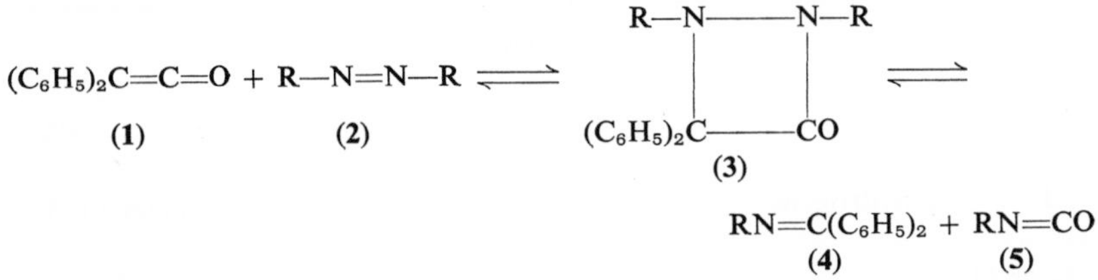

In an attempt to determine the tendency of carbon–carbon double bonds and nitrogen–nitrogen double bonds to undergo cycloaddition reactions with each other to form four-membered heterocyclic compounds,

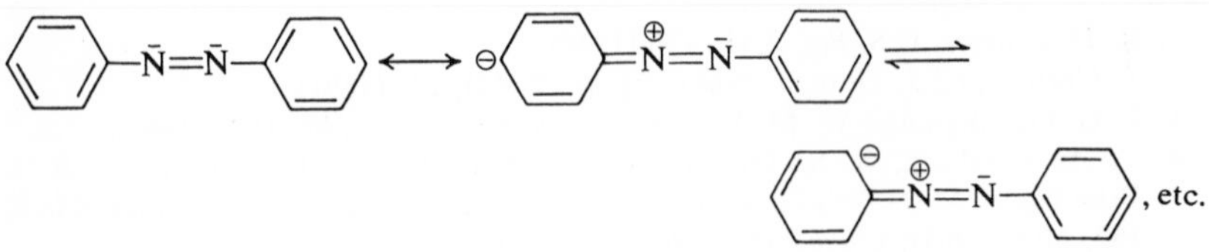

Ingold and Weaver [15,16] found that the azo group in azobenzene possessed a very small additive power. They reported that the cycloaddition reaction occurs much more readily when the phenyl groups are replaced by other groups such as the carbethoxy group. Ethylphenylazocarboxylate (6) com-

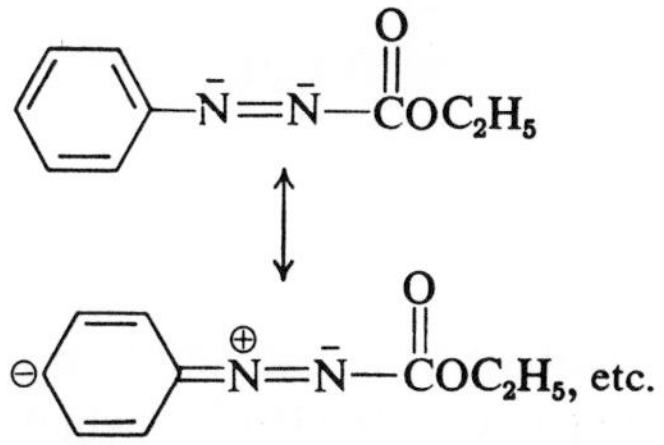

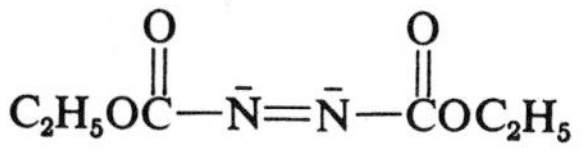

bined with great ease with diphenylketene (1) forming the diazetidinone (originally termed a keto-diimine), 1,4,4-triphenyl-2-carbethoxy-1,2-diazetidin-3-one (7), in 70% yield.[15,16]

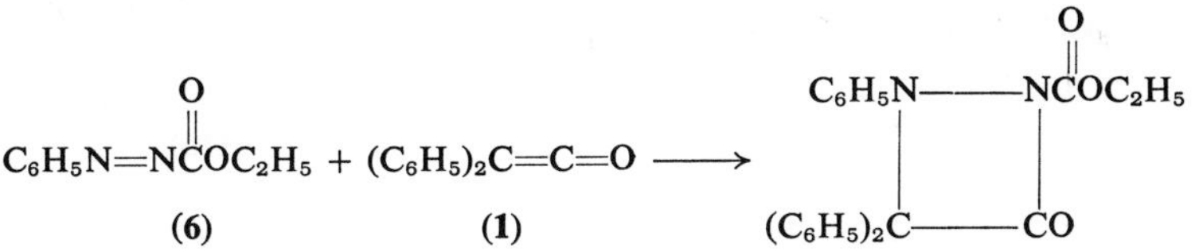

It was reported [15] that the diazetidinone (7) isomerized in the presence of hydrochloric acid in ethanol; the isomer was assigned the structure 8, envisaged as arising from an *ortho*-semidine rearrangement.[31] This acid-catalyzed rearrangement of the diphenylketene-ethylphenyl-azocarboxylate

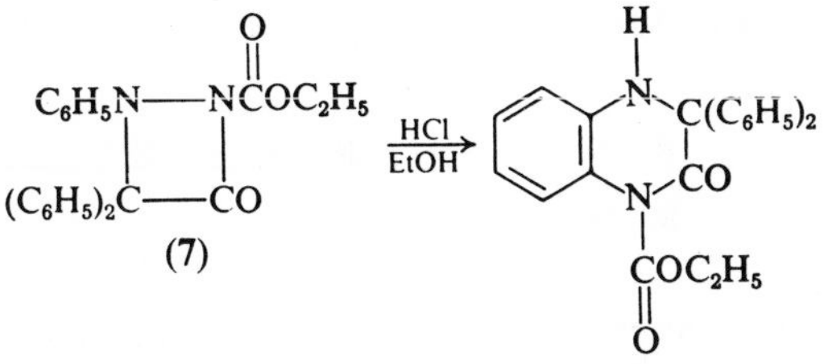

adduct (7) was reexamined [2] and found to give mainly 1-ethoxycarbonyl-amine-3,3-diphenyloxindole (9). The rearrangement of these diazetidinones may be readily rationalized by the assumption that the initial step consists of the protonation of N-2 or the 2-acyl group. Subsequent fission of the 2,3-bond would lead to the carbonium ion $Ph_2C^{\oplus} \cdot CO \cdot NPh \cdot NH \cdot COR$, which may attack N-2, the 2-acyl group, or the N-phenyl group, with formation of the observed products such as 9. Bird also reported [1] the

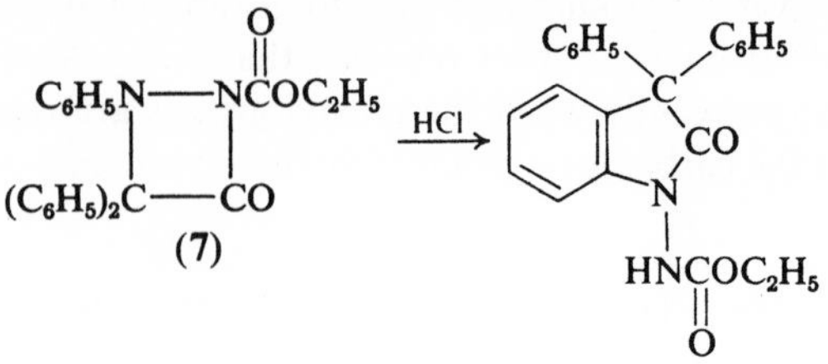

$$C_6H_5N \underset{|}{\overset{|}{\phantom{x}}} \overset{\overset{O}{\parallel}}{N}COC_2H_5 \qquad \xrightarrow{HCl}$$

$$(C_6H_5)_2C \underset{}{\overset{}{\phantom{x}}} CO$$

$$(7)$$

$$(9)$$

formation of the diazetidinone (**11a**)—resulting from the addition of di-phenylketene (**1**) to *para*-chlorobenzenediazocyanide (**10**),[18]—which iso-merized to **12** when refluxed in xylene. The structures of the compounds were determined by their infrared absorption spectra.

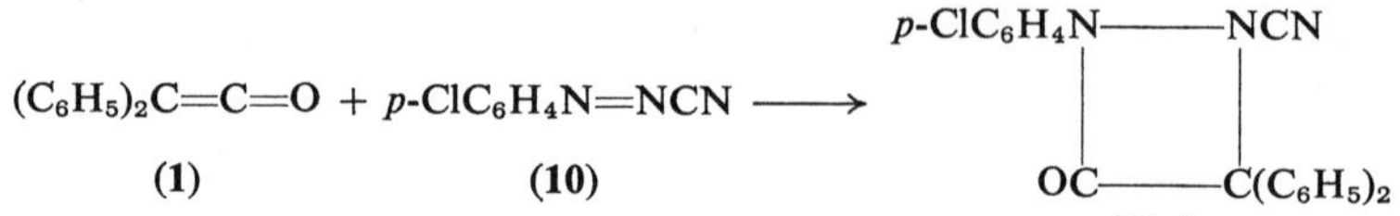

$$(C_6H_5)_2C{=}C{=}O + p\text{-}ClC_6H_4N{=}NCN \longrightarrow$$

$$(1) \qquad\qquad (10)$$

$$p\text{-}ClC_6H_4N \underset{}{\overset{}{\phantom{x}}} NCN$$

$$OC \underset{}{\overset{}{\phantom{x}}} C(C_6H_5)_2$$

$$(11a)$$

$$11a \longrightarrow$$

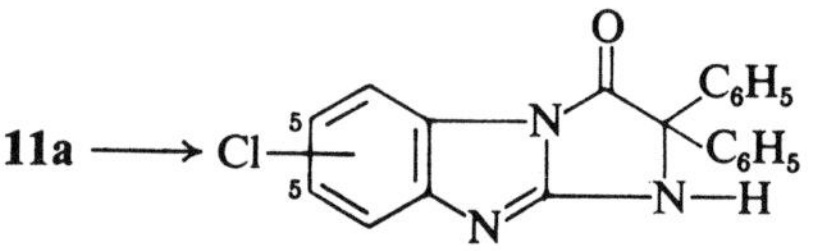

$$(2)$$

In an effort to provide a method of differentiation between *cis*- and *trans*-azobenzene, Cook and Jones[4] focused their attention to addition reactions of the type

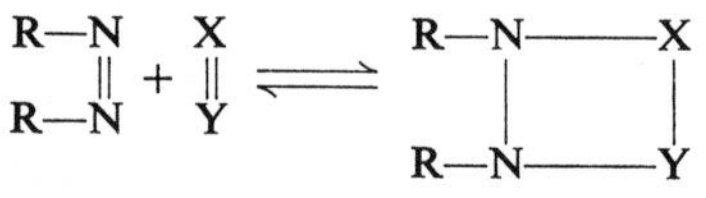

$$\begin{array}{c} R{-}N \\ \parallel \\ R{-}N \end{array} + \begin{array}{c} X \\ \parallel \\ Y \end{array} \rightleftharpoons \begin{array}{c} R{-}N \underset{}{\overset{}{\phantom{x}}} X \\ \phantom{x} \\ R{-}N \underset{}{\overset{}{\phantom{x}}} Y \end{array}$$

Here, the *cis* form was expected to react more rapidly than the *trans*-form. Diazoacetic ester[20] and diphenylketene[15] readily reacted with azodicarb-oxylic ester to give the cyclic adducts, but did not react under mild condi-tions with purely aromatic *cis*- or *trans*-azo compounds. Staudinger[27] mentions that reactions with diphenylketene and azo-compounds had been observed when the reaction mixture was heated at 150°C for several hours. Staudinger's brief report was confirmed by Cook and Jones,[4] who ob-tained a small amount of the adduct (**14**) of *trans*-azobenzene (**13**) and diphenylketene (**1**) only after heating at 125–130°C for 24 hr. When *cis*-azobenzene (**15**) was added to diphenylketene (**1**), a vigorous reaction

$(C_6H_5)_2C{=}C{=}O + C_6H_5N$      $C_6H_5N\text{———}NC_6H_5$

              $\longrightarrow$

(1)       $NC_6H_5$      $(C_6H_5)_2C\text{———}CO$

          (13)            (14)

occurred at room temperature resulting in the same adduct (14), as that obtained from the *trans*-azobenzene. Irradiation of a petroleum ether

$(C_6H_5)_2C{=}C{=}O + C_6H_5N$      $C_6H_5N\text{———}NC_6H_5$

              $\longrightarrow$

        $C_6H_5N$      $(C_6H_5)_2C\text{———}CO$

(1)        (15)          (14)

solution of *trans*-azobenzene provided a more convenient route to the adduct, as did the irradiation of the *cis*-isomeride.[4]

Chemical analysis showed that the product (14) contained one molecule each of the reactants[4]:

$C_6H_5N\text{———}NC_6H_5$    $\xrightarrow{\text{NaOCH}_3}$   $C_6H_5N{=}NC_6H_5$

$(C_6H_5)_2C\text{———}CO$     $\xrightarrow{190°}$   $C_6H_5N{=}C(C_6H_5)_2$

    (14)

These facts indicated that the diazetidinone structure for the adduct (14) proposed by Staudinger[27] was correct, and similar to that of the compound obtained by Ingold and Weaver.[15] Analogous adducts were obtained from *meta*- and *para*-azotoluene.[4] The *cis*-form reacted rapidly at room temperature while a high temperature was necessary when the *trans*-form was used.

Diphenylketene was found to react with substituent groups of azo compounds, for example, amino- or hydroxyazo-compounds. With *p*-amino-azobenzene (16) diphenylketene (1) gave *p*-(diphenylacetamido)azobenzene (17).[4]

$p\text{-}NH_2C_6H_4N{=}NC_6H_5 + (C_6H_5)_2C{=}C{=}O \longrightarrow$
    (16)           (1)

$$\underset{\text{(17)}}{(C_6H_5)_2CH\overset{\displaystyle O}{\overset{\|}{C}}\underset{\underset{H}{|}}{-N}C_6H_4N{=}NC_6H_5}$$

The great difference in reactivity of the *cis*- and *trans*-forms suggested that other pairs of nitrogen–nitrogen double bond isomers might show similar differences in reactivity. *Cis*- and *trans-p*-chlorobenzenediazo-cyanide (10)[18] both reacted readily with diphenylketene (1) in petroleum ether, yielding the same colorless adduct (11b). This adduct (11b) is

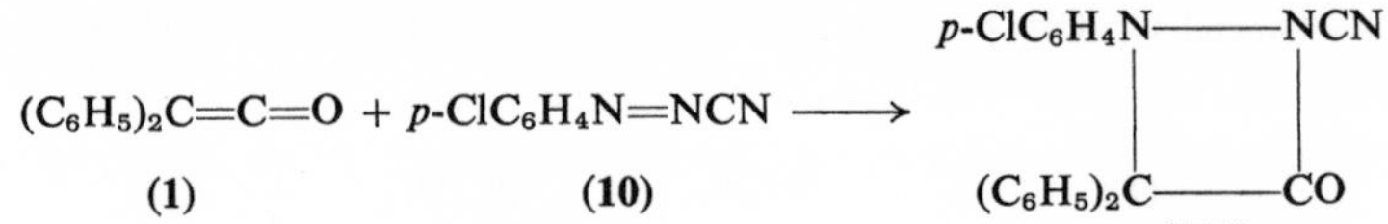

$$p\text{-ClC}_6\text{H}_4\text{N}\text{———}\text{NCN}$$

$$(\text{C}_6\text{H}_5)_2\text{C}=\text{C}=\text{O} + p\text{-ClC}_6\text{H}_4\text{N}=\text{NCN} \longrightarrow$$

$$(\text{C}_6\text{H}_5)_2\text{C}\text{———}\text{CO}$$

(1)                        (10)                                    (11b)

regarded as being formed by addition across the azo-linkage,[4] in agreement with Ingold and Weaver's experiment.[15] More recently, however, Bird[1] proposed that the structure of the adduct of diphenylketene (1) and p-chlorobenzenediazocyanide (10) was not that of 11b but 11a. This structure was characterized by its infrared absorption spectra.

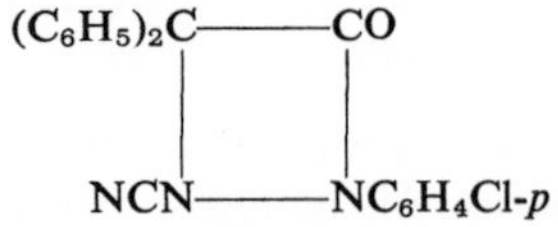

$$(\text{C}_6\text{H}_5)_2\text{C}\text{———}\text{CO}$$

$$\text{NCN}\text{———}\text{NC}_6\text{H}_4\text{Cl-}p$$

(11a)

In a photochemical investigation of ketenes, Schenck and Engelhard[24] found that the addition of ketene to phenylazocarboxylic esters does not succeed thermally or by irradiation. They found, however, that from cis-azobenzene (15) and ketene (18) in hexane at 15°C arose the cycloadduct, 1,2-diphenyl-1,2-diazetidin-3-one (19). The diazetidinone (19) was also

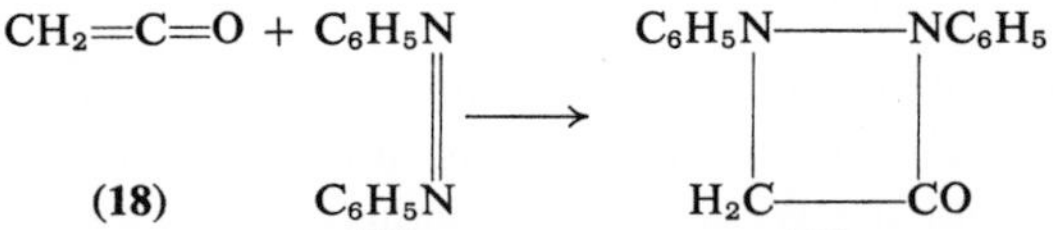

$$\text{CH}_2=\text{C}=\text{O} + \text{C}_6\text{H}_5\text{N}$$

$$\text{C}_6\text{H}_5\text{N}\text{———}\text{NC}_6\text{H}_5$$

$$\text{C}_6\text{H}_5\text{N} \longrightarrow \text{H}_2\text{C}\text{———}\text{CO}$$

(18)          (15)                          (19)

prepared by irradiation of azobenzene in hexane with introduction of ketene. Other azo compounds, capable of forming the cis-derivative, produced analogous cycloadducts.

In a study of the behavior of diazoketones (20) toward ultraviolet light, Horner and co-workers[12-14] found that unstable ketenes (21)[17,23,30] were formed, which would easily polymerize, as is shown here.

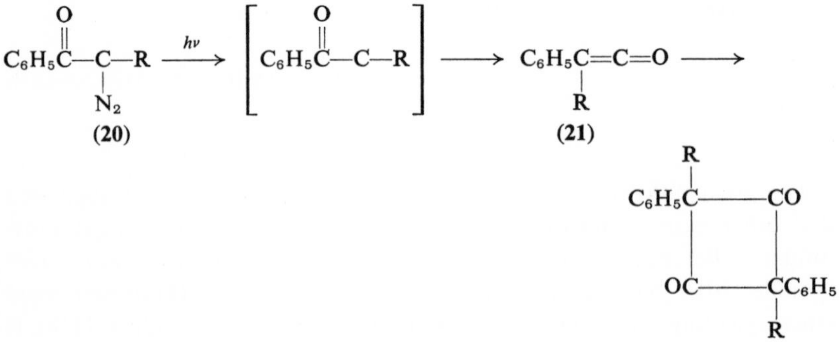

$$\text{C}_6\text{H}_5\overset{\text{O}}{\overset{\|}{\text{C}}}\text{—C—R} \xrightarrow{h\nu} \left[ \text{C}_6\text{H}_5\overset{\text{O}}{\overset{\|}{\text{C}}}\text{—C—R} \right] \longrightarrow \text{C}_6\text{H}_5\text{C}=\text{C}=\text{O} \longrightarrow$$

with $\text{N}_2$ under (20) and $\text{R}$ under (21)

$$\text{C}_6\text{H}_5\overset{\text{R}}{\text{C}}\text{———}\text{CO}$$

$$\text{OC}\text{———}\overset{}{\text{C}}\text{C}_6\text{H}_5$$

$$\text{R}$$

If, however, the irradiation is carried out in the presence of azobenzene (15), the ketene could be trapped as the adduct (22), a diazetidinone. The reaction occurs with the *cis*-form of azobenzene (15).[14]

$$C_6H_5C{=}C{=}O + C_6H_5N{=}NC_6H_5 \longrightarrow$$

$$\underset{(21)}{\overset{\displaystyle R}{\big|}} \qquad\qquad \underset{(15)}{}$$

$$\begin{array}{c} C_6H_5 \\ | \\ R{-}C{\rule[0.5ex]{2em}{0.4pt}}CO \\ | \qquad\quad | \\ C_6H_5N{\rule[0.5ex]{2em}{0.4pt}}NC_6H_5 \\ (22) \end{array}$$

The reactions of the 1,2-diazetidinones with alkoxides, organolithium compounds, and lithium aluminum hydride have been further substantiated by Hall.[9]

Neumann and Fischer[22] found that polyisocyanates form polycarbodiimides (23)[10,29] containing nitrogen–carbon–oxygen end groups which could combine with carbodiimide groups, resulting in ring formation. For example, by thermal treatment of diphenylmethane-4,4′-disocyanate, a

$$OCN{-}R{-}N{=}C{=}N{-}(R{-}N{=}C{=}N)_x{-}R{-}NCO$$
$$(23)$$

carbodiimide with free nitrogen–carbon–oxygen groups is obtained to which excess diisocyanate is added to form the 1,3-diazetidine-2,4-dione-4-imine (24).[7] It has also been reported that isocyanates and carbodiimides

$$OCN{-}R{-}N{=}C{=}N{-}R{-}NCO + OCN{-}R{-}NCO \longrightarrow$$

$$(R = {-}C_6H_4CH_2C_6H_4{-})$$

$$\begin{array}{c} OCN{-}R{-}N{\rule[0.5ex]{2em}{0.4pt}}CO \\ | \qquad\qquad | \\ OCN{-}R{-}N{=}C{\rule[0.5ex]{2em}{0.4pt}}N{-}R{-}NCO \\ (24) \end{array}$$

combine to give thermally unstable adducts,[3,11] for which formulas 25 and 26 have been considered. Structure 25 is preferred on the basis of the infra-

$$R{-}NCO + R{-}N{=}C{=}N{-}R \longrightarrow$$

$$\begin{array}{c} R{-}N{\rule[0.5ex]{2em}{0.4pt}}CO \\ | \qquad\quad | \\ R{-}N{=}C{\rule[0.5ex]{2em}{0.4pt}}N{-}R \\ (25) \end{array} \quad \text{or}$$

$$\begin{array}{c} R{-}N{=}C{\rule[0.5ex]{2em}{0.4pt}}O \\ | \qquad\qquad | \\ R{-}N{\rule[0.5ex]{2em}{0.4pt}}C{=}C{-}R \\ (26) \end{array}$$

red absorption spectra showing a characteristic band at 5.7–5.8 µ and a second weaker band at 7.2–7.5 μ.[22] These compounds are 1,3-diazetidine-2,4-dione-4-imines (uretidinedione-imines or uretoneimines), by analogy to the 1,3-diazetidine-2,4-diones (27) (uretidinediones),[27] the dimerization products of aromatic isocyanates.

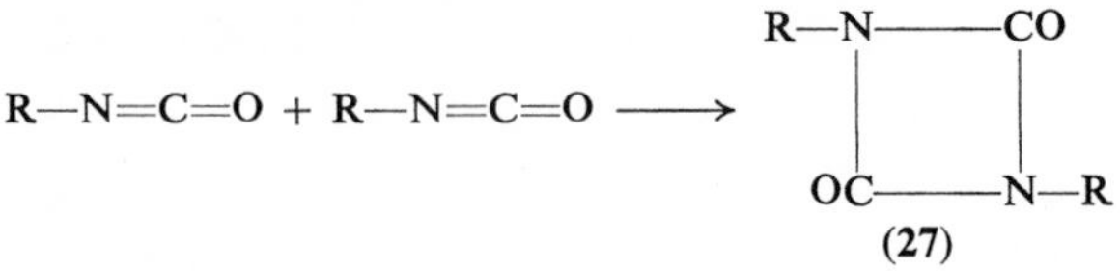

$$R-N=C=O + R-N=C=O \longrightarrow \begin{array}{cc} R-N & CO \\ | & | \\ OC & N-R \end{array}$$
$$(27)$$

The 1,3-diazetidine-2,4-dione-4-imine (28) from an isocyanate, R′—N=C=O, and a carbodiimide, R²—N=C=N—R², cleaves on heating not only in the direction of formation, but also in such a way that a new isocyanate, R²—N=C=O, and a mixed carbodiimide,

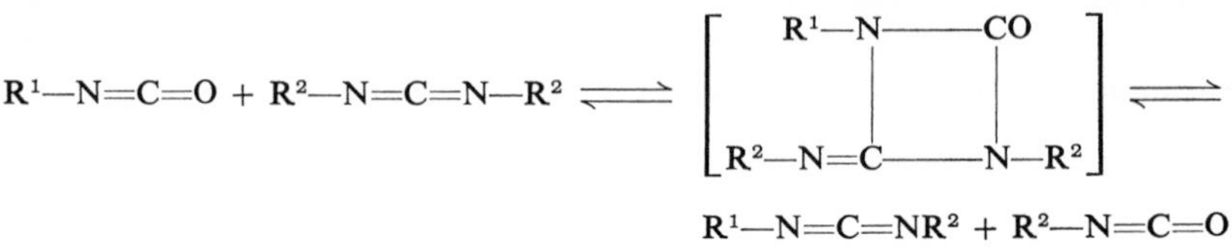

$$R^1-N=C=O + R^2-N=C=N-R^2 \rightleftharpoons \left[ \begin{array}{cc} R^1-N & CO \\ | & | \\ R^2-N=C & N-R^2 \end{array} \right] \rightleftharpoons$$
$$R^1-N=C=NR^2 + R^2-N=C=O$$
$$(28)$$

R¹—N=C=N—R², are formed (Table 1).[22] By removing R²—N=C=O, the equilibrium is shifted toward the direction of the mixed carbodiimide (Table 2). By selection of the molar ratios of isocyanate and carbodiimide, both substituents of the original carbodiimide can be replaced, so that another symmetrical carbodiimide is formed resulting from a twofold 1,3-diazetidine-2,4-dione-4-imine formation and cleavage (Table 3)[22]:

$$R^2-N=C=N-R^2 + 2R^1-N=C=O \rightleftharpoons$$
$$R^1-N=C=N-R^1 + 2R^2-N=C=O$$

A branched triisocyanate (31) may be formed in the presence of excess diisocyanate (30) by 1,3-diazetidine-2,4-dione-4-imine formation from a carbodiimide (29); a similar triisocyanate is also obtained by elimination

$$O=C=N-(CH_2)_6-[N=C=N-(CH_2)_6]_x-N=C=O$$
$$(x = 1) \qquad\qquad (29)$$

of carbon dioxide from diphenylmethane-4,4′-diisocyanate (23).[22] The

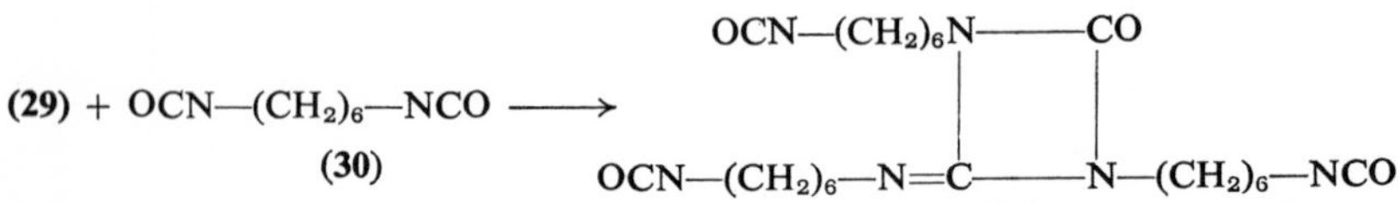

$$(29) + OCN-(CH_2)_6-NCO \longrightarrow \begin{array}{cc} OCN-(CH_2)_6N & CO \\ | & | \\ OCN-(CH_2)_6-N=C & N-(CH_2)_6-NCO \end{array}$$
$$(30) \qquad\qquad\qquad (31)$$

formation of 1,3-diazetidine-2,4-dione-4-imines—an equilibrium reaction —is largely repressed when sterically hindered isocyanate and carbodiimide groups are involved, or when the equilibrium is frozen on the side of the cleavage products, the free isocyanate or carbodiimide groups.

It has also been reported[21] that benzoylisocyanate (32) in anhydrous ether and $N,N'$-diphenylcarbodiimide (33) undergo a cycloaddition reaction forming the 1,3-diazetidine-2,4-dione-4-imine, 1-benzoyl-3-phenyl-1,3-diazetidine-2,4-dione-4-phenylimine (34). Analogously benzoyliso-

$$
\begin{array}{cc}
\overset{\displaystyle O}{\underset{\displaystyle \|}{C_6H_5\overset{}{C}}}-N{=}C{=}O \; + \; C_6H_5N{=}C{=}N{-}C_6H_5 \longrightarrow \\
(32) \qquad\qquad (33)
\end{array}
$$

$$
\begin{array}{c}
C_6H_5N\text{------}C{=}NC_6H_5 \\
\big| \qquad\qquad \big| \\
OC\text{------}N\underset{\displaystyle \underset{\|}{O}}{C}C_6H_5
\end{array}
$$

(34)

cyanate (32) reacts with $N,N'$-dicyclohexylcarbodiimide (35) to yield the 1,3-diazetidine-2,4-dione-4-imine, 1-benzoyl-3-phenyl-1,3-diazetidine-2,4-dione-4-cyclohexylimine (36) (Table 4).[21]

$$
\begin{array}{cc}
\overset{\displaystyle O}{\underset{\displaystyle \|}{C_6H_5\overset{}{C}}}-N{=}C{=}O \; + \; C_6H_{11}N{=}C{=}NC_6H_{11} \longrightarrow \\
(32) \qquad\qquad (35)
\end{array}
$$

$$
\begin{array}{c}
C_6H_{11}N\text{------}C{=}NC_6H_{11} \\
\big| \qquad\qquad \big| \\
OC\text{------}N\underset{\displaystyle \underset{\|}{O}}{C}C_6H_5
\end{array}
$$

(36)

In conclusion, the only authentic members of the 1,3-diazetidin-2-one series have been prepared by the cycloaddition of an isocyanate to a carbon–nitrogen double bond,[19] paralleling the formation of $\beta$-lactams by the addition of ketenes to azomethines. The reaction of phenylisocyanate (37) or $\alpha$-naphthylisocyanate (38) with methylene-aniline (39) gave 1,3-diphenyl- (40) and 1-phenyl-3-$\alpha$-naphthyl-1,3-diazetidin-2-one (41)[25], respectively. The reaction was extended by Hale and Lange[8] to the preparation

$$
\begin{array}{cc}
C_6H_5N{=}C{=}O \; + \; CH_2{=}NC_6H_5 \longrightarrow \\
(37) \qquad\qquad (39)
\end{array}
$$

$$
\begin{array}{c}
H_2C\text{------}NC_6H_5 \\
\big| \qquad\qquad \big| \\
C_6H_5N\text{------}CO
\end{array}
$$

(40)

(38)

$+ (39) \longrightarrow$

(41)

of 1,4-diphenyl-1,3-diazetidin-2-ones (**44**) from cyanic acid (**42**) and benzalaniline (**43**). A similar addition of cyanic acid, generated *in situ* from

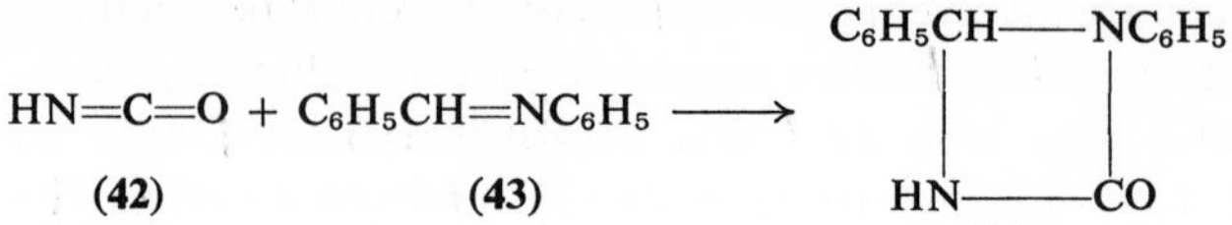

$$HN{=}C{=}O + C_6H_5CH{=}NC_6H_5 \longrightarrow$$

$$\begin{array}{c} C_6H_5CH{-\!\!\!-}NC_6H_5 \\ | \qquad\qquad | \\ HN{-\!\!\!-}CO \end{array}$$

(**42**)          (**43**)          (**44**)

urea, was postulated by Frerich and Hartwig[5,6] to occur with the carbon–nitrogen triple bond of ethylcyanoacetate, giving an acidic product assigned the 1,3-diazet-2-one structure (**45**).

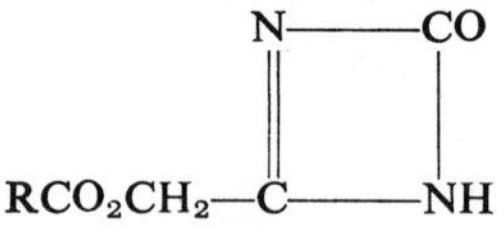

$$\begin{array}{c} N{-\!\!\!-}CO \\ \| \qquad | \\ RCO_2CH_2{-}C{-\!\!\!-}NH \end{array}$$

(**45**)

**Table 1**

Preparation of Diazetidinones from the Cycloaddition Reaction of Ketenes and Azo-Compounds

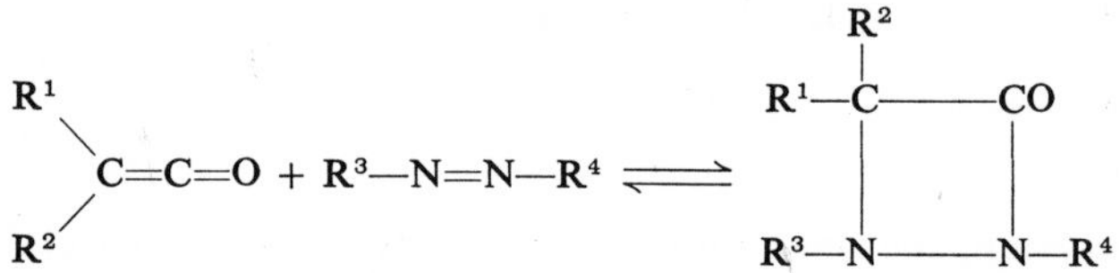

$$\begin{array}{c} R^1 \\ \diagdown \\ \qquad C{=}C{=}O + R^3{-}N{=}N{-}R^4 \rightleftharpoons \\ \diagup \\ R^2 \end{array} \qquad \begin{array}{c} R^2 \\ | \\ R^1{-}C{-\!\!\!-}CO \\ | \qquad\qquad | \\ R^3{-}N{-\!\!\!-}N{-}R^4 \end{array}$$

| $R^1$ | $R^2$ | $R^3$ | $R^4$ | MP (°C) | Ref. |
|-------|-------|-------|-------|---------|------|
| $C_6H_5$ | $C_6H_5$ | $C_6H_5$ | $CO_2C_2H_5$ | 132–133[a] | 15 |
|  |  |  |  | 129–130 | 2 |
| $C_6H_5$ | $C_6H_5$ | CN | $p$-ClC$_6$H$_4$ | — | 1 |
|  |  |  |  | 121 | 4 |
| $C_6H_5$ | $C_6H_5$ | $C_6H_5$ | $C_6H_5$ | 175 | 4 |
|  |  |  |  |  | 27 |
|  |  |  |  | 173 | 13, 14 |
| $C_6H_5$ | $C_6H_5$ | $m$-CH$_3$C$_6$H$_4$ | $m$-CH$_3$C$_6$H$_4$ | 118 | 4 |
| $C_6H_5$ | $C_6H_5$ | $p$-CH$_3$C$_6$H$_4$ | $p$-CH$_3$C$_6$H$_4$ | 172 | 4 |
| H | H | $C_6H_5$ | $C_6H_5$ | 115 | 24 |
| H | $C_6H_5$ | $C_6H_5$ | $C_6H_5$ | 92 | 13, 14 |
| $C_6H_5$ | $C_6H_5$ | $C_6H_5CO$ | $C_6H_5CO$ | 191 | 13 |
| $C_6H_5$ | $C_6H_5$ | $C_6H_5CH_2$ | $C_6H_5CH_2$ | 154 | 13 |
| $C_6H_5$ | $C_6H_5$ | $o$-CH$_3$C$_6$H$_4$ | $o$-CH$_3$C$_6$H$_4$ | 162 | 4 |
| $C_6H_5$ | $C_6H_5$ | $\beta$-C$_{10}$H$_7$ | $\beta$-C$_{10}$H$_7$ | 222 | 4 |
| H | H | $m$-CH$_3$C$_6$H$_4$ | $m$-CH$_3$C$_6$H$_4$ | — | 24 |

[a] 70% yield.

**Table 2**

Unsymmetrical Carbodiimides Prepared by the Exchange Reaction[22]:

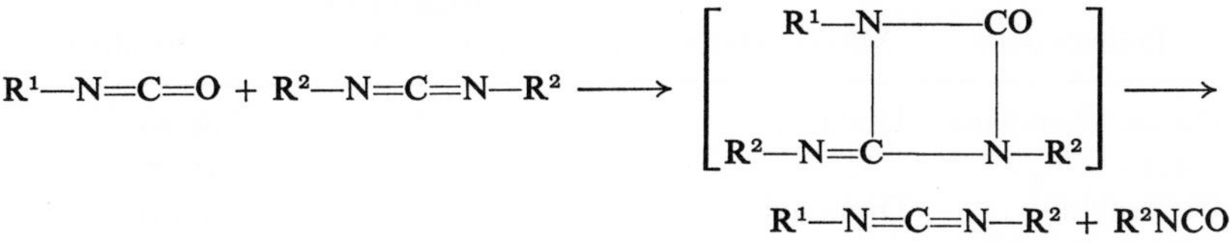

$$R^1{-}N{=}C{=}O + R^2{-}N{=}C{=}N{-}R^2 \longrightarrow \begin{bmatrix} R^1{-}N\text{------}CO \\ \quad\mid\qquad\qquad\mid \\ R^2{-}N{=}C\text{------}N{-}R^2 \end{bmatrix} \longrightarrow$$

$$R^1{-}N{=}C{=}N{-}R^2 + R^2NCO$$

| Isocyanate | Carbodiimide | Unsymmetrical carbodiimide |
|---|---|---|
| 1-Naphthyl | Dicyclohexyl | 1-Naphthylcyclohexyl |
| Octadecyl | Dicyclohexyl | Octadecylcyclohexyl |
| 2,6-Diethyl-4-methylphenyl | Diphenyl | Phenyl-2,6-diethyl-4-methylphenyl |

**Table 3**

Polycarbodiimides and Polyisocyanates from
Isocyanate–Carbodiimide Interchange[22]

| Diioscyanate | Monocarbodiimide | Molar ratio —NCO:—NCN— | Product |
|---|---|---|---|
| Hexamethylene-1,6- | Diethyl | 1:2 | Polycarbodiimide |
| Hexamethylene-1,6 | Dicyclohexyl | 1:2 | Polycarbodiimide |
| Dicyclohexyl-methane-4,4′- | Dicyclohexyl | 1:3 | Polycarbodiimide |
| Toluylene-2,4/2,6- | Diphenyl | 1:2 | Polycarbodiimide |
| 1-Chlorophenyl-ene-2,4/2,6- | Dicyclohexyl | 1:2.5 | Polycarbodiimide |
| Diphenyldimethyl-methane-4,4′- | Diphenyl | 1:3.5 | Polycarbodiimide |
| Hexamethylene-1,6- | Dicyclohexyl | 4:1 | Polycarbodiimide, modified polyisocyanate |
| Toluylene-2,4/2,6- | Diphenyl | 20:1 | Polyisocyanate |

(*continued*)

**Table 3** (*continued*)

| Diioscyanate | Monocarbodiimide | Molar ratio —NCO:—NCN— | Product |
|---|---|---|---|
| Diphenylmethane-4,4′- | Diphenyl | 20:1 | Polyiso-cyanate |
| Diphenyldimethylmethane-4,4′- | Diphenyl | 5:1 | Polyiso-cyanate |
| 1,3,5-Triisopropylphenylene-2,4- | Diphenyl | 2:1 | Polyiso-cyanate |
| 3,5′5,5′-Tetraethyldiphenylmethane-4,4′- | Diphenyl | 2:1 | Polyiso-cyanate |
| Naphthylene-1,5- | Dicyclohexyl | 40:1 | Polyiso-cyanate |

**Table 4**

1,3-Diazetidin-2,4-dione-4-imines from Benzoylisocyanate and Carbodiimides[21]

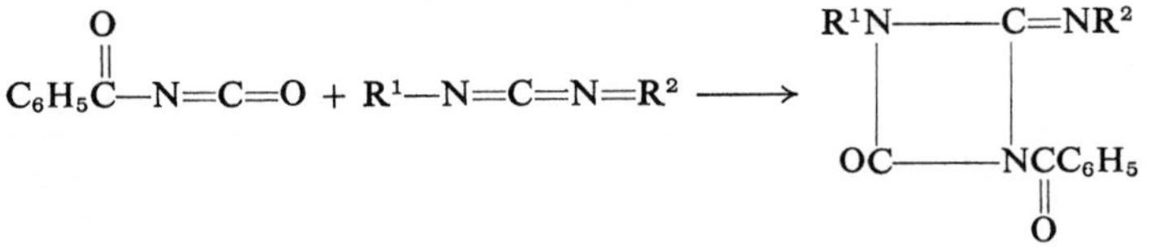

$$\underset{\substack{\| \\ O}}{C_6H_5C}-N{=}C{=}O + R^1-N{=}C{=}N{=}R^2 \longrightarrow$$

R¹N——C=NR²
|          |
OC——NCC₆H₅
‖
O

| R¹— | R²— | MP (°C) |
|---|---|---|
| $C_6H_5$ | $C_6H_5$ | 188–189 |
| $C_6H_{11}$ | $C_6H_{11}$ | 138–139 |

REFERENCES

1. C. W. Bird, *Chem. Ind.* (*London*), **1963**, 1556.
2. C. W. Bird, *J. Chem. Soc.*, **1963**, 674.
3. Brit. Pat. 795,720 (1955).
4. A. H. Cook and D. G. Jones, *J. Chem. Soc.*, **1941**, 184.
5. G. Frerich and L. Hartwig, *J. Prakt. Chem.*, 3 (72), 489 (1905).
6. G. Frerich and L. Hartwig, *J. Prakt. Chem.*, 3 (73), 44 (1906).
7. P. Fischer and E. Meisert, Ger. Pat. 1,092,007 (1960).
8. W. J. Hale and N. A. Lange, *J. Am. Chem. Soc.*, **41**, 379 (1919).
9. J. H. Hall, *J. Org. Chem.*, **29**, 3188 (1964).
10. A. W. Hofmann, *Chem. Ber.*, **18**, 765 (1885).
11. R. Hofmann, E. Schmidt, A. Reichle, and F. Moosmüller, Ger. Pat. 1,012,601 (1957).

12. L. Horner and E. Spietschka, *Chem. Ber.*, **85**, 225 (1952).
13. L. Horner and E. Spietschka, *Chem. Ber.*, **89**, 2765 (1956).
14. L. Horner, E. Spietschka, and A. Gross, *Ann. Chem.*, **573**, 17 (1951).
15. C. K. Ingold and S. D. Weaver, *J. Chem. Soc.*, **127**, 378 (1925).
16. C. K. Ingold and S. D. Weaver, *J. Chem. Soc.*, **128i**, 58 (1925).
17. R. N. Lacey, in *Advances in Organic Chemistry*, Vol. II, R. A. Raphael, E. C. Taylor, and H. Wynberg, Eds., Interscience, New York, 1960, pp. 226 ff.
18. R. J. W. Le Feure and H. Vine, *J. Chim. Soc.*, **1938**, 436.
19. J. A. Moore, in *Three- and Four-Membered Rings* (*The Chemistry of Heterocyclic Compounds*, Vol. 19, A. Weissberger, Ed.), Wiley, New York, 1964, pp. 885 ff.
20. E. Müller, *Chem. Ber.*, **47**, 3001 (1914).
21. R. Neidlein, *Arch. Pharm.*, **297**, 623 (1964).
22. W. Neumann and P. Fischer, *Angew. Chem.*, **74**, 801 (1962).
23. G. Quadbeck, *Angew. Chem.*, **68**, 361 (1956).
24. G. O. Schenck and H. Engelhard, *Angew. Chem.*, **68**, 71 (1956).
25. A. Seiner and F. G. Shepheard, *J. Chem. Soc.*, **95**, 494 (1909).
26. S. Skraup and O. Binder, *Chem. Ber.*, **62B**, 1127 (1929).
27. H. Staudinger, *Die Ketene*, F. Enke, Stuttgart, 1912, p. 91.
28. H. Staudinger, *Helv. Chim. Acta*, **5**, 103 (1922).
29. R. Stolle, *Chem. Ber.*, **41**, 1125 (1908).
30. F. Weygand and H. Bestmann, *Angew. Chem.*, **72**, 548 (1960).
31. H. Wieland, *Ann. Chem.*, **381**, 200 (1911).

## 2. Oxygen and Nitrogen

### a. Oxazetidines

It was proposed by Ingold[40,41,43] that four-membered ring systems might be formed by reversible cycloaddition reactions of the type

$$A = B + C = D \rightleftharpoons \begin{array}{c} A\text{——}B \\ | \quad\quad | \\ C\text{——}D \end{array} \rightleftharpoons A = C + B = D$$

It had been reported[43,44] that certain types of azomethines and nitroso compounds formed stable cyclic "bimerides." By reacting certain olefins and nitrosoarene compounds, Ingold[42,47,48] found that the noncatalyzed reaction in solution led to the formation of 1:1 adducts which were assigned the 1,2-oxazetidine ring structure (**1**) (originally named 1,2-oxaimine).[21,40,41,43-48] The two gem-substituted ethylenes (**2** and **3**) reported for the preparation of the 1,2-oxazetidine derivatives were chosen because of their stabilizing effect on the ring. The only other alkene used

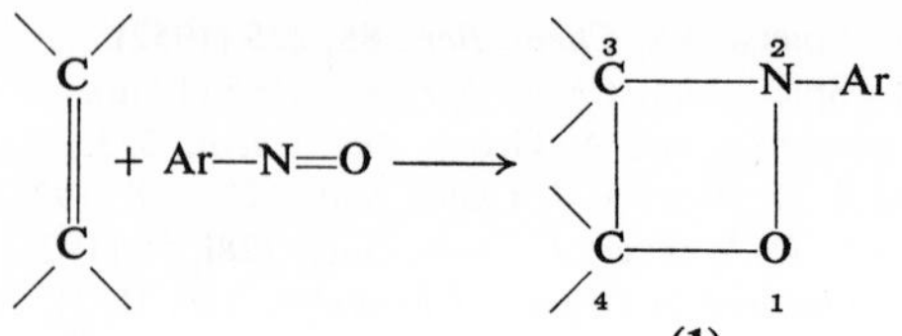

**(1)**

by Ingold and Weaver was styrene, for which the nitrone, benzylidene-*N*-

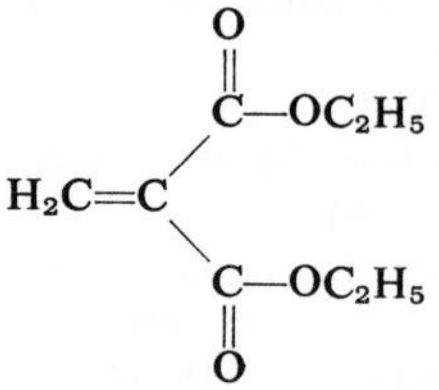

phenylnitrone, $C_6H_5N(\rightarrow O)=CHC_6H_5$, was the reaction product with nitrosobenzene. They accounted for its presence by postulating the formation of an unstable six-membered ring system (**4**) which they presumed decomposed as shown here.

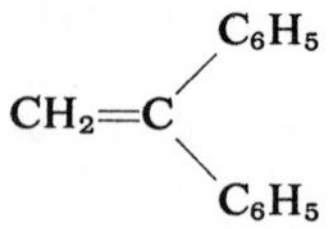

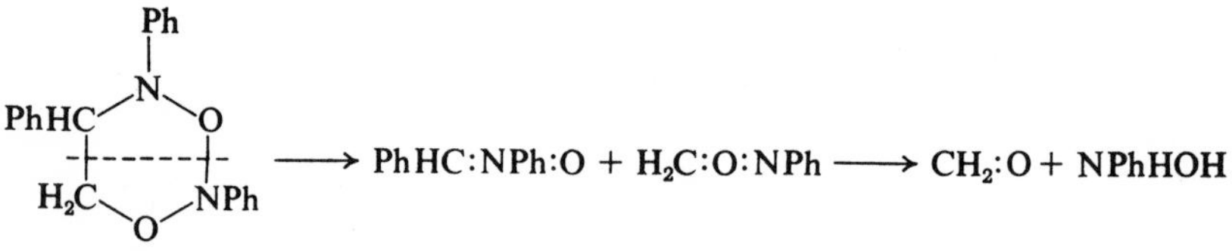

$$\longrightarrow PhHC:NPh:O + H_2C:O:NPh \longrightarrow CH_2:O + NPhHOH$$

The nitrone, benzylidene-*N*-phenylnitrone, was also reported as the product in the reaction of styrene and nitrosobenzene by Alessandri.[1] Its formation was said to have been due to the cleavage of the terminal methylene group[1] of styrene.

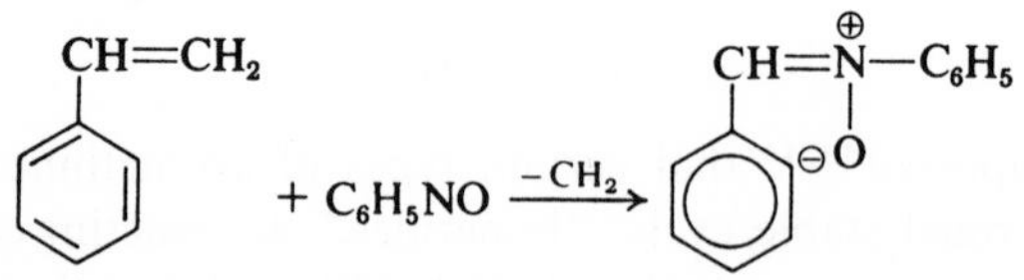

The "direction of the addition"[47,48] of **2** or **3** with nitrosobenzene was found to be at variance with that required by "the theory of alternate polarities."[52] Thus, it was reported that diethyl methylenemalonate (**2**) reacted exothermically with nitrosobenzene to give 2-phenyl-4,4-dicarbethoxy-1,2-oxazetidine (**5**) and not 2-phenyl-3,3-dicarbethoxy-1,2-oxazetidine

(6), which should not be the case if oxygen key-atoms determine the polarities: $Ar\overset{\oplus}{=}\overset{\ominus}{N}\overset{\oplus}{=}\overset{\ominus}{O}$; $CH_2\overset{\ominus}{=}\overset{\oplus}{C}$; $(\overset{\oplus\ominus}{CO_2Et})_2$.

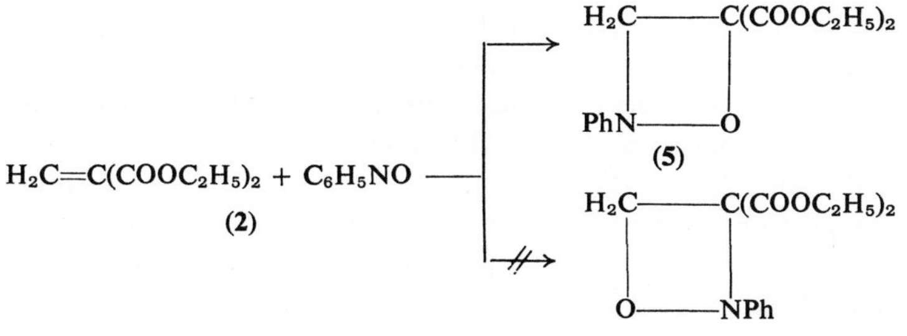

$$H_2C=C(COOC_2H_5)_2 + C_6H_5NO \longrightarrow$$

(2)

H$_2$C————C(COOC$_2$H$_5$)$_2$

PhN————O

**(5)**

H$_2$C————C(COOC$_2$H$_5$)$_2$

O————NPh

**(6)**

The 1,2-oxazetidine was reported to decompose after 4 hr at 100° to give a compound which was identified as dicarbethoxyacetanilide (7). Analogous reactions with *p*-bromo- and *p*-chloronitrosobenzene were reported to yield oxazetidines with similar postulated structures.

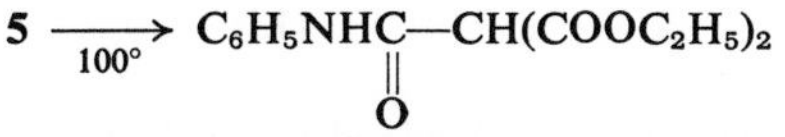

$$5 \xrightarrow{100°} C_6H_5NHC-CH(COOC_2H_5)_2$$
$$\underset{O}{\|}$$

**(7)**

In a similar reaction[47,48] 1,1-diphenylethylene (3) and nitrosobenzene gave a 1:1 adduct. Pyrolysis of the adduct at 250° gave benzhydrylidene aniline (8) and formaldehyde. On the basis of analysis, reactivity, and pyrolysis data, the product was assigned the cyclic structure of 2,3,-triphenyl-1,2-oxazetidine (9)

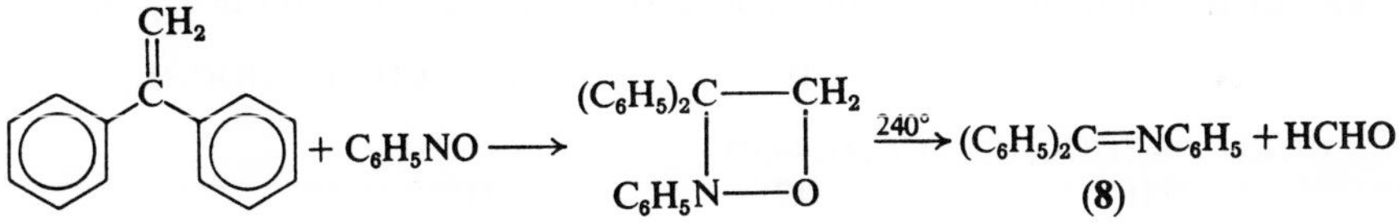

$$+ C_6H_5NO \longrightarrow \begin{matrix}(C_6H_5)_2C———CH_2\\ | \quad\quad | \\ C_6H_5N———O\end{matrix} \xrightarrow{240°} (C_6H_5)_2C=NC_6H_5 + HCHO$$

**(9)** **(8)**

Ingold[42] also postulated the formation of four-membered heterocyclic compounds, 1,3-oxazetidines (10) (originally called 1,3-oxaimines) which were too unstable to be isolated, but the equilibrium reaction could be determined in either direction by choice of a suitable solvent.

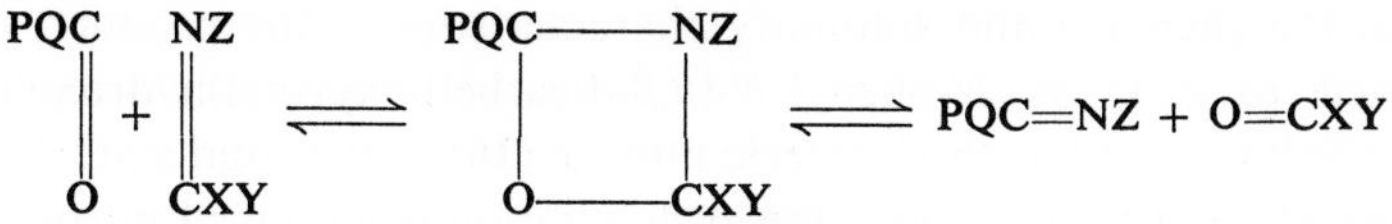

$$\begin{matrix}PQC & NZ \\ \| & \| \\ O & CXY\end{matrix} \rightleftharpoons \begin{matrix}PQC———NZ\\ | \quad\quad |\\ O———CXY\end{matrix} \rightleftharpoons PQC=NZ + O=CXY$$

**(10)**

Due to the lack of sufficient chemical evidence used to assign the structure of the oxazetidines and a misinterpretation of the "polarity theory," Lapworth and co-workers[14,16] reinvestigated these reactions. It should be noted that the work of Lapworth,[14-16] controverting Ingold's conclusions, has been overlooked by more recent investigators.[7,21,29,38] Lapworth and co-workers[14,16] found that Ingold's oxazetidine (9) was in reality the benzhydrylidene-$N$-phenylnitrone (11), which can be synthesized from the benzylidene-$N$-phenylnitrone (12) by the method of Angeli, Alessandri, and Alazzi-Mancini[5]; that is, normal Grignard addition of phenylmagnesium bromide to 12 gives a 1,3-addition product which on hydrolysis yields $N$-benzhydryl-$N$-phenylhydroxyl amine (13), which can then be oxidized by a variety of methods to the nitrone (11).

$$\underset{(12)}{\overset{\displaystyle CH=\overset{+}{N}-C_6H_5}{\underset{\displaystyle O^-}{\bigcirc}}} + C_6H_5MgBr \longrightarrow \underset{(13)}{(C_6H_5)_2CH\underset{OH}{\overset{|}{N}}C_6H_5} \longrightarrow \underset{(11)}{(C_6H_5)_2C=\overset{+}{\underset{O_-}{N}}C_6H_5}$$

This same product was also synthesized from diphenyl diazomethane and nitrosobenzene by Staudinger and Miescher.[72]

Lapworth and co-workers[16] also found no direct evidence in the pyrolysis products of 11 for the formation of formaldehyde reported by Ingold.

By using an alternate route to 5 consisting of the reaction of diethyl hydroxymethylenemalonate (14) and $N$-phenylhydroxylamine (17), Lapworth and co-workers[14] showed that 5 was a 1:1 adduct of nitrosobenzene and diethylmethylenemalonate. The acyclic structure was proposed and,

$$\underset{(14)}{HOCH=C(COOC_2H_5)_2} + \underset{(17)}{C_6H_5\overset{\displaystyle H}{\overset{|}{N}}OH} \longrightarrow \underset{(15)}{\overset{\displaystyle C_6H_5-NCH=C(COOC_2H_5)_2}{\underset{\displaystyle OH}{\overset{|}{\phantom{x}}}}}$$

$$\underset{(16)}{\overset{\displaystyle C_6H_5\overset{\oplus}{N}=CHCH(COOC_2H_5)_2}{\underset{\displaystyle \overset{\ominus}{O}}{\overset{|}{\phantom{x}}}}}$$

due to the chemical and solubility characteristics of the product, it was assumed to exist as $N$-phenyl-$N$-($\beta,\beta$-dicarbethoxyvinyl)hydroxylamine (15) in solution and as the isomeric nitrone (16) in the solid state.

In an attempt to investigate the cycloaddition reactions of nitroso compounds with nonhalogenated olefins and to study the physical properties and chemical reactivity of the 1,2-oxazetidine formed, Hepfinger[25,26,36] repeated the work of Ingold and Weaver[47,48] with 1,1-diphenylethylene and diethylmethylenemalonate and nitrosobenzene, and found no cyclic products. Infrared, ultraviolet, and proton magnetic resonance spectra confirmed the structure of the compound from the reaction of diethyl-methylenemalonate and nitrosobenzene as the $N$-phenyl-$\beta,\beta$-dicarbethoxy-vinylhydroxylamine (15) proposed by Lapworth.[14] In a similar manner Hepfinger[25,26,37] confirmed the structure of the 1:1 adduct of the 1,1-di-phenylethylene and nitrosobenzene to be that of the benzhydrylidene-$N$-phenylnitrone (11) proposed by Lapworth,[16] and not the 1,2-oxazetidine structure proposed by Ingold and Weaver.[47,48]

Recently Hamer and Macaluso,[28,29,53] attempting reactions with the nitrosoarene–olefin series somewhat similar to those of Ingold and Weaver,[47,48] found that the reaction of 1,1-diphenylethylene (3) with nitrosobenzene and with 3-bromonitrosobenzene did not yield a cyclo-addition product. They observed in the cases of cyclopentene, cyclohexene, propylene, and the isomeric butenes that the major product of the reaction was an azoxy compound.

In a series of investigations of perfluoroalkylnitroso derivatives, Barr and Haszeldine[7,10] found that in reactions with halogenated olefins 1,2-oxazetidines and copolymers were formed. The reaction of trifluoro-nitrosomethane (18) and tetrafluoroethylene (19) at $-45°C$ gave a color-less gas (30% yield) and a viscous oil (65% yield).[7,10] When the reaction was repeated at room temperature in the absence of light, the amount of colorless gas was increased (30–65% yield), as was that of the viscous oil (35–70% yield).[7] An investigation of the possible structures (20, 21, 22, and 23) led to the assignment of the cyclic perfluoro-2-methyl-1,2-oxa-zetidine structure (20) to the gaseous product and a 1:1 linear copolymer structure (24) to the viscous oil.

The structural assignments were made on the basis of physical proper-ties, spectral evidence, and chemical activity. Strong support for the per-fluoro-2-methyl-1,2-oxazetidine (20) and the copolymer (24) was given by their pyrolysis at 550°C at low pressure in the absence of air to yield carbonyl fluoride (26) and perfluoro(methylenemethylamine) (25).

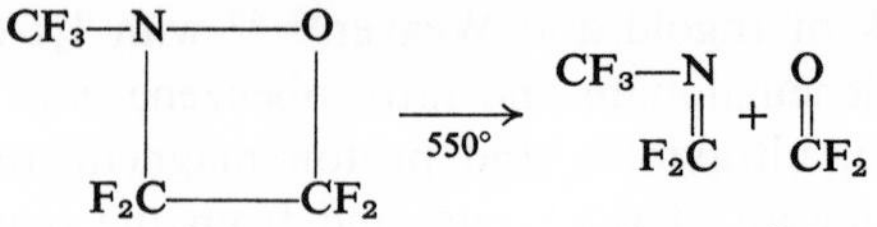

$$\begin{array}{c} \text{CF}_3\text{—N}\text{———O} \\ | \qquad\qquad | \\ \text{F}_2\text{C}\text{———CF}_2 \\ (20) \end{array} \xrightarrow{550°} \begin{array}{cc} \text{CF}_3\text{—N} & \text{O} \\ \| \ + \ \| \\ \text{F}_2\text{C} & \text{CF}_2 \\ (25) \quad (26) \end{array}$$

$$\begin{array}{c} (\text{—N—O—CF}_2\text{—CF}_2\text{—})_n \\ | \\ \text{CF}_3 \\ (24) \end{array} \xrightarrow{500°} (25) + (26)$$

This reaction was extended to nitrosyl halides,[9,11a,50,58,61] which underwent analogous reactions to give an oxazetidine (27) and a copolymer (28). It was hoped that the oxazetidine (29) and the polymer (30) would be

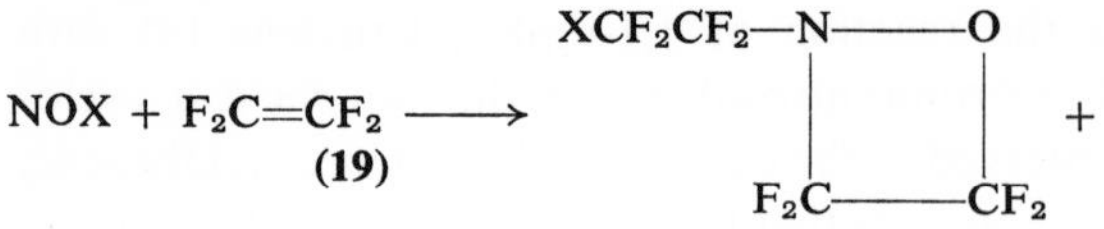

$$\text{NOX} + \text{F}_2\text{C}=\text{CF}_2 \longrightarrow \begin{array}{c} \text{XCF}_2\text{CF}_2\text{—N}\text{———O} \\ | \qquad\qquad\qquad | \\ \text{F}_2\text{C}\text{———CF}_2 \end{array} +$$

$$\qquad (19)$$

$$(27) \quad (\text{—N(CF}_2\text{CF}_2\text{X})\text{—O—CF}_2\text{CF}_2\text{—})_n$$

$$(28)$$

(X = Cl, F)

formed and isolated. However, this was not the case, as oxazetidines of the

$$\begin{array}{c} \text{X—N}\text{———O} \\ | \qquad\qquad | \\ \text{F}_2\text{C}\text{———CF}_2 \end{array} \qquad \left( \begin{array}{c} \text{—N—O—CF}_2\text{—CF}_2\text{—} \\ | \\ \text{X} \end{array} \right)_n$$

(X = Cl, F)

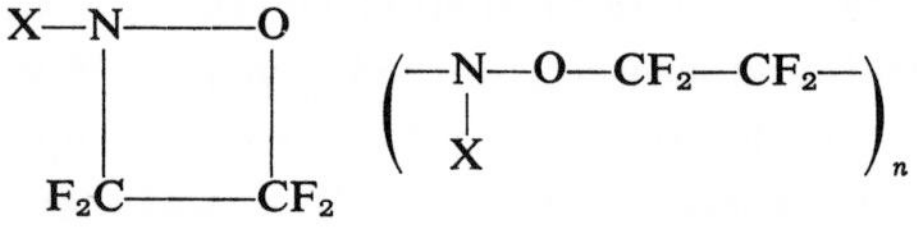

$$\qquad (29) \qquad\qquad\qquad (30)$$

structure 27 were obtained. The formation of this oxazetidine and not the oxazetidine 29 can be explained by the following reaction sequences A and B, as shown below.

A. Equimolar amounts of nitrosyl chloride and tetrafluoroethylene are reacted:

$$\text{NOCl} + \text{F}_2\text{C}=\text{CF}_2 \longrightarrow \text{CF}_2\text{ClCF}_2\text{Cl} + (\text{NO}_2 + \text{N}_2) + \text{CF}_2\text{ClCF}_2\text{NO}$$

$$\qquad (19)$$

$$\text{CF}_2\text{ClCF}_2\text{NO} + \text{NOCl(NO}_2) \longrightarrow \text{CF}_2\text{ClCF}_2\text{NO}_2$$

or

$$\text{CF}_2\text{ClCF}_2\text{NO} \longrightarrow \text{CF}_2\text{ClCF}_2\cdot + \text{NO} \uparrow \xrightarrow{\text{NO}_2}$$

$$\qquad\qquad\qquad\qquad\qquad\qquad \text{CF}_2\text{ClCF}_2\text{NO}_2 + \text{CF}_2\text{ClCF}_2\text{ONO}$$

$$\text{CF}_2\text{ClCF}_2\text{ONO} \longrightarrow \text{CF}_2\text{ClCF}_2\text{O}\cdot + \text{NO} \uparrow \longrightarrow \text{CF}_2\text{ClCOF}$$

The rapid oxidation of the nitroso compound, $\text{CF}_2\text{ClCF}_2\text{NO}$, by nitrosyl chloride is in agreement with the known properties of perfluoroalkynitroso compounds.[7,8,32] Also, the formation of the acyl fluoride,

$CF_2ClCOF$, by the above scheme is consistent with known reactions of perfluoroalkyl and perfluoroalkoxy radicals.[18,33-35]

B. Reaction of nitrosyl chloride with an excess of tetrafluoroethylene:

$$NOCl + F_2C{=}CF_2 \longrightarrow CF_2ClCF_2Cl + CF_2ClCF_2NO$$
$$(19)$$

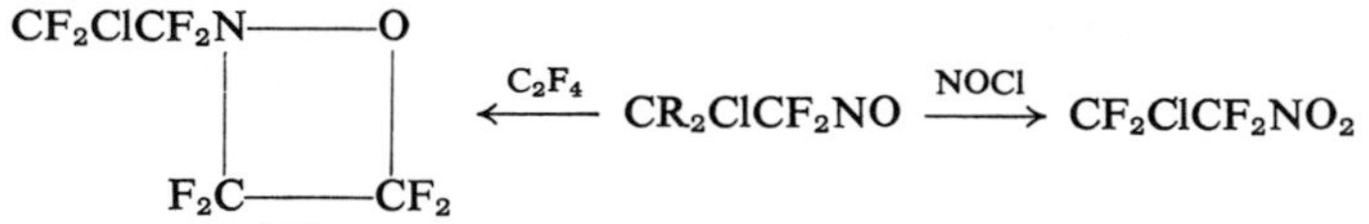

$$CF_2ClCF_2N\text{------}O$$
$$\left|\qquad\right|$$
$$F_2C\text{------}CF_2 \quad \xleftarrow{\;C_2F_4\;} \quad CR_2ClCF_2NO \quad \xrightarrow{\;NOCl\;} \quad CF_2ClCF_2NO_2$$
$$(27)$$

The isolation of $CF_2ClCF_2NO$ strongly suggests that it, rather than the oxazetidine (**29**, X = Cl), is the intermediate in the formation of the oxazetidine (**27**, X = Cl).[9]

The reaction was further extended to other perfluoroalkynitroso compounds,[8] which also reacted analogously, and it was found that the oxazetidine formation is favored at increased temperatures and the polymer formation predominates at room temperature. Finally, the reaction was extended by these and other workers in this area to include larger variations in the nitroso compounds[23] and unsymmetrical olefins of the type $CF_2{=}CXY$[11,60]; also reported were reactions of nitric oxide and fluoroolefins.[12,59,60]

Oxazetidine formation has been observed by Andreads[3,4] during a study of the reaction of nitrosyl fluoride (**31**) with tetrafluoroethylene (**19**). Irradiation of a mixture of tetrafluoroethylene (**19**) and nitrosyl fluoride (**31**) gave hexafluorocyclopropane (**32**) (63% yield), perofluoro-2-methyl-1,2-oxazetidine (**20**) (12.5% yield), and some perfluoro-2-ethyl-1,2-oxa-

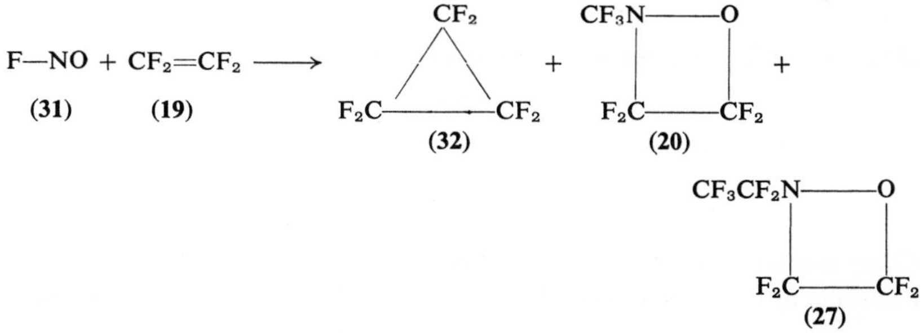

$$F\text{---}NO + CF_2{=}CF_2 \longrightarrow$$
$$(31) \qquad (19)$$

$$\overset{CF_2}{\triangle} \atop F_2C\text{------}CF_2 \qquad + \qquad \overset{CF_3N\text{------}O}{\underset{F_2C\text{------}CF_2}{|\qquad\;|}} \qquad +$$
$$(32) \qquad\qquad\qquad (20)$$

$$\overset{CF_3CF_2N\text{------}O}{\underset{F_2C\text{------}CF_2}{|\qquad\quad\;|}}$$
$$(27)$$

zetidine (**27**, X = F). Analysis of the reaction products indicated that the difluorocarbene intermediate, $:CF_2$, was inserted in the nitrogen–fluorine bond of the nitrosyl fluoride; that is, the formation of **32** indicates that the difluorocarbene intermediate was produced by the photolytic cleavage of tetrafluoroethylene, since **32** is presumed to arise from the reaction of the difluorocarbene intermediate with an excess of tetrafluoroethylene **19**.[6,62] It is much more likely that the oxazetidine (**20**) was formed according to equation a rather than b, since attempts to isolate **29** (X = F) from

$$:CF_2 + F-N{=}O \longrightarrow CF_3N{=}O \xrightarrow{C_2F_4}$$

(**31**)

$$\begin{array}{cc} CF_3N\!\!-\!\!-\!\!-\!\!O \\ | \quad\quad | \\ F_2C\!\!-\!\!-\!\!-\!\!CF_2 \end{array} \qquad (a)$$

(**20**)

↑ :CF₂

$$CF_2{=}CF_2 + F-N{=}O \longrightarrow$$

$$\begin{array}{cc} F-N\!\!-\!\!-\!\!-\!\!O \\ | \quad\quad | \\ F_2C\!\!-\!\!-\!\!-\!\!CF_2 \end{array} \qquad (b)$$

(**29**)

thermal[2,9,32,50] or photolytic reactions have failed.

It is possible that the relatively low bond energy of nitrogen–fluorine bonds in nitrosyl fluoride (**31**) (55.4 kcal/mole)[49] is the cause of the competition reaction in the insertion of difluorocarbene intermediate between the formation of the oxazetidine (**20**) and the cyclopropane (**22**). The heat of formation of difluorocarbene has been estimated as −17 kcal/mole[56] and is probably more negative,[13] indicating that it should be rather selective in contrast to the extremely indiscriminate carbene intermediate, :CH₂.[17]

Adducts which have been assigned the 1,2-oxazetidine structure were reported to have been formed by the reaction of trifluoronitrosomethane (**18**) with styrene, methyl methacrylate, diphenylketene,[54,55] and other unsaturated compounds.[20] The reaction of **18** with styrene gave both 1:1 and 2:1 adducts; the 1:1 adduct was assigned the oxazetidine ring structure (**33**), but the 2:1 adduct was not characterized.

$$CF_3NO + C_6H_5CH{=}CH_2 \longrightarrow$$

$$\begin{array}{cc} CF_3N\!\!-\!\!-\!\!-\!\!O \\ | \quad\quad | \\ H_2C\!\!-\!\!-\!\!-\!\!CHC_6H_5 \end{array} \quad + \text{ 2:1 adduct}$$

(**33**)

Compounds having the 1,2-oxazetidine structure have been reported in the reactions of tetramethoxyethylene and nitrosobenzene,[39] and compounds

$$(CH_3O)_2C{=}C(OCH_3)_2 + C_6H_5NO \longrightarrow$$

$$\begin{array}{cc} C_6H_5N\!\!-\!\!-\!\!-\!\!O \\ | \quad\quad | \\ CH_3OC\!\!-\!\!-\!\!-\!\!C(OCH_3)_2 \\ | \\ OCH_3 \end{array}$$

(mp 83°C, quant. yield)

having the 1,3-oxazetidine structure have been reported as intermediates in the reactions of carbonyl compounds and acyl hydrazones.[19]

$$
\overset{\text{O}}{\overset{\|}{\text{ArC}}}-\text{NHN}=\text{CRR}^1 + \text{R}^2\overset{\text{C}}{\underset{\overset{\|}{\text{O}}}{}}\text{R}^3 \longrightarrow
\begin{array}{c}
\text{R}^1 \\
\text{O}-\!\!\!-\!\!\!\overset{\text{R}}{\underset{}{}} \\
\text{R}^2\overset{}{\underset{\text{R}^3}{}}-\!\!\!-\text{NNHCAr} \\
\overset{\|}{\text{O}}
\end{array}
\longrightarrow
$$

$$
\overset{\text{O}}{\overset{\|}{\text{ArCNHN}}}=\text{CR}^2\text{R}^3 + \text{RCR}^1\overset{}{\underset{\overset{\|}{\text{O}}}{}}
$$

Finally, the oxazetidinone structure was proposed by Staudinger[65,67] and Staudinger and Jelagin[69] for the product of the reactions of nitroso compounds and diphenylketene (**34**). If nitrosobenzene was reacted with

$$
(\text{C}_6\text{H}_5)_2\text{C}{=}\text{C}{=}\text{O} + \text{R}-\text{N}{=}\text{O} \longrightarrow
\begin{array}{c}
(\text{C}_6\text{H}_5)_2\text{C}-\!\!\!-\!\!\!-\text{CO} \\
|\qquad\qquad| \\
\text{O}-\!\!\!-\!\!\!-\text{N}-\text{R}
\end{array}
\quad \text{or}
$$

(**34**)                         (**35**)

$$
\begin{array}{c}
(\text{C}_6\text{H}_5)_2\text{C}-\!\!\!-\!\!\!-\text{CO} \\
|\qquad\qquad| \\
\text{R}-\text{N}-\!\!\!-\!\!\!-\text{O}
\end{array}
$$

(**36**)

**34** the cycloaddition product was a stable 1,2-oxazetidinone-3 (**35**, R = $\text{C}_6\text{H}_5$, 63% yield), which decomposed upon heating into benzophenone

$$
(\text{C}_6\text{H}_5)_2\text{C}{=}\text{C}{=}\text{O} + \text{C}_6\text{H}_5\text{NO} \longrightarrow
\begin{array}{c}
(\text{C}_6\text{H}_5)_2\text{C}-\!\!\!-\!\!\!-\text{CO} \\
|\qquad\qquad| \\
\text{O}-\!\!\!-\!\!\!-\text{NC}_6\text{H}_5
\end{array}
$$

(**34**)                         (**35**)

(**37**) and phenylisocyanate (**38**).[65,67,69] The four-membered ring (**35**, R = $\text{C}_6\text{H}_5$) was also synthesized by reacting diphenylchloroacetic acid

$$
\begin{array}{c}
(\text{C}_6\text{H}_5)_2\text{C}-\!\!\!-\!\!\!-\text{CO} \\
|\qquad\qquad| \\
\text{O}-\!\!\!-\!\!\!-\text{NC}_6\text{H}_5
\end{array}
\xrightarrow{\Delta}
\begin{array}{c}
(\text{C}_6\text{H}_5)_2\text{C}\qquad\text{CO} \\
\|\qquad\quad + \quad\| \\
\text{O}\qquad\quad\text{NC}_6\text{H}_5
\end{array}
$$

(**35**)                         (**37**)     (**38**)

chloride (**39**) with phenylhydroxylamine (**40**).[69] Staudinger and Jelagin[67,69] found that diphenylketene (**34**) reacts with p-dimethylamino-

$$(\text{C}_6\text{H}_5)_2\text{CClCOCl} + 3\text{C}_6\text{H}_5\text{NHOH} \longrightarrow (\textbf{35}) + 2\text{C}_6\text{H}_5\text{NHOH}\cdot\text{HCl}$$

(**39**)                  (**40**)

nitrosobenzene (41) to give an unstable 1,2-oxazetidinone-4 (42) which decomposes prior to its isolation to a Schiff's base (43) and carbon dioxide. The Schiff's base (43) then reacts with another molecule of 34 giving a β-lactam (44).[64, 69]

$$(C_6H_5)_2C{=}C{=}O + p\text{-}NOC_6H_4N(CH_3)_2 \longrightarrow$$

(34)                              (41)

$$
\begin{array}{ccc}
(C_6H_5)_2C & \!\!\!\!\!\text{---} & CO \\
| & & | \\
(CH_3)_2NC_6H_4\text{---}N & \!\!\!\!\!\text{---} & O
\end{array}
$$
(42)

$$
\begin{array}{ccc}
(C_6H_5)_2C & \!\!\!\!\!\text{---} & CO \\
| & & | \\
(CH_3)_2NC_6H_4N & \!\!\!\!\!\text{---} & O
\end{array}
$$
(42)

$$\xrightarrow{\Delta} CO_2 + (CH_3)_2NC_6H_4N{=}C(C_6H_5)_2$$
(43)

$$(C_6H_5)_2C{=}C{=}O + (43) \longrightarrow$$
(34)

$$
\begin{array}{ccc}
(C_6H_5)_2C & \!\!\!\!\!\text{---} & CO \\
| & & | \\
(C_6H_5)_2C & \!\!\!\!\!\text{---} & NC_6H_4N(CH_3)_2
\end{array}
$$
(44)

An unstable 1,3-oxazetidinone-4 (45) was postulated to have been formed by the reaction of dimethylaminobenzaldehyde (46) and phenyliso-cyanate (47),[65] which decomposed into carbon dioxide and a Schiff's base (48).

$$(CH_3)_2NC_6H_5CHO + C_6H_5N{=}C{=}O \longrightarrow$$
(46)                              (47)

$$
\begin{array}{ccc}
(CH_3)_2NC_6H_4CH & \!\!\!\!\!\text{---} & O \\
| & & | \\
C_6H_5N & \!\!\!\!\!\text{---} & CO
\end{array}
$$
(45)

$$(45) \longrightarrow (CH_3)_2NC_6H_4CH{=}NC_6H_5 + CO_2$$
(48)

Kresze and Trede[51] repeated the work of Staudinger and Jelagin[69] and determined the effects of substituents in nitroso compounds on the direction of the reaction with ketenes. p-Dimethylaminonitrosobenzene (41) and p-methoxynitrosobenzene were found to add to the ketene via a polar addition to give the unstable 1,2-oxazetidinone-4 (42), which decomposed prior to isolation to give carbon dioxide and an azomethine (43). Nitroso-benzene and its p-chloro, p-bromo, and p-methyl derivatives were found to add in a reversed direction to give the stable cyclic adducts containing the 1,2-oxazetidinone-3 structure proposed by Staudinger.[69]

It has been reported[22] recently that an unstable 1,3-oxazetidinone-4-N-sulfonyl fluoride acts as an intermediate in the reaction of benzaldehyde and other substituted aldehydes with N-carbonylsulfamoyl halides

(OCNSO$_2$F or OCNSO$_2$Cl) in the formation of $N$-benzalsulfamic acid halides, which then react with ketene to form $\beta$-lactam-$N$-sulfonyl halides (see Table 4-A, Section III-A-2b), as is shown below.

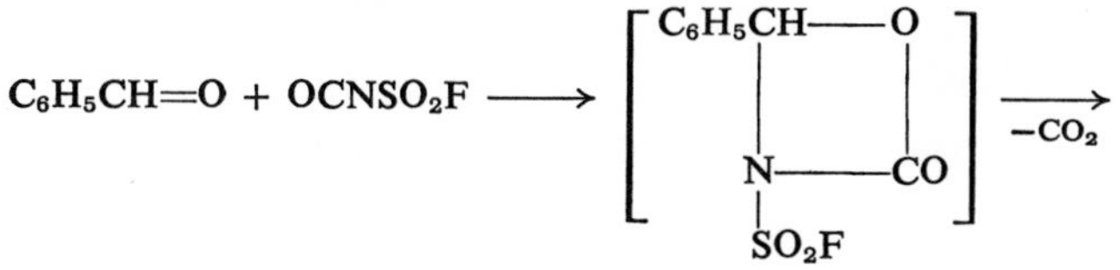

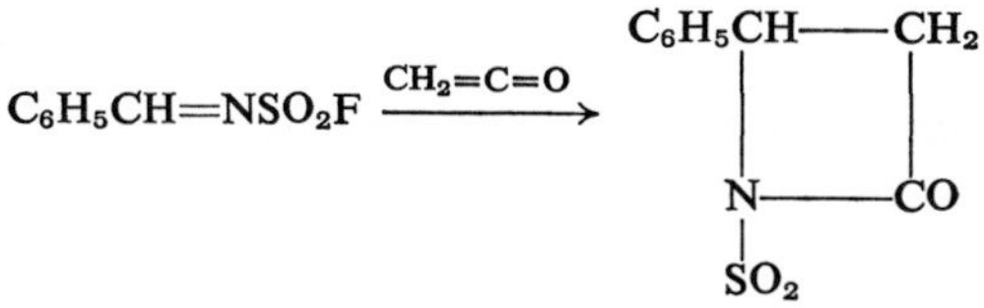

$$C_6H_5CH{=}O + OCNSO_2F \longrightarrow \left[ \begin{array}{c} C_6H_5CH{-\!\!-}O \\ | \qquad \quad | \\ N{-\!\!-\!\!-}CO \\ | \\ SO_2F \end{array} \right] \xrightarrow[-CO_2]{}$$

$$C_6H_5CH{=}NSO_2F \xrightarrow{CH_2=C=O} \begin{array}{c} C_6H_5CH{-\!\!-}CH_2 \\ | \qquad \quad | \\ N{-\!\!-\!\!-}CO \\ | \\ SO_2 \end{array}$$

Staudinger and Miescher[71] postulated the formation of a 1,2-oxazetidinone-4 derivative (49) in the reaction of diphenylketene (34) and di-

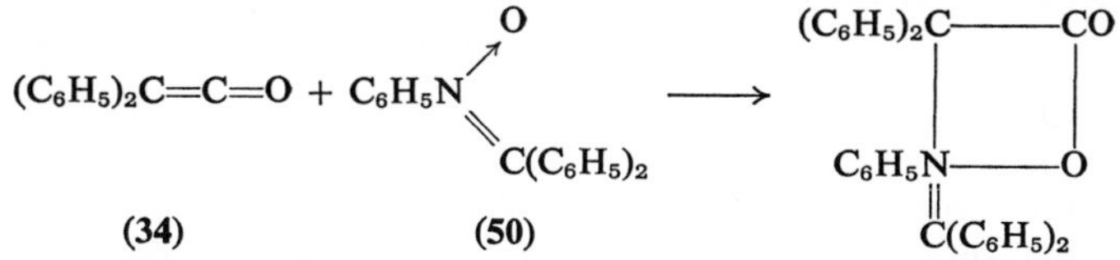

$$(C_6H_5)_2C{=}C{=}O + C_6H_5N \overset{O}{\underset{C(C_6H_5)_2}{\diagdown}} \longrightarrow \begin{array}{c} (C_6H_5)_2C{-\!\!-\!\!-}CO \\ | \qquad \qquad | \\ C_6H_5N{-\!\!-\!\!-}O \\ \| \\ C(C_6H_5)_2 \end{array}$$

$$(34) \qquad\qquad (50) \qquad\qquad\qquad\qquad (49)$$

phenyl-$N$-phenylnitrone (50). The cyclic adduct (49) when heated released carbon dioxide and a "nitrene"* (51) which could not be isolated. Diphenyl-

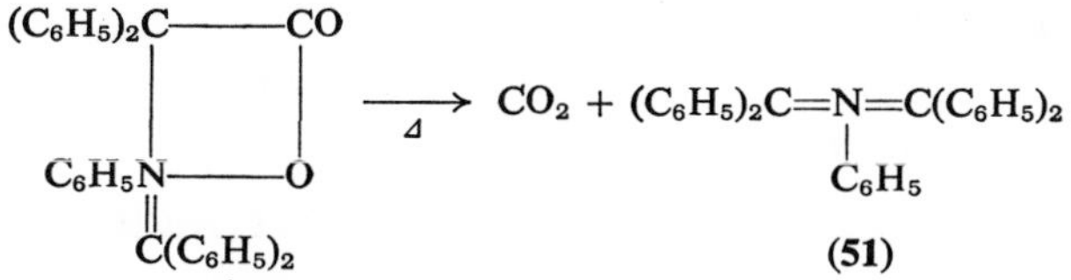

$$\begin{array}{c} (C_6H_5)_2C{-\!\!-\!\!-}CO \\ | \qquad \qquad | \\ C_6H_5N{-\!\!-\!\!-}O \\ \| \\ C(C_6H_5)_2 \end{array} \xrightarrow{\Delta} CO_2 + (C_6H_5)_2C{=}N{=}C(C_6H_5)_2$$

$$\qquad\qquad\qquad\qquad\qquad\qquad\qquad\qquad\qquad C_6H_5$$

$$(49) \qquad\qquad\qquad\qquad\qquad\qquad (51)$$

$N$-methylnitrone (52) was reported[71] to have reacted in the same manner:

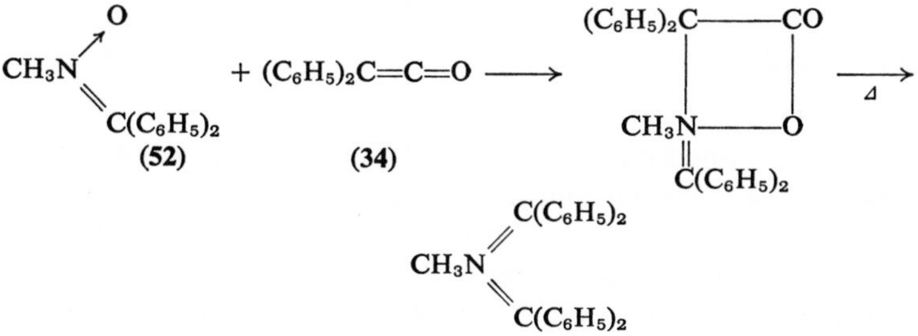

$$CH_3N \overset{O}{\underset{C(C_6H_5)_2}{\diagdown}} + (C_6H_5)_2C{=}C{=}O \longrightarrow \begin{array}{c} (C_6H_5)_2C{-\!\!-\!\!-}CO \\ | \qquad \qquad | \\ CH_3N{-\!\!-\!\!-}O \\ \| \\ C(C_6H_5)_2 \end{array} \xrightarrow{\Delta}$$

$$(52) \qquad\qquad (34)$$

$$CH_3N \overset{C(C_6H_5)_2}{\underset{C(C_6H_5)_2}{\diagdown}}$$

*Staudinger's "nitrenes" should not be confused with electron-deficient species R—$\underline{N}$|.

Analogously, Staudinger[70] attempted to react *N,N*-dimethylaniline oxide and diphenylketene (34) to obtain a 1,2-oxazetidinone-4, which would decompose into an aminomethylene derivative, but the oxide acted as an

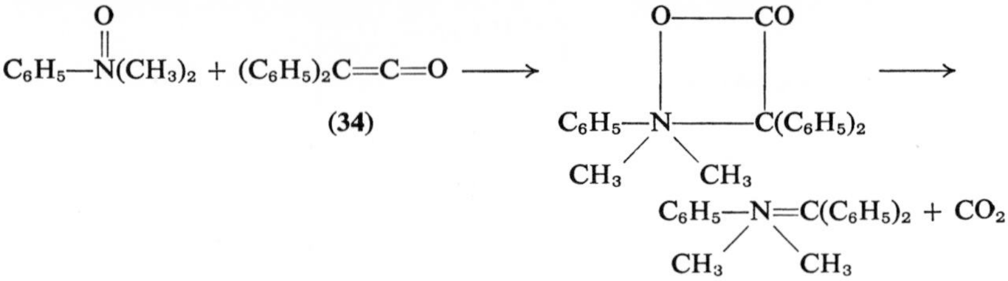

$$C_6H_5—\overset{\overset{O}{\|}}{N}(CH_3)_2 + (C_6H_5)_2C{=}C{=}O \longrightarrow$$

(34)

$$
\begin{array}{c}
\overset{O\text{———}CO}{|\qquad\quad|} \\
C_6H_5{—}N{———}C(C_6H_5)_2 \\
\underset{CH_3}{\diagup}\quad\underset{CH_3}{\diagdown}
\end{array}
\longrightarrow
$$

$$C_6H_5{—}N{=}C(C_6H_5)_2 + CO_2$$
$$\underset{CH_3}{\diagup}\quad\underset{CH_3}{\diagdown}$$

oxidizing medium and reacted with diphenylketene in two directions (equations a and b).

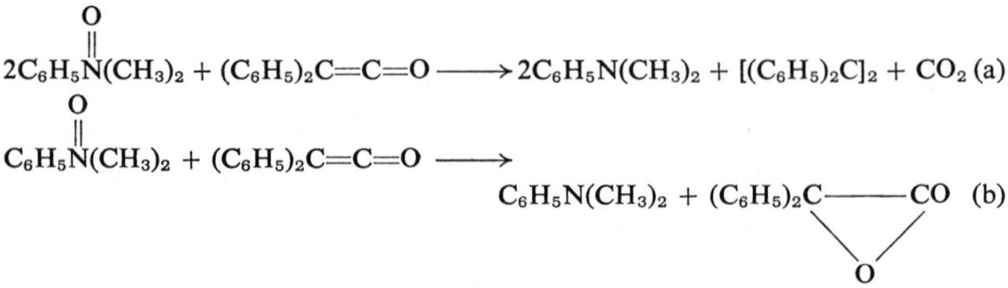

$$2C_6H_5\overset{\overset{O}{\|}}{N}(CH_3)_2 + (C_6H_5)_2C{=}C{=}O \longrightarrow 2C_6H_5N(CH_3)_2 + [(C_6H_5)_2C]_2 + CO_2 \text{ (a)}$$

$$C_6H_5\overset{\overset{O}{\|}}{N}(CH_3)_2 + (C_6H_5)_2C{=}C{=}O \longrightarrow$$

$$C_6H_5N(CH_3)_2 + (C_6H_5)_2C{———}CO \text{ (b)}$$
$$\diagdown\;\diagup$$
$$O$$

Staudinger's work[71] was cited in a review article on nitrones[63] in which the "nitrenes" postulated by Staudinger were regarded as derivatives of ethyleneimine-ring compounds.[57] The pentavalent formula for the "nitrene" was untenable, and further investigations were undertaken by Taylor, Owen, and Whittaker,[73] whose evidence led them to an ethyleneimine structure, as shown below.

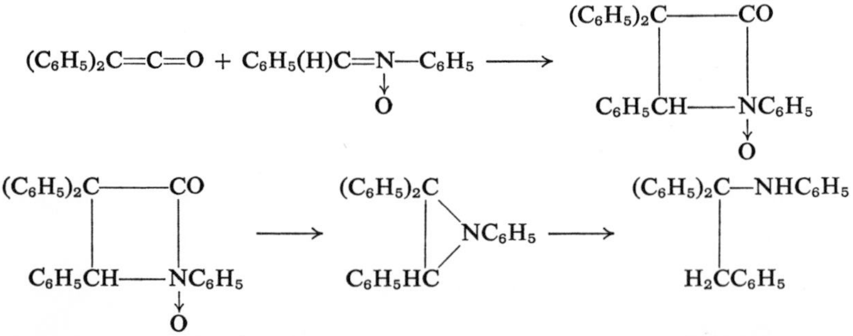

$$(C_6H_5)_2C{=}C{=}O + C_6H_5(H)C{=}\underset{\downarrow}{N}{—}C_6H_5 \longrightarrow$$
$$\qquad\qquad\qquad\qquad\qquad\qquad O$$

$$
\begin{array}{c}
(C_6H_5)_2C{———}CO \\
|\qquad\qquad\quad| \\
C_6H_5CH{———}\underset{\downarrow}{N}C_6H_5 \\
\qquad\qquad\quad O
\end{array}
$$

$$
\begin{array}{c}
(C_6H_5)_2C{———}CO \\
|\qquad\qquad\quad| \\
C_6H_5CH{———}\underset{\downarrow}{N}C_6H_5 \\
\qquad\qquad\quad O
\end{array}
\longrightarrow
\begin{array}{c}
(C_6H_5)_2C \\
\diagdown \\
\qquad NC_6H_5 \\
\diagup \\
C_6H_5HC
\end{array}
\longrightarrow
\begin{array}{c}
(C_6H_5)_2C{—}NHC_6H_5 \\
| \\
H_2CC_6H_5
\end{array}
$$

However, Hassall and Lippman[30] reported that the reaction of diphenylketene (34) with an *N*-phenylnitrone is suggested by the structure of the addition product. It was reported that the electrophilic character of the nitrogen atom had been transmitted to the *N*-phenyl nucleus, so that the diphenylmethylidene group becomes attached to the *ortho*-position. This is followed by a prototropic change to 53, as is illustrated here.

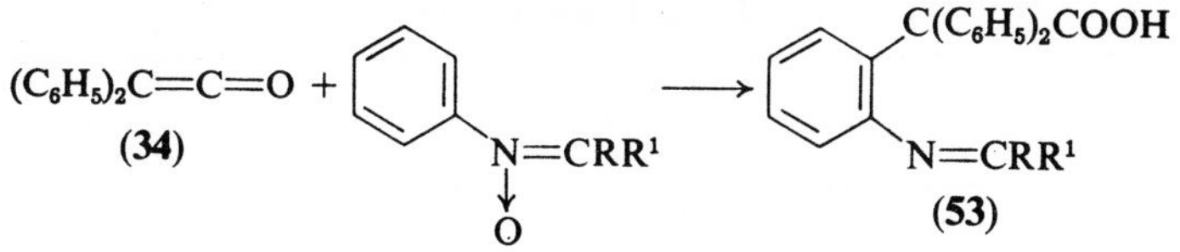

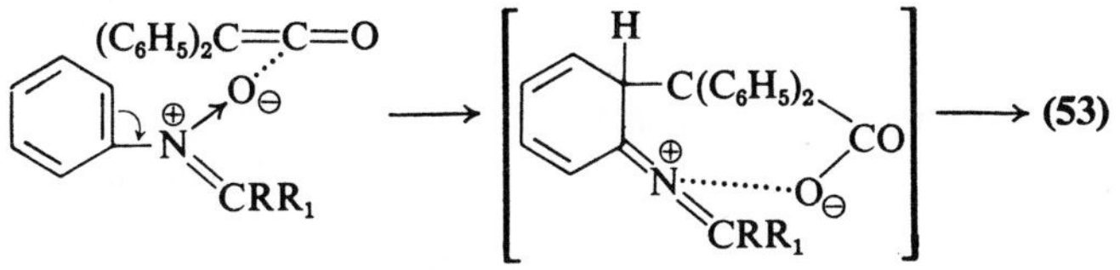

This is in accord with known properties of ketenes,[66] but it is an exceptional mode of reaction for the nitrones which normally undergo 1,3-cycloaddition reactions.[28, 63]

## Table 1

Preparation of Oxazetidines from Perhalonitroso- or Perhaloalkylnitroso Compounds and Haloolefins

| Nitroso derivative | Alkene | 1,2-Oxazetidine | BP (°C) | Yield (%) | Ref. |
|---|---|---|---|---|---|
| $CF_3NO$ | $CF_2{=}CF_2$ | 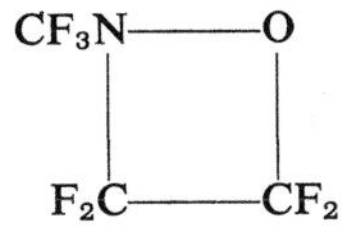 $CF_3N{-}{-}{-}O$ / $F_2C{-}{-}{-}CF_2$ | −6.8 Isoteniscope | 28 / 62 | 7, 10 |
| $CF_3CF_2NO$ | $CF_2{=}CF_2$ | 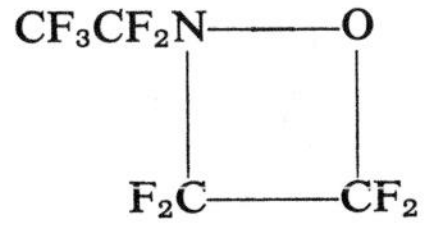 $CF_3CF_2N{-}{-}{-}O$ / $F_2C{-}{-}{-}CF_2$ | 26.0 Isoteniscope | 90 | 9 |
| $CF_2ClCF_2NO$ | $CF_2{=}CF_2$ | 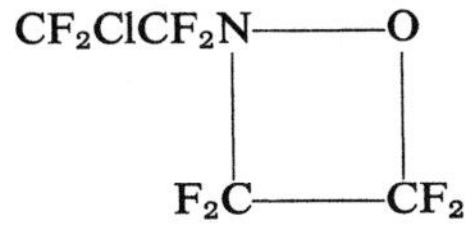 $CF_2ClCF_2N{-}{-}{-}O$ / $F_2C{-}{-}{-}CF_2$ | 57.0 Isoteniscope | 72 | 9 |
| $NOCl$ | $CF_2{=}CF_2$ | 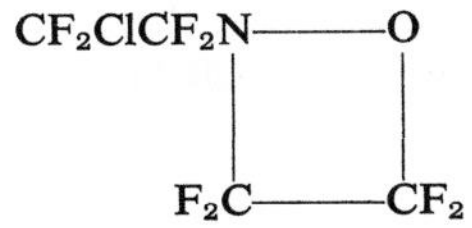 $CF_2ClCF_2N{-}{-}{-}O$ / $F_2C{-}{-}{-}CF_2$ | 57.0 Isoteniscope | 58 / 1.6 | 9, 58, 61 |
| $NOF$ | $CF_2{=}CF_2$ | 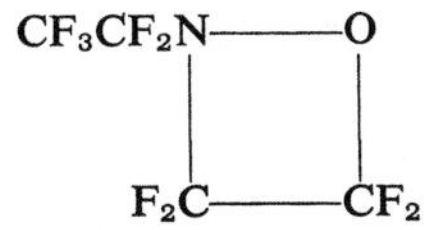 $CF_3CF_2N{-}{-}{-}O$ / $F_2C{-}{-}{-}CF_2$ | 26.0 Isoteniscope | 13–22 / — / 55 | 4, 9, 50 |

(continued)

**Table 1** (*continued*)

| Nitroso derivative | Alkene | 1,2-Oxazetidine | BP (°C) | Yield (%) | Ref. |
|---|---|---|---|---|---|
| NOF | $CF_2{=}CF_2$ | 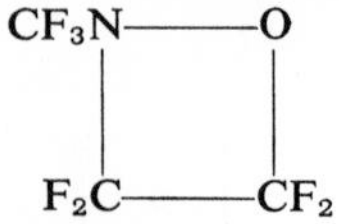 $CF_3N$——O<br><br>$F_2C$——$CF_2$ | $-6.8$ | 12.5 | 3 |
| $CF_3CF_2CF_2NO$ | $CF_2{=}CF_2$ | 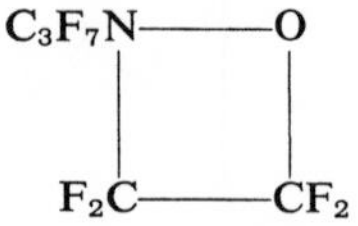 $C_3F_7N$——O<br><br>$F_2C$——$CF_2$ | 50.5<br>Isoteniscope | 63(75) | 8 |
| $CF_3NO$ | $CF_2{=}CFCl$ | 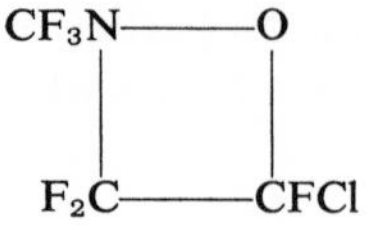 $CF_3N$——O<br><br>$F_2C$——$CFCl$ | 30.0<br>Isoteniscope | 85 | 11 |
| $CF_3NO$ | $CF_2{-}CCl_2$ | 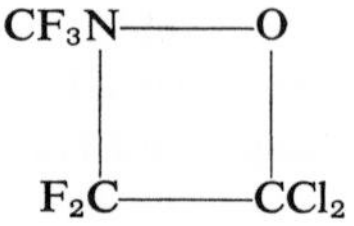 $CF_3N$——O<br><br>$F_2C$——$CCl_2$ | 63.0<br>Isoteniscope | 65 | 11 |
| $CF_3NO$ | $CF_3CF{=}CF_2$ | 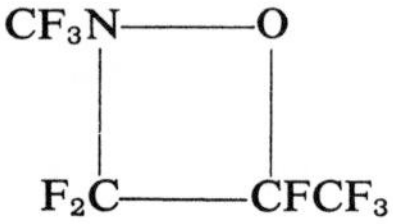 $CF_3N$——O<br><br>$F_2C$——$CFCF_3$ | 22.3 | 90 | 11 |
| | | 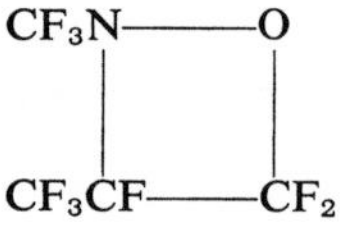 $CF_3N$——O<br><br>$CF_3CF$——$CF_2$ | — | 10 | 11 |
| $CF_2{=}CFNO$ | $CF_2{=}CF_2$ | 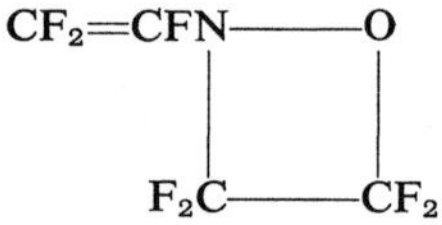 $CF_2{=}CFN$——O<br><br>$F_2C$——$CF_2$ | 41–43 | 69<br>— | 23, 24<br>31 |
| $CF_2{=}CFNO$ | $CFCl{=}CF_2$ | 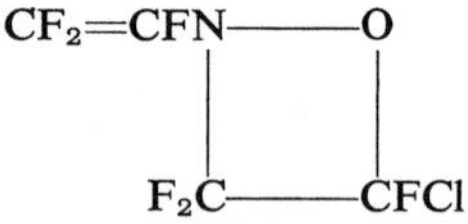 $CF_2{=}CFN$——O<br><br>$F_2C$——$CFCl$ | 73–75 | 57 | 23, 24,<br>31 |
| $CF_2ClCF(Cl)NO$ | $CFCl{=}CF_2$ | 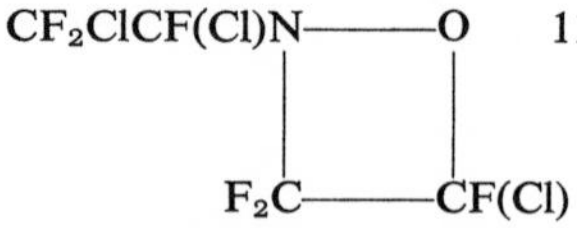 $CF_2ClCF(Cl)N$——O<br><br>$F_2C$——$CF(Cl)$ | 116–117 | 17 | 23, 24 |
| $CF_2ClCF(Cl)NO$ | $CF_2{=}CF_2$ | 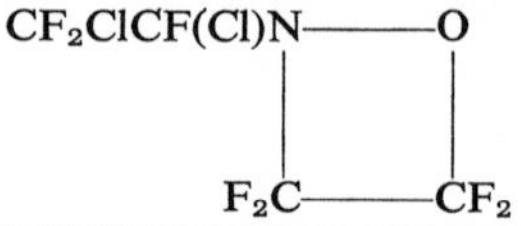 $CF_2ClCF(Cl)N$——O<br><br>$F_2C$——$CF_2$ | — | — | 23, 24 |

(*continued*)

**Table 1** (*continued*)

| Nitroso derivative | Alkene | 1,2-Oxazetidine | BP (°C) | Yield (%) | Ref. |
|---|---|---|---|---|---|
| $(CF_3)_2CFNO$ | $CF_2{=}CF_2$ | $(CF_3)_2CFN\text{---}O$ $\phantom{xxx}\mid\phantom{xxxx}\mid$ $F_2C\text{---}CF_2$ | 48–52 | 45 | 4 |
| NO | $CF_2{=}CFCF_2CF_2Cl$ | $ClCF_2CF_2N\text{---}O$ $\phantom{xxx}\mid\phantom{xxxx}\mid$ $F_2C\text{---}CF_2$ | 76°/630 mm | 12 | 60 |
| NO | $CF_2{=}CF_2$ | $NO_2CF_2CF_2N\text{---}O$ $\phantom{xxx}\mid\phantom{xxxx}\mid$ $F_2C\text{---}CF_2$ | — | — | 59 |
|  |  |  | — | 5–85%[a] | 12 |

[a] The reaction conditions (temperature, pressure, and molar ratio of reactants) were varied to produce the wide percentage yield range. The infrared and ultraviolet absorption spectra data were given.

**Table 2**
Characteristic Infrared Absorption Band of Perhalogenated
Oxazetidines[11]

| Oxazetidine | Absorption band ($\mu$) | Oxazetidine | Absorption band ($\mu$) |
|---|---|---|---|
| $CF_3N\text{---}O$ $\phantom{xx}\mid\phantom{xxx}\mid$ $F_2C\text{---}CF_2$ | 7.05 7.05 | $CF_3N\text{---}O$ $\phantom{xx}\mid\phantom{xxx}\mid$ $F(Cl)C\text{---}CF_2$ | 7.06 |
| $C_2F_5N\text{---}O$ $\phantom{xx}\mid\phantom{xxx}\mid$ $F_2C\text{---}CF_2$ | 7.06 | $CF_3N\text{---}O$ $\phantom{xx}\mid\phantom{xxx}\mid$ $Cl_2C\text{---}CF_2$ | 7.55 |
| $C_3F_7N\text{---}O$ $\phantom{xx}\mid\phantom{xxx}\mid$ $F_2C\text{---}CF_2$ | 7.06 | $CF_3N\text{---}O$ $\phantom{xx}\mid\phantom{xxx}\mid$ $(CF_3)CF\text{---}CF_2$ | 7.30 |
| $CF_2ClCF_2N\text{---}O$ $\phantom{xx}\mid\phantom{xxx}\mid$ $F_2C\text{---}CF_2$ | 7.06 | $CF_3N\text{---}O$ $\phantom{xx}\mid\phantom{xxx}\mid$ $FCH\text{---}CF_2$ | 7.08 |

**Table 3**

Preparation of 1:1 Adducts (Assumed Oxazetidines) by Reaction of
Trifluoronitrosomethane with Unsaturated Compounds

| Alkene | Postulated adduct structure | BP (°C/mm) | $d_{20}^{20}$ | $n_D^{20}$ | Ref. |
|---|---|---|---|---|---|
| $CH_2=C(Me)CO_2Me$ | $CF_3N$——$O$ <br><br> $H_2C$——$C(Me)CO_2Me$ | 99°/5 | 1.338 | 1.6150 | 54, 55 |
| $C_6H_5CH=CH_2$ | $CF_3N$——$O$ <br><br> $H_2C$——$CHC_6H_5$ | oil <br> 90°/5 | 1.372 <br> 1.250 | 1.4855 <br> 1.4730 | 54, 55 <br> 20 |
| $CF_3C\equiv CCl$ | $CF_3N$——$O$ <br><br> $ClC$===$CCF_3$ | 37°/2 | 1.725 | 1.3702 | 54, 55 |
| $CF_3C\equiv CBr$ | $CF_3N$——$O$ <br><br> $BrC$===$CF_2Cl$ | 48°/2 | 1.994 | 1.3920 | 54, 55 |
| $CF_2ClC\equiv CCl$ | $CF_3N$——$O$ <br><br> $ClC$===$CF_2Cl$ | 50°/2 | 1.735 | 1.4132 | 54, 55 |
| $CF(Cl)_2C\equiv CCl$ | $CF_3N$——$O$ <br><br> $ClC$===$C(F)Cl_2$ | 57°/2 | 1.773 | 1.4379 | 54, 55 |
| $2CH_3NC$ | $CF_3N$——$O$ <br><br> $CH_3N$ $\diagdown$ $NCH_3$ | 52–54°/44 | 1.273 | 1.349 | 54, 55 |
| $CF_2=CF_2$ | $CF_3N$——$O$ <br><br> $F_2C$——$CF_2$ | — | — | — | 54, 55 |
| $CF_2=CFCl$ | $CF_3N$——$O$ <br><br> $F_2C$——$CFCl$ | — | — | — | 54, 55 |

*(continued)*

**Table 3** (*continued*)

| Alkene | Postulated adduct structure | BP (°C/mm) | $d_{20}^{20}$ | $n_D^{20}$ | Ref. |
|---|---|---|---|---|---|
| $CF_2{=}CFC_6H_5$ | 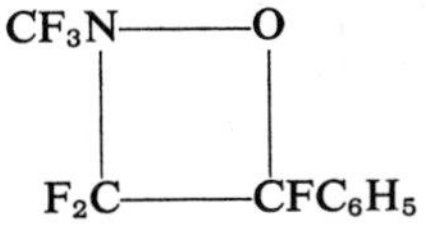 $CF_3N{-}O$ / $F_2C{-}CFC_6H_5$ | 73°/75 | 1.401 | 1.4065 | 20 |

**Table 4**

Preparation of 1,2-Oxazetidinones-3 by the Reaction of Nitroso Compounds with Ketenes

| Nitroso derivative | Ketene | Adduct | MP (°C) | Yield (%) | Ref. |
|---|---|---|---|---|---|
| $C_6H_5NO$ | $(C_6H_5)_2C{=}C{=}O$ | 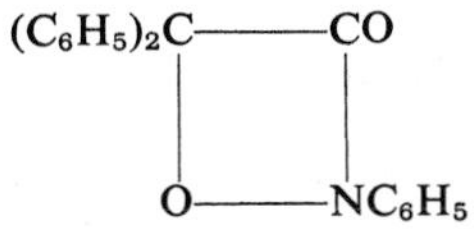 $(C_6H_5)_2C{-}CO$ / $O{-}NC_6H_5$ | 72.5° / 73–73.5° | 63 / 45 | 69 / 51 |
| $p$-$ClC_6H_4NO$ | $(C_6H_5)_2C{=}C{=}O$ | 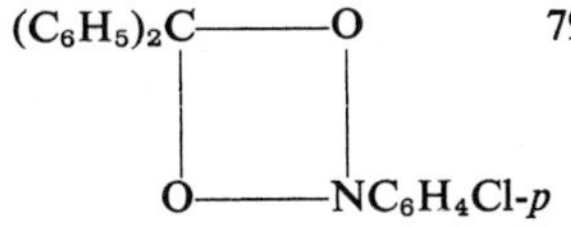 $(C_6H_5)_2C{-}O$ / $O{-}NC_6H_4Cl$-$p$ | 79–79.5° | 48 | 51 |
| $C_6H_5NO$ | $p$-$ClC_6H_4(C_6H_5)C{=}CO$ | 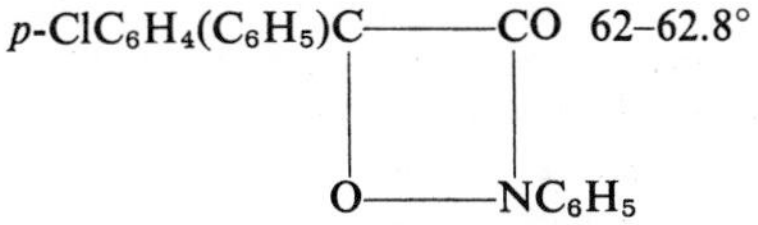 $p$-$ClC_6H_4(C_6H_5)C{-}CO$ / $O{-}NC_6H_5$ | 62–62.8° | 52 | 51 |
| $p$-$ClC_6H_4NO$ | $p$-$ClC_6H_4(C_6H_5)C{=}CO$ | 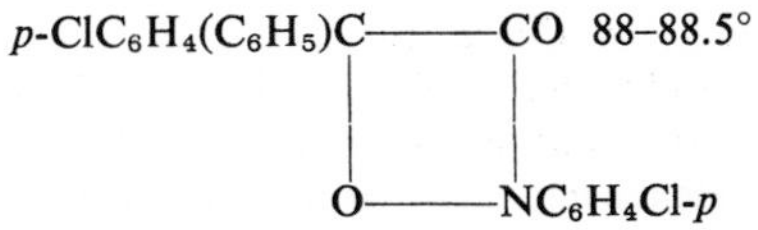 $p$-$ClC_6H_4(C_6H_5)C{-}CO$ / $O{-}NC_6H_4Cl$-$p$ | 88–88.5° | 38 | 51 |
| $p$-$BrC_6H_4NO$ | $(C_6H_5)_2C{=}C{=}O$ | 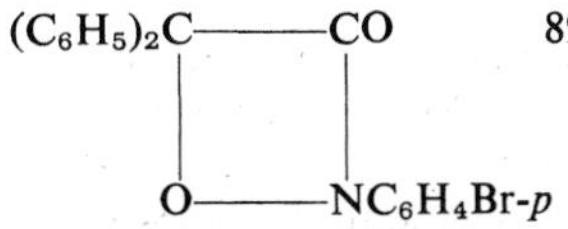 $(C_6H_5)_2C{-}CO$ / $O{-}NC_6H_4Br$-$p$ | 89.5–90° | 19 | 51 |
| $p$-$CH_3C_6H_4NO$ | $(C_6H_5)_2C{=}C{=}O$ | 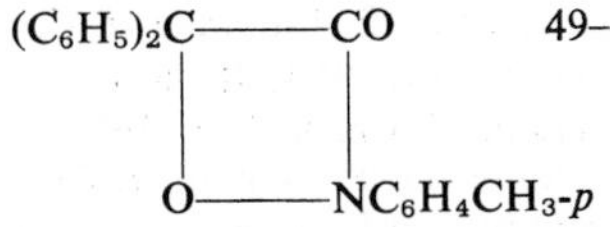 $(C_6H_5)_2C{-}CO$ / $O{-}NC_6H_4CH_3$-$p$ | 49–49.7° | 38 | 51 |
| $CF_3NO$ | $(C_6H_5)_2C{=}C{=}O$ | 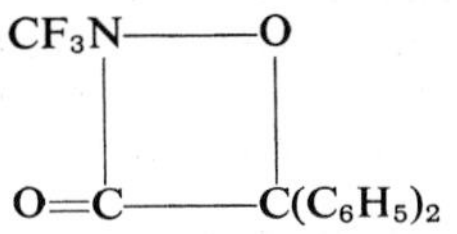 $CF_3N{-}O$ / $O{=}C{-}C(C_6H_5)_2$ | Decom. (gas) 300° | — | 54, 55 |

## REFERENCES

1. L. Alessandri, *Gazz. Chim. Ital.*, **54**, 426 (1924); *Chem. Abstr.*, **19**, 45 (1925).
2. S. Andreads, *Abstr. 139th Mtg. Am. Chem. Soc., St. Louis, Missouri, March 1961,* pp. 26–30.
3. S. Andreads, *Chem. Ind.* (*London*), **1962**, 782.
4. S. Andreads, *J. Org. Chem.*, **27**, 4163 (1962).
5. A. Angeli, L. Alessandri, and M. Alazzi-Mancini, *Atti Accad. Lincei*, **20** (I), 546 (1911); *Chem. Abstr.*, **5**, 3403 (1911).
6. B. Atkins, *J. Chem. Soc.*, **1952**, 2684.
7. D. A. Barr and R. N. Haszeldine, *J. Chem. Soc.*, **1955**, 1881.
8. D. A. Barr and R. N. Haszeldine, *J. Chem. Soc.*, **1956**, 3416.
9. D. A. Barr and R. N. Haszeldine, *J. Chem. Soc.*, **1960**, 1151.
10. D. A. Barr and R. N. Haszeldine, *Nature*, **175**, 991 (1955).
11. D. A. Barr, R. N. Haszeldine, and C. J. Willis, *J. Chem. Soc.*, **1961**, 1351.
11a. D. A. Barr, R. N. Haszeldine, and C. J. Willis, *Proc. Chem. Soc.* (*London*), **1959**, 230.
12. J. M. Birchall, A. L. Bloom, R. N. Haszeldine, and C. J. Willis, *J. Chem. Soc.*, **1962**, 3021.
13. L. Brewer, J. L. Margrave, R. F. Porter, and W. Wieland, *J. Phys. Chem.*, **65**, 1913 (1961).
14. A. Lapworth and G. N. Burkhardt, *J. Chem. Soc.*, **127**, 1748 (1925).
15. A. Lapworth and G. N. Burkhardt, *J. Chem. Soc.*, **127**, 2234 (1925).
16. A. Lapworth, G. N. Burkhardt, and J. Walkden, *J. Chem. Soc.*, **127**, 2458 (1925).
17. W. E. Doering, R. G. Buttery, R. G. Laughlin, and N. Chaudhuri, *J. Am. Chem. Soc.*, **78**, 3224 (1956).
18. W. C. Francis and R. N. Haszeldine, *J. Chem. Soc.*, **1955**, 2151.
19. A. Gautier, J. Renault, and C. Fauran, *Bull. Soc. Chim.* (*France*), **1963**, 2738.
20. V. A. Ginsburg, S. S. Dubov, A. N. Medvedev, L. L. Martynova, B. I. Tetel'baum, M. N. Vasil'eva, and A. Ya. Yakubovich, *Dokl. Akad. Nauk SSSR*, **152**, 1104 (1963); *Chem. Abstr.*, **60**, 1570 (1964).
21. B. G. Gowenlock and W. Lüttke, *Quart. Rev.*, **12**, 321 (1958).
22. R. Graf, *Ann. Chem.*, **661**, 111 (1963).
23. C. E. Griffin and R. N. Haszeldine, *J. Chem. Soc.*, **1960**, 1398.
24. C. E. Griffin and R. N. Haszeldine, *Proc. Chem. Soc.*, **1959**, 369.
25. N. F. Hepfinger, C. E. Griffin, and B. L. Shapiro, *J. Am. Chem. Soc.*, **85**, 2683 (1963).
26. N. F. Hepfinger, C. E. Griffin, and B. L. Shapiro, *Tetrahedron Letters*, **1963**, 1365.
27. J. Hamer and A. Macaluso, *Chem. Rev.*, **64**, 473 (1964).
28. J. Hamer and A. Macaluso, *Chem. Rev.*, **64**, 482 (1964).
29. J. Hamer and A. Macaluso, *Tetrahedron Letters*, **1963**, 381.
30. C. H. Hassall and A. E. Lippman, *J. Chem. Soc.*, **1953**, 1059.
31. R. N. Haszeldine, Brit. Pat. 963,634 (1963).
32. R. N. Haszeldine, *J. Chem. Soc.*, **1953**, 2075.
33. R. N. Haszeldine and F. Nyman, *J. Chem. Soc.*, **1959**, 387.
34. R. N. Haszeldine and F. Nyman, *J. Chem. Soc.*, **1959**, 420.
35. R. N. Haszeldine and F. Nyman, *J. Chem. Soc.*, **1959**, 1804.
36. N. F. Hepfinger, "A Study of the Reactions of Nitroso Compounds with Olefins," Ph.D. Thesis, University of Pittsburgh, Pittsburgh, Pennsylvania, 1963, pp. 34 ff.
37. N. F. Hepfinger, *Ibid.*, pp. 43 ff.

38. W. J. Hickinbottom, in *Chemistry of Carbon Compounds*, Vol. 3A, E. H. Rodd, Ed., Elsevier, Amsterdam, 1957.
39. R. W. Hoffmann and H. Häuser, *Angew. Chem.*, **76**, 346 (1964); *Angew. Chem. Int. Ed. Engl.*, **3**, 380 (1964).
40. C. K. Ingold, *J. Chem. Soc.*, **125**, 87 (1924).
41. C. K. Ingold, *J. Chem. Soc.*, **126i**, 322 (1924).
42. C. K. Ingold, *J. Chem. Soc.*, **127**, 1141 (1925).
43. C. K. Ingold and H. A. Piggott, *J. Chem. Soc.*, **121**, 2793 (1922).
44. C. K. Ingold and H. A. Piggott, *J. Chem. Soc.*, **123**, 2745 (1923).
45. C. K. Ingold and H. A. Piggott, *J. Chem. Soc.*, **125**, 168 (1924).
46. C. K. Ingold and H. A. Piggott, *J. Chem. Soc.*, **126i**, 323 (1924).
47. C. K. Ingold and S. D. Weaver, *J. Chem. Soc.*, **125**, 1456 (1924).
48. C. K. Ingold and S. D. Weaver, *J. Chem. Soc.*, **126i**, 116 (1924).
49. H. S. Johnston and H. J. Bertin, Jr., *J. Am. Chem. Soc.*, **81**, 6402 (1959).
50. I. L. Knunyants, E. G. Bykhovskaya, V. N. Frosin, and Ya. M. Kisel, *Dokl. Akad. Nauk SSSR*, **132**, 123 (1960); *Chem. Abstr.*, **54**, 20840 (1960).
51. G. Kresze and A. Trede, *Tetrahedron*, **19**, 133 (1963).
52. T. M. Lowry, *J. Chem. Soc.*, **123**, 822 (1923).
53. A. Macaluso, "Exploratory Investigations into the Reactions of Aromatic Nitroso Compounds with Alkenes," M.S. Thesis, Tulane University, New Orleans, Louisiana, 1963.
54. S. P. Makarov, V. A. Shpanskii, V. A. Ginsberg, A. I. Shchekotikhin, A. S. Filatov, L. L. Martynova, I. V. Pavlovskaya, A. F. Golovaneva, and Ya. Yakubovich, *Dokl. Akad. Nauk SSSR*, **142**, 354 (1962); *Chem. Abstr.*, **57**, 4528 (1962).
55. S. P. Makarov, V. A. Shpanskii, V. A. Ginsburg, A. I. Shchekotikhin, A. S. Filatov, L. L. Martynova, I. V. Pavlovskaya, A. F. Golovaneva, and Ya. Yakubovich, *Dokl. Akad. Nauk SSSR*, **142**, 596 (1962); *Chem. Abstr.*, **57**, 4528 (1962).
56. J. R. Majer and C. R. Patrick, *Nature*, **192**, 866 (1961).
57. E. Oliveri-Mandala and E. Calderaro, *Gazz. Chim. Ital.*, **451**, 311 (1915); *Chem. Abstr.*, **10**, 596 (1916).
58. J. D. Park and A. P. Stefani, U.S. Pat. 3,072,705 (1963).
59. J. D. Park, A. P. Stefani, G. H. Crawford, and J. R. Lacher, *J. Org. Chem.*, **26**, 3316 (1961).
60. J. D. Park, A. P. Stefani, and J. R. Lacher, *J. Org. Chem.*, **26**, 3319 (1961).
61. J. D. Park, A. P. Stefani, and J. R. Lacher, *J. Org. Chem.*, **26**, 4017 (1962).
62. J. P. Simons and A. J. Yarwood, *Nature*, **192**, 943 (1961).
63. L. E. Smith, *Chem. Rev.*, **23**, 193 (1938).
64. H. Staudinger, *Ann. Chem.*, **356**, 61 (1907).
65. H. Staudinger, *Chem. Ber.*, **44**, 521 (1911).
66. H. Staudinger, *Die Ketene*, F. Enke, Stuttgart, 1912.
67. H. Staudinger, *Helv. Chim. Acta*, **5**, 103 (1923).
68. H. Staudinger and R. Endle, *Chem. Ber.*, **50**, 1042 (1917).
69. H. Staudinger and S. Jelagin, *Chem. Ber.*, **44**, 365 (1911).
70. H. Staudinger and J. Meyer, *Helv. Chim. Acta.* **2**, 608 (1919).
71. H. Staudinger and K. Miescher, *Helv. Chim. Acta*, **2**, 554 (1919).
72. H. Staudinger and K. Miescher, *Helv. Chim. Acta*, **2**, 568 (1919).
73. T. W. J. Taylor, J. S. Owen, and D. Whittaker, *J. Chem. Soc.*, **1938**, 207.

### 3. Oxygen and Sulfur

#### a. Oxathietane 1-Oxides and Oxathietane 1,1-Dioxides

In studying the reactions of diphenylketene, Staudinger and Pfenninger[27] reported that diphenylketene (1) and sulfur dioxide (2) combined via a cycloaddition reaction to form the unstable oxathietane derivative, 4,4-diphenyl-1,2-oxathietan-3-one 1-oxide (3), which decomposed into a sulfur-containing compound (4), and at higher temperatures into tetraphenylethylene (5).

$$(C_6H_5)_2C{=}C{=}O + O{=}S{=}O \longrightarrow$$

    (1)          (2)

$$(C_6H_5)_2C\text{----}CO$$
$$OS\text{----}O$$
$$(3) \longrightarrow$$

$$(C_6H_5)_2C + CO_2 \longrightarrow (C_6H_5)_2C{=}C(C_6H_5)_2$$
$$\underset{O}{\overset{\parallel}{\underset{\downarrow}{S}}}$$

    (4)                       (5)

If, on the other hand, sulfur trioxide (6) is introduced into a mixture of dioxane and ethylene chloride cooled to 15°C, to which ketene (7) is simultaneously added, the resulting cycloadduct, 1,2-oxathietan-3-one 1,1-dioxide (8) is obtained.[12, 22, 26]

$$SO_3 + CH_2{=}C{=}O \longrightarrow$$

    (6)        (7)

$$CH_2\text{----}CO$$
$$O_2S\text{----}O$$
$$(8)$$

Reactions of olefins with sulfur trioxide are vigorous, and therefore need to be moderated by use of inert diluents or by use of complexes of sulfur trioxide with pyridine or dioxane.[29] These reactions have been extensively studied[1-7, 28-32] in an effort to determine whether the intermediate in the sulfonation reaction is a $\beta$-sultone or a cyclic sulfonate–sulfate anhydride. In one instance—the reaction of styrene (9) with sulfur trioxide (6)—the isolation of a $\beta$-sultone, 4-phenyl-1,2-oxathietane 1,1-dioxide (10), has been reported[1, 4] in 80% yield. Analogously, a $\beta$-sultone was assumed to

$$SO_3 + C_6H_5CH{=}CH_2 \longrightarrow$$

    (6)        (9)

$$C_6H_5CH\text{----}CH_2$$
$$O_2S\text{----}O$$
$$(10)$$

act as an intermediate in the reaction of ethylene and excess sulfur tri-oxide[19, 23-25] and substituted olefins and the sulfur trioxide-dioxane complex, resulting in the cyclic sulfonate–sulfate anhydride.[2, 5, 21, 28, 29, 33] For example, 1-hexene (12) and the sulfur trioxide–dioxane complex (11) combine rapidly to form the $\beta$-sultone, 3-$n$-butyl-1,2-oxathietane 1,1-dioxide (13), which reacts slowly with a second molecule of the sulfur trioxide–dioxane complex to form the cyclic sulfonate–sulfate anhydride (14).

$$n\text{-}C_4H_9CH{=}CH_2 + C_4H_8O_2 \cdot SO_3 \xrightarrow{\text{Fast}} \begin{array}{c} n\text{-}C_4H_9CH\text{---}CH_2 \\ | \qquad\qquad | \\ O\text{----}SO_2 \end{array} + C_4H_8O_2$$

$$(12) \qquad\qquad (11) \qquad\qquad\qquad\qquad (13)$$

$$(13) \xrightarrow[\text{Slow}]{C_4H_8O_2 \cdot SO_3} \begin{array}{c} n\text{-}C_4H_9CH\text{---}CH_2 \\ O \qquad\qquad SO_2 \\ SO_2\text{---}O \end{array}$$

$$(14)$$

Bordwell and Peterson[3] further substantiated the existence of a $\beta$-sultone in the reactions of olefins and sulfur trioxide, depending on the reaction conditions. Sulfonation of cyclopentene with an equimolar quantity of dioxane–sulfur trioxide complex after hydrolysis gave 3% sulfuric acid, 8% of an unsaturated sulfonic acid, and 79% of a $\beta$-hydroxycyclopentane-sulfonic acid. A mixed melting point determination of the $p$-toluidine salt of the above acid with an identical sample obtained by the reaction of cyclopentene oxide or *trans*-chlorocyclopentanol with ammonium sulfite proved that the salt was that of *trans*-2-hydroxycyclopentanesulfonic acid (16),[3] since *trans*-opening of an epoxide ring in reactions with nucleophilic reagents has been established.[17, 34] *Trans*-products are also the rule for displacement reactions of cyclic halohydrins.[3]

The formation of *trans*-2-hydroxycyclopentanesulfonic acid (16) from the hydrolysis of the sulfonation solution is consistent with the presence of a $\beta$-sultone (15) intermediate analogous to **A**.[3] The fusion of the four- and

$$\begin{array}{c} RHC\text{---}CH_2 \\ | \qquad | \\ O\text{---}SO_2 \end{array} \qquad\qquad \xrightarrow{H_2O} \qquad\qquad$$

$$\textbf{A} \qquad\qquad (15) \qquad\qquad (16)$$

five-membered rings in **15** must of necessity be *cis*; therefore the ring opening of **15** by the attack of the water molecule is expected to lead to inversion regardless of whether the hydrolysis proceeds via an $S_N1$ or $S_N2$

type mechanism.[3] A minimum of 57% of the *trans* isomer present was isolated.

Additional evidence for the presence of the β-sultone intermediate (15) was obtained by the formation of a dipolar ion, *trans*-2-(1-proto-1-pyridyl)-cyclopentanesulfonate (17), by addition of pyridine to the sulfonation solution.[3]

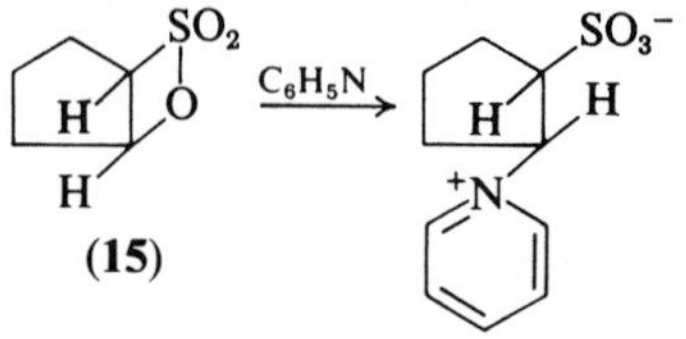

Reaction of cyclopentene with a two-molar quantity of dioxane–sulfur trioxide gave different results[3, 8–10, 20]; this seems to indicate the presence

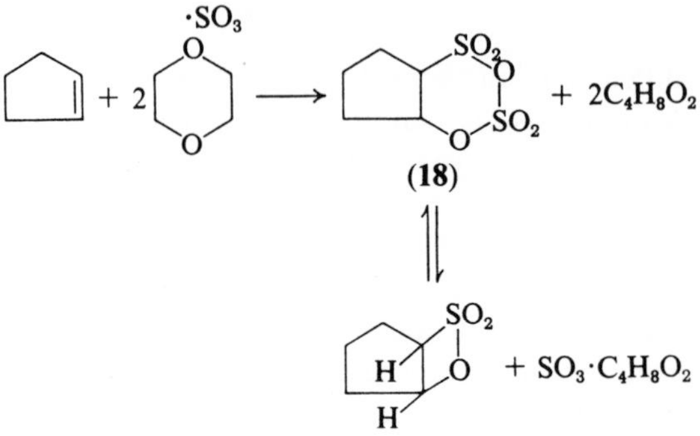

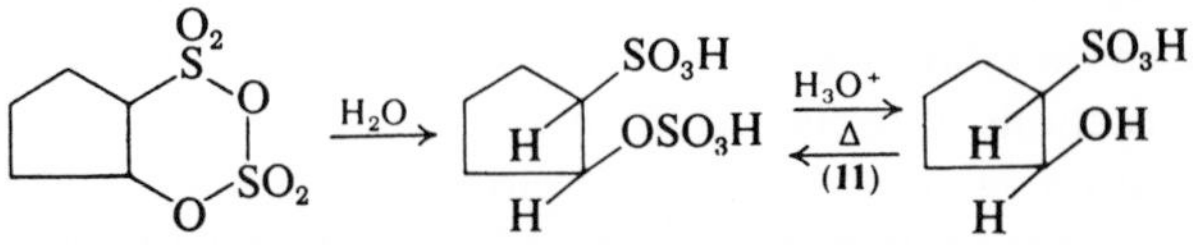

of a cyclic sulfonate–sulfate anhydride (18). The sulfonation, and its mechanism, of cyclohexene has also been discussed.[3]

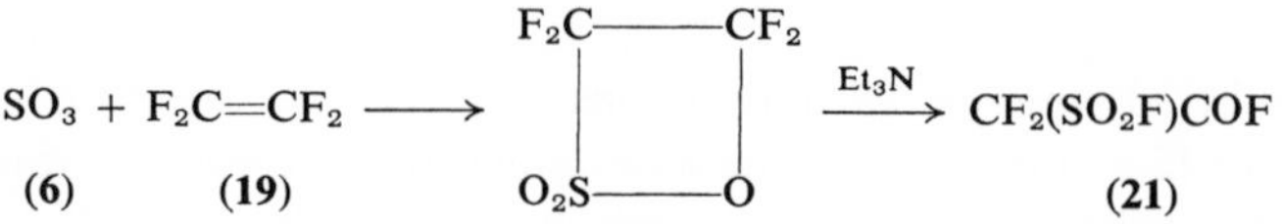

In contrast, it was reported[11, 18] that fluoroolefins react with sulfur trioxide in the absence of a complexing agent or diluent to give β-sultones and cyclic sulfonate–sulfate anhydrides. Tetrafluoroethylene (19) reacted rapidly and exothermically with freshly distilled sulfur trioxide (6) to give the cycloadduct, 3,4-perfluoro-1,2-oxathietane 1,1-dioxide (20), in nearly quantitative yield,[11,13,14] which rearranges to 21 when treated with triethylamine.[13,14] Hexafluoropropene (22) was observed to react analogously with sulfur trioxide (6), resulting in the formation of the oxathietane derivative 4-trifluoromethyl-3,3,4-trifluoro-1,2-oxathietane 1,1-dioxide

$$SO_3 + CF_3CF{=}CF_2 \longrightarrow$$

(6)    (22)

$$\begin{array}{cc} CF_3CF\!\!-\!\!-\!\!CF_2 \\ | \quad\quad | \\ O_2S\!\!-\!\!-\!\!O \end{array}$$

(23)

(23).[11,13] The structure of the $\beta$-sultones (20 and 23) were determined by elemental analysis, neutral equivalent determinations, and fluorine nuclear magnetic resonance and infrared (asymmetric S—O stretch at 6.9 $\mu$) spectra.[13,14,16,18]

$\beta$-Sultones were also prepared from several chlorofluoroolefins (Table 1)[11,14,18] by mildly heating the olefin and sulfur trioxide at atmospheric pressure. Chlorotrifluoroethylene (14) gave equal amounts of two possible isomeric $\beta$-sultones (25 and 26)[11,14,18] which codistilled, but the fluorine nuclear magnetic resonance spectrum of the mixture was interpreted as consisting of a single peak (CFCl) and a weak, strong, strong, weak combination or AB pattern (CF$_2$ in an unsymmetrical ring) for each of the two isomers present (Table 2).[14]

$$SO_3 + ClCF{=}CF_2 \longrightarrow$$

(6)    (24)

$$\begin{array}{cc} ClCF\!\!-\!\!-\!\!CF_2 \\ | \quad\quad | \\ O_2S\!\!-\!\!-\!\!O \end{array} \quad\quad \begin{array}{cc} F_2C\!\!-\!\!-\!\!FCCl \\ | \quad\quad | \\ O_2S\!\!-\!\!-\!\!O \end{array}$$

(25)    (26)

Treatment of the $\beta$-sultone (27) with a catalytic amount of triethylamine (29) resulted in the quantitative rearrangement to sulfonic–carboxylic acid halides (30) via the following proposed mechanism [14] in which the triethylamine attacks the sulfur atom and a ring opening at the sulfur–oxygen bond occurs. A halogen ion, X$^-$, is expelled, the chloride ion always being expelled where there is a choice between chloride or fluoride ions. The expelled anion displaces triethylamine from the cation to give the final products (30) (Table 3) observed. There was a decreasing tendency toward $\beta$-sultone formation when a series of hydrofluoroolefins were used; for

$$\begin{array}{cc} F \quad\; R \\ | \quad\;\; | \\ X_1C\!\!-\!\!-\!\!CX_2 + (C_2H_5)_3N \longrightarrow \\ | \quad\quad | \\ O\!\!-\!\!-\!\!SO_2 \end{array} \quad (29) \quad\quad \begin{array}{cc} F \quad\; R \\ | \quad\;\; | \\ X_1C\!\!-\!\!-\!\!CX_2 \\ | \quad\quad | \\ O \quad\; {}^+SO_2 \\ {}^- \quad\quad | \\ \quad\quad N(C_2H_5)_3 \end{array} \longrightarrow$$

(27)

$$\underset{O}{\overset{F}{\underset{\|}{C}}}\text{—}\underset{{}^{+}SO_2}{\overset{R}{\underset{|}{C}X_2}}$$

$$X_1^- + \underset{\underset{N(C_2H_5)_3}{|}}{\underset{O}{\overset{F}{\underset{\|}{C}}}}\text{—}\underset{{}^{+}SO_2}{\overset{R}{\underset{|}{C}X_2}} \longrightarrow (C_2H_5)_3N + \underset{O}{\overset{F}{\underset{\nearrow}{C}}}\text{—}\underset{\underset{X_1}{|}}{\underset{SO_2}{\overset{R}{\underset{|}{C}X_2}}}$$

**(30)**

example, trifluoroethylene under conditions comparable to those used with tetrafluoroethylene gave only 60% of the $\beta$-sultone 3,3,4-trifluoro-1,2-oxathietane 1,1-dioxide (**32**), which could be rearranged to fluorosulfonyl-fluoroacetyl fluoride and 34% of a higher boiling product shown by chemical and spectral analysis to be a 1:2 ethylene/sulfur trioxide adduct,[2,3,5,11,18] the cyclic sulfonate–sulfate anhydride (**34**).[1]

$$SO_3 + CHF{=}CF_2 \longrightarrow$$
**(6)**      **(31)**

$$\begin{array}{c} FCH\text{——}CF_2 \\ | \qquad\quad | \\ | \qquad\quad | \\ O_2S\text{——}O \end{array}$$
**(32)**

FO$_2$SCHFCOF

**(33)**

$$\begin{array}{c} \overset{O}{F_2C\diagup\;\;\diagdown SO_2} \\ |\qquad\qquad| \\ FHC\diagdown\;\;\diagup O \\ \underset{SO_2}{} \end{array}$$
**(34)**

The $\beta$-sultones undergo reactions with nucleophilic reagents such as alcohols, sodium methoxide, primary and secondary amines, urea, thiols and potassium thiocyanate.[4,14–16,18]

For example, sulfur trioxide (**6**) and perfluoro-1-heptene (**35**) combine via a cycloaddition reaction resulting in 4-perfluoropentyl-3,3,4-trifluoro-1,2-oxathietane 1,1-dioxide (**36**) in a 58% yield.[15] When **36** is treated with ammonia in the presence of perfluorodimethylcyclobutane, 4-perfluoro-pentyl-4-fluoro-3-imino-1,2-oxathietane 1,1-dioxide (**37**) is obtained.[15]

$$SO_3 + CF_3(CF_2)_4CF{=}CF_2 \longrightarrow$$
**(6)**          **(35)**

$$\begin{array}{c} F \\ CF_3(CF_2)_4\overset{|}{C}\text{————}CF_2 \\ |\qquad\qquad\quad| \\ |\qquad\qquad\quad| \\ O_2S\text{————}O \end{array}$$
**(36)**

$$\mathbf{(36)} + NH_3 \longrightarrow$$

$$\begin{array}{c} F \\ CF_3(CF_2)_4\overset{|}{C}\text{————}C{=}NH \\ |\qquad\qquad\quad| \\ |\qquad\qquad\quad| \\ O_2S\text{————}O \end{array}$$
**(37)**

## Table 1
### 1,2-Oxathietane 1,1-Dioxides from the Cycloaddition of Sulfur Trioxide and Olefins

| Olefin | Cycloadduct | $d_4^t$ | $n_D^t$ | BP (°C/mm) | Yield (%) | Ref. |
|---|---|---|---|---|---|---|
| $CF_2=CF_2$ | F$_2$C——CF$_2$<br>&#124;  &#124;<br>O$_2$S——O | 1.6219 (20) | 1.3050 (20) | 42<br>33 | 93<br>— | 13, 14<br>11 |
| $CF_3CF=CF_2$ | CF$_3$CF——CF$_2$<br>&#124;  &#124;<br>O$_2$S——O | 1.6670 (20) | 1.3000 (20) | 46.5<br>—<br>47–48<br>42–43 | —<br>85<br>94<br>— | 13<br>14<br>16<br>11 |
| $ClCF=CF_2$ | ClCF——CF$_2$<br>&#124;  &#124;<br>O$_2$S——O<br><br>F$_2$C——FCCl<br>&#124;  &#124;<br>O$_2$S——O | 1.71 (22)<br>1.7269 (20) | 1.3672 (21)<br>1.3676 (20) | 76–78<br>76–76.5<br>77–78 | 85[a]<br>quant.<br>— | 14<br>18<br>11 |
| $ClCF=C(Cl)F$ | ClCF——FCCl<br>&#124;  &#124;<br>O$_2$S——O | | | 110–113 | 80[b] | 14 |

(continued)

**Table 1** (*continued*)

| Olefin | Cycloadduct | $d^{t°}$ | $n_D^{t°}$ | BP (°C/mm) | Yield (%) | Ref. |
|---|---|---|---|---|---|---|
| $Cl_2C{=}CF_2$ | 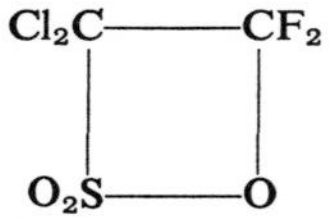 $Cl_2C{-}CF_2$ / $O_2S{-}O$ | | | 110–112 | 56 | 14 |
| $FCH{=}CF_2$ | 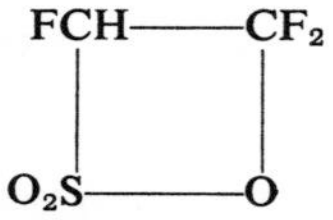 $FCH{-}CF_2$ / $O_2S{-}O$ | 1.7082 (20) | 1.3530 (20) | 103 | 61 | 14 |
| | | | | 104–105 | — | 11 |
| $C_4H_9CF{=}CF_2$ | 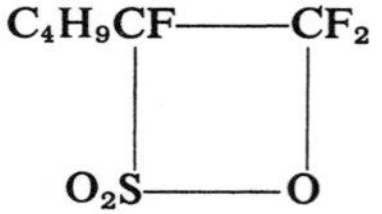 $C_4H_9CF{-}CF_2$ / $O_2S{-}O$ | | | 63–65/20 | 72 | 14 |
| $H(CF_2)_6CF{=}CF_2$ | 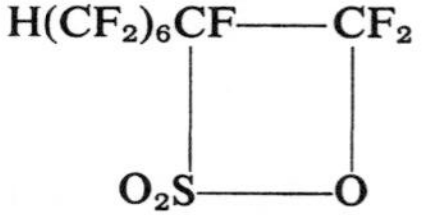 $H(CF_2)_6CF{-}CF_2$ / $O_2S{-}O$ | | | 76/22 | 90 | 14 |
| $(C_5F_{11})CF{=}CF_2$ | 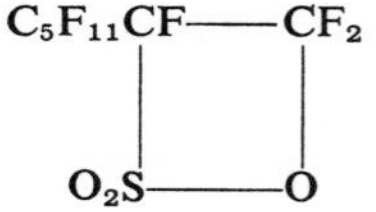 $C_5F_{11}CF{-}CF_2$ / $O_2S{-}O$ | — | — | 134–36.5 | 58 | 15, 16 |

| Starting material | Product | Density | $n$ | b.p. | Yield | Ref. |
|---|---|---|---|---|---|---|
| $CF_2ClCFClCF_2CF{=}CF_2$ | $CF_2ClCFClCF_2CF{-}CF_2$, ring $O{-}SO_2$ | — | 1.3642 (22) | 79.8–80/63.7 | 72 | 18 |
| $CF_2Cl(CFClCF_2)_2CF{=}CF_2$ | $CF_2Cl(CFClCF_2)_2CF{-}CF_2$, ring $O{-}SO_2$ | 1.881 (20) | 1.3800 (20.5) | 56/0.17 | 77.5 | 18 |
| $CF_2Cl(CFClCF_2)_3CF{=}CF_2$ | $CF_2Cl(CFClCF_2)_3CF{-}CF_2$, ring $O{-}SO_2$ | — | 1.3893 (20) | 81–2/0.08 | 73 | 18 |
| $CF_2Cl(CFClCF_2)_4CF{=}CF_2$ | $CF_2Cl(CFClCF_2)_4CF{-}CF_2$, ring $O{-}SO_2$ | 1.993 (23.8) | 1.3949 (20) | 115–116/ 0.04 | 82 | 18 |
| $CFCl_2CF_2CF{=}CF_2$ | $CFCl_2CF_2CF{-}CF_2$, ring $O{-}SO_2$ | 1.776 (23.8) | 1.3720 (20) | 129–131.5 | 73.4 | 18 |
| $CF_3CCl{=}C(CF_3)Cl$ | $CF_3CCl{-}C(CF_3)Cl$, ring $O{-}SO_2$ | — | 1.3740 (22) | 132–33.8 | 59.8 | 18 |

<sup></sup>

[a] Mixture of isomers.    [b] Mixture of *cis-* and *trans-* isomers.

**Table 2**

Fluorine Nuclear Magnetic Resonance Spectral Data for $\beta$-Sultones[14]

| $\beta$-Sultone | FNMR (cps) | | | |
|---|---|---|---|---|
| | $CF_3$ | $CF_2$ | CF | CHF |
| $F_2C$——$CF_2$ <br> $\mid$　　$\mid$ <br> $O_2S$——$O$ | | 768[a] <br><br> 1305[a] | | |
| $CF_3CF$——$CF_2$ <br> $\mid$　　$\mid$ <br> $O_2S$——$O$ | −150 | 309[b] <br> 419[b] <br> 645[b] <br> 756[b] | 4320 | |
| $ClCF$——$CF_2$ <br> $\mid$　　$\mid$ <br> $O_2S$——$O$ | | 296[b] <br> 391[b] <br> 520[b,c] <br> 615[b,c] <br> 703[b] | −287[c] <br> 1418[c] | |
| $F_2C$——$CF(Cl)$ <br> $\mid$　　$\mid$ <br> $O_2S$——$O$ | | 857[b] <br> 963[b,c] <br> 1117[b,c] | | |
| $ClCF$——$C(Cl)F$ <br> $\mid$　　$\mid$ <br> $O_2S$——$O$ | | | −890[c] <br> −601[c] <br> 691[c] <br> 979[c] | |
| $Cl_2C$——$CF_2$ <br> $\mid$　　$\mid$ <br> $O_2S$——$O$ | | 107 | | |
| $FCH$——$CF_2$ <br> $\mid$　　$\mid$ <br> $O_2S$——$O$ | | 254[b] <br> 362[b] <br> 564[b] <br> 674[b] | | 5123[c] <br> 5172[c] |

[a] Triplet.
[b] Weak, strong, strong, weak.
[c] Doublet.

**Table 3**

Sulfonic–Carboxylic Acid Halides from Rearrangements of
β-Sultones with Triethylamine

$$\begin{array}{ccc}
F & R & \\
| & | & \\
C & \!\!\!\!-\!\!\!\!- C\!\!-\!\!X_2 & \\
O^{/\!/} & SO_2 & \\
& | & \\
& X_1 & \\
\end{array}$$

| $X_1$ | $X_2$ | R | Ref. |
|-------|-------|-----------|------|
| F | F | F | 14 |
| Cl | Cl | F | 14 |
| F | Cl | Cl | 14 |
| F | F | Cl | 14 |
| Cl | F | F | 14 |
| F | F | $C_5F_{11}$ | 15 |
| F | F | $CF_3$ | 15 |

REFERENCES

1. F. G. Bordwell, F. B. Colton, and M. Knell, *J. Am. Chem. Soc.*, **76**, 3950 (1954).
2. F. G. Bordwell and M. L. Peterson, *J. Am. Chem. Soc.*, **76**, 3952 (1954).
3. F. G. Bordwell and M. L. Peterson, *J. Am. Chem. Soc.*, **76**, 3957 (1954).
4. F. G. Bordwell, M. L. Peterson, and C. S. Rondestvedt, Jr., *J. Am. Chem. Soc.*, **76**, 3945 (1954).
5. F. G. Bordwell and C. S. Rondestvedt, Jr., *J. Am. Chem. Soc.*, **70**, 2429 (1948).
6. F. G. Bordwell, C. M. Suter, J. M. Holbert, and C. S. Rondestvedt, Jr., *J. Am. Chem. Soc.*, **68**, 139 (1946).
7. F. G. Bordwell, C. M. Suter, and A. J. Webber, *J. Am. Chem. Soc.*, **67**, 827 (1945).
8. G. N. Burkhardt, W. K. Ford, and E. Singleton, *J. Chem. Soc.*, **1936**, 17.
9. R. L. Burwell, Jr., *J. Am. Chem. Soc.*, **67**, 220 (1945).
10. R. L. Burwell, Jr., *J. Am. Chem. Soc.*, **71**, 1769 (1949).
11. M. A. Dmitriev, G. A. Sokol'skii, and I. L. Knunyants, *Khim. Nauka Prom.*, **3**, 826 (1958); *Dokl. Akad. Nauk SSSR*, **124**, 581 (1959); *Chem. Abstr.*, **53**, 11211 (1959).
12. W. D. Emmons, in *Compounds with Three- and Four-Membered Rings* (*The Chemistry of Heterocyclic Compounds*, Vol. 19, A. Weissberger, Ed.), Interscience, New York, 1964, pp. 978 ff.
13. D. C. England, U.S. Pat. 2,852,554 (1958).
14. D. C. England, M. A. Dietrich, and R. V. Lindsey, *J. Am. Chem. Soc.*, **82**, 6181 (1960).
15. H. H. Gibbs, U.S. Pat. 3,091,619 (1963).
16. H. H. Gibbs and M. I. Bro, *J. Org. Chem.*, **26**, 4002 (1961).
17. W. E. Grigsby, J. Hind, J. Chanley, and F. H. Westheimer, *J. Am. Chem. Soc.*, **64**, 2606 (1942).
18. S. Hsi-Kwei Jiang, *Hua Hsüeh Hsüeh Pao*, **23**, 330 (1957); *Chem. Abstr.*, **52**, 15493 (1958).

19. A. Michael and N. Weiner, *J. Am. Chem. Soc.*, **58**, 294 (1936).
20. M. S. Neuman, *J. Am. Chem. Soc.*, **72**, 3853 (1950).
21. H. Pepouse, *Bull. Soc. Chim. Belges*, **34**, 133 (1925).
22. G. Quadbeck, *Angew. Chem.*, **68**, 361 (1956).
23. H. V. Regnault, *Ann. Chem.*, **25**, 32 (1838).
24. H. V. Regnault, *Ann. Chem.*, **27**, 11 (1838).
25. H. V. Regnault, *Ann. Chim. Phys.*, **45**, 98 (1838).
26. C. W. Smith, U.S. Pat. 2,566,810 (1951).
27. H. Staudinger and F. Pfenninger, *Chem. Ber.*, **49**, 1941 (1916).
28. C. M. Suter and F. G. Bordwell, *J. Am. Chem. Soc.*, **65**, 507 (1943).
29. C. M. Suter, P. B. Evans, and J. M. Kiefer, *J. Am. Chem. Soc.*, **60**, 538 (1938).
30. C. M. Suter and J. D. Malkemus, *J. Am. Chem. Soc.*, **63**, 978 (1941).
31. C. M. Suter, J. D. Malkemus, and S. Archer, *J. Am. Chem. Soc.*, **63**, 1594 (1941).
32. C. M. Suter and W. E. Truce, *J. Am. Chem. Soc.*, **66**, 1105 (1944).
33. W. E. Truce and P. F. Gunberg, *J. Am. Chem. Soc.*, **72**, 2401 (1950).
34. C. E. Wilson and H. J. Lucas, *J. Am. Chem. Soc.*, **58**, 2396 (1936).

## 4. Nitrogen and Sulfur

### a. Thiazetidine 1,1-Dioxides and Thiazetidinone 1-Oxides

In an attempt to prepare diphenylsulfene (**2**), a compound with characteristics similar to those of the ketenes,[17] Staudinger and Pfenninger reacted diphenyldiazomethane (**1**) with sulfur dioxide[16]; however, the sulfene (**2**) was not obtained. Assuming that the sulfene (**2**) was formed as

$$(C_6H_5)_2C{=}N_2 + SO_2 \longrightarrow (C_6H_5)_2C{=}SO_2 + N_2$$
$$\text{(1)} \qquad\qquad\qquad\qquad \text{(2)}$$

an intermediate between the reaction of (**1**) and sulfur dioxide, the reaction was undertaken in the presence of Schiff bases, which should trap the sulfene intermediate by forming a cycloaddition product. The sulfene intermediate (**2**) was reacted with benzylideneaniline (**3**) yielding

$$(C_6H_5)_2C{=}SO_2 + C_6H_5CH{=}NC_6H_5 \longrightarrow$$
$$\text{(2)} \qquad\qquad \text{(3)}$$

$$
\begin{array}{ccc}
(C_6H_5)_2C & \!\!\!\!\!\!-\!\!\!\!\!\! & SO_2 \\
| & & | \\
C_6H_5CH & \!\!\!\!\!\!-\!\!\!\!\!\! & NC_6H_5 \\
\end{array}
$$
$$\text{(4)}$$

the cycloaddition product 2,3,4,4-tetraphenyl-1,2-thiazetidine-1,1-dioxide

(4).[16] The Schiff base (3) would not react with either the diphenyldiazomethane (1) or the sulfur dioxide in the pure form.[5,6]

More recently, in an attempt to show the similarity between the nitrogen–oxygen double bond and the nitrogen–sulfur–oxygen group,[9] reactions
analogous to the cycloaddition reaction of nitrosobenzene (5) and diphenylketene (6) to form the oxazetidinone (7) by Staudinger and Jelagin[15]

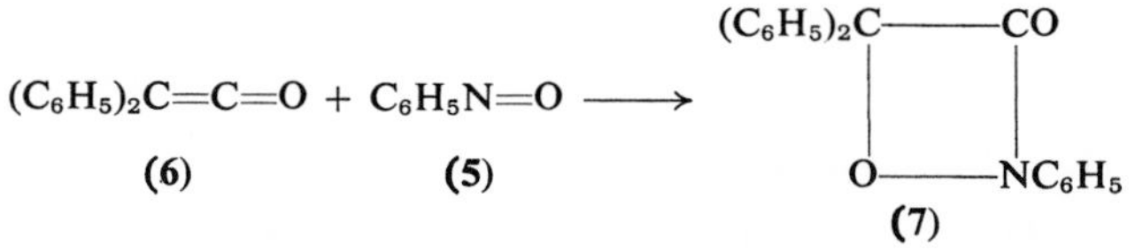

$$(C_6H_5)_2C{=}C{=}O + C_6H_5N{=}O \longrightarrow$$

(6)                    (5)

$$(C_6H_5)_2C{-}{-}{-}{-}CO$$
$$O{-}{-}{-}{-}{-}NC_6H_5$$

(7)

were conducted. N-Sulfinylaniline did not react with diphenylketene, but
the more reactive N-sulfinyl-p-toluenesulfonamide (8) combined with
diphenylketene in dilute petroleum ether solution at room temperature to
form the cycloadduct 2-p-toluenesulfonyl-4,4-diphenyl-1,2-thiazetidin-3-
one-1-oxide (9), in 78% yield.[9] An analogous reaction occurred with butyl-

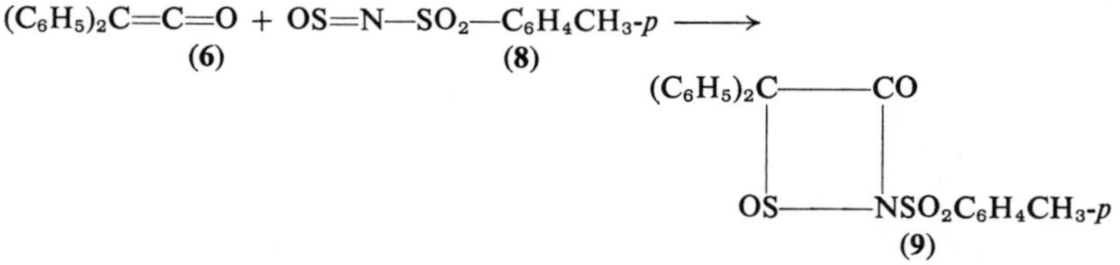

$$(C_6H_5)_2C{=}C{=}O + OS{=}N{-}SO_2{-}C_6H_4CH_3{-}p \longrightarrow$$

(6)                              (8)

$$(C_6H_5)_2C{-}{-}{-}{-}CO$$
$$OS{-}{-}{-}{-}{-}NSO_2C_6H_4CH_3{-}p$$

(9)

ethylketene (10) and 8[4] with the formation of 2-p-toluenesulfonyl-4-ethyl-
4-butyl-1,2-thiazetidin-3-one-1-oxide (11).

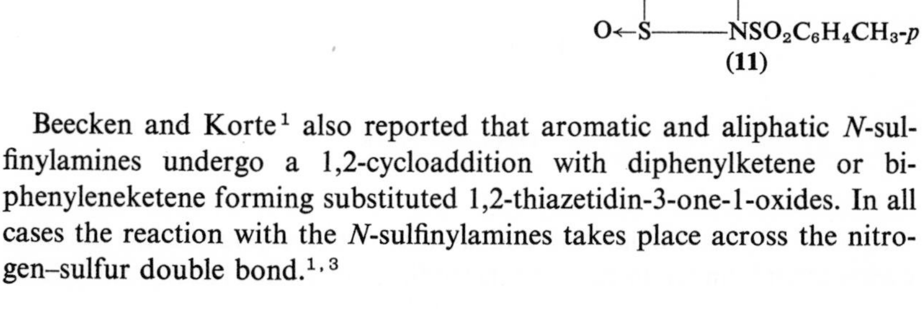

$$C_4H_9C{=}C{=}O + OS{=}N{-}SO_2C_6H_4CH_3{-}p \longrightarrow$$
$$\quad\ \ |$$
$$\quad\ \ C_2H_5$$

(10)                              (8)

$$C_2H_5$$
$$\ \ |$$
$$C_4H_9C{-}{-}{-}{-}CO$$
$$O{\leftarrow}S{-}{-}{-}{-}{-}NSO_2C_6H_4CH_3{-}p$$

(11)

Beecken and Korte[1] also reported that aromatic and aliphatic N-sulfinylamines undergo a 1,2-cycloaddition with diphenylketene or biphenyleneketene forming substituted 1,2-thiazetidin-3-one-1-oxides. In all
cases the reaction with the N-sulfinylamines takes place across the nitrogen–sulfur double bond.[1,3]

As already mentioned, Kresze and co-workers[9] reported that $N$-sulfinyl-aniline (12a) would not react with diphenylketene (6); however, Beecken and Korte[1] found that this limitation did not exist. That is, equimolar amounts of $N$-sulfinylaniline (12a) or other aromatic sulfinylamines (12c–g) and diphenylketene (6) were converted into $N$-aryl-4,4-diphenyl-1,2-thiazetidin-3-one-1-oxides (13a, c–g) (Table 1) generally at room temperature with or without the presence of a solvent.[1] It was reported

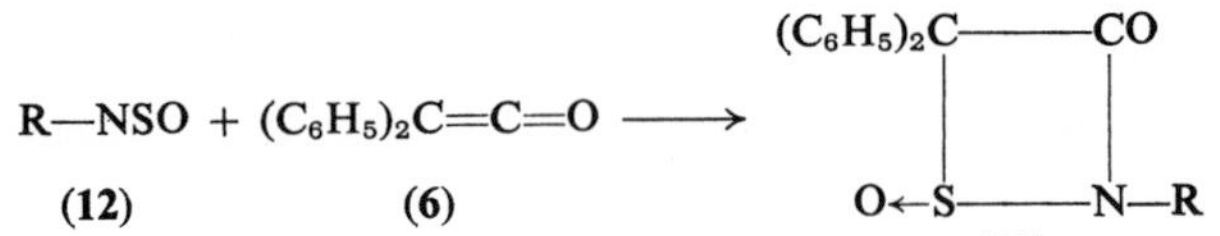

$$R{-}NSO + (C_6H_5)_2C{=}C{=}O \longrightarrow$$

(12)                    (6)

$$(C_6H_5)_2C{-}\!\!-\!\!-CO$$
$$O{\leftarrow}S{-}\!\!-\!\!-N{-}R$$
(13)

that the sterically unfavorable aliphatic $N$-sulfinylcyclohexylamine (12b) was much more reactive than were the aromatic $N$-sulfinylamines.

Biphenyleneketene (14) also adds smoothly to $N$-sulfinylamines in petroleum ether with formation of spirothiazetidinoneoxides (15) (Table 1).[1] The strained four-membered ring was identified by its very intensive

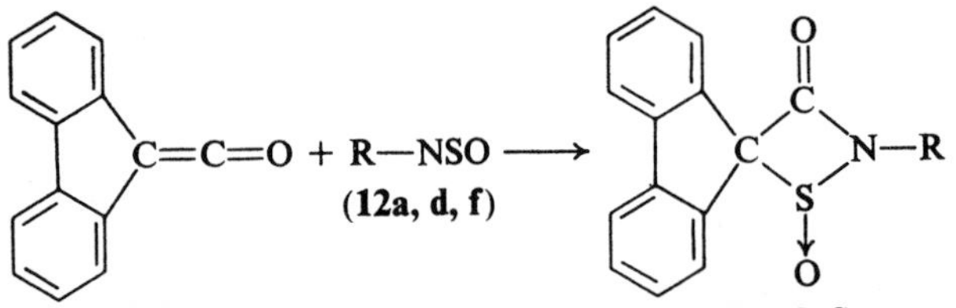

$$C{=}C{=}O + R{-}NSO \longrightarrow$$
(12a, d, f)

(14)                    (15a, d, f)

carbonyl and sulfur–oxygen infrared absorption bands ($\nu$ (C=O) = 1730–1760 cm$^{-1}$; $\nu$(S $\rightarrow$ O) = 1130–1143 cm$^{-1}$).

1,2-Thiazetidin-3-one-1,1-dioxides (16) are prepared by cyclization reactions,[2,7,8,11–13] and not by the oxidation of the 1,2-thiazetidin-3-one-1-oxides.[1] In comparison, it was recently found that in the cycloaddition

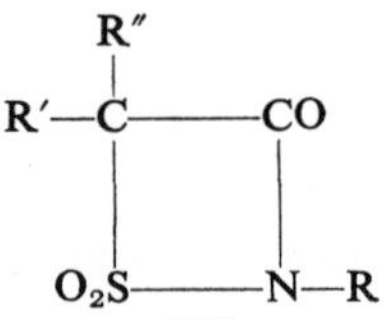

$$R'{-}C{-}\!\!-\!\!-CO$$
with R'' above and $O_2S{-}\!\!-\!\!-N{-}R$ below
(16)

reactions of $N$-sulfinylaniline and unsaturated compounds, the resulting cycloadduct (similar to the 1,2-thiazetidin-3-ones) was readily oxidized to the dioxide by a peroxide–acetic acid mixture; for example, *N*-sulfinylaniline (**12a**) and norbornene (**17**) combine to form the cycloadduct (**18**),

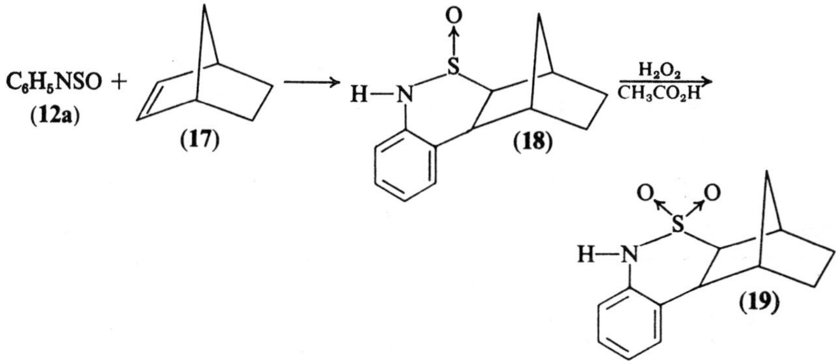

which is oxidized to the dioxide (**19**).[3,10] Analogously, *N*-sulfinylaniline (**12a**) reacts with norbornadiene (**26**); the resulting cycloadduct (**21**) is readily oxidized by peroxide–acetic acid mixture to the dioxide (**22**).[10]

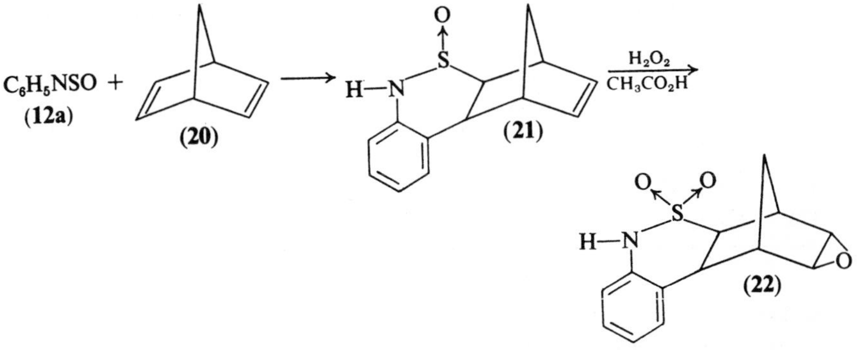

In conclusion, Staudinger and Endle reported[14] that Michler's ketone (**23**) and phenylisocyanate (**24**) were reacted at 180°C resulting in the formation of the cycloadduct, 2-bis(*N*,*N*-dimethylaniline)-3-phenyl-1,3-thiazetidin-4-one (**25**), which decomposed into carbon oxysulfide and the imine (**26**).

$$\underset{(\mathbf{23})}{[(CH_3)_2NC_6H_4]_2C{=}S} + \underset{(\mathbf{24})}{C_6H_5N{=}C{=}O} \longrightarrow$$

$$\underset{(\mathbf{25})}{\begin{array}{lcl} [(CH_3)_2NC_6H_4]_2C & — & S \\ \quad\quad | & & | \\ \quad C_6H_5N & — & CO \end{array}} \longrightarrow \underset{(\mathbf{26})}{[(CH_3)_2NC_6H_4]_2C{=}NC_6H_5} + S{=}C{=}O$$

**Table 1**

Preparation of Thiazetidinone-oxides from *N*-Sulfinylamines
and Ketenes

$$R\text{—}NSO + R^1R^2C\text{=}C\text{=}O \longrightarrow \begin{array}{ccc} & R^2 & \\ & | & \\ R^1\text{—}C & \text{—————} & CO \\ | & & | \\ OS & \text{—————} & N\text{—}R \end{array}$$

| No. | R | $R^1$ | $R^2$ | Yield (%) | MP (°C) | Ref. |
|-----|---|-------|-------|-----------|---------|------|
| **12** | | | | | | |
| a | $C_6H_5$ | $C_6H_5$ | $C_6H_5$ | 95.1 | 116–117.5 | 1 |
| b | $C_6H_{11}$ | $C_6H_5$ | $C_6H_5$ | 99.8 | 154–157 | 1 |
| c | $p$-$ClC_6H_4$ | $C_6H_5$ | $C_6H_5$ | 99.5 | 120–123.5 | 1 |
| d | $m$-$ClC_6H_4$ | $C_6H_5$ | $C_6H_5$ | 89 | 127.5–129 | 1 |
| e | $o$-$ClC_6H_4$ | $C_6H_5$ | $C_6H_5$ | 93 | 108–109.5 | 1 |
| f | $2,4$-$Cl_2C_6H_3$ | $C_6H_5$ | $C_6H_5$ | 82.5 | 116–119 | 1 |
| g | $p$-$NO_2C_6H_4$ | $C_6H_5$ | $C_6H_5$ | 86 | 184–187 | 1 |
| **8** | $p$-$CH_3C_6H_4$ | $C_6H_5$ | $C_6H_5$ | 78 | 140–141 | 9 |
| **12** | | | | | | |
| a | $C_6H_5$ | —$(C_6H_4)_2$— | — | — | 161–163 | 1 |
| d | $m$-$ClC_6H_4$ | —$(C_6H_4)_2$— | — | — | 165–167 | 1 |
| f | $2,4$-$Cl_2C_6H_3$ | —$(C_6H_4)_2$— | — | — | 195–199 (dec) | 1 |
| **8** | $p$-$CH_3C_6H_4$ | $C_4H_9$ | $C_2H_5$ | — | — | 4 |
| **12a** | $C_6H_5$ | $C_4H_9$ | $C_2H_5$ | — | — | 4 |

**REFERENCES**

1. H. Beecken and F. Korte, *Tetrahedron*, **18**, 1527 (1962).
2. E. Bellasio, G. Pagani, and E. Testa, *Gazz. Chim. Ital.*, **94**, 639 (1964); *Chem. Abstr.*, **61**, 12005 (1964).
3. C. R. Collins, *J. Org. Chem.*, **29**, 1688 (1964).
4. Eastman Technical Data on Butylethylketene, TDS NoX-163.
5. A. Eibner, *Ann. Chem.*, 302, 335 (1898).
6. A. Eibner, *Ann. Chem.*, **316**, 89 (1901).
7. G. G. Gallo, C. R. Pasqualucci, and G. Tuan, *Ann. Chim.*, **52**, 352 (1962).
8. H. H. Gibbs, U.S. Pat. 3,091,619 (1963).
9. G. Kresze, A. Maschke, R. Albrecht, K. Bederke, H. P. Patzscheke, H. Smalla, and A. Trede, *Angew. Chem. Intern. Ed. Engl.*, **1**, 97 (1962).
10. A. Macaluso, Ph.D. Thesis, Tulane University, New Orleans, Louisiana, 1965.
11. B. J. R. Nicholaus, E. Bellasio, and E. Testa, Brit. Pat. 963,500 (1964).
12. B. J. R. Nicholaus, E. Bellasio, and E. Testa, *Helv. Chim. Acta*, **45**, 717 (1962).
13. B. J. R. Nicholaus, E. Bellasio, and E. Testa, *Helv. Chim. Acta*, **46**, 450 (1963).

14. H. Staudinger and R. Endle, *Chem. Ber.*, **50**, 1042 (1917).
15. H. Staudinger and S. Jelagin, *Chem. Ber.*, **44**, 365 (1911).
16. H. Staudinger and F. Pfenninger, *Chem. Ber.*, **49**, 1941 (1916).
17. E. Wedekind and D. Schenk, *Chem. Ber.*, **44**, 198 (1911).

### 5. Sulfur Only

#### a. *Dithiacyclobutanes, Desaurins, and 1,2-Dithietenes*

The photochemical dimerization of thiophosgene (**1**) was first observed by Rathke,[21, 22, 25] and the dimeric character of the product was confirmed by Carrara.[2] Rathke originally assigned the trichloromethylchlorodithioformate structure (**2**) to the photodimer; however, Schönberg and Stephenson[27] reinvestigated the reaction and proposed the cyclic 2,2,4,4-tetra-

$$2Cl-\overset{\overset{\textstyle S}{\|}}{C}-Cl \xrightarrow{h\nu} S = C\overset{\textstyle S-C-Cl_3}{\underset{\textstyle Cl}{\diagdown}}$$

$$\qquad (1) \qquad\qquad\qquad (2)$$

chloro-1,3-dithiacyclobutane structure (**3**), which was supported by Delépine et al.[3, 4] Schönberg and Stephenson found that the dimer (**3**) upon controlled hydrolysis gave 4,4,-dichloro-1,3-dithiacyclobutanone-2 (**4**), and

$$2 \overset{\textstyle Cl}{\underset{\textstyle Cl}{\diagdown}}C = S \underset{h\nu\ or\ \varDelta}{\overset{h\nu}{\rightleftharpoons}} Cl_2C\overset{\diagup S \diagdown}{\underset{\diagdown S \diagup}{}}CCl_2$$

$$\qquad (1) \qquad\qquad\qquad (3)$$

when treated with aniline (**5**), the imine (**6**) which decomposed upon heat-

$$Cl_2C\overset{\diagup S \diagdown}{\underset{\diagdown S \diagup}{}}CCl_2 \xrightarrow{H_2O} Cl_2C\overset{\diagup S \diagdown}{\underset{\diagdown S \diagup}{}}C{=}O + 2HCl$$

$$\qquad (3) \qquad\qquad\qquad (4)$$

ing into thiophosgene (**1**) and phenylisothiocyanate (**7**) was obtained.

$$\underset{(3)}{Cl_2C\overset{S}{\underset{S}{\diamond}}CCl_2} + \underset{(5)}{3H_2NC_6H_5} \longrightarrow \underset{(6)}{Cl_2C\overset{S}{\underset{S}{\diamond}}C{=}NC_6H_5}$$

$$\underset{(6)}{Cl_2C\overset{S}{\underset{S}{\diamond}}C{=}NC_6H_5} \xrightarrow{\Delta} \underset{(1)}{Cl_2C{=}S} + \underset{(7)}{S{=}C{=}NC_6H_5}$$

White[38] suggested the name "carbon sulphoxy chloride" for the dimeric product to avoid structural implications, as he doubted the correctness of the hydrolysis product (4). The structures of the dithiacyclobutane (3) and the dithiacyclobutanone (4) were determined by infrared analysis.[8]

The spectrum of a carbon disulfide solution (10%) of thiophosgene (1) has three very strong bands at 1120, 810, and 780 cm$^{-1}$. These correspond to the 1138 cm$^{-1}$ band and the doublet at 811 and 794 cm$^{-1}$ reported by Haszeldine and Kidd,[7] the former representing the carbon–sulfur double bond stretching mode, the others representing the carbon–chlorine stretching vibrations. In the spectrum of the dimer (3) a strong band occurred at 810 cm$^{-1}$ adjacent to a broad region of strong absorption ($D > 1.5$) extending from 800 cm$^{-1}$ to beyond 650 cm$^{-1}$. The solid film spectrum of the hydrolysis product (4) showed a weak band at 1837 cm$^{-1}$, two strong bands at 1767 and 1717 cm$^{-1}$, and a weak shoulder at 1656 cm$^{-1}$. In solution, however, the spectrum showed only two strong bands at 1780 and 1710 cm$^{-1}$. Strong absorption was also observed in the region 880–700 cm$^{-1}$. The absence of any absorption between 1400 and 1000 cm$^{-1}$ (calculated region for carbon–sulfur double bond stretch) strongly supported the cyclic structure (3) for the thiophosgene dimer. Similar cyclic structures were postulated for related silicon oxyhalides, thiohalides, and selenohalides.[6, 31, 37] Thioaldehydes and thioketones also polymerize easily to give the dimeric and trimeric cyclic compounds, from which the carbon–sulfur double bond group is absent.[23]

Middleton[18] reported the dimerization of thiophosgene (1) in the presence of base to the dithiacyclobutane (3). It was also observed[18, 19] that

$$2 \underset{(1)}{\overset{Cl}{\underset{Cl}{\diagdown}}C{=}S} \xrightarrow{\text{base}} \underset{(3)}{Cl_2C\overset{S}{\underset{S}{\diamond}}CCl_2}$$

thioketones, such as hexafluorothioacetone (8), dimerize in the presence of a trace amount of base to give the perfluorodithiacyclobutane (9). Middleton also reported the photodimerization of thiocarbonyl halides, such as trifluorothioacetyl fluoride (10), to a *cis-trans* mixture of the dithiacyclobutane derivative (11), 2,4-bis-(trifluoromethyl)-2,4-difluoro-1,3-dithietane.

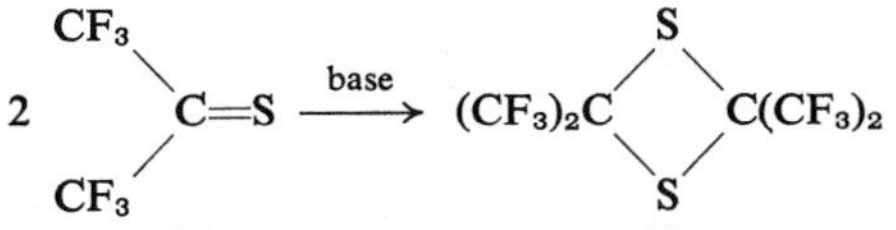

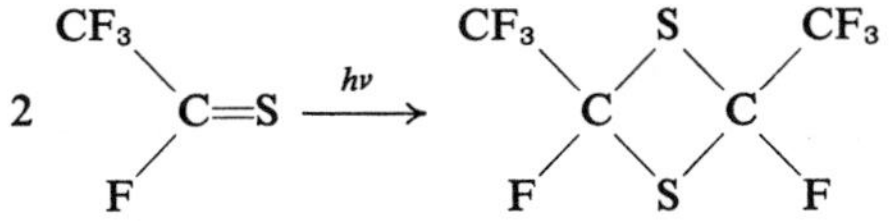

Recently, 1,3-dithietanes have been reported[13,17] in the reactions of perfluoroolefins and sulfur. Martin[13] found that the reaction of hexafluoropropene (12) and sulfur vapor resulted in the formation of the dimer (9), 2,2,4,4-tetrakis(trifluoromethyl)-1,3-dithietane, and hexafluorothioacetone (8). The structure of 9 was determined by infrared analysis (700,

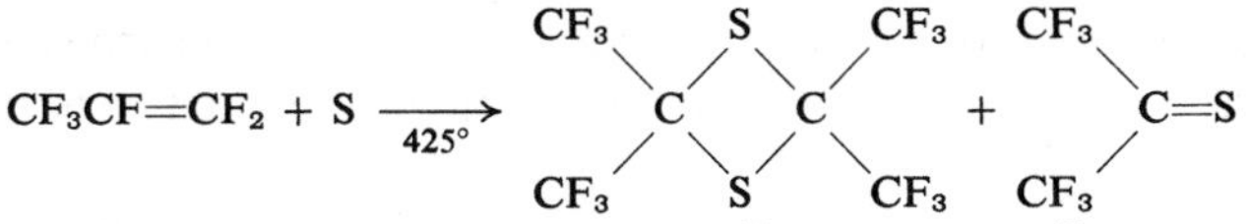

747, and 940 $cm^{-1}$: carbon–sulfur stretching or carbon–fluorine bending or rocking frequencies; 1150–1300 $cm^{-1}$ carbon–fluorine stretching frequency) and fluorine[19] nuclear magnetic resonance spectrum. Middleton[17] also reported that if hexafluoropropene (12) and molten sulfur were heated at 425–625°, hexafluorothioacetone (8) was obtained which when treated with 13 in ether at −80° and allowed to warm to room temperature yielded the 1,3-dithietane (9). The 1,1-dioxide (14) was obtained by treating the 1,3-diethietane (9) with fuming nitric acid and chromic oxide. When the dioxide (14) was sublimed at 1 mm through a platinum tube

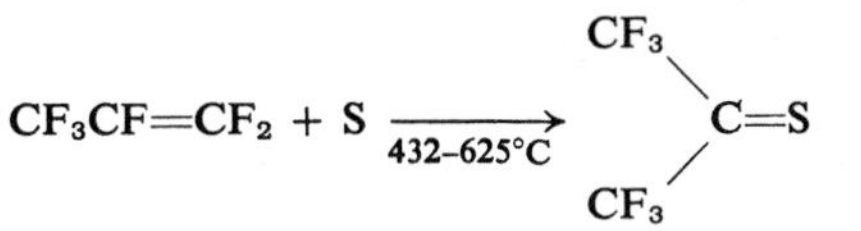

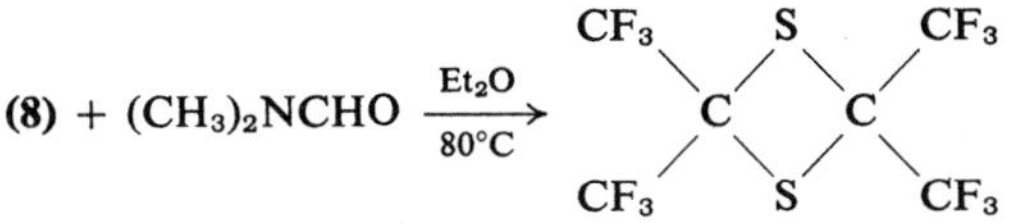

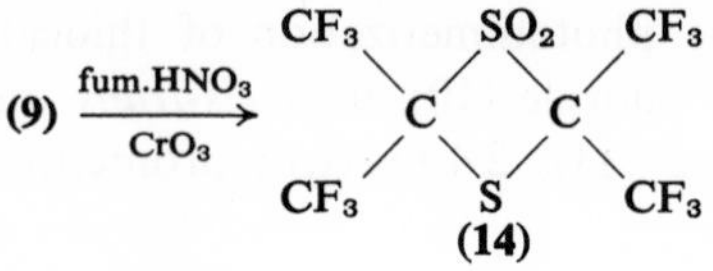

$$(9) \xrightarrow[\text{CrO}_3]{\text{fum.HNO}_3}$$

**(14)**

heated at 550°, sulfur dioxide and the thiirane **(15)** were obtained. Other olefins were employed (Table 1).

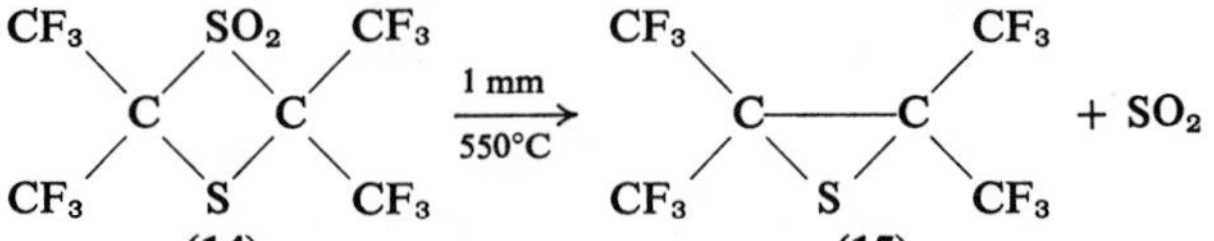

**(14)**                    **(15)**

O-Ethyl thioacetate, irradiated with light of 254 mμ wavelengh at 40° in the absence of a solvent, gave 2,3-diethoxy-2-butene in 65% yield,[24] while 3,4-diethoxy-3-hexene was formed in 60% yield upon irradiation of O-ethyl thiopropionate. As for the mechanism of this reaction, it is still undecided as to whether the dialkoxy olefins were formed by the dimerization of the thiocarboxylic esters to 1,2- or 1,3-dithiacyclobutanes followed by stepwise elimination of sulfur via ethylene sulfides, or whether an ethoxycarbene is formed first and reacts with the thiocarboxylic ester giving ethylene sulfides. Small amounts of ethylene sulfides were reported.

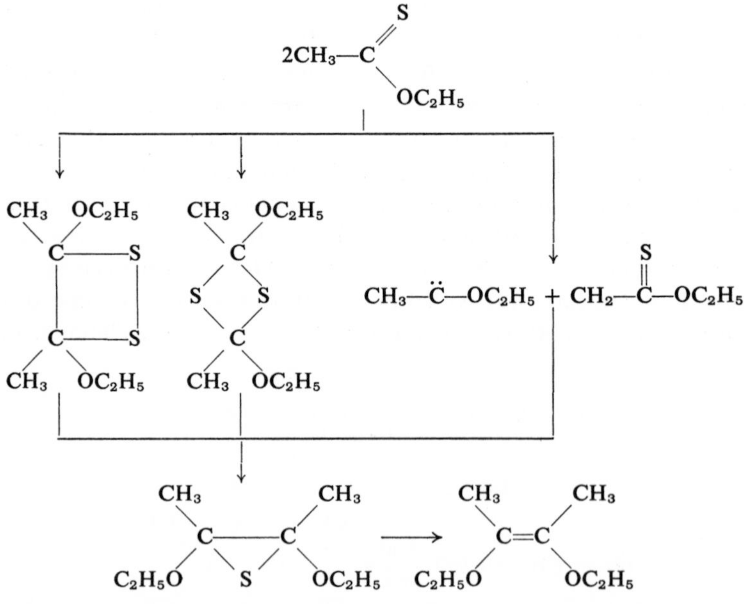

Schönberg and co-workers[28-30] found that when thio compounds of the

type **16**, **17**, **18**, or **19** were heated above 250° the dimer of diphenylthio-
ketene (**20**) was obtained. The dimer (**20**) is commonly referred to as a
desaurin. This class of stable, high-melting, neutral, yellow compounds
was first reported [1, 14 – 16, 20, 36] in the reactions of certain ketones with base

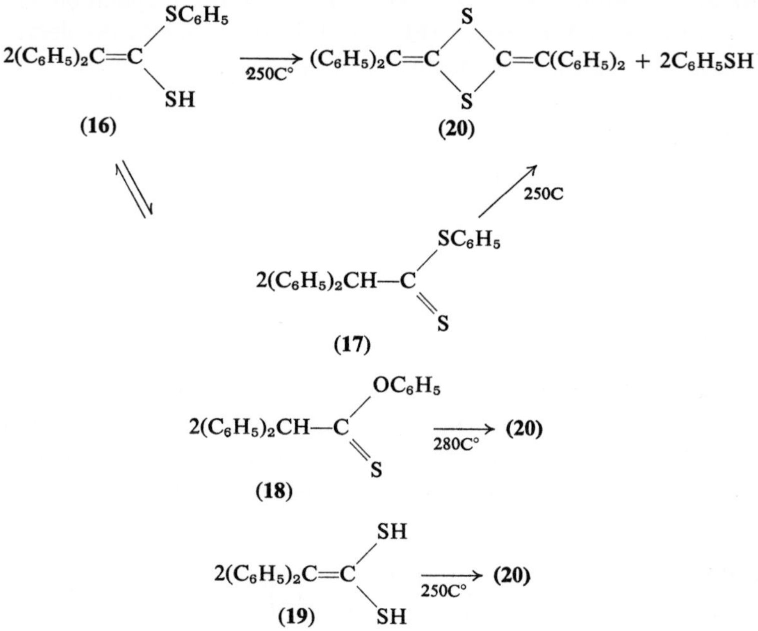

$$2(C_6H_5)_2C{=}C\diagup^{SC_6H_5}_{\diagdown SH} \xrightarrow[250C°]{} (C_6H_5)_2C{=}C\diagup^S_{\diagdown S}C{=}C(C_6H_5)_2 + 2C_6H_5SH$$

$$\qquad\qquad (16) \qquad\qquad\qquad\qquad\qquad (20)$$

$$250C$$

$$2(C_6H_5)_2CH{-}C\diagup^{SC_6H_5}_{\diagdown\!\!\parallel\, S}$$

$$(17)$$

$$2(C_6H_5)_2CH{-}C\diagup^{OC_6H_5}_{\diagdown\!\!\parallel\, S} \xrightarrow[280C°]{} (20)$$

$$(18)$$

$$2(C_6H_5)_2C{=}C\diagup^{SH}_{\diagdown SH} \xrightarrow[250C°]{} (20)$$

$$(19)$$

and carbon disulfide. Structure **21** was suggested for the prototype, the
desaurin from desoxybenzoin,[9, 10] although the proposal was accepted
without experimental support. Yates and Moore [39] have substantiated this

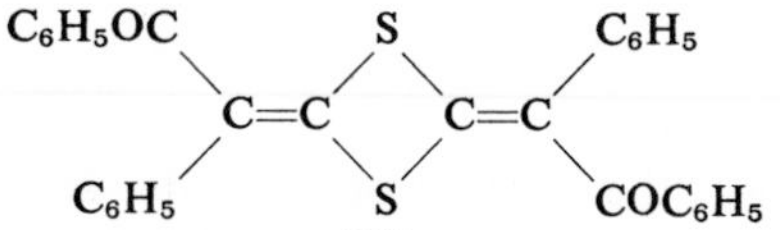

$$C_6H_5OC\diagdown_{\diagup}\,\overset{S}{\underset{S}{\diagup\diagdown}}\,{C_6H_5}$$
$$\qquad C{=}C \qquad C{=}C$$
$$C_6H_5\diagup \qquad\diagdown COC_6H_5$$

$$(21)$$

type of structure for two desaurins, one from desoxybenzoin (**21**) and one
from phenylacetone (**22**). The structures were ascertained on the basis of

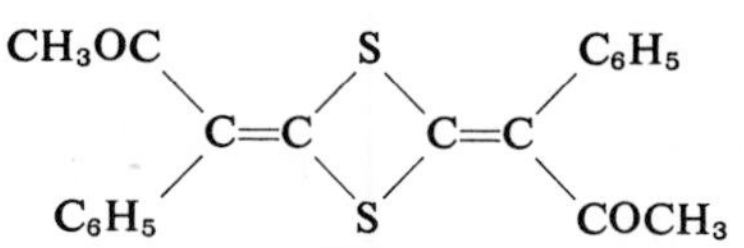

$$CH_3OC\diagdown_{\diagup}\,\overset{S}{\underset{S}{\diagup\diagdown}}\,{C_6H_5}$$
$$\qquad C{=}C \qquad C{=}C$$
$$C_6H_5\diagup \qquad\diagdown COCH_3$$

$$(22)$$

chemical evidence, elemental analysis, and infrared, ultraviolet, and nu-
clear magnetic resonance absorption spectra [**22**: $\lambda_{max}$ 6.05 $\mu$; $\lambda_{max}$ 246 m$\mu$

(log $\varepsilon$ 3.96); 374 m$\mu$ (log $\varepsilon$ 4.44); (21: $\lambda_{max}$ 6.17 $\mu$, $\lambda_{max}$ 266 m$\mu$ (log $\varepsilon$ 4.36), 419 m$\mu$ (log $\varepsilon$ 4.58)]. The abnormally weak carbonyl stretching band of 21 was attributed to the *s-cis* conformation of the $\alpha,\beta$-unsaturated carbonyl system.

Recently, Dittmar and co-workers[5] reported the preparation of dicyanomethylene-1,3-dithietane (23), which is analogous to the desaurins but has only one exocyclic methylene group and is much more reactive. This 1,3-dithietane was, however, prepared not as were the other desaurins, but rather via the following procedure.

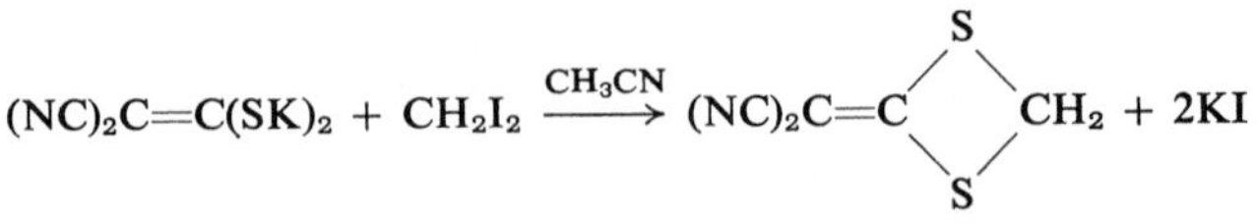

$$(NC)_2C{=}C(SK)_2 + CH_2I_2 \xrightarrow{CH_3CN} (NC)_2C{=}C\overset{S}{\underset{S}{\diagup\diagdown}}CH_2 + 2KI$$

(23)

Schönberg[26] reported two new methods of preparing desaurins; for example, diphenyldiazomethane (24) and carbon disulfide were heated, and the resulting intermediate (25), which can be isolated, was desulfurized with copper powder yielding the desaurin (20) (Table 2) The second

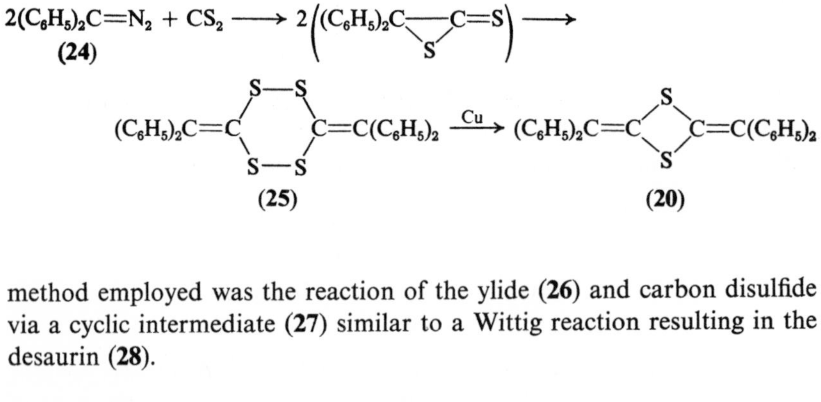

$$2(C_6H_5)_2C{=}N_2 + CS_2 \longrightarrow 2\Big((C_6H_5)_2C\overset{}{\underset{S}{\diagup\diagdown}}C{=}S\Big) \longrightarrow$$

(24)

$$(C_6H_5)_2C{=}C\overset{S-S}{\underset{S-S}{\diagup\diagdown}}C{=}C(C_6H_5)_2 \xrightarrow{Cu} (C_6H_5)_2C{=}C\overset{S}{\underset{S}{\diagup\diagdown}}C{=}C(C_6H_5)_2$$

(25)                                   (20)

method employed was the reaction of the ylide (26) and carbon disulfide via a cyclic intermediate (27) similar to a Wittig reaction resulting in the desaurin (28).

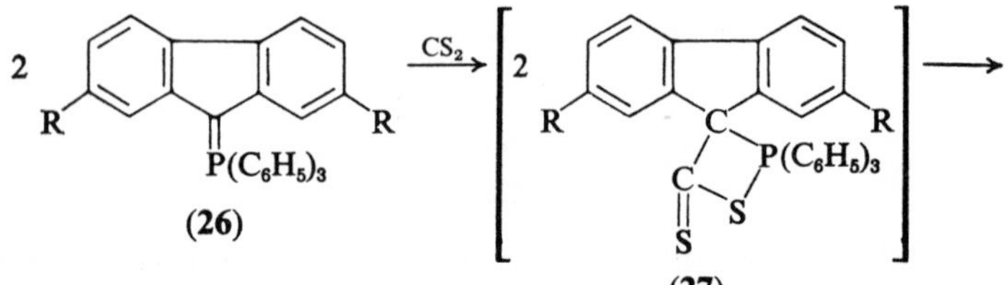

(26)                                   (27)

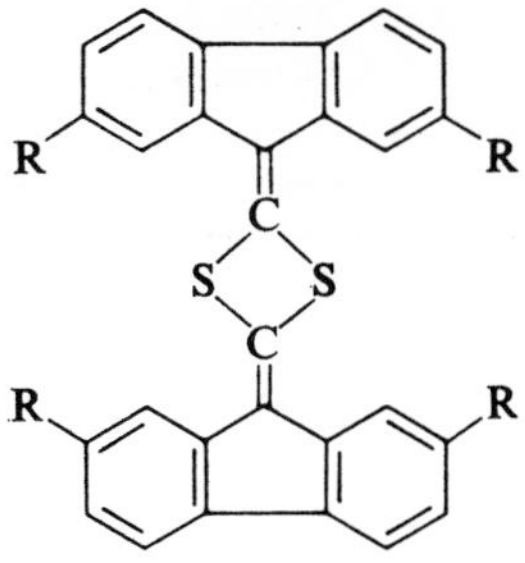

**(28)**

The formation of 1,2-dithietenes has been reported by Krespan and co-workers.[11,12] Hexafluoro-2-butyne (**29**) reacted with boiling sulfur at 1 atm pressure forming an 80% yield of bis(trifluoromethyl)-1,2-dithietene (**30**), which is capable of reacting further with various olefins.[12] Hexafluoro-2-butyne (**29**), sulfur, and iodine heated to 200° and the iodine re-

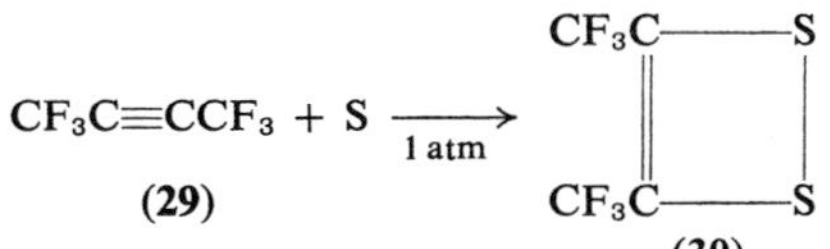

$$CF_3C{\equiv}CCF_3 + S \xrightarrow[\text{1 atm}]{}$$

**(29)**

**(30)**

moved were also reported[11] to give the 1,2-dithietene (**30**). Analogously, hexafluoro-2-butyne (**29**) and sulfur heated to 222° or to 180° in a benzene solution, without iodine, or the butyne passed through refluxing sulfur at 1 atm, yield the 1,2-dithietene (**30**) (Table 3). Similarly, 1,2-dithietenes were obtained from 1,12-dehydroeicosafluoro-6-dodecyne and 1,3,4,6-tetrachlorooctafluoro-3-hexene (Table 3).

In conclusion, other 1,2-dithietene compounds (**32**) have been reported in the reactions of disodium dimercaptofumaronitrile (**31**).[32–35]

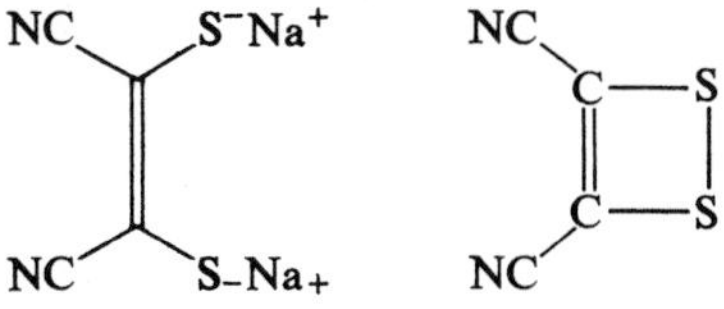

**(31)**                    **(32)**

**Table 1**
1,3-Dithietanes

| Dimer | Yield | MP (°C) | BP (°C/mm) | $n_D^t$ | Ref. |
|---|---|---|---|---|---|
| $Cl_2C$———S<br><br>S———$CCl_2$ | | 116<br>119 | | | 21, 22<br>27 |
| $(CF_3)_2C$———S<br><br>S———$C(CF_3)_2$ | 100 | 23.6 | 110[a]<br><br>112<br>109–111 | [25]1.3357 | 18<br>19<br>13<br>17 |
| $F(CF_3)C$———S<br><br>S———$C(CF_3)F$ | 60 | | 73[a]<br><br>69 | [25]1.3378 | 18<br>17<br>19 |
| $F(CF_2Cl)C$———S<br><br>S———$C(CF_2Cl)F$ | 83 | | 44/23<br><br>137 | [24]1.4131<br>[25]1.4127 | 17<br>19 |
| $(CF_3)(C_2F_5)C$———S<br><br>S———$C(CF_3)(C_2F_5)$ | 100 | | 142–144 | [25]1.3479 | 19 |
| $(CF_2Br)FC$———S<br><br>S———$C(CF_2Br)F$ | 58 | | 40–41/3 | 1.4572 | 19 |
| $(CF_3Cl)C$———S<br><br>S———$C(CF_3)Cl$ | 93 | | 66–68/25 | 1.4162 | 19 |
| $(CF_2Cl)ClC$———S<br><br>S———$C(CF_2Cl)Cl$ | 45 | | 76/9 | 1.4852 | 19 |
| $(CF_3)(CF_3S)C$———S<br><br>S———$C(CF_3)(SCF_3)$ | 100 | | 55–56/10 | 1.3391 | 19 |

[a] *Cis-trans* mixture.

**Table 2**

Desaurins

| Desaurin | MP (°C) | Yield (%) | Ref. |
|---|---|---|---|
| 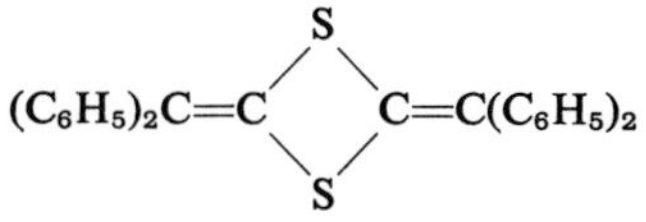 $(C_6H_5)_2C=C\underset{S}{\overset{S}{\diamond}}C=C(C_6H_5)_2$ | 257–258 | | 25 |
| | 263 | 88 | 26 |
| 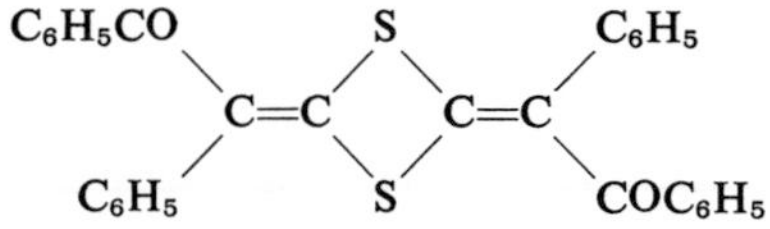 $\underset{C_6H_5}{\overset{C_6H_5CO}{>}}C=C\underset{S}{\overset{S}{\diamond}}C=C\underset{COC_6H_5}{\overset{C_6H_5}{<}}$ | 300–302 | | 39 |
| 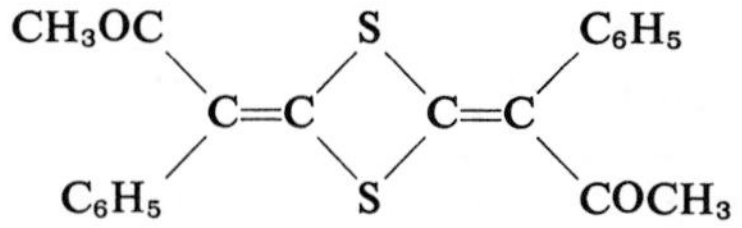 $\underset{C_6H_5}{\overset{CH_3OC}{>}}C=C\underset{S}{\overset{S}{\diamond}}C=C\underset{COCH_3}{\overset{C_6H_5}{<}}$ | 233–233.5 | | 39 |
| 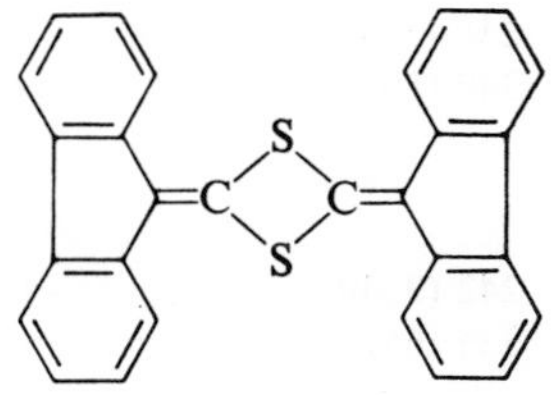 | 373 | 80.8 | 26 |
| 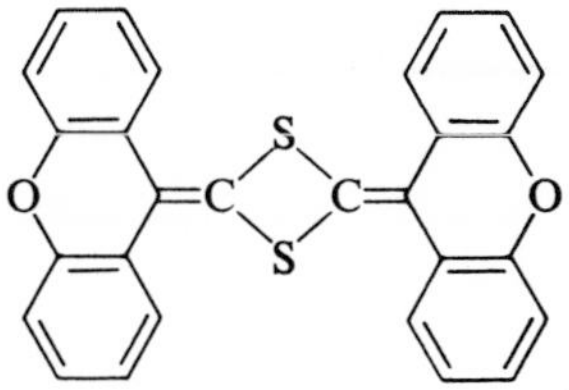 | 294 dec | 88 | 26 |
| 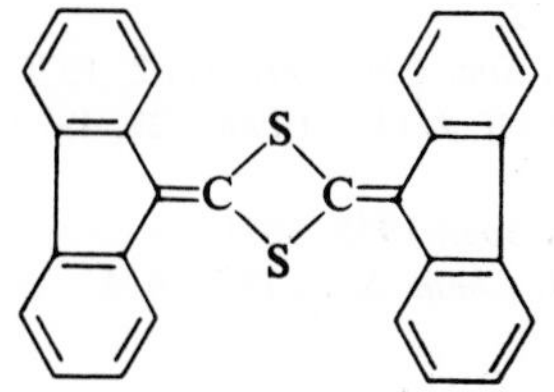 | 376–377 | 68.3 | 26 |

*(continued)*

**Table 2** (*continued*)

| Desaurin | MP (°C) | Yield (%) | Ref. |
|---|---|---|---|
| 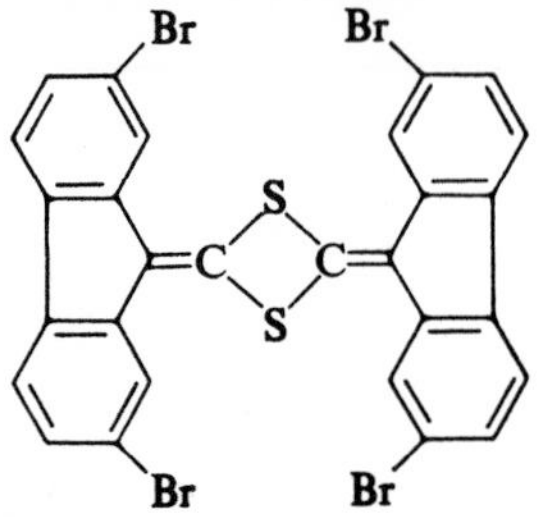 | over 400 | 66 | 26 |

**Table 3**
1,2-Dithietenes[11, 12]

| Dithietene | BP (°C) | Yield (%) | IR, $\lambda$ (C=C)$\mu$ | UV, $\lambda_{max}m\mu(\epsilon)$ | NMR (cps) | | |
|---|---|---|---|---|---|---|---|
| | | | | | CF$_3$ | CF$_2$[a] | CF$_2$Cl |
| 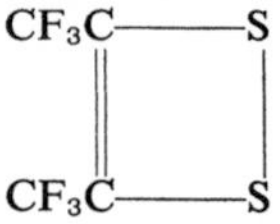 CF$_3$C———S / CF$_3$C———S | 95–96 | 80 | 6.14 | 238 (7740) 340 (80) | −811 | | |
| 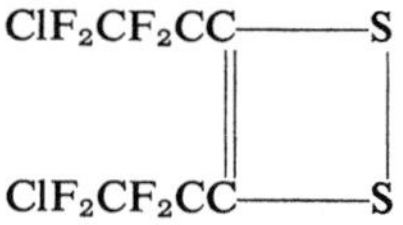 ClF$_2$CF$_2$CC———S / ClF$_2$CF$_2$CC———S | 98/40 mm | — | 6.24 | 242 (9540) 335 (65) | | −1585 | −465 |

[a] Adjacent to dithietene ring.

REFERENCES

1. H. Bergreen, *Chem. Ber.*, **21**, 337 (1888).
2. G. Carrara, *Gazz. Chim. Ital.*, **23**, 12 (1893).
3. M. Delépine, *Ann. Chim. Phys.*, **25**, 529 (1912).
4. M. Delépine, L. Labro, and F. Lange, *Bull. Soc. Chim. France*, **2**, 1970 (1935).
5. D. C. Dittmer, H. E. Simmons, and R. D. Vest, *J. Org. Chem.*, **29**, 497 (1964).
6. Y. Etienne, *Bull. Soc. Chim. France*, **1953**, 791.
7. R. N. Haszeldine and J. M. Kidd, *J. Chem. Soc.*, **1955**, 3871.
8. J. I. Jones, W. Kynaston, and J. L. Hales, *J. Chem. Soc.*, **1957**, 614.
9. C. Kelber, *Chem. Ber.*, **43**, 1252 (1910).
10. C. Kelber and A. Schwarz, *Chem. Ber.*, **45**, 137 (1912).
11. C. G. Krespan, *J. Am. Chem. Soc.*, **83**, 3434 (1961).
12. C. G. Krespan, B. C. McKusick, and T. L. Cairns, *J. Am. Chem. Soc.*, **82**, 1515 (1960).

13. K. Martin, *J. Chem. Soc.*, **1964**, 2944.
14. V. Meyer, *Chem. Ber.*, **21**, 353 (1888).
15. V. Meyer, *Chem. Ber.*, **23**, 1571 (1890).
16. V. Meyer and H. Wege, *Chem. Ber.*, **24**, 3535 (1891).
17. W. J. Middleton, U.S. Pat. 3,136,781 (1964).
18. W. J. Middleton, E. G. Howard, and W. H. Sharkey, *J. Am. Chem. Soc.*, **83**, 2589 (1961).
19. W. J. Middleton, E. G. Howard, and W. H. Sharkey, *J. Org. Chem.*, **30**, 1375 (1965).
20. P. Petrenko-Kritschenko, *Chem. Ber.*, **25**, 2239 (1892).
21. B. Rathke, *Ann. Chem.*, **167**, 205 (1873).
22. B. Rathke, *Chem. Ber.*, **21**, 2539 (1888).
23. E. H. Rodd, *Chemistry of Carbon Compounds*, Vol. 1A, Elsevier, London, 1951, pp. 487, 521; Vol. 3A, 1954, p. 516.
24. U. Schmidt and K. H. Kabitzke, *Angew. Chem. Intern. Ed. Engl.*, **3**, 641 (1964).
25. A. Schönberg, *Präparative Organische Photochemie*, Springer, Berlin, 1958, p. 36.
26. A. Schönberg, E. Frese, and K.-H. Brosowski, *Chem. Ber.*, **95**, 3077 (1962).
27. A. Schönberg and A. Stephenson, *Chem. Ber.*, **66**, 567 (1933).
28. A. Schönberg, A. Stephenson, H. Kaltschmitt, E. Peterson, and H. Schulten, *Chem. Ber.*, **66**, 237 (1933).
29. A. Schönberg and L. v. Vargha, *Chem. Ber.*, **64**, 1390 (1931).
30. A. Schönberg, L. v. Vargha, and H. Kaltschmitt, *Chem. Ber.*, **64**, 2582 (1931).
31. W. C. Schumb and D. F. Holloway, *J. Am. Chem. Soc.*, **63**, 2753 (1941).
32. H. E. Simmons, D. C. Blomstrom, and R. D. Vest, *J. Am. Chem. Soc.*, **84**, 4756 (1962).
33. H. E. Simmons, D. C. Blomstrom, and R. D. Vest, *J. Am. Chem. Soc.*, **84**, 4772 (1962).
34. H. E. Simmons, D. C. Blomstrom, and R. D. Vest, *J. Am. Chem. Soc.*, **84**, 4782 (1962).
35. H. E. Simmons, R. D. Vest, D. C. Blomstrom, J. R. Roland, and T. L. Cairns, *J. Am. Chem. Soc.*, **84**, 4746 (1962).
36. W. Wachter, *Chem. Ber.*, **25**, 1727 (1892).
37. A. Weiss and A. Weiss, *Angew. Chem.*, **66**, 714 (1954).
38. R. W. White, *Can. J. Chem.*, **32**, 867 (1954).
39. P. Yates and D. Moore, *J. Am. Chem. Soc.*, **80**, 5577 (1958).

## C. MISCELLANEOUS

### 1. Oxadiazetidine Derivatives

In studying the formation and properties of four-membered heterocyclic compounds, Ingold[5,9,10] postulated that imines and nitroso compounds combined via a cycloaddition reaction to give a stable 1,2,4-oxadiazetidine (originally termed 1,2,4-oxadiimine) (Table 1). For example, nitrosobenzene (1) and methylene-*p*-tolylaniline (2) were thought to give the cycloadduct, 2-phenyl-4-*p*-tolyl-1,2,4-oxadiazetidine (3).[9,10]

$$C_6H_5N=O + CH_2=NC_6H_4CH_3\text{-}p \longrightarrow$$

$$\begin{array}{cc} C_6H_5N\!\!-\!\!-\!\!-\!\!-\!\!O \\ | \qquad\qquad | \\ H_2C\!\!-\!\!-\!\!-\!\!-\!\!NC_6H_4CH_3\text{-}p \end{array}$$

(1)                    (2)                                            (3)

Subsequently, Ingold[3,4] discovered that the product (3) was not a ring compound but an *N*-hydroxyamidine (4) which is formed by the isomerization of the cycloadduct (3). Lapworth and co-workers[2] re-examined the

$$\begin{array}{c} C_6H_5N\!\!-\!\!-\!\!-\!\!-\!\!O \\ | \qquad\qquad | \\ H_2C\!\!-\!\!-\!\!-\!\!-\!\!NC_6H_4CH_3\text{-}p \end{array} \qquad \longrightarrow \qquad \overset{\displaystyle OH}{\underset{}{C_6H_5N\!\!-\!\!CH\!\!=\!\!NC_6H_4CH_3\text{-}p}}$$

(3)                                                            (4)

process of the reaction with *p*-chloromethyleneaniline (5) and *p*-bromonitrosobenzene (6) and proposed that if such a cycloadduct (7) were formed it would cleave exclusively in one direction. Lapworth's hydrolysis

$$CH_2=NC_6H_4Cl\text{-}p + p\text{-}BrC_6H_4N=O \longrightarrow$$

$$\begin{array}{c} p\text{-}BrC_6H_4N\!\!-\!\!-\!\!-\!\!-\!\!O \\ | \qquad\qquad | \\ H_2C\!\!-\!\!-\!\!-\!\!-\!\!NC_6H_4Cl\text{-}p \end{array}$$

(5)                              (6)                                            (7)

product of the above-mentioned reaction differed from that reported by Ingold.[3,4]

Staudinger and Endle[11] reported that at high temperatures phenylisocyanate (8) reacted with unsaturated compounds (for example, nitrosobenzene (1)) in a manner analogous to that of diphenylketene. The cycloadduct 2,3-diphenyl-1,2,3-oxadiazetidin-4-one (9), however, could not be isolated since the four-membered ring was unstable at high temperatures, decomposing into azobenzene (10) and carbon dioxide.[11]

$$C_6H_5N=C=O + C_6H_5N=O \longrightarrow \begin{array}{c} C_6H_5N\!\!-\!\!-\!\!-\!\!-\!\!O \\ | \qquad\qquad | \\ C_6H_5N\!\!-\!\!-\!\!-\!\!-\!\!CO \end{array} \qquad \begin{array}{c} C_6H_5N + CO_2 \\ \| \\ C_6H_5N \end{array}$$

(8)                    (1)                                (9)                              (10)

In a study of nitrones, Staudinger and Miescher[12] reported that diphenyl-*N*-phenylnitrone (11) and phenylisocyanate (8) formed a cycloadduct (12) which decomposed into carbon dioxide and a "hydrazine

derivative" (13) upon heating. However, the cycloaddition of phenylisocyanate and nitrones has been found[1,6-8,13-15] to give an oxadiazolinone

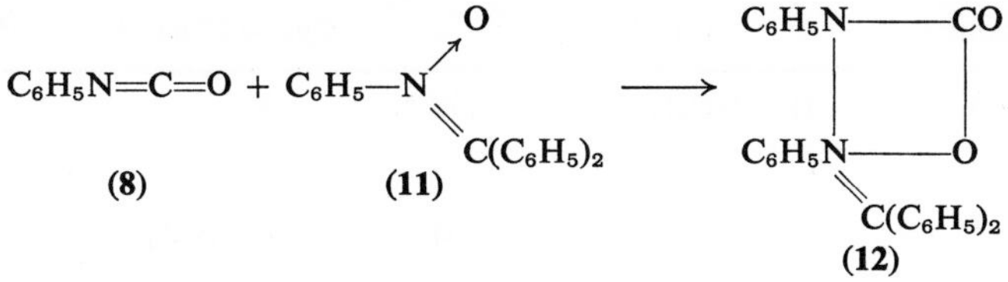

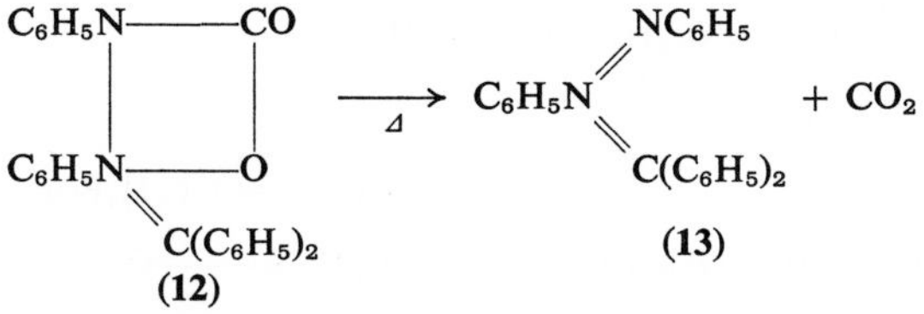

$$C_6H_5N=C=O + C_6H_5-N \overset{O}{\underset{C(C_6H_5)_2}{\nearrow}} \longrightarrow$$

(8)                    (11)

$$\begin{array}{cc} C_6H_5N & CO \\ | & | \\ C_6H_5N & O \\ \| & \\ C(C_6H_5)_2 & \end{array}$$

(12)

$$\begin{array}{cc} C_6H_5N & CO \\ | & | \\ C_6H_5N & O \\ \| & \\ C(C_6H_5)_2 & \end{array} \overset{\Delta}{\longrightarrow} C_6H_5N \overset{NC_6H_5}{\underset{C(C_6H_5)_2}{\Bigg\backslash}} + CO_2$$

(12)                                    (13)

derivative and not the oxadiazetidinone (12); that is, phenylisocyanate (8)
and α,α,N-triphenylnitrone gives the oxadiazolinone, 2,3,3,4-tetraphenyl-
1,2,4-oxadiazolin-5-one (13).

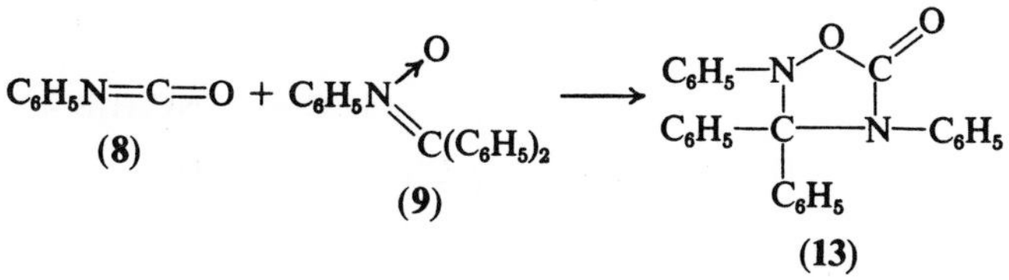

$$C_6H_5N=C=O + C_6H_5N \overset{O}{\underset{C(C_6H_5)_2}{\nearrow}} \longrightarrow$$

(8)                    (9)

$$\begin{array}{c} C_6H_5-N \overset{O}{\diagdown} \overset{O}{C} \\ | \quad \quad \| \\ C_6H_5-C \quad N-C_6H_5 \\ | \\ C_6H_5 \end{array}$$

(13)

### Table 1
Proposed Oxadiazetidines via Cycloaddition Reactions of
Nitroso Compounds and Imines[9]

| Nitroso compounds | Imine | Cycloadduct | MP (°C) |
|---|---|---|---|
| $C_6H_5NO$ | $CH_2=NC_6H_4CH_3$-$p$ | 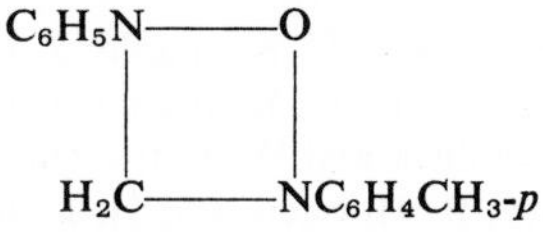 $\begin{array}{cc} C_6H_5N & O \\ \| & \| \\ H_2C & NC_6H_4CH_3\text{-}p \end{array}$ | 150 |
| $p$-$CH_3C_6H_4NO$ | $CH_2=NC_6H_4Cl$-$p$ | 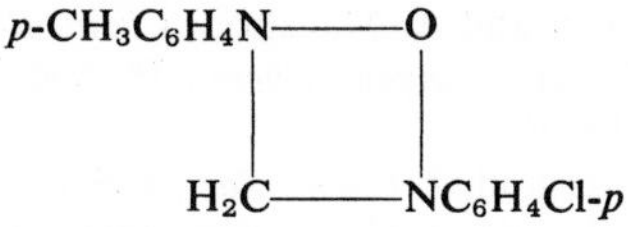 $\begin{array}{cc} p\text{-}CH_3C_6H_4N & O \\ \| & \| \\ H_2C & NC_6H_4Cl\text{-}p \end{array}$ | 163 |
| $p$-$CH_3C_6H_4NO$ | $CH_2=NC_6H_4Br$-$p$ | 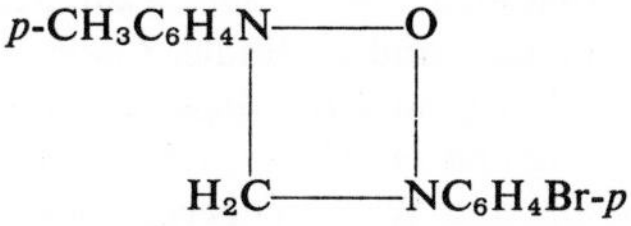 $\begin{array}{cc} p\text{-}CH_3C_6H_4N & O \\ \| & \| \\ H_2C & NC_6H_4Br\text{-}p \end{array}$ | 158 |

(continued)

**Table 1** (*continued*)

| Nitroso compounds | Imine | Cycloadduct | MP (°C) |
|---|---|---|---|
| $C_6H_5NO$ | $CH_2=NC_6H_4Cl\text{-}p$ | 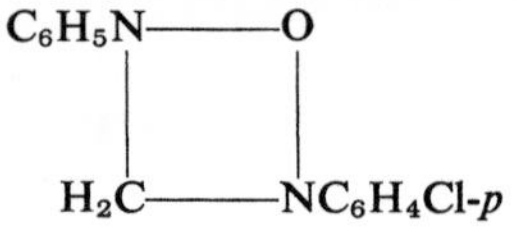 $C_6H_5N$————$O$<br><br>$H_2C$————$NC_6H_4Cl\text{-}p$ | 162 |
| $C_6H_5NO$ | $CH_2=NC_6H_4Br\text{-}p$ | 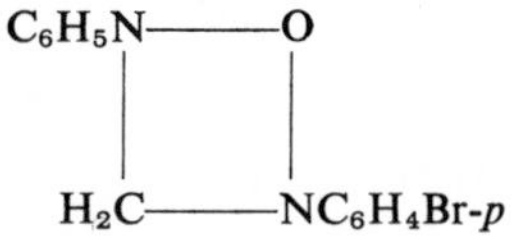 $C_6H_5N$————$O$<br><br>$H_2C$————$NC_6H_4Br\text{-}p$ | 171 |
| $p\text{-}ClC_6H_4NO$ | $CH_2=NC_6H_4Cl\text{-}p$ | 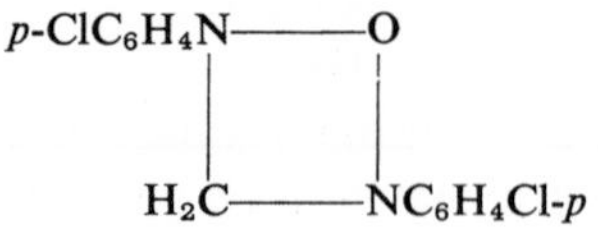 $p\text{-}ClC_6H_4N$————$O$<br><br>$H_2C$————$NC_6H_4Cl\text{-}p$ | 171 |
| $p\text{-}BrC_6H_4NO$ | $CH_2=NC_6H_4Br\text{-}p$ | 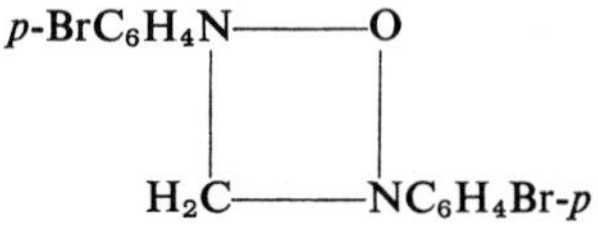 $p\text{-}BrC_6H_4N$————$O$<br><br>$H_2C$————$NC_6H_4Br\text{-}p$ | 175 |
| $p\text{-}ClC_6H_4NO$ | $CH_2=NC_6H_4Br\text{-}p$ | 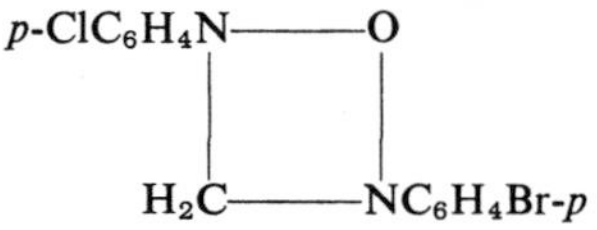 $p\text{-}ClC_6H_4N$————$O$<br><br>$H_2C$————$NC_6H_4Br\text{-}p$ | 171 |

REFERENCES

1. E. Beckmann, *Chem. Ber.*, **27**, 1957 (1894).
2. G. N. Burkhardt, A. Lapworth, and E. B. Robinson, *J. Chem. Soc.*, **127**, 2234 (1925).
3. M. D. Farrow and C. K. Ingold, *J. Chem. Soc.*, **125**, 2543 (1924).
4. M. D. Farrow and C. K. Ingold, *J. Chem. Soc.*, **128i**, 155 (1925).
5. B. G. Lowenlock and W. Lütte, *Quart. Rev.*, **12**, 321 (1958).
6. R. Grashey, R. Huisgen, and H. Leitermann, *Tetrahedron Letters*, **1960**, 9.
7. J. Hamer and A. Macaluso, *Chem. Rev.* **64**, 473 (1964).
8. R. Huisgen, *Angew. Chem.*, **75**, 604 (1963); *Angew. Chem. Intern. Ed. Engl.*, **2**, 633 (1963).
9. C. K. Ingold, *J. Chem. Soc.*, **125**, 87 (1924).
10. C. K. Ingold, *J. Chem. Soc.*, **126i**, 322 (1924).
11. H. Staudinger and R. Endle, *Chem. Ber.*, **50**, 1042 (1917).
12. H. Staudlinger and K. Miescher, *Helv. Chim. Acta*, **2**, 554 (1919).
13. J. Thesing and H. Mayer, *Chem. Ber.*, **89**, 2159 (1956).
14. J. Thesing and W. Sirrenberg, *Chem. Ber.*, **92**, 1748 (1959).
15. G. E. Utzinger and F. A. Regenass, *Helv. Chim. Acta*, **37**, 1892 (1954).

## 2. Wittig Type Reactions

In order to give some background material for this section it is necessary that the reaction of alkylidene phosphoranes and carbonyl compounds, known as the Wittig reaction, be briefly mentioned since the reactions to be discussed here are analogous to the Wittig reaction, in that a cyclic intermediate containing phosphorus or phosphorus and other heteroatoms such as nitrogen, oxygen, and sulfur has been postulated.

In 1953 Wittig and Geissler[91] found that benzophenone (1) and methylenetriphenylphosphorane (2) gave 1,1-diphenylethylene (3) and triphenylphosphine oxide (4); this led in the following years to the development of

$$(C_6H_5)_2C{=}O + (C_6H_5)_3P{=}CH_2 \longrightarrow (C_6H_5)_2C{=}CH_2 + (C_6H_5)_3P \rightarrow O$$
$$\quad (1) \qquad\qquad (2) \qquad\qquad\qquad (3) \qquad\qquad (4)$$

a new method for the synthesis of olefins[88-90,92,93] known as the Wittig reaction, which soon attained importance in preparative organic chemistry. This new method of preparation possessed two distinct advantages over the older method of converting the carbonyl compounds to olefins by using the Grignard reaction followed by dehydration of the resulting carbinol: (1) mixtures of isomeric olefins are eliminated, and (2) the reaction is conducted under alkaline medium and very mild conditions, permitting the preparation of sensitive olefins such as carotenoids, methylene steroids, and other natural products.

The Wittig reaction has been reviewed extensively[45,47,49,59,62,79,80,96]; therefore, only a brief description will be presented in order to show the postulated mechanism and stereochemistry of the reaction as background material.

It is necessary to mention that phosphorus, unlike nitrogen, is capable of being pentacovalent, since it can expand its valency shell to ten electrons by inclusion of $d$ orbitals, as shown by the existence of pentaphenylphosphorane.[92a] Alkylidene phosphoranes are therefore considered as resonance hybrids of two limiting structures, the ylid form (5a) and the ylene form (5b). Effects of substituent groups on the reactivity of the alkylidene

$$(R)_3\overset{\oplus}{P}{-}\overset{\ominus}{C}\overset{R^1}{\underset{R_2}{\diagdown}} \rightleftharpoons (R)_3P{=}C\overset{R_1}{\underset{R_2}{\diagdown}}$$
$$\qquad (5a) \qquad\qquad (5b)$$

phosphoranes were discussed in detail in the recent review of the Wittig reaction by Maercker.[49]

Since definitive kinetic studies of reactions of unstabilized alkylidene phosphoranes have not yet been made, it is not possible to make a final statement concerning the mechanism of the Wittig reaction; however, using available facts an outline of the path of this reaction has been given.[49] It has been postulated that olefin formation from the alkylidene phosphoranes and carbonyl compounds occurs via the intermediates shown in the following scheme. In step A, nucleophilic addition of the

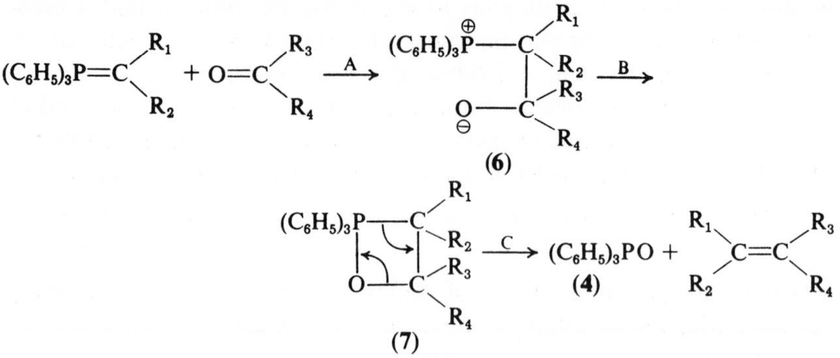

alkylidene phosphorane in its ylid form to the polarized carbonyl group gives the phosphonium betaine (6). Because of the great affinity of phosphorus for oxygen and the possibility of expansion of the valence shell of phosphorus, the phosphorus–oxygen bond is formed (step B), resulting in the formation of the four-membered ring compound (7), which subsequently decomposes via *cis* elimination of triphenylphosphine oxide (4) into an olefin (8) (step C). At present it cannot be decided whether the four-membered ring compound (7) with a pentavalent phosphorus atom is actually an intermediate or a transition state, since step C has never been observed to be the slowest and, therefore, rate-determining step, in a Wittig reaction. However, depending on the reactants, either step A or B may become rate-determining.[9,40–42,81,82] Recent kinetic studies with resonance-stabilized alkylidene phosphoranes indicated that the overall reaction was best described as a slow, reversible formation of the betaine (rate-controlling) with rapid decomposition of the betaine into phosphine oxide and olefin.[67–69]

A completely different case was found in the reaction of carbonyl compounds with reactive alkylidene phosphoranes, which constitute the majority of the Wittig reagents.[95] Here the addition of the ylid to the carbonyl compound occurs within only a few minutes, whereas the subsequent decomposition of the betaines into phosphine oxide and olefins often require prolonged standing at room temperature or heating.[49] Thus step B, decomposition of the betaine, is rate-determining. Consequently, electron-releasing groups on phosphorus will impede the decomposition of B via the four-membered cyclic intermediate, since phosphorus is less able to accept the anionic betaine oxygen. It has been found that introduction of phenyl groups on the $\beta$-carbon atom of the carbonyl compound facilitated the decomposition of the betaine into phosphine oxide and olefin.[49]

Experiments with optically active phosphonium salts have shown that the Wittig reaction occurs with retention of configuration on phosphorus.[12, 13, 49] If the ylid and the carbonyl components are symmetrically substituted, a mixture of *cis* and *trans* olefins is usually obtained, with the *trans* olefin predominating. For example, the reaction of benzylidenetriphenylphosphorane (9) and benzaldehyde (10) results in a mixture con-

$$(C_6H_5)_3P{=}CHC_6H_5 + C_6H_5CHO \longrightarrow$$

| H        C$_6$H$_5$ | C$_6$H$_5$    C$_6$H$_5$ |
| C$_6$H$_5$    H  +  | H        H |
| 70% | 30% |
| (11a) | (11b) |

(9)                (10)

taining 70% *trans*- and 30% *cis*-stilbene (11a and b).[93] Instances have been observed in which the *cis* isomer predominates, although for steric reasons the *trans* compound was preferred.[15, 39, 84, 87] If resonance-stabilized alkylidene phosphoranes are employed, the *trans* isomer is always formed predominately or exclusively. The isomer ratio may be shifted further in favor of the *trans* products if the stability of the initially formed betaines (12a and b) is increased, thus preventing further reaction before equilibrium has been reached.[49] This was accomplished by substituting cyclohexyl groups for the phenyl groups on phosphorus,[9] thus rendering the phosphorus less electrophilic and the conversion of 12 to the end products via the four-membered heterocycle (13) becomes more difficult. If the rate of conversion of 12 to 13 occurs rapidly enough so that the equilibrium (12a $\rightleftharpoons$ 12b) cannot be established, large amounts of *cis* olefins in addition to the *trans* compounds will result. If, on the other hand, the equilibrium is established, the betaine (12a) leading to the *trans* isomer will be energetically favored.[49] Numerous studies have been made [4, 9, 31, 44, 69, 70] in an effort to account for the predominance of *trans* compounds from resonance-stabilized phosphoranes, while other studies conducted indicated that reactive phosphoranes with aldehydes tend to give increased amounts of *cis* isomers in the products if Lewis bases were present.[3 − 8, 65]

Recently, a phosphonate modification of the Wittig reaction has been found very useful in preparing sensitive olefins not preparable by the standard Wittig synthesis.[34, 44, 60, 85, 93] While stable ylids furnish predominantly *trans* olefins, mixtures of isomers are often obtained with more transient phosphoranes. Phosphonate carbanions, however, have been reported to furnish a great preponderance of *trans* olefins.[35]

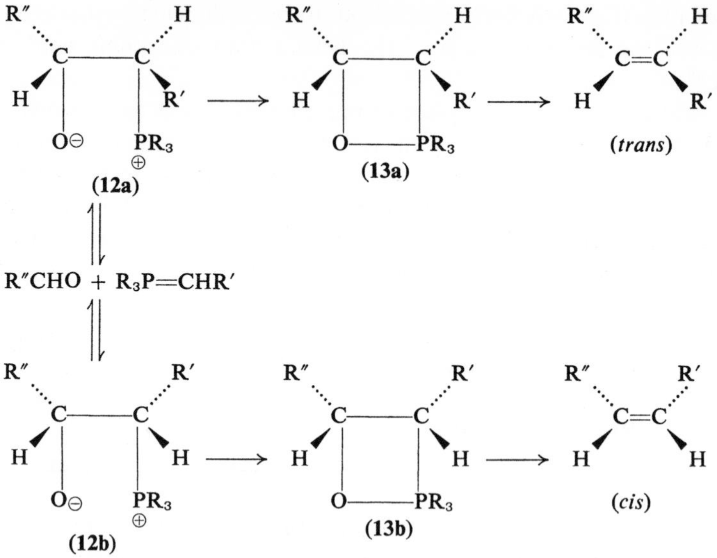

R″ — C(H) — C(H)(R′) with O⊖ and PR₃⊕ (12a) → R″ — C(H) — C(H)(R′) with O—PR₃ (13a) → R″(H)C=C(H)(R′) (*trans*)

R″CHO + R₃P=CHR′

R″ — C(H) — C(R′)(H) with O⊖ and PR₃⊕ (12b) → R″ — C(H) — C(R′)(H) with O—PR₃ (13b) → R″(H)C=C(R′)(H) (*cis*)

Pati and Schwartz[58] reported the preparation of a mixture of *cis*- and *trans*-ethyl *p*-nitrocinnamate from the condensation of *p*-nitrobenzalde-hyde and *O,O*-diethylcarbethoxymethylphosphonate. However, since only the *trans*-product was isolated, it was concluded that the originally formed *cis-trans* mixture of isomers was isomerized upon heating or re-crystallization. Repetition of this work showed the crude product to be a 10:90% mixture of *trans-p*-nitrocinnamate and *p*-nitrobenzaldehyde which was identified by gas chromatography.[86] A 90:10% sample mixture of *p*-nitrobenzaldehyde (mp 106.5°) and *trans*-ethyl *p*-nitrocinnamate (mp 137°) melted at 80–85°, corresponding roughly to that of the "*cis-trans*" mixture reported by Pati and Schwartz.

Of a number of stilbene analogs, distyrylbenzene, ethyl cinnamate, β-styrylacrylic acid, and cinnamic acid (Table 1) prepared by the phosphon-ate modification of the Wittig reaction, only the *trans* products were isolated, although vapor phase chromatography indicate the presence of trace amounts of the *cis*-isomers.[86] To determine the degree of stereo-specificity of the reaction several experiments under adverse conditions were devised, based on the generally accepted mechanism[34,85] which should have been more favorable for the preparation of *cis* olefins. In only one case, however, was a significant amount of a *cis*-isomer formed (6.4% *cis*-1,2-(1,1′-dinaphthyl)ethylene in a 1:10 *cis-trans* mixture), demonstrat-ing the great stereospecific tendency of the reaction.

Wittig reagents have also been made to react with a number of com-pounds that undergo reactions similar to those of carbonyl compounds;

for example, thiobenzophenone (14) reacts with methylenetriphenylphosphorane (2) to give 1,1-diphenylethylene (3).[30,62]

$$(C_6H_5)_3P=CH_2 + (C_6H_5)_2C=S \longrightarrow$$

(2)          (14)

$$\begin{array}{c} (C_6H_5)_3P\text{------}CH_2 \\ | \qquad\qquad | \\ S\text{------}C(C_6H_5)_2 \end{array}$$

$$\begin{array}{c} (C_6H_5)_3P\text{------}CH_2 \\ | \qquad\qquad | \\ S\text{------}C(C_6H_5)_2 \end{array} \longrightarrow (C_6H_5)_2C=CH_2 + (C_6H_5)_3P{\to}S$$

(3)

In an effort to obtain a pentavalent phosphorus compound as 17, Staudinger and Meyer[71,76] combined diphenylketene (15) and diphenylmethylenetriphenylphosphorane (16). However, such an addition product was not obtained; the diphenylketene (15) and phosphine–methylene derivative (16) did not react. Staudinger also noted that it was remarkable

$$(C_6H_5)_2C=C=O + (C_6H_5)_3P=C(C_6H_5)_2 \longrightarrow$$

(15)          (16)

$$\begin{array}{c} (C_6H_5)_3P\text{------}C(C_6H_5)_2 \\ | \qquad\qquad\qquad | \\ OC\text{------}C(C_6H_5)_2 \end{array}$$

(17)

that the reaction of 15 and 16 had not reacted in the following sense with the formation of triphenylphosphine oxide (4) and the unsaturated compound (18). The reaction of diphenylketene (15) and the phosphorane (16)

$$(C_6H_5)_2C=C=O + (C_6H_5)_3P=C(C_6H_5)_2 \longrightarrow$$

(15)          (16)

$$\begin{array}{c} (C_6H_5)_3P\text{------}C(C_6H_5)_2 \\ | \qquad\qquad\qquad | \\ O\text{------}C=C(C_6H_5)_2 \end{array}$$

$$\begin{array}{c} (C_6H_5)_3P\text{------}C(C_6H_5)_2 \\ | \qquad\qquad\qquad | \\ O\text{------}C=C(C_6H_5)_2 \end{array} \longrightarrow (C_6H_5)_3P^{\nearrow O} + (C_6H_5)_2C=C=C(C_6H_5)_2$$

(4)          (18)

giving triphenylphosphine oxide (4) and the unsaturated compound (18) was reported[48,52,53] to occur only under forcing conditions at 140°C in benzene under pressure.

More recently, Zbiral[97-99] has reported that alkylidene phosphoranes undergo addition reactions with dehydroaromatics (Table 2). For example, the alkylidene phosphorane (19) was reported to have reacted with benzyne (20) resulting in the formation of the addition product (21). Since the existing information about the reactions of arynes with various nucleo-

philes indicated that the addition resulted stepwise and not synchro-
nously,[38,46] Zbiral[97,99,100] formulated the following reaction for arynes
(20) with alkylidene phosphoranes (19):

$$(C_6H_5)_3P{=}CHR + \overset{(20)}{\bigcirc\!|} \longrightarrow (C_6H_5)_2P{-}\underset{(21)}{\bigcirc}\overset{\overset{C_6H_5\diagdown\quad R}{CH}}{}$$

(19)

$$(C_6H_5)_3P{=}CHR + \overset{(20)}{\bigcirc\!|} \longrightarrow [(C_6H_5)_3\overset{\oplus}{P}{-}CHR]\,\underset{\ominus}{\bigcirc} \longrightarrow (C_6H_5)_3P{-}CHR$$

(19)
(R = C₆H₅)

[(C₆H₅)₃P̟—CHR]

(C₆H₅)₃P—CHR
(22)

(C₆H₅)₂PCHR
C₆H₅
(23)

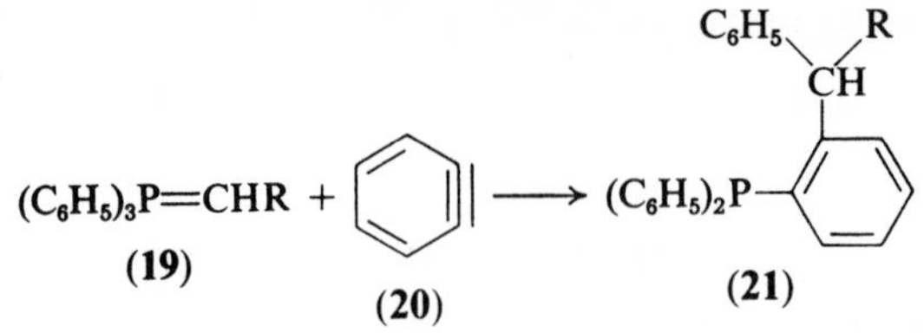

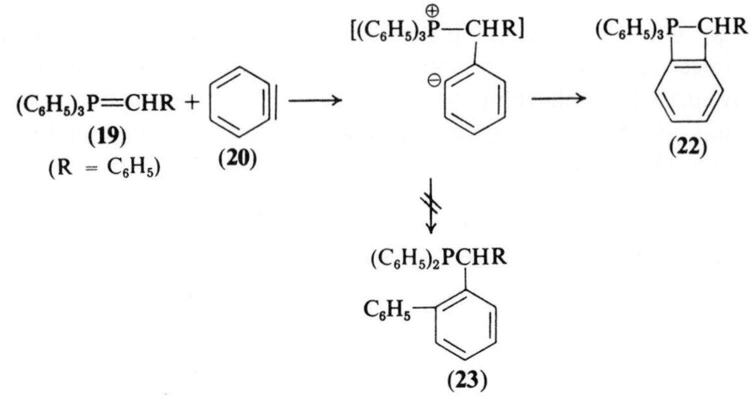

The benzophosphacyclobutene derivative (22) and not the phosphine (23)
(obtained from a phenyl migration) was the intermediate, although not
isolated, postulated by Zbiral since the carbon–hydrogen-R-radical had
been removed from the phosphorus atom as shown by the final product
(21).

In support of the formation of the phosphacyclobutene intermediate (22)
another group of workers[10,21-33] independently reported the formation
of a phosphacyclobutene intermediate (24) in the reaction of alkylidene
phosphoranes (19) with acetylenedicarboxylic acid esters (23) (Table 2).
The phosphacyclobutene intermediate (24) resulted from the insertion of

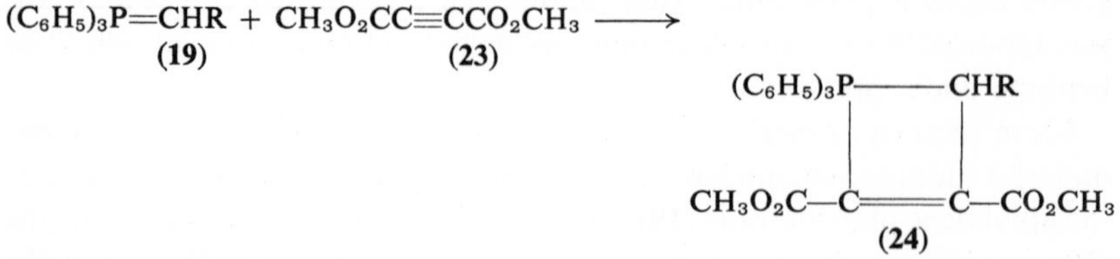

$$(C_6H_5)_3P{=}CHR + CH_3O_2CC{\equiv}CCO_2CH_3 \longrightarrow$$
(19)                    (23)

$$(C_6H_5)_3P{-}\!-\!-\!-CHR$$
$$CH_3O_2C{-}C{=\!=\!=}C{-}CO_2CH_3$$
(24)

the second carbon atom of the ester (23) into the phosphorus–carbon

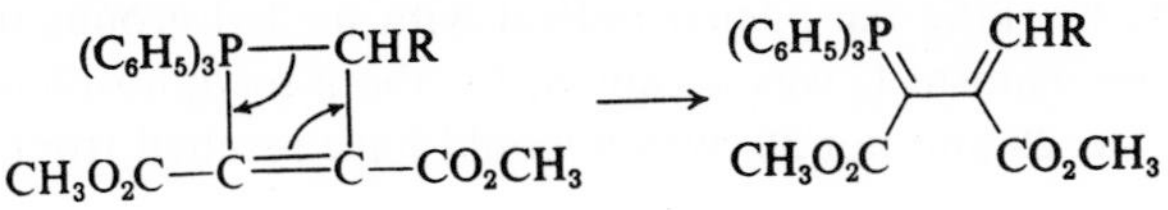

$$(C_6H_5)_3P\text{—}CHR \qquad\qquad (C_6H_5)_3P \qquad CHR$$
$$\qquad\qquad\qquad\qquad\longrightarrow$$
$$CH_3O_2C\text{—}C\text{=}C\text{—}CO_2CH_3 \qquad CH_3O_2C \qquad CO_2CH_3$$

double bond of the alkylidene phosphorane (19). A similar phenomenon exists in the reaction of benzyne (20) and the alkylidene phosphorane (19).

A cyclobutene intermediate (26) similar to that mentioned above was postulated[18] for the reaction of dimethylacetylenedicarboxylate (23) with

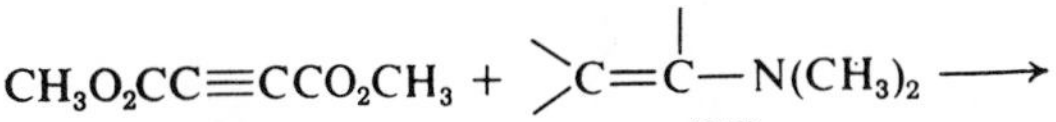

$$CH_3O_2CC\text{≡}CCO_2CH_3 + \quad >C\text{=}C\text{—}N(CH_3)_2 \longrightarrow$$
$$\qquad\quad \textbf{(23)} \qquad\qquad\qquad\qquad \textbf{(25)}$$

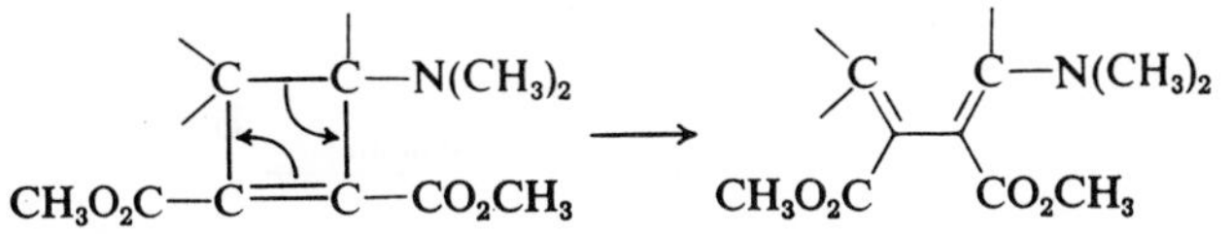

$$C\text{—}C\text{—}N(CH_3)_2 \qquad\qquad C \qquad C\text{—}N(CH_3)_2$$
$$\qquad\qquad\qquad\qquad\qquad\qquad \longrightarrow$$
$$CH_3O_2C\text{—}C\text{=}C\text{—}CO_2CH_3 \qquad CH_3O_2C \qquad CO_2CH_3$$
$$\qquad\qquad \textbf{(26)}$$

enamines (25). Other analogous cyclobutene derivatives formed by the cycloaddition of benzyne (20) and olefins[46, 66] are shown below.

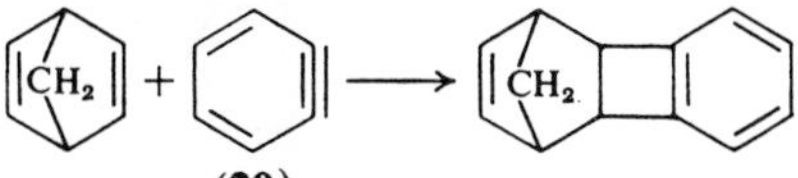

$$(CH_2) + \bigcirc \longrightarrow (CH_2)\square$$
$$\qquad\qquad \textbf{(20)}$$

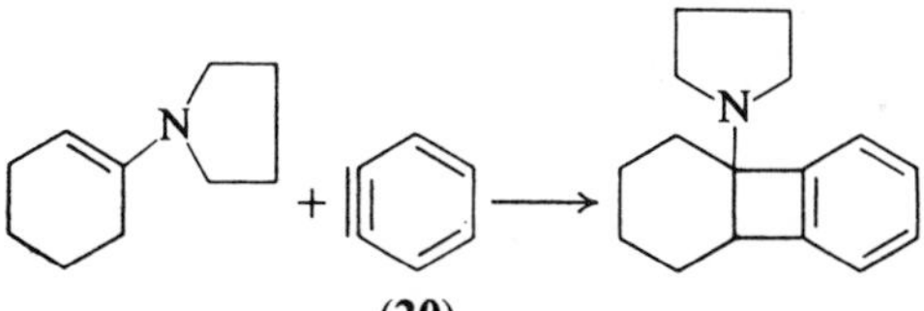

$$\bigcirc\text{—N} + \bigcirc \longrightarrow \square$$
$$\qquad\qquad \textbf{(20)}$$

By analogy, Zbiral[97, 99, 100] proposed three mechanisms for the ultimate formation of the phosphine (21): A (in essence a "no-mechanism reaction")[29]; B and C, intramolecular nucleophilic substitutions of the polar structural intermediate (28) analogous to the Truce-Smiles rearrange-

Mechanism A:

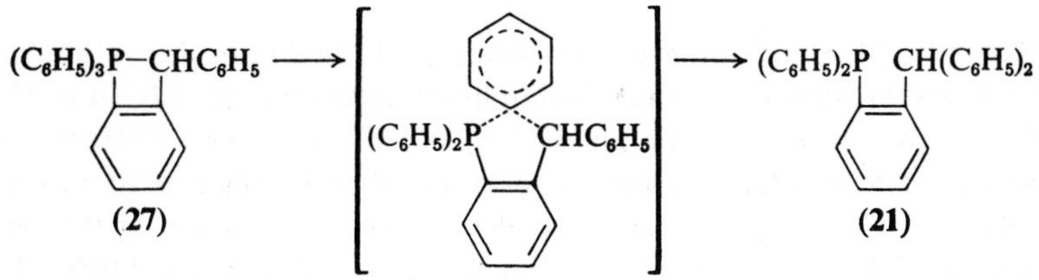

$$(C_6H_5)_3P\text{—}CHC_6H_5 \longrightarrow \left[ \begin{array}{c} \bigcirc \\ (C_6H_5)_2P \quad CHC_6H_5 \end{array} \right] \longrightarrow (C_6H_5)_2P \quad CH(C_6H_5)_2$$
$$\quad \textbf{(27)} \qquad\qquad\qquad\qquad\qquad\qquad\qquad\qquad\qquad \textbf{(21)}$$

ment.[83] By marking the phenyl radical with methyl groups in the *ortho*-position, mechanism C was accepted, for the *p*-tolylphosphine derivative obtained was **29** and not **30**, which would have resulted from B.

Mechanism B:

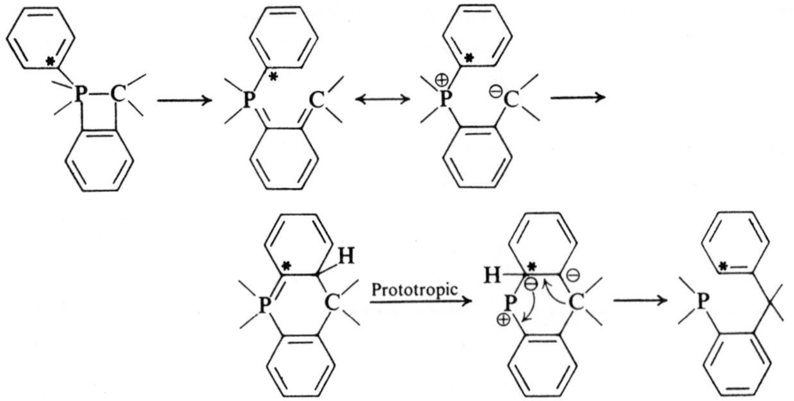

Mechanism C:

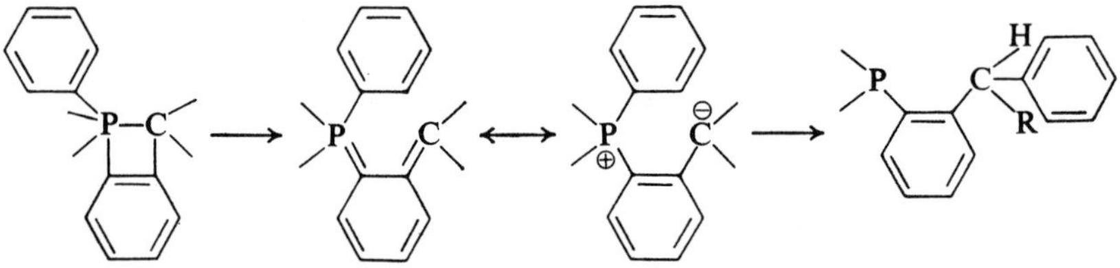

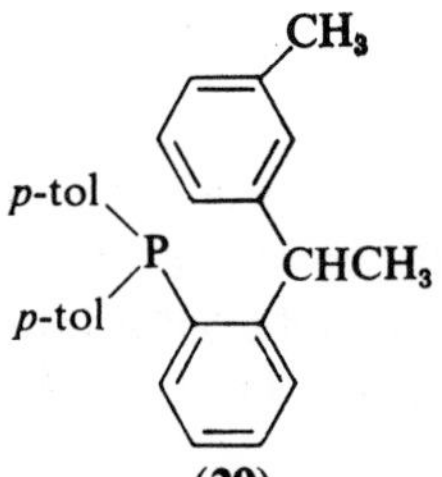

**(29)** 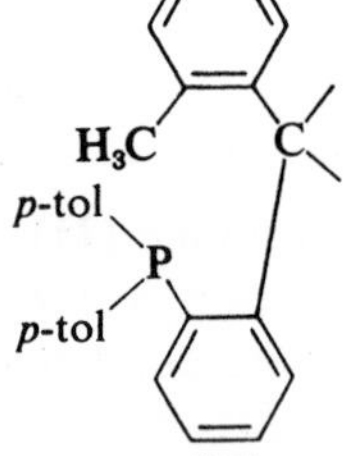                **(30)**

Recently, Mahler[50] reported the isolation of the diphosphacyclobutene 1,2,3,4-tetrakis(trifluoromethyl)-3,4-diphosphacyclobutene (**33**), in a 55% yield via the reaction of the phosphine, $(CF_3P)_4$ (**31**), and bis(trifluoro-methyl)acetylene (**32**) extending the reactions of biphosphine with multiple bonds.[23, 27] The vapor pressure was determined to be 6 mm at 0°C and 26 mm at 25°C, from which the boiling point was estimated at 110°C. The

$$(CF_3P)_4 + CF_3C{\equiv}CCF_3 \longrightarrow$$

(31)              (32)

$$\begin{array}{c} CF_3C{-}{-}{-}{-}PCF_3 \\ \| \quad\quad | \\ CF_3C{-}{-}{-}{-}PCF_3 \end{array}$$

(33)

cyclopolyphosphine (33) is spontaneously flammable in air, but in isolation it is stable at 200°C. The structure of 33 was determined by infrared (double bond absorption at 1625 cm$^{-1}$) and fluorine[19] nuclear magnetic resonance spectra.

The fluorine[19] nuclear magnetic resonance spectrum of 33 shows two kinds of fluorine in equal amounts. The trifluoromethyl groups, $CF_3$ attached to the phosphorus atom have the X pattern of an $X_3AA'X_3$ system[1,16] in which light lines were resolved.[50] The coupling constants obtained from the fluorine[19] magnetic resonance spectrum are given in Table 3; at high resolution there is further splitting (1.5 cps) from the other set of trifluoromethyl groups; this fluorine–fluorine coupling is seen in the fluorine[19] spectrum of the trifluoromethyl groups on the carbon and can be removed by double resonance.

Earlier[51] Mahler had argued that the (formally) nonbonding electron pair on each phosphorus atom in polyphosphines was delocalized in π-type orbitals. This concept is further supported by the observation that the heterocyclic polyphosphines absorb ultraviolet light at longer wavelengths than the corresponding open-chain di- and triphosphine (Table 4),[50] clearly suggesting that the orbitals of the polyphosphine portion of the ring overlap with the carbon–carbon π-orbitals.

Earlier in this section reference was made to the phosphacyclobutene intermediate in the addition of phosphoranes to acetylenes. It was also reported[20] that phosphinimines (34)* react with dimethyl acetylenedicarboxylate (23) to form 1:1 adducts (36) (Table 5), the structures of which were determined by x-ray analysis and ultraviolet absorption spectra. It has been concluded[22] that the reaction must proceed through the intermediate 35, which then breaks the phosphorus–nitrogen bond.

$$(C_6H_5)_3P{=}N{-}\langle{\bigcirc}\rangle{-}R + CH_3O_2CC{\equiv}CCO_2CH_3 \longrightarrow$$

(34)                                        (23)

$$(C_6H_5)_3P{-}{-}N{-}\langle{\bigcirc}\rangle{-}R \longrightarrow (C_6H_5)_3P{=}C{-}C{=}N{-}\langle{\bigcirc}\rangle{-}R$$

$$CH_3O_2C{-}C{=}C{-}CO_2CH_3 \quad\quad\quad CO_2CH_3$$

(35)                                        (36)

(R = (a) H, (b) Br, (c) $CO_2CH_3$, (d) $COCH_3$, (e) $NO_2$.)

* For a review on phosphinimines see N. L. Paddock.[57]

The imine (**37**), which could have undergone a Michael addition resulting in **38**, reacted analogously forming the adduct **39** (N–H band 3380 cm$^{-1}$). Phosphinimines with the nitrogen atom less nucleophilic than in **36e**, as in

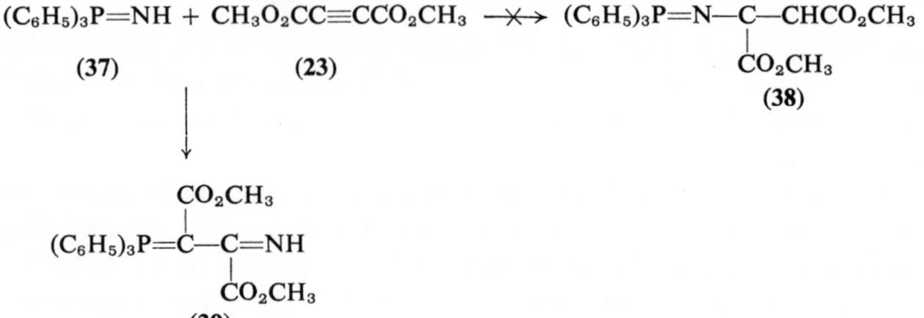

$$(C_6H_5)_3P{=}NH + CH_3O_2CC{\equiv}CCO_2CH_3 \ \longrightarrow\hspace{-1.2em}\times\hspace{0.6em} \ (C_6H_5)_3P{=}N{-}C{-}CHCO_2CH_3$$

(**37**)                    (**23**)                                    $\overset{|}{C}O_2CH_3$

(**38**)

$$\text{CO}_2\text{CH}_3$$
$$(C_6H_5)_3P{=}\overset{|}{C}{-}C{=}NH$$
$$\underset{|}{\overset{}{}}CO_2CH_3$$

(**39**)

the *N*-2,4-dinitrophenyl-, -benzoyl-, -ethoxycarbonyl, or -*p*-toluenesulfonylinimes, failed to add to the acetylene (**23**) as did phosphinimines of type **40**.[22]

$$(C_2H_5O)_3P{=}NR$$
(**40**)

$$(R = C_6H_5, COC_6H_5, p\text{-}SO_2C_6H_4CH_3)$$

Phosphazines (**41**) containing α-hydrogen atoms gave adducts with dimethyl acetylenedicarboxylate formed by Michael addition while phosphazines (**42**) with no α-hydrogen atoms added via the phosphazacyclobutene intermediate to give the adduct **43**.[22]

$$(C_6H_5)_3P{=}N{-}N{=}CHCOOR$$
(**41**)
$$(R = CH_3, C_2H_5)$$

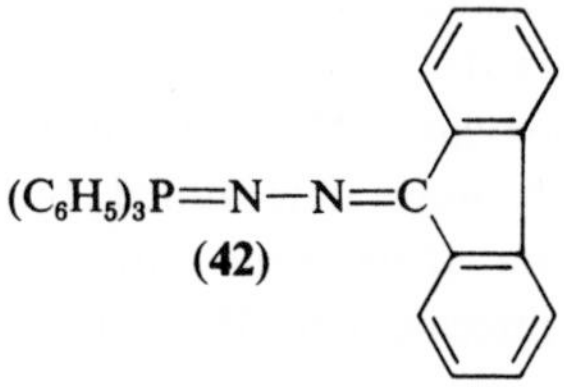

$$(C_6H_5)_3P{=}N{-}N{=}C$$
(**42**)

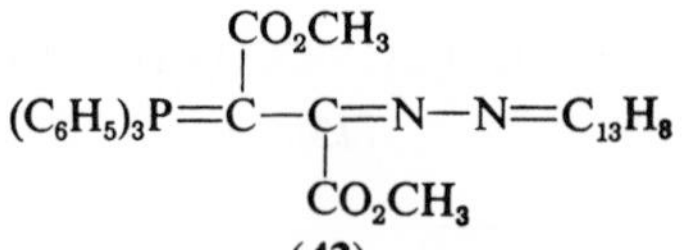

$$\text{CO}_2\text{CH}_3$$
$$(C_6H_5)_3P{=}\overset{|}{C}{-}\overset{|}{C}{=}N{-}N{=}C_{13}H_8$$
$$CO_2CH_3$$
(**43**)

$$(R = CH_3, C_2H_5)$$

The facile opening of the phosphacyclobutene and phosphazacyclobutene rings is somewhat similar to the isomerization of the cyclobutene systems[2,17,36,37] from addition of dimethyl acetylenedicarboxylate to enamines.

Staudinger[73] also reported a four-membered heterocyclic intermediate in the reactions of the phosphazine (44) and sulfur dioxide or thionylaniline, which decomposed with evolution of nitrogen to give benzophenone (1), phosphine oxide (4), and sulfur.

$$(C_6H_5)_3P=N—N=C(C_6H_5)_2 + O=S=O \longrightarrow$$
$$\quad (44)$$

$$(C_6H_5)_3P\underset{\displaystyle O\underline{\hspace{1em}}S=O}{\overline{\hspace{1em}}}N—N=C(C_6H_5)_2 \qquad \longrightarrow$$

$$(C_6H_5)_3P{\to}O + O=S=N—N=C(C_6H_5)_2$$
$$(4)$$

$$O=S=N—N=C(C_6H_5)_2 \xrightarrow{-N_2} (C_6H_5)_2C=S=O \longrightarrow (C_6H_5)_2C=O + S$$
$$\qquad\qquad (1)$$

Referring again to the work of Staudinger, it was reported[75,76] that $N$-phenyltriphenylphosphinimine (45) and carbon dioxide reacted via a cycloaddition to form the intermediate oxaphosphazacyclobutanone (46), which easily decomposed into triphenylphosphine oxide (4) and phenylisocyanate (47).

$$(C_6H_5)_3P=NC_6H_5 + O=C=O \longrightarrow$$
$$(45)$$

$$(C_6H_5)_3P\underset{\displaystyle O\underline{\hspace{1em}}C=O}{\overline{\hspace{1em}}}NC_6H_5 \qquad \longrightarrow$$
$$(46)$$

$$(C_6H_5)_3P\underset{\displaystyle O\underline{\hspace{1em}}C=O}{\overline{\hspace{1em}}}NC_6H_5 \longrightarrow (C_6H_5)_3P{\to}O + O=C=NC_6H_5$$
$$(46) \qquad\qquad (4) \qquad\qquad (47)$$

An analogous reaction occurs with carbon disulfide, phenylisocyanate, and phenylisothiocyanate; for example, phenylisocyanate (47) and $N$-phenyltriphenylphosphinimine (45) undergo a cycloaddition reaction to form the unstable intermediate (48) which decomposed into triphenylphosphine oxide (31) and the diimide (49).[75-77] Likewise, diphenylketene (15) reacts with the phosphinimine (45) via an unstable cyclic intermediate (50)

$$(C_6H_5)_3P=NC_6H_5 + O=C=NC_6H_5 \longrightarrow$$
$$(45) \qquad\qquad (47)$$

$$(C_6H_5)_3P\underset{\displaystyle O\underline{\hspace{1em}}C=NC_6H_5}{\overline{\hspace{1em}}}NC_6H_5 \qquad \longrightarrow$$
$$(48)$$

$$(C_6H_5)_3P \to O + C_6H_5N=C=NC_6H_6$$
$$(4) \qquad\qquad (49)$$

resulting in the addition product (51) and triphenylphosphine oxide
(4).[74-76] It is remarkable to note that here the diphenylketene molecule

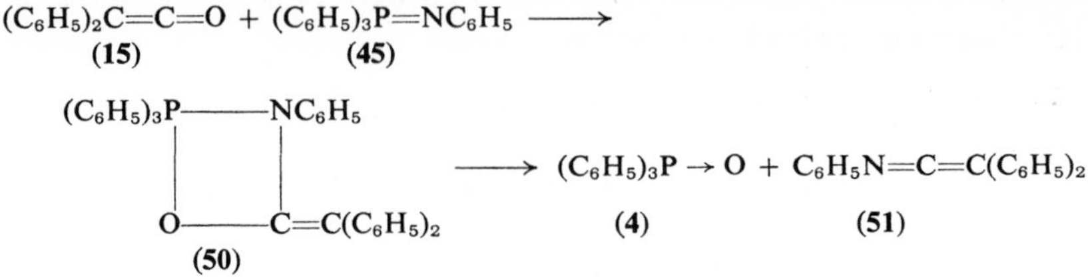

$(C_6H_5)_2C{=}C{=}O + (C_6H_5)_3P{=}NC_6H_5 \longrightarrow$
    (15)              (45)

$(C_6H_5)_3P{\text----}NC_6H_5$

$\longrightarrow (C_6H_5)_3P \to O + C_6H_5N{=}C{=}C(C_6H_5)_2$

$O{\text----}C{=}C(C_6H_5)_2$      (4)           (51)
    (50)

reacted via the carbonyl group and not the unsaturated carbon–carbon
bond as was observed in previous cases,[72] for example:

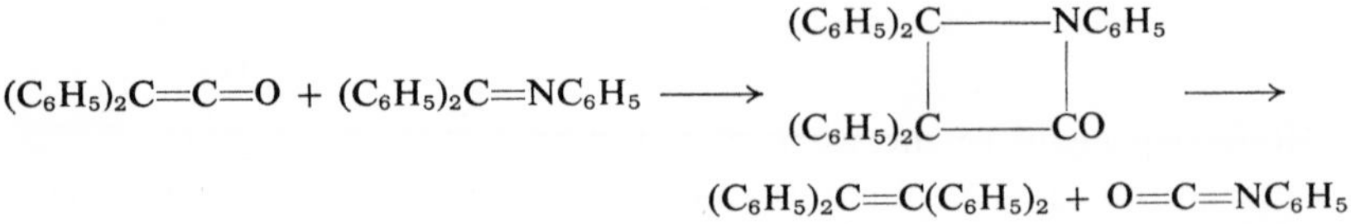

$(C_6H_5)_2C$ ———— $NC_6H_5$

$(C_6H_5)_2C{=}C{=}O + (C_6H_5)_2C{=}NC_6H_5 \longrightarrow$            $\longrightarrow$

$(C_6H_5)_2C$ ———— $CO$

$(C_6H_5)_2C{=}C(C_6H_5)_2 + O{=}C{=}NC_6H_5$

The addition product (51) (originally termed a ketene imide by Staudinger) was also prepared by the decomposition of the cyclic intermediate (52)
obtained by the cycloaddition of phenylisocyanate (47) and the alkylidene
phosphorane (16).[75, 76]

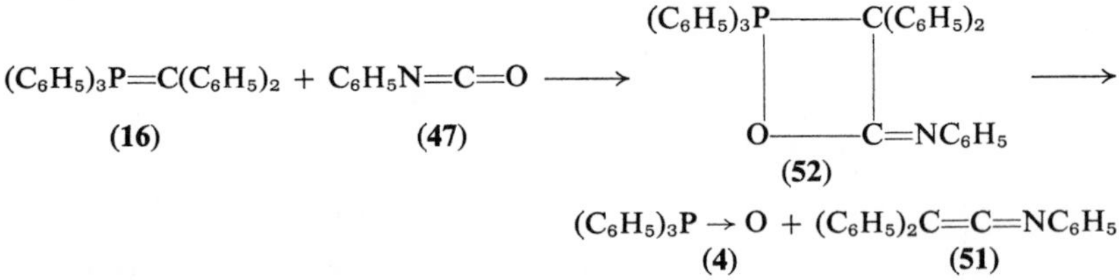

$(C_6H_5)_3P$ ———— $C(C_6H_5)_2$

$(C_6H_5)_3P{=}C(C_6H_5)_2 + C_6H_5N{=}C{=}O \longrightarrow$          $\longrightarrow$

    (16)               (47)

$O$ ———— $C{=}NC_6H_5$
          (52)

$(C_6H_5)_3P \to O + (C_6H_5)_2C{=}C{=}NC_6H_5$
      (4)          (51)

More recently, the formation of benzophenone-aniline (55) was reported[64] during the reaction of triphenylphosphine diphenylene (16) and
nitrosobenzene (53). The reaction was postulated to proceed through a
cyclic intermediate (54) which readily decomposed into the anilide (55) and
triphenylphosphine oxide (4). The reaction was repeated with triphenyl-

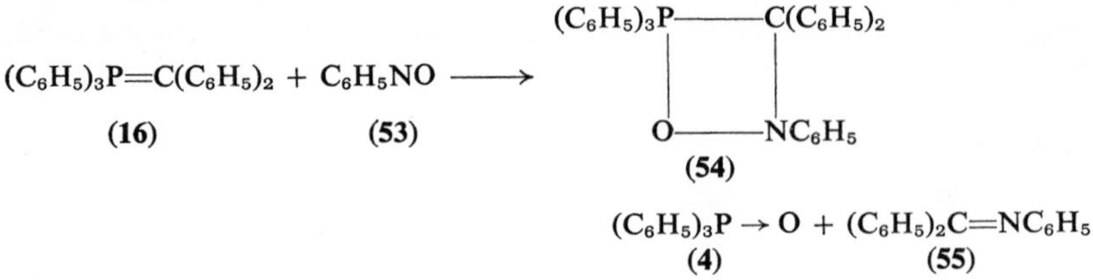

$(C_6H_5)_3P$ ———— $C(C_6H_5)_2$

$(C_6H_5)_3P{=}C(C_6H_5)_2 + C_6H_5NO \longrightarrow$

    (16)              (53)

$O$ ———— $NC_6H_5$
          (54)

$(C_6H_5)_3P \to O + (C_6H_5)_2C{=}NC_6H_5$
      (4)          (55)

phosphine fluorenylene, benzophenonetriphenylphosphazine (56), and

2,4-dichloro-1,3,5-triazine aldehyde-6-triphenylphosphazine. The addition of nitrosobenzene (53) to the phosphazine (56) was postulated to proceed through the six-membered heterocyclic intermediate (57), which decomposed with evolution of nitrogen to form triphenylphosphine oxide (4) and benzophenone-anilide (55).[64]

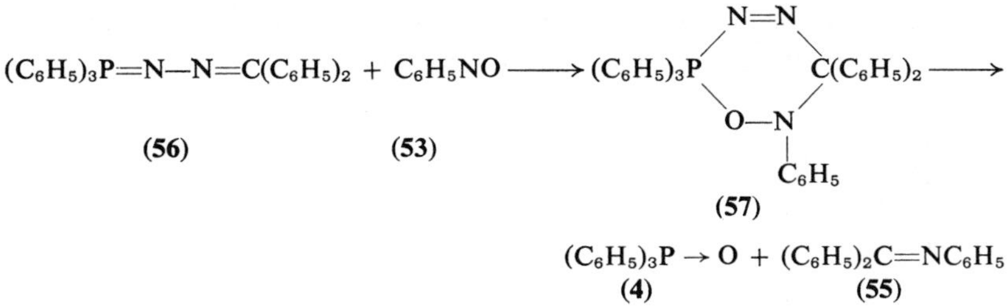

$$(C_6H_5)_3P{=}N{-}N{=}C(C_6H_5)_2 + C_6H_5NO \longrightarrow$$

(56)  (53)

(57)

$$(C_6H_5)_3P \rightarrow O + (C_6H_5)_2C{=}NC_6H_5$$

(4)  (55)

Nitrosobenzene[62,63,94] was also found to react with alkylidene triphenylphosphoranes to give Schiff bases (azomethines) which could be hydrolyzed yielding aldehydes and ketones. For instance, benzylidenetriphenylphosphorane (9) is converted to benzaldehyde (10) by way of benzalaniline (58).

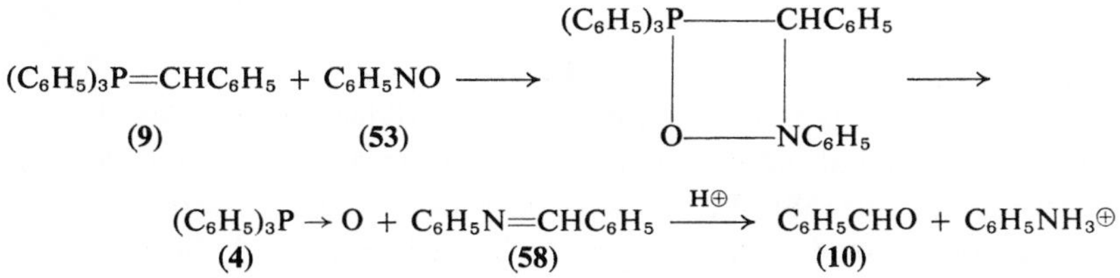

$$(C_6H_5)_3P{=}CHC_6H_5 + C_6H_5NO \longrightarrow$$

(9)  (53)

$$(C_6H_5)_3P \rightarrow O + C_6H_5N{=}CHC_6H_5 \xrightarrow{H^\oplus} C_6H_5CHO + C_6H_5NH_3^\oplus$$

(4)  (58)  (10)

The formation of imines similar to (55) was also reported[14] in the reactions of carbonyl compounds and phosphinimines via the formation of a cyclic intermediate.

$$R_2CO + R'N{=}PR_3 \longrightarrow R'N{=}CR_2 + R_3PO$$

Concerning phosphorylations via oxidation of phosphites,[19,28,43,54,61,78] a study was recently made[54] with a view to producing diesters of phosphorous acid (59) via a metaphosphite intermediate (60) under the assumption that the intermediate might be generated by reacting ethyl N-phenylimino phosphite (59) with benzaldehyde (10), in a manner analogous to the Wittig reaction, as shown below. The results of this study

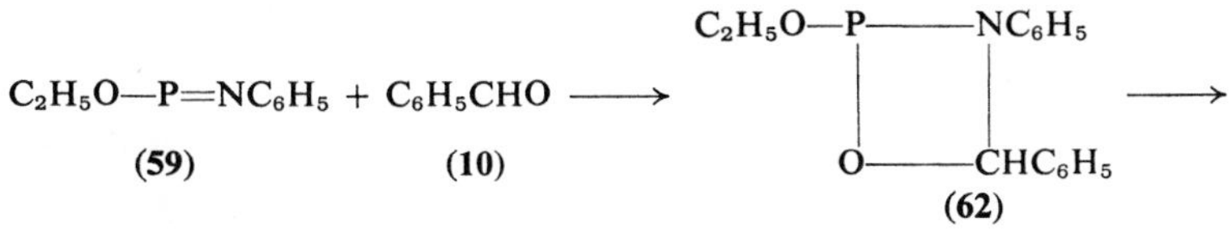

$$C_2H_5O{-}P{=}NC_6H_5 + C_6H_5CHO \longrightarrow$$

(59)  (10)

(62)

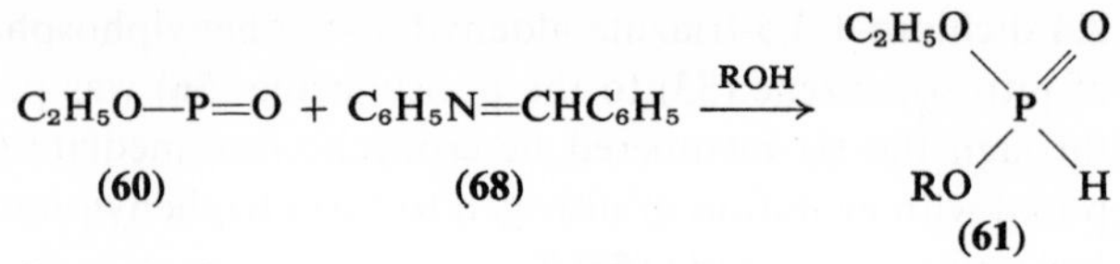

$$C_2H_5O\text{—}P\text{=}O + C_6H_5N\text{=}CHC_6H_5 \xrightarrow{\text{ROH}}$$

(60)                    (68)

$$\begin{array}{c} C_2H_5O \\ RO \end{array}\!\!\!P\!\!\!\begin{array}{c} O \\ H \end{array}$$

(61)

(R = alkyl)

suggested that the following mechanism is preferable to the metaphosphite intermediate (60) reaction mechanism illustrated here:

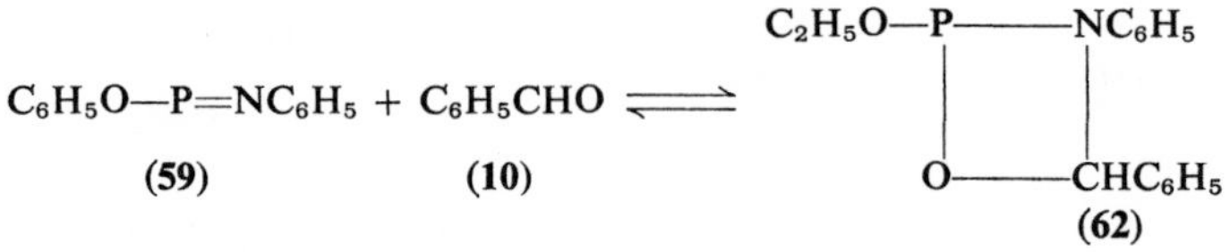

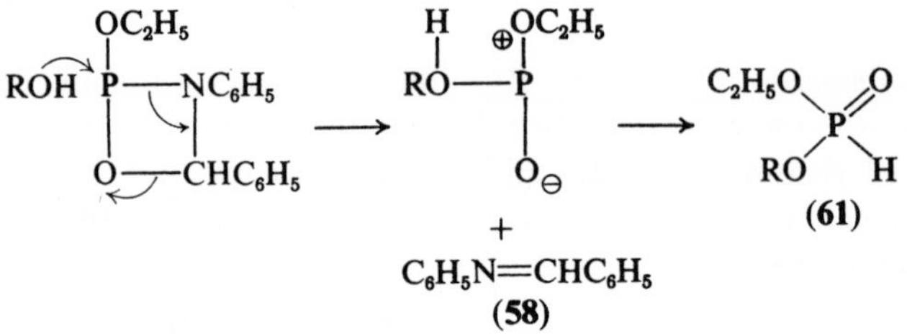

$$C_6H_5O\text{—}P\text{=}NC_6H_5 + C_6H_5CHO \rightleftharpoons$$

(59)                    (10)

$$\begin{array}{ccc} C_2H_5O\text{—}P & \text{——} & NC_6H_5 \\ | & & | \\ O & \text{——} & CHC_6H_5 \end{array}$$

(62)

ROH  $\overset{OC_2H_5}{\underset{O\text{——}CHC_6H_5}{P\text{—}NC_6H_5}}$  →  $\overset{H\ \overset{\oplus}{O}C_2H_5}{\underset{\underset{\ominus}{O}}{RO\text{—}P}}$  →  $\begin{array}{c} C_2H_5O \\ RO \end{array}\!\!\!P\!\!\!\begin{array}{c} O \\ H \end{array}$

                                                                                           (61)

+

$$C_6H_5N\text{=}CHC_6H_5$$

(58)

The formation of 62 was considered to be reversible, and 62 did not decompose into metaphosphite (60) and benzylideneaniline (58). In the presence of alcohol, 62 decomposed, giving the dialkyphosphite 61 and benzylideneaniline (58). When a secondary alcohol such as isopropyl alcohol was used instead of the primary alcohol, ethylisopropyl phosphite was not isolated but 68% of crude benzaldehyde (10), 77% of 59, and a small amount of white crystalline solid (mp 180–182°C) was obtained whose elemental analysis agreed with the formula 62.[54]

The conversion of arylisocyanates 63 to carbodiimides (66) through the use of phospholene oxide catalysts (64) has been described[24–26,55] in the literature (Table 6). The most active catalyst was 1-ethyl-3-methyl-3-phospholene 1-oxide. Studies of the kinetics of the reaction support the formation of a phosphinimide intermediate (65), as described by the mechanism shown below.

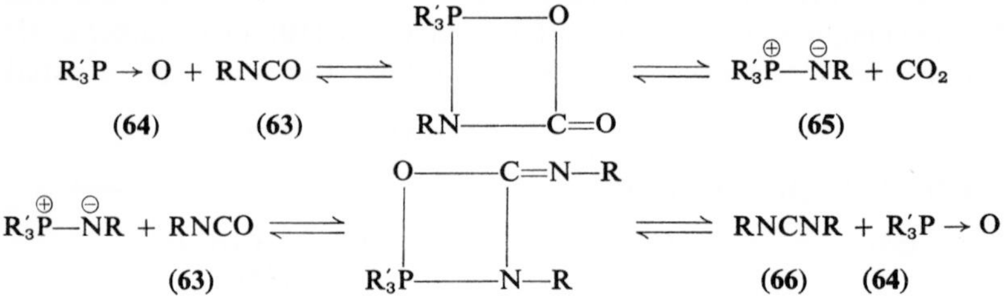

$$R_3'P \rightarrow O + RNCO \rightleftharpoons \begin{array}{ccc} R_3'P & \text{——} & O \\ | & & | \\ RN & \text{——} & C\text{=}O \end{array} \rightleftharpoons R_3'P\overset{\oplus}{\text{—}}\overset{\ominus}{N}R + CO_2$$

(64)        (63)                                        (65)

$$R_3'P\overset{\oplus}{\text{—}}\overset{\ominus}{N}R + RNCO \rightleftharpoons \begin{array}{ccc} O & \text{——} & C\text{=}N\text{—}R \\ | & & | \\ R_3'P & \text{——} & N\text{—}R \end{array} \rightleftharpoons RNCNR + R_3'P \rightarrow O$$

(63)                        (66)        (64)

On the basis of this mechanism, Campbell and co-workers[56] reasoned that a reaction of benzoyl isocyanate (67) with phospholene oxide catalysts (64) should yield benzonitrile (68) by the route shown below. In ether

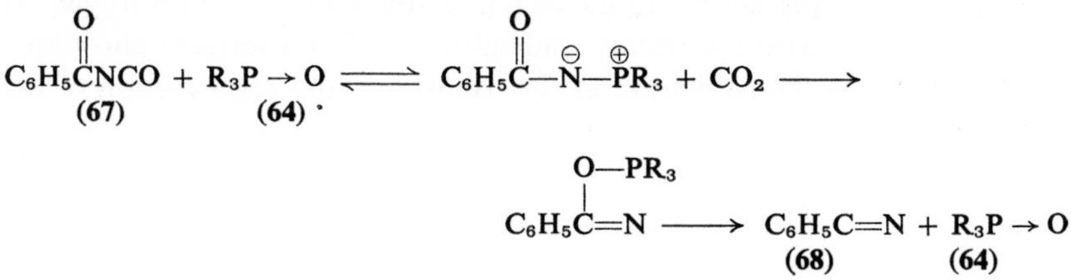

$$
\underset{(67)}{C_6H_5\overset{\overset{\displaystyle O}{\|}}{C}NCO} + \underset{(64)}{R_3P \to O} \; \rightleftharpoons \; C_6H_5\overset{\overset{\displaystyle O}{\|}}{C}-\overset{\ominus}{N}-\overset{\oplus}{P}R_3 + CO_2 \longrightarrow
$$

$$
\underset{(68)}{C_6H_5\overset{\overset{\displaystyle O-PR_3}{|}}{C}=N} \longrightarrow \underset{}{C_6H_5C=N} + \underset{(64)}{R_3P \to O}
$$

solution,[25] or in xylene, however, benzoylisocyanate (67) reacted with 1-ethyl-3-methyl-3-phospholene 1-oxide to give a good yield of a solid product (69), 2,6-diphenyl-4-benzoylimino-1,3,5-oxadiazine, which decomposed into benzonitrile (68), carbon dioxide, and other products at temperatures of 200°C.[56] The mechanism postulated for the formation of the oxadiazine (69) is illustrated below.

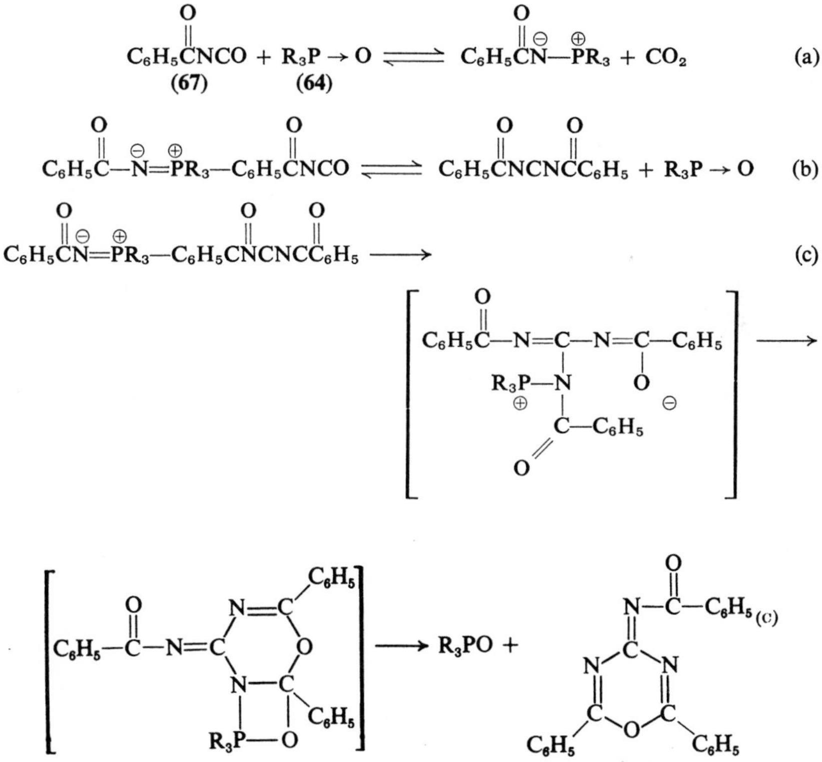

$$
\underset{(67)}{C_6H_5\overset{\overset{\displaystyle O}{\|}}{C}NCO} + \underset{(64)}{R_3P \to O} \; \rightleftharpoons \; C_6H_5\overset{\overset{\displaystyle O}{\|}}{C}\overset{\ominus}{N}-\overset{\oplus}{P}R_3 + CO_2 \qquad (a)
$$

$$
C_6H_5\overset{\overset{\displaystyle O}{\|}}{C}-\overset{\ominus}{N}=\overset{\oplus}{P}R_3-C_6H_5\overset{\overset{\displaystyle O}{\|}}{C}NCO \; \rightleftharpoons \; C_6H_5\overset{\overset{\displaystyle O}{\|}}{C}NCN\overset{\overset{\displaystyle O}{\|}}{C}C_6H_5 + R_3P \to O \qquad (b)
$$

$$
C_6H_5\overset{\overset{\displaystyle O}{\|}}{C}\overset{\ominus}{N}=\overset{\oplus}{P}R_3-C_6H_5\overset{\overset{\displaystyle O}{\|}}{C}NCN\overset{\overset{\displaystyle O}{\|}}{C}C_6H_5 \longrightarrow \qquad (c)
$$

$$
\longrightarrow R_3PO +
$$

(69)

Steps a and b have been well documented for arylisocyanates.[24 – 26, 55] The dibenzoylcarbodiimide formed is best represented by a number of resonance forms, and it was postulated that its electron-poor carbon atom would be highly susceptible to nucleophilic attack by the ylid nitrogen, as in step c. Subsequent cyclization and splitting off of a tertiary phosphine oxide resulted in the formation of the oxadiazine and regeneration of the catalyst.

**Table 1**

Disubstituted Ethylenes via a Phosphonate Modification of the Wittig Reaction[86]

| Olefin | Phosphonate[a] | Carbonyl | MP (°C) | Yield, % cis | Yield, % trans |
|---|---|---|---|---|---|
| $C_6H_5CH=CHC_6H_5$ | A | $C_6H_5CHO$ | — | 1.2 | 86.9 |
| | | | | 0.9 | 97.9 |
| $C_6H_5CH=CH(p\text{-}NO_2C_6H_4)$ | A | $p\text{-}NO_2C_6H_4CHO$ | 154–155 | 0.8 | 36.3 |
| $C_6H_5CH=CH(p\text{-}NO_2C_6H_5)$ | D | $C_6H_5CHO$ | 154–155 | 1.9 | 74.5 |
| $C_6H_5CH=CH(p\text{-}CH_3OC_6H_4)$ | A | $p\text{-}CH_3OC_6H_4CHO$ | 135–136 | 0.0 | 100 |
| $C_6H_5CH=CH(p\text{-}C_2H_5O_2CC_6H_4)$ | C | $C_6H_5CHO$ | 102–102.5 | 0.0 | 76.3 |
| | | | | | 78.5 |
| $C_6H_5CH=CH(p\text{-}CH_3OC_6H_4)$ | C | $C_6H_5CHO$ | 159.5–160 | — | 36.7 |
| $p\text{-}NO_2C_6H_4CH=CH(p\text{-}C_2H_5O_2CC_6H_4)$ | C | $p\text{-}NO_2C_6H_4CHO$ | 165.5–166.5 | 1.9 | 63.5 |
| $p\text{-}CH_3C_6H_4CH=CH(p\text{-}C_2H_5O_2CC_6H_4)$ | C | $p\text{-}CH_3C_6H_4CHO$ | 134–135 | 0.0 | 64.8 |
| $4\text{-}CH_3OC_6H_4CH=CH(p\text{-}NO_2C_6H_4)$ | D | $p\text{-}CH_3OC_6H_4CHO$ | 130–131 | 0.0 | 15.8 |
| $1\text{-}C_{10}H_7CH=CH(1\text{-}C_{10}H_7)$ | F | $1\text{-}C_{10}H_7CHO$ | 164–165 | 6.4 | 66.7 |
| $C_6H_5(CH=CH)_2(C_2H_5O_2CC_6H_4)$ | C | $C_6H_5CH=CHCHO$ | 129.5–130.5 | 0.0 | 85.1 |
| $C_6H_5CH=CHCH_2CO_2C_2H_5$ | B | $C_6H_5CH_2CHO$ | — | 0.0 | 93.4 |
| $C_6H_5CH_2CH=CHCO_2C_2H_5$ | B | $C_6H_5CH_2CHO$ | — | 0.0 | — |
| $CH_3CH=CHCO_2C_2H_5$ | B | $CH_3CHO$ | — | 0.0 | — |
| $CH_3(CO_2C_2H_5)C=CHCO_2C_2H_5$ | B | $CH_3COCH_2CO_2C_2H_5$ | — | 16.3 | 17.9 |
| $n\text{-}C_3H_7CH=CHCO_2C_2H_5$ | B | $n\text{-}C_3H_7CHO$ | — | 0.0 | 66.5 |
| $n\text{-}C_5H_{11}(CH_3)C=CHCO_2C_2H_5$ | B | — | — | 19.0 | 40.6 |
| 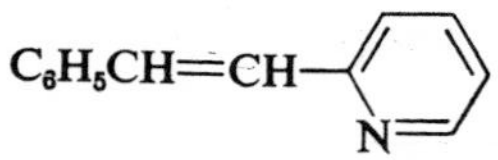 $C_6H_5CH=CH-$ (pyridin-2-yl) | A | $C_5H_5NCHO$ | 92.5–93 | 0.0 | 75.0 |

(continued)

**Table 1** (*continued*)

| Olefin | Phosphonate[a] | Carbonyl | MP (°C) | Yield, % cis | Yield, % trans |
|---|---|---|---|---|---|
|  $C_6H_5CH=CH-$ ⟨structure⟩ $-CH=CHC_6H_5$ | A | $1,4\text{-}(HCO)_2C_6H_5$ | 265–266 | — | 74.0 |
|  $(CH_3)_2N-$ ⟨structure⟩ $-CH=CH-$ ⟨structure $N(CH_3)_2$⟩ | E | $p\text{-}(CH_3)_2NC_6H_4CHO$ | 318–325 dec. | — | 77.5 |
|  $CH_3O-$ ⟨structure⟩ $-CH=CH-$ ⟨structure $OCH_3$⟩ | E | $p\text{-}CH_3OC_6H_4CHO$ | 272–275 | — | 41.0 |
| 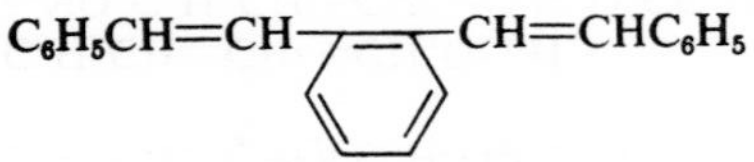 $C_6H_5CH=CH-$ ⟨structure⟩ $-CH=CHC_6H_5$ | I | $C_6H_5CHO$ | 117–119 | — | 44.6 |
| 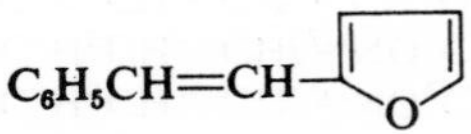 ⟨furyl⟩ $-CH=CH-$ ; $C_6H_5CH=CH-$ | G | $C_6H_5CHO$ | 49–52 | — | 73.0 |
| 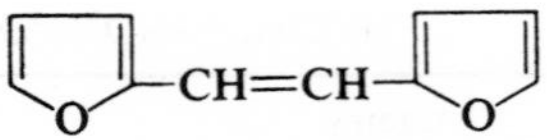 ⟨furyl⟩ $-CH=CH-$ ⟨furyl-CHO⟩ | G | 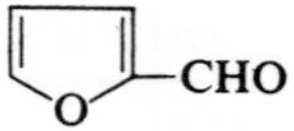 ⟨furyl⟩$CHO$ | 96–98 | — | 42.0 |
| $3,4\text{-}(CH_3O)_2C_6H_3CH=CHC_6H_5$ | A | $3,4\text{-}(CH_3O)_2C_6H_3CHO$ | 110–110.5 | — | 92.0 |
| $p\text{-}(CH_3)_2NC_6H_4CH=CHC_6H_5$ | A | $p\text{-}(CH_3)_2NC_6H_4CHO$ | 150–153 | — | 80.0 |

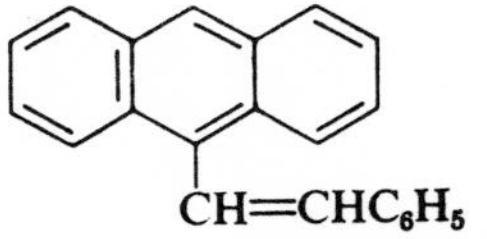

| Reactant | Product | Code | M.p. (°C) | | Yield (%) |
|---|---|---|---|---|---|
| 9-(2-phenylvinyl)anthracene (CH=CHC₆H₅) | 9-anthraldehyde (CHO) | A | 133–134.5 | — | 58.5 |
| 9,10-bis(2-phenylvinyl)anthracene (CH=CHC₆H₅, CH=CHC₆H₅) | 9,10-anthracenedicarboxaldehyde (CHO, CHO) | A | 275.5–277.5 | — | 78.5 |
| $C_6H_5CH{=}CHCH{=}CHCH{=}CHC_6H_5$ | $C_6H_5CH{=}CHCHO$ | A | 152.2–153.5 | — | 76.0 |
| $3,4\text{-}(CH_3O)_2C_6H_3CH{=}CH{-}CH{=}CHC_6H_5$ | $3,4\text{-}(CH_3O)_2C_6H_3CHO$ | H | 142–143 | — | 37.0 |
| $C_6H_5CH{=}CHC_6H_5$ | $C_6H_5CHO$ | A | 126–127 | — | 85.0 |
| $C_6H_5CH{=}CH{-}$(2-pyridyl) | (2-pyridyl)CH | A | 92.5–93 | — | 75.0 |
| $C_6H_5CH{=}CH{-}$(2-furyl) | (2-furyl)CHO | A | 54–55 | — | 84.0 |
| $C_6H_5CH{=}CH{-}$(2-furyl) | $C_6H_5CHO$ | G | 49–52 | — | 77.0 |
| $C_6H_5CH{=}CH{-}CH{=}CH{-}$(2-pyridyl) | (2-pyridyl)CHO | H | 122.5–123.5 | — | Poor |

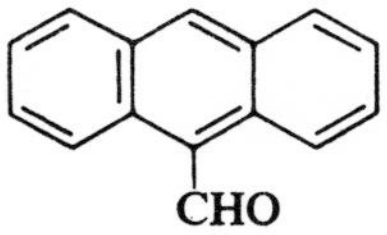

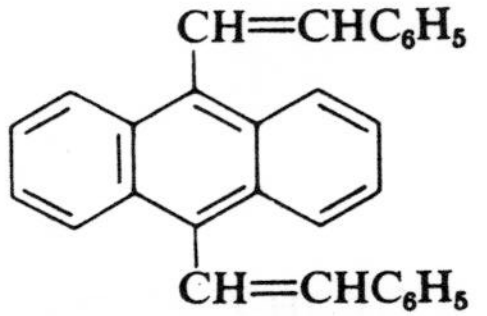

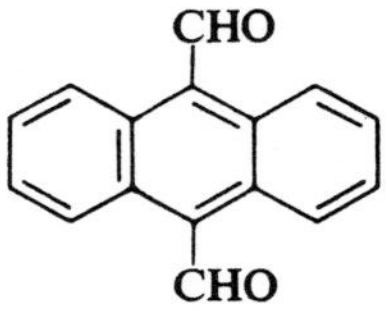

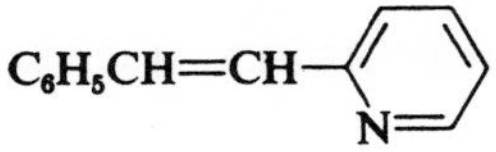

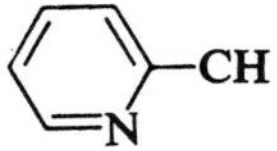

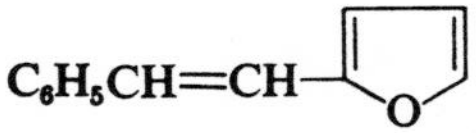

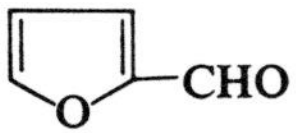

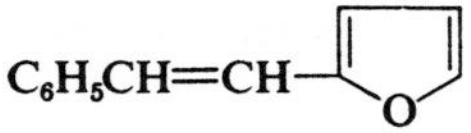

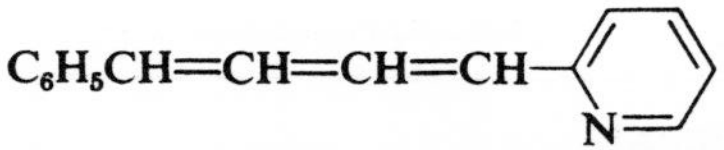

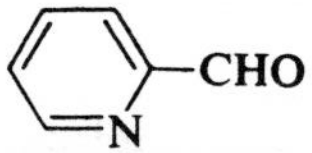

[a] A, diethyl benzylphosphonate; B, diethyl carbethoxymethylphosphonate; C, diethyl p-carbethoxybenzylphosphonate; D, diethyl p-nitrobenzylphosphonate; E, tetraethyl p-xylenediphosphonate; F, dimethyl 1-naphthylmethylphosphonate; G, diethyl 2-furylmethylphosphonate; H, diethyl styrylmethylphosphonate; I, tetraethyl o-xylenediphosphonate.

## Table 2
### Products from the Reaction of Alkylene Phosphoranes and Arynes

| Alkylene phosphorane | Aryne | Addition product | MP (°C) | Yield (%) | Ref. |
|---|---|---|---|---|---|
| $(C_6H_5)_3P{=}CHCN_3$ | $(CH_3O_2CC)_2$ | 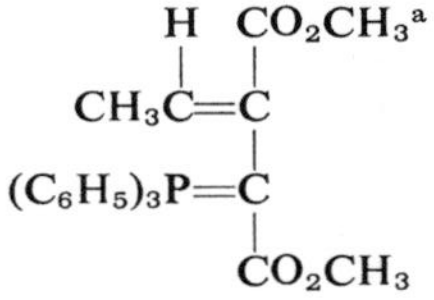 $CH_3C{=}C\begin{smallmatrix}H & CO_2CH_3{}^a\end{smallmatrix}$ ; $(C_6H_5)_3P{=}C{-}CO_2CH_3$ | 174–176 | 77 | 10 |
| $(C_6H_5)_3P{=}CH(CH_2)_2CH_3$ | $(CH_3O_2CC)_2$ | 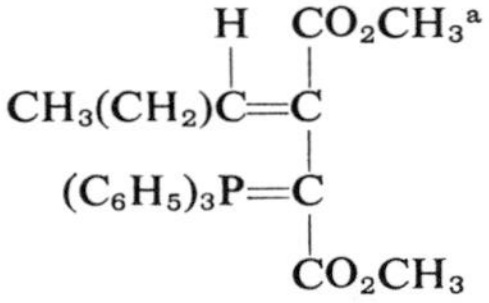 $CH_3(CH_2)C{=}C\begin{smallmatrix}H & CO_2CH_3{}^a\end{smallmatrix}$ ; $(C_6H_5)_3P{=}C{-}CO_2CH_3$ | 133–137 | 47 | 10 |
| $(C_6H_5)_3P{=}CHC_6H_5$ | $(CH_3O_2C{-}C)_2$ | 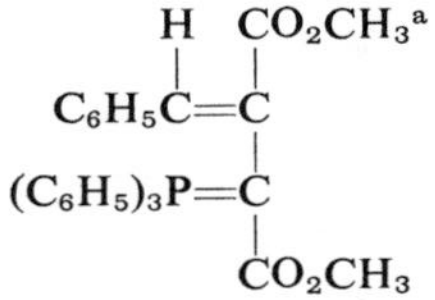 $C_6H_5C{=}C\begin{smallmatrix}H & CO_2CH_3{}^a\end{smallmatrix}$ ; $(C_6H_5)_3P{=}C{-}CO_2CH_3$ | 182–184 | 72 | 10 |
| $(C_6H_5)_3P{=}CHCH{=}CHC_6H_5$ | $(CH_3O_2C{-}C)_2$ | 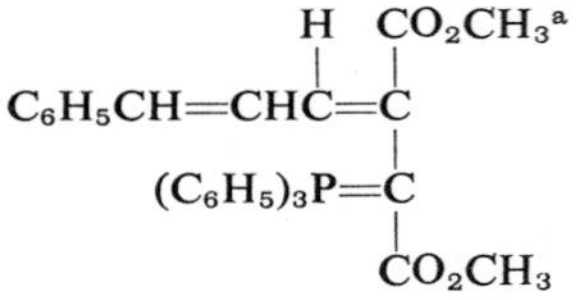 $C_6H_5CH{=}CHC{-}C\begin{smallmatrix}H & CO_2CH_3{}^a\end{smallmatrix}$ ; $(C_6H_5)_3P{=}C{-}CO_2CH_3$ | 173–178 | 48 | 10 |

| | | | | |
|---|---|---|---|---|
| $(C_6H_5)_3P=C(CH_3)-C_6H_5$ | $(CH_3O_2C-C)_2$ | $C_6H_5C-C=C-CO_2CH_3$ with $CH_3$, $CO_2CH_3{}^{[a]}$, $(C_6H_5)_3P$, $CO_2CH_3$ | 213–216 | 60 | 10 |
| $(C_6H_5)_3P=C(C_6H_5)_2$ | $(CH_3O_2C-C)_2$ | $CO_2CH_3{}^{[a]}$ $(C_6H_5)_2C=C-C=C$ $(C_6H_5)_3P$ $CO_2CH_3$ | $\overline{257}{}^{[b]}$ | — | 10 / 22 |
| $(C_6H_5)_3P=CHC_6H_5$ | $C_6H_4$ | 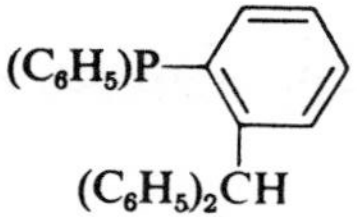 $(C_6H_5)_2P$ — $(C_6H_5)_2CH$ (benzene ring) | 158–160 | 30 | 97 |
| $(C_6H_5)_3P=CHC_3H_7\text{-}n$ | $C_6H_4$ | $(C_6H_5)_2P-C_6H_4-(o\text{-})-CH$ with $C_3H_7\text{-}n$ and $C_6H_5$ | — | 60 | 97 |
| $(C_6H_5)_3P=CHCH_3$ | $C_6H_4$ | $(C_6H_5)_2P-C_6H_4(o\text{-})-CH$ with $CH_3$ and $C_6H_5$ | — | 50 | 97 |
| $(C_6H_5)_3P=C(CH_3)_2$ | $C_6H_4$ | $(C_6H_5)_2P-C_6H_4-(o\text{-})-C(CH_3)_2$ with $C_6H_5$ | — | 70 | 97 |

(continued)

### Table 2 (continued)

| Alkylene phosphorane | Aryne | Addition product | MP (°C) | Yield (%) | Ref. |
|---|---|---|---|---|---|
| $(C_6H_5)_3P=CH_2$ | $C_6H_4$ | $(C_6H_5)_2P-C_6H_4-(o-)-CH_2C_6H_5$ | — | 1 | 97 |
| $(C_6H_5)_3P=CHC_3H_{7}-n$ | $CH_3OC_6H_3$ | 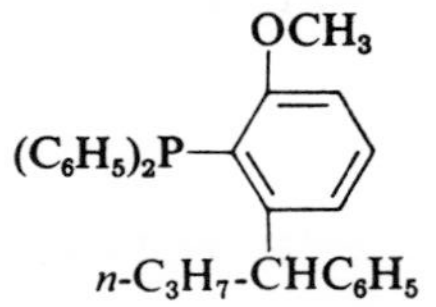 | — | 70 | 97 |
| $(p-CH_3C_6H_4)_3P=CHCH_3$ | $CH_3OC_6H_3$ | 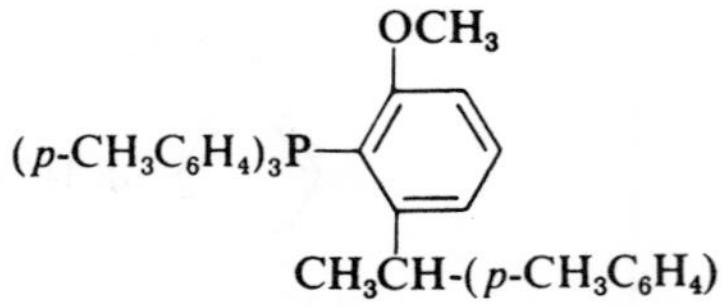 | — | 33 | 97 |
| 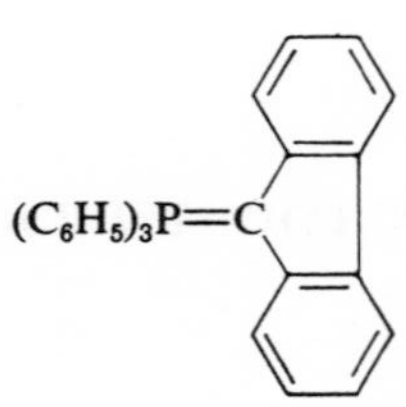 | $(CH_3O_2CC)_2$ | 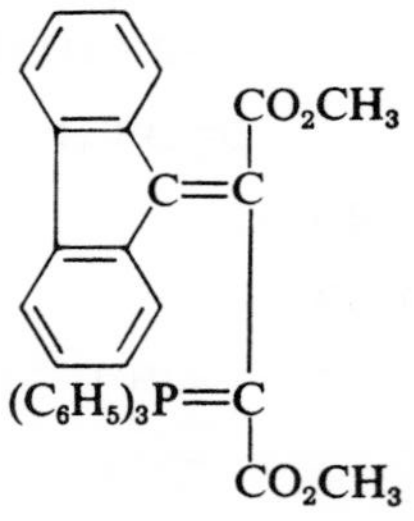 | 211° | — | 22 |

Structure 1 labels: $OCH_3$, $(C_6H_5)_2P$, $n\text{-}C_3H_7\text{-}CHC_6H_5$

Structure 2 labels: $OCH_3$, $(p\text{-}CH_3C_6H_4)_3P$, $CH_3CH\text{-}(p\text{-}CH_3C_6H_4)$

Structure 3 labels: $CO_2CH_3$, $CO_2CH_3$, $(C_6H_5)_3P=C$

Structure 4 label: $(C_6H_5)_3P$

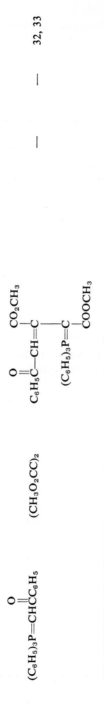

| | | | | | |
|---|---|---|---|---|---|
| $(C_6H_5)_3P{=}CHC({=}O)C_6H_5$ | $(CH_3O_2CC)_2$ |  | — | — | 32, 33 |

[a] The structures were determined by chemical analysis, infrared carbonyl band at 6.15–6.20$\mu$ characteristic for phosphine alkylene with an ester group on the carbon atom of the carbon–phosphorus double bond[11] and nuclear magnetic resonance [olefinic protons at 4.4$\tau$ in a quadruplet ($J$=3.9 cps) and methyl groups at 8.14$\tau$ and 8.25$\tau$ in two doublets ($J$=3.9 cps)].

[b] Ultraviolet absorption: $\lambda_{max}$ 365 m$\mu$ ($\varepsilon$ 3000).

[c] Ultraviolet absorption: $\lambda_{max}$ 427 m$\mu$ ($\varepsilon$ 10000).

**Table 3**

Nuclear Magnetic Resonance Parameters[50]

| | $J_{P-P'}$ (cps) | $J_{P-F}$ (cps) | $J_{P'-F}$ (cps) | $\partial F$, ppm CF$_3$COOH=O | $\partial P$, ppm, H$_3$PO$_4$=O |
|---|---|---|---|---|---|
| F$_3$C—P—P'—CF$_3'$ | 55 | 59 | 18 | −25 | +40 |
| F$_3$C—C=C—CF$_3$ | | $J_{P-F} + J_{P'-F} = 10$ | | −13 | |

**Table 4**

Gas Phase Ultraviolet Absorption Maxima A°($\varepsilon$)[50]

| C$_2$P$_2$(CF$_3$)$_4$[a] | C$_2$P$_3$(CF$_3$)$_5$[a] | H$_2$(CF$_3$P$_2$)$_2$[b] | H$_2$(CF$_3$P)$_3$[b] |
|---|---|---|---|
| 2480 (2300) | 2750 (3600) | 2040 (7400) | 2240 (5500) |
| 2150 (4500) | 2160 (9200) | | 2075 (7600) |
| 2000 (8400) | | | |

[a] Ref. 50.
[b] Ref. 51.

**Table 5**

Addition Products via the Reaction of Phosphinimines or
Phosphazines and Dimethyl acetylenedicarboxylate[21, 22]

$$(C_6H_5)_3P=N—R + CH_3CO_2CC\equiv CCO_2CH_3 \longrightarrow (C_6H_5)_3P=C\overset{\displaystyle CO_2CH_3}{\underset{\displaystyle CO_2CH_3}{|}}—C—C=N—R$$

| R | MP (°C) | Ultraviolet absorption (max, m$\mu$) | |
|---|---|---|---|
| C$_6$H$_5$ | 197–198 | 313 | 8300 |
| BrC$_6$H$_4$ | 180 | 321 | 11100 |
| p-CH$_3$O$_2$CC$_6$H$_4$ | 243 | 340 | 10500 |
| p-CH$_3$OC$_6$H$_4$ | 235 | 346 | 16600 |
| p-NO$_2$C$_6$H$_4$ | 244 | 377 | 16000 |
| H | 170 | 289 | 5000 |
| 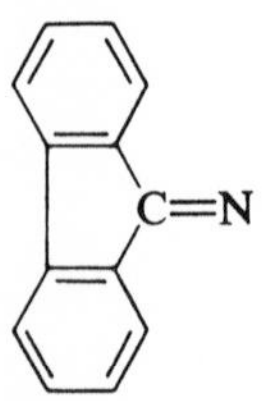 | 225 | 417 | 18000 |

## Table 6

### Carbodiimides via Reaction of Arylisocyanates and 1-Ethyl-3-methyl-3-phospholene 1-Oxide Catalyst[25,26]

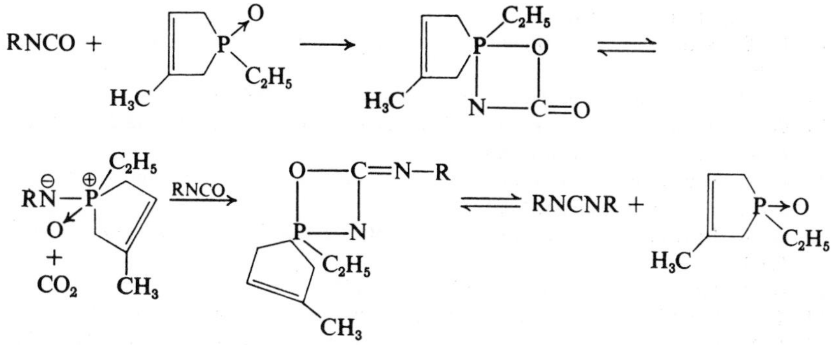

| R | Yield (%) | R | Yield (%) |
|---|---|---|---|
| $C_6H_5$ | 94 | $p\text{-}ClC_6H_4$ | 91 |
| $o\text{-}CH_3C_6H_4$ | 87 | $o\text{-}NO_2C_6H_4$ | 95 |
| $m\text{-}CH_3C_6H_4$ | 98 | $m\text{-}NO_2C_6H_4$ | 91 |
| $p\text{-}CH_3C_6H_4$ | 88 | $p\text{-}NO_2C_6H_4$ | 52 |
| $o\text{-}CH_3OC_6H_4$ | 92 | $\alpha\text{-}C_{10}H_7$ | 99 |
| $p\text{-}CH_3OC_6H_4$ | 99 | $n\text{-}C_4H_9$ | 60 |
| $m\text{-}ClC_6H_4$ | 99 | $2\text{-}C_8H_7$ | 89 |

REFERENCES

1. F. A. L. Anet, *J. Am. Chem. Soc.*, **84**, 747 (1962).
2. G. A. Berchtold and G. F. Uhlig, *J. Org. Chem.*, **28**, 1459 (1963).
3. L. D. Bergelson and M. M. Shemyakin, *Angew. Chem. Intern. Ed. Engl.*, **3**, 250 (1964).
4. L. D. Bergelson and M. M. Shemyakin, *Tetrahedron*, **19**, 149 (1963).
5. L. D. Bergelson, V. A. Vaver, L. I. Barsukov, and M. M. Shemyakin, *Dokl. Akad. Nauk SSSR*, **143**, 111 (1962); *Chem. Abstr.*, **57**, 7298 (1962).
6. L. D. Bergelson, V. A. Vaver, V. Yu. Kovtun, L. B. Senyavina, and M. M. Shemyakin, *Zh. Obshch. Khim.*, **32**, 1802 (1962); *Chem. Abstr.*, **58**, 4415 (1963).
7. L. D. Bergelson, V. A. Vaver, and M. M. Shemyakin, *Izv. Akad. Nauk SSSR, Otd. Khim. Nauk*, **1960**, 1900; *Chem. Abstr.*, **55**, 14294 (1961).
8. L. D. Bergelson V. A. Vaver, and M. M. Shemyakin, *Izv. Akad. Nauk SSSR, Otd. Khim. Nauk*, **1961**, 729; *Chem. Abstr.*, **55**, 22196 (1961).
9. H. J. Bestmann and O. Kratzer, *Chem. Ber.*, **95**, 1894 (1962).
10. H. J. Bestmann and O. Rothe, *Angew. Chem. Int. Ed. Engl.*, **3**, 512 (1964).
11. H. J. Bestmann and H. Schulz, *Chem. Ber.*, **95**, 2921 (1962).
12. A. Bladé-Font, W. McEwen, and C. A. VanderWerf, *J. Am. Chem. Soc.*, **82**, 2646 (1960).
13. A. Bladé-Font, C. A. VanderWerf, and W. McEwen, *J. Am. Chem. Soc.*, **82**, 2396 (1960).

14. H. Bode, K. Bütow, and G. Lienau, *Chem. Ber.*, **81**, 547 (1948).
15. F. Bohlmann, E. Inhoffen, and P. Herbst, *Chem. Ber.*, **90**, 1661 (1957).
16. A. A. Bothner-By and C. Naar-Colin, *J. Am. Chem. Soc.*, **84**, 743 (1962).
17. K. C. Brannock, R. D. Burpitt, V. W. Goodlett, and J. G. Thweatt, *J. Org. Chem.*, **28**, 1464 (1963).
18. K. C. Brannock, R. D. Burpitt, and J. G. Thweatt, *J. Org. Chem.*, **28**, 1462 (1963).
19. D. M. Brown and P. R. Hammond, *J. Chem. Soc.*, **1960**, 4229.
20. G. W. Brown, R. C. Cookson, I. D. R. Stevens, T. C. W. Mak, and J. Trotter, *Proc. Chem. Soc. London*, **1964**, 84.
21. G. W. Brown, R. C. Cookson, I. D. R. Stevens, T. C. W. Mak, and J. Trotter, *Proc. Chem. Soc. London*, **1964**, 86.
22. G. W. Brown, R. C. Cookson, and I. D. R. Stevens, *Tetrahedron Letters*, **1964**, 1263.
23. A. B. Burg, *J. Am. Chem. Soc.*, **83**, 2226 (1961).
24. T. W. Campbell and J. J. Monagle, *J. Am. Chem. Soc.*, **84**, 1493 (1962).
25. T. W. Campbell, J. J. Monagle, and V. S. Foldi, *J. Am. Chem. Soc.*, **84**, 3673 (1962).
26. T. W. Campbell, J. J. Monagle, and H. F. McShane, *J. Am. Chem. Soc.*, **84**, 4288 (1962).
27. J. Chatt, F. A. Hart, and H. C. Fielding, U.S. Pat. 2,922,819 (1960).
28. N. S. Corby, G. W. Kenner, and A. R. Todd, *J. Chem. Soc.*, **1952**, 3669.
29. S. J. Rhoads, in *Molecular Rearrangements*, Part 1, P. de Mayo, Ed., Interscience, New York, 1963, p. 656.
30. P. Duffner, Doctoral Dissertation, Universität Tübingen, 1957.
31. H. Goetz, F. Nerdel, and H. Michaelis, *Naturwissenschaften*, **50**, 496 (1963).
32. J. B. Hendrickson, R. Rees, C. Hall, and J. F. Templeton, *J. Org. Chem.*, **30**, 3312 (1965).
33. J. B. Hendrickson, R. Rees, and J. F. Templeton, *J. Am. Chem. Soc.*, **86**, 107 (1964).
34. L. Horner, H. Hoffmann, W. Klink, H. Ertel, and V. Toscano, *Chem. Ber.*, **95**, 581 (1962).
35. L. Horner, H. Hoffmann, H. Whippel, and G. Klabre, *Chem. Ber.*, **92**, 2499 (1959).
36. C. F. Huebner and E. Donoghue, *J. Org. Chem.*, **28**, 1732 (1963).
37. C. F. Huebner, L. Dorfman, M. M. Robinson, E. Donoghue, W. G. Pierson, and P. Strachan, *J. Org. Chem.*, **28**, 3134 (1963).
38. R. Huisgen and J. Sauer, *Angew. Chem.*, **72**, 91 (1961).
39. H. H. Inhoffen, K. Brückner, G. F. Domagk, and H.-M. Erdmann, *Chem. Ber.* **88**, 1415 (1955).
40. A. Wm. Johnson, *J. Org. Chem.*, **24**, 282 (1959).
41. A. Wm. Johnson and R. B. La Count, *Chem. Ind. (London)*, **1959**, 52.
42. A. Wm. Johnson and R. B. La Count, *Tetrahedron*, **9**, 130 (1960).
43. G. W. Kenner, A. R. Todd, and F. J. Weymouth, *J. Chem. Soc.*, **1952**, 3675.
44. R. Ketcham, D. Jambotkar, and L. Martinelli, *J. Org. Chem.*, **27**, 4666 (1962).
45. Kostka, *Wiadomosci Chemi*, **12**, 521 (1958).
46. M. E. Kuehne, *J. Am. Chem. Soc.*, **84**, 837 (1962).
47. J. Levisalles, *Bull. Soc. Chim. France*, **1958**, 1021.
48. G. Lüscher, Doctoral Dissertation, Eidg. Hochschule, Zürich, 1922.

49. A. Maercker, "The Wittig Reaction," in *Organic Reactions*, Vol. 14, A. Cope, Ed.-in-Chief, Wiley, New York, 1965, p. 270.
50. W. Mahler, *J. Am. Chem. Soc.*, **86**, 2306 (1964).
51. W. Mahler and A. B. Burg, *J. Am. Chem. Soc.*, **80**, 6161 (1958).
52. J. Meyer, *Chem. Ber.*, **89**, 842 (1956).
53. J. Meyer, *Helv. Chim. Acta*, **40**, 1052 (1957).
54. O. Mitsunobu and T. Mukaiyama, *J. Org. Chem.*, **29**, 3005 (1964).
55. J. J. Monagle, *J. Org. Chem.*, **27**, 3851 (1962).
56. L. A. McGrew, W. Sweeny, T. W. Campbell, and V. S. Foldi, *J. Org. Chem.*, **29**, 3002 (1964).
57. N. L. Paddock, *Quart. Rev.* (*London*), **18**, 168 (1964).
58. S. Pati and A. Schwartz, *J. Org. Chem.*, **25**, 1232 (1960).
59. B. Pelc, *Chem. Listy*, **53**, 177 (1959); *Chem. Abstr.*, **53**, 7965 (1959).
60. H. Pommer, *Angew. Chem.*, **72**, 911 (1960).
61. D. Samuel and D. B. Silver, *J. Org. Chem.*, **28**, 2089 (1963).
62. U. Schöllkopf, *Angew. Chem.*, **71**, 260 (1959).
63. U. Schöllkopf, Doctoral Dissertation, Universität Tübingen, 1956.
64. A. Schönberg and K.-H. Brosowski, *Chem. Ber.*, **92**, 2606 (1959).
65. M. M. Shemyakin, L. D. Bergelson, and V. A. Vaver, *Chem. Eng. News*, **40**, 36 (1962).
66. H. E. Simmons, *J. Am. Chem. Soc.*, **83**, 1657 (1961).
67. A. J. Speziale and D. E. Bissing, *J. Am. Chem. Soc.*, **85**, 1888 (1963).
68. A. J. Speziale and D. E. Bissing, *J. Am. Chem. Soc.*, **85**, 3878 (1963).
69. A. J. Speziale and K. W. Ratts, *J. Am. Chem. Soc.*, **85**, 2790 (1963).
70. A. J. Speziale and K. W. Ratts, *J. Org. Chem.*, **28**, 465 (1963).
71. H. Staudinger, *Chem. Ber.*, **41**, 1355 (1908).
72. H. Staudinger, *Chem. Ber.*, **44**, 525 (1911).
73. H. Staudinger and W. Braunholtz, *Helv. Chim. Acta*, **4**, 897 (1921).
74. H. Staudinger and E. Hauser, *Helv. Chim. Acta*, **4**, 861 (1921).
75. H. Staudinger and J. Meyer, *Chem. Ber.*, **53**, 72 (1920).
76. H. Staudinger and J. Meyer, *Helv. Chim. Acta*, **2**, 635 (1919).
77. H. Staudinger, G. Rathsam, and F. Kjelsberg, *Helv. Chim. Acta*, **3**, 853 (1920).
78. A. R. Todd, *Proc. Chem. Soc.* (*London*), **1962**, 199.
79. S. Trippet, "The Wittig Reaction," in *Advances in Organic Chemistry*, Vol. 1, R. Adams, Ed.-in-Chief, Wiley, New York, 1960, p. 83.
80. S. Trippet, *Quart. Rev.* (*London*), **17**, 406 (1963).
81. S. Trippet and D. M. Walker, *Chem. Ind.* (*London*), **1960**, 933.
82. S. Trippet and D. M. Walker, *J. Chem. Soc.*, **1961**, 1266.
83. W. E. Truce and W. J. Ray, Jr., *J. Am. Chem. Soc.*, **81**, 481 (1959).
84. E. Truscheit and K. Eiter, *Ann. Chem.*, **658**, 65 (1962).
85. W. S. Wadsworth and W. D. Emmons, *J. Am. Chem. Soc.*, **83**, 1732 (1960).
86. D. H. Wadsworth, O. E. Schupp, III, E. J. Seus, and J. A. Ford, Jr., *J. Org. Chem.*, **30**, 680 (1965).
87. P. C. Wailes, *Chem. Ind.* (*London*), **1958**, 1086.
88. G. Wittig, *Angew. Chem.*, **68**, 505 (1956).
89. G. Wittig, *Experientia*, **12**, 41 (1956).
90. G. Wittig, *Festschr. Arthur Stoll*, **1957**, 48; *Chem. Abstr.*, **52**, 15414 (1958).
91. G. Wittig and G. Geissler, *Ann. Chem.*, **580**, 44 (1953).
92. G. Wittig and W. Haag, *Chem. Ber.*, **88**, 1654 (1955).
92a. G. Wittig and M. Rieber, *Ann. Chem.*, **567**, 187 (1949).

93. G. Wittig and U. Schöllkopf, *Chem. Ber.*, **87**, 1318 (1954).

94. G. Wittig, U. Schöllkopf, and H. Pommer, Ger. Pat. 1,048,568 (1961).

95. G. Wittig, H.-D. Weigmann, and M. Schlosser, *Chem. Ber.*, **94**, 676 (1961).

96. L. A. Yanoaskaya, *Usp. Khim.*, **30**, 813 (1961); *Chem. Abstr.*, **56**, 1323 (1962).

97. E. Zbiral, *Montash. Chem.*, **95**, 1759 (1964).

98. E. Zbiral, *Tetrahedron Letters*, **1964**, 1649.

99. E. Zbiral, *Tetrahedron Letters*, **1964**, 3963.

100. E. Zbiral, Second Communication given at the IUPAC Symposium of Organophosphorus Compounds, Heidelberg, Germany, May 20, 1964.

### 3. "Quasi-" Wittig Reactions

This section deals with a series of miscellaneous reactions that form four-membered heterocyclic intermediates via the cycloaddition of the reactants. For instance, Schönberg and Brosowski[8] reported the cycloaddition of nitrosobenzene (1) to aromatic thioketones, such as $p,p'$-dimethoxythiobenzophenone (2), resulting in the formation of the heterocyclic intermediate (3) which readily decomposed into the imine (4) sulfur dioxide, and sulfur.

$$(p\text{-}CH_3OC_6H_4)_2C{=}S + C_6H_5NO \longrightarrow$$

$$\begin{array}{cc} (p\text{-}CH_3OC_6H_4)_2C\!\!-\!\!\!-\!\!\!-\!\!S \\ | \qquad\qquad | \\ C_6H_5N\!\!-\!\!\!-\!\!\!-\!\!O \end{array} \longrightarrow$$

(2)                    (1)                    (3)

$$(p\text{-}CH_3OC_6H_4)_2C{=}NC_6H_5 + \tfrac{1}{2}SO_2 + \tfrac{1}{2}S$$

(7)

Kresze and Albrecht[2,4] reported that the reactions of $N$-sulfinyl compounds (5) with carbonyl compounds (6) were transformations analogous to a Wittig reaction (Section III-C-2) in which the carbonyl oxygen is replaced by the group R—N= or R—SO₂N= with elimination of sulfur dioxide (Table 1). For the preparation of sulfonyl derivatives, this reaction, in contrast to the direct condensation of sulfonamides and carbonyl compounds,[6,7,12] affords higher yields and fewer side reactions. Kresze and co-workers[1,5] reported the analogous reactions of $N$-sulfinyl-$p$-toluene-

$$R\text{—}N{=}SO + O{=}CH\text{—}R' \longrightarrow \begin{bmatrix} R\text{—}N\!\!-\!\!\!-\!\!SO \\ | \qquad | \\ R'\text{—}CH\!\!-\!\!\!-\!\!O \end{bmatrix} \longrightarrow$$

(5)          (6)

$$R\text{—}N{=}CH\text{—}R' + SO_2$$

sulfonamide (7) with α-diketones (8), which result in the formation of the corresponding imine (10) via decomposition of the four-membered heterocyclic intermediate (9) (Table 2). Diacetyl (8, R = R' = CH₃) reacted readily with the amide (7) yielding the imine (10, R = R' = CH₃),

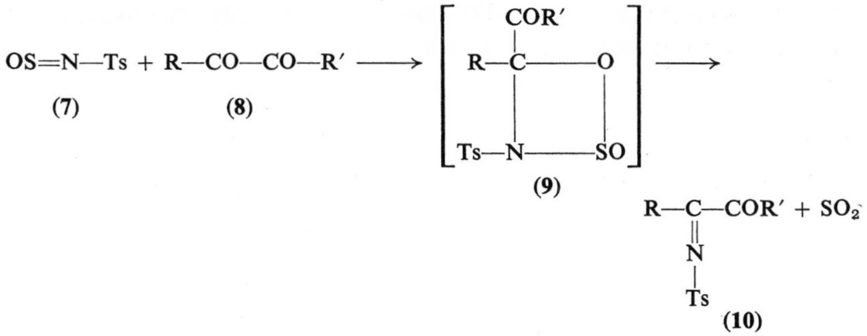

$$OS{=}N{-}Ts + R{-}CO{-}CO{-}R' \longrightarrow \begin{bmatrix} & COR' & \\ & | & \\ R{-}C & \quad\quad O \\ & | & | \\ Ts{-}N & \quad\quad SO \end{bmatrix} \longrightarrow$$

(7)            (8)                                    (9)

$$R{-}C{-}COR' + SO_2$$
$$\overset{\|}{N}$$
$$\overset{|}{Ts}$$
(10)

which was identified by infrared [$\lambda$(NH) at 3190 cm$^{-1}$; $\lambda$(CO) at 1695 cm$^{-1}$; $\lambda$(C=C) at 1630 cm$^{-1}$] and nuclear magnetic resonance [only 6H = 2 methyl groups with $\delta$ = 2.2 ppm; a AB-system for the vinyl group at 5.4 and 6.1 ppm)] analysis.

Senning[10,11] described the preparation of N-sulfonylazomethines, N-sulfonylguanidines, and N-sulfonylamidines from N-sulfinylsulfonyl-amides and azomethine thiourea derivatives and thioamides, respectively (Table 3). The name quasi-Wittig reaction was proposed for these reactions. The reaction sequence postulated for the reaction of benzalazine (11) and N-sulfinylbenzenesulfonamide (12)[11] forming the N-benzalbenzol-sulfonamide (13) and the unstable sulfinyl hydrazine (14)[3] was verified by the reaction of N-sulfinylbenzenesulfonamide (12) and the azomethine

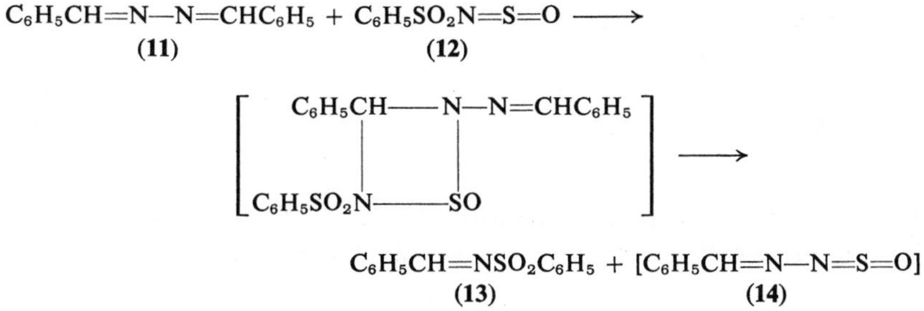

$$C_6H_5CH{=}N{-}N{=}CHC_6H_5 + C_6H_5SO_2N{=}S{=}O \longrightarrow$$
(11)                              (12)

$$\begin{bmatrix} C_6H_5CH & \quad N{-}N{=}CHC_6H_5 \\ | & | \\ C_6H_5SO_2N & \quad SO \end{bmatrix} \longrightarrow$$

$$C_6H_5CH{=}NSO_2C_6H_5 + [C_6H_5CH{=}N{-}N{=}S{=}O]$$
(13)                              (14)

(N-benzalaniline) (15), for which the following sequence was formulated[10]:

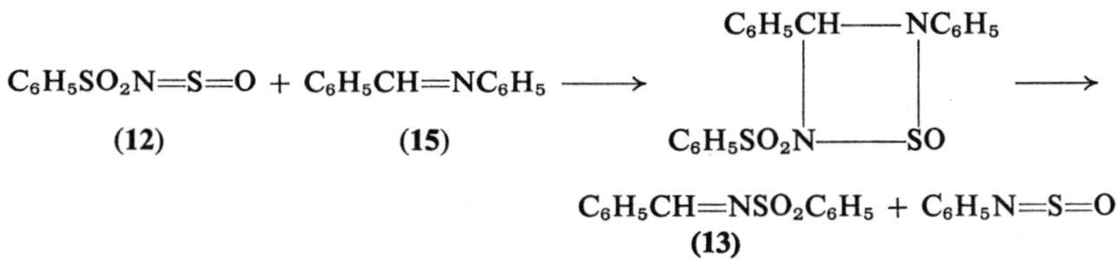

$$C_6H_5SO_2N{=}S{=}O + C_6H_5CH{=}NC_6H_5 \longrightarrow \begin{matrix} C_6H_5CH & \quad NC_6H_5 \\ | & | \\ C_6H_5SO_2N & \quad SO \end{matrix} \longrightarrow$$

(12)                    (15)

$$C_6H_5CH{=}NSO_2C_6H_5 + C_6H_5N{=}S{=}O$$
(13)

With thiourea derivatives and thioamides (16) the reaction proceeded with cleavage of disulfur monoxide (17), which spontaneously decomposed into sulfur dioxide and sulfur, as is shown below.

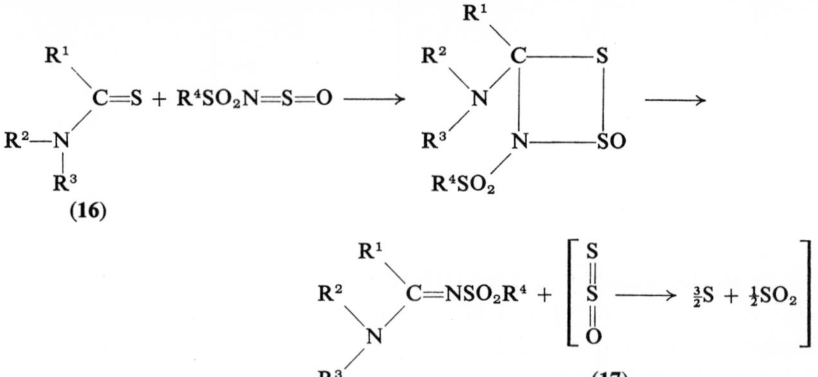

$$
\begin{array}{c}
R^1 \\
\diagdown \\
C{=}S + R^4SO_2N{=}S{=}O \longrightarrow \\
\diagup \\
R^2{-}N \\
| \\
R^3 \\
(16)
\end{array}
\qquad
\begin{array}{c}
R^1 \\
R^2 \quad C{-\!-\!-}S \\
\diagdown\diagup \quad | \qquad | \\
N \qquad | \qquad | \longrightarrow \\
\diagup \quad | \qquad | \\
R^3 \quad N{-\!-\!-}SO \\
R^4SO_2
\end{array}
$$

$$
\begin{array}{c}
R^1 \\
\diagdown \\
R^2 \qquad C{=}NSO_2R^4 + \left[\begin{array}{c} S \\ \| \\ S \\ \| \\ O \end{array}\right] \longrightarrow \tfrac{3}{2}S + \tfrac{1}{2}SO_2 \\
\diagdown \\
N \\
\diagup \\
R^3 \qquad\qquad\qquad\qquad (17)
\end{array}
$$

In conclusion, sulfoxides (18), like aldehydes and formamides, react with N-sulfinylsulfonamides (19) via a "Wittig" reaction forming N-sulfonyl-sulfidimines (20) with evolution of sulfur dioxide[9] (Table 4). The reaction takes place readily with aliphatic sulfoxides at room temperature in inert

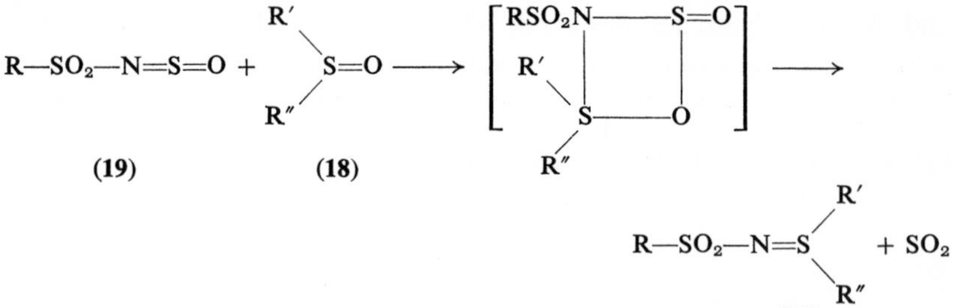

$$
\begin{array}{c}
R' \\
\diagdown \\
R{-}SO_2{-}N{=}S{=}O + \qquad S{=}O \longrightarrow \left[\begin{array}{c} RSO_2N{-\!-\!-}S{=}O \\ | \qquad\qquad | \\ R' \qquad\qquad | \\ \diagdown \qquad | \\ S{-\!-\!-}O \\ \diagup \\ R'' \end{array}\right] \longrightarrow \\
\diagup \\
R'' \\
(19) \qquad\qquad (18)
\end{array}
$$

$$
\begin{array}{c}
R' \\
\diagup \\
R{-}SO_2{-}N{=}S \qquad + SO_2 \\
\diagdown \\
R'' \\
(20)
\end{array}
$$

solvents such as benzene, while aromatic sulfoxides must be heated at 80°C for several hours in benzene or at 100°C without solvents.

## Table 1
### Reactions Leading to Azomethines and Amidines[4,5]

$$R-N{=}S{=}O + O{=}CH-R' \longrightarrow R-N{=}CH{=}R' + SO_2$$

| R | R' | MP (°C) | Yield (%) |
|---|----|---------|-----------|
| $C_6H_5$ | $C_6H_5$ | 48 | 70 |
| $C_6H_5$ | $CCl_3$ | 4 (bp 136–39/10 mm) | 40 |
| $C_7H_7SO_2$ | $C_6H_5$ | 107 | 71 |
| $C_7H_7SO_2$ | $p$-$NO_2C_6H_4$ | 206–207 | 78 |
| $C_7H_7SO_2$ | $CCl_3$ | 105–111 | 80 |
| $C_7H_7SO_2$ | H | 166 | — |
| $C_7H_7SO_2$ | 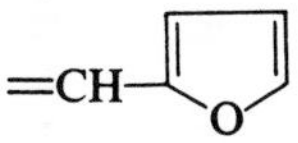 $={}CH-$ <br> (furan) | 100–102 | 85 |
| $C_7H_7SO_2$ | 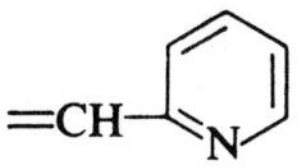 $={}CH-$ <br> (pyridine) | 121–122 | 92 |
| $C_7H_7SO_2$ | $N(CH_3)_2$ | 135–137 | 96 |
| $C_7H_7SO_2$ | $N(CH_3)C_6H_5$ | 101 | 20 |
| $C_6H_5SO_2$ | $N(CH_3)_2$ | 129–130 | 97 |
| $p$-$ClC_6H_4SO_2$ | $C_6H_5$ | 110 | 37 |

## Table 2
### Reactions of *N*-Sulfinyl-*p*-toluenesulfonamide with Diketones[5]

$$R-CO-CO-R' + O{=}S{=}NSO_2C_6H_4CH_3\text{-}p \longrightarrow$$

$$\underset{p\text{-}CH_3C_6H_4SO_2N}{R-\overset{\|}{C}-CO-R'} + SO_2$$

| R | R' | MP (°C) | Yield (%) |
|---|----|---------|-----------|
| $C_6H_5$ | $C_6H_5$ | 132 | 68 |
| $p$-$ClC_6H_4$ | $C_6H_5$ | 167.5 | 55 |
| $p$-$ClC_6H_4$ | $p$-$ClC_6H_4$ | 173.5 | 65 |
| $p$-$CH_3C_6H_4$ | $p$-$CH_3C_6H_4$ | 164.5 | 75 |
| $CH_3$ | $CH_3$ | — | — |

**Table 3**

"Quasi-Wittig" Reaction of *N*-Sulfinyl Compounds[10,11]

| Double-bond systems | *N*-Sulfinyl compound | Product | Yield | MP |
|---|---|---|---|---|
| $C_6H_5CH=NC_6H_5$ | $C_6H_5SO_2N=S=O$ | $C_6H_5CH=NSO_2C_6H_5$ | 49 | 83.5–85.5[a] |
| $[(CH_3)_2N]_2C=S$ | $4\text{-}CH_3C_6H_4SO_2N=S=O$ | $4\text{-}CH_3C_6H_4SO_2N=C[N(CH_3)_2]_2$ | 65 | 143–145 |
| $CH_3(C_6H_5)N-\overset{\overset{\displaystyle S}{\|}}{C}-NHC_6H_5$ | $4\text{-}CH_3C_6H_4SO_2N=S=O$ | $4\text{-}CH_3C_6H_4SO_2N=C(NHC_6H_5)N(C_6H_5)CH_3$ | 15 | 119–120.5 |
| $C_6H_5NH-\overset{\overset{\displaystyle O}{\|}}{C}-NHCCH_3$ | $4\text{-}CH_3C_6H_4SO_2N=S=O$ | $4\text{-}CH_3C_6H_4SO_2N=C(NHC_6H_5)NHCCH_3$ $\overset{\displaystyle O}{\|}$ | 10 | 160–161.5 |
| $(CSNHCH_3)_2$ | $4\text{-}CH_3C_6H_4SO_2N=S=O$ | $[C(=NC_6H_4CH_3\text{-}4)-NHCH_3]_2$ | 20 | 268.5–271 |

[a] Literature[6] mp 80–82°.

## Table 4

Sulfidimines via the Reaction of *N*-Sulfinylsulfonamides with Sulfoxides[9]

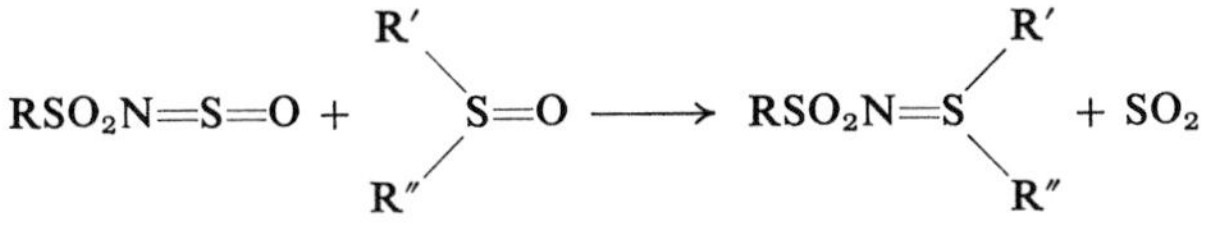

$$RSO_2N=S=O + \underset{R''}{\overset{R'}{\diagdown}} S=O \longrightarrow RSO_2N=S\underset{R''}{\overset{R'}{\diagup}} + SO_2$$

| R | R' | R'' | MP (°C) | Yield (%) |
|---|---|---|---|---|
| $CH_3$ | $CH_3$ | $CH_3$ | 122–123 | 61 |
| $p\text{-}CH_3C_6H_4$ | $CH_3$ | $CH_3$ | 158–159 | 82 |
| $p\text{-}CH_3C_6H_4$ | $C_2H_5$ | $C_2H_5$ | 144–145 | 83 |
| $CH_3$ | —$(CH_2)_4$— | | 101 | 50 |
| $p\text{-}CH_3C_6H_4$ | —$(CH_2)_4$— | | 135–136 | 58 |
| $CH_3$ | $CH_3$ | $CH_3$ | 124–126 | 46 |
| $CH_3$ | $C_6H_5$ | $C_6H_5$ | 91.5–92 | 38 |

REFERENCES

1. R. Albrecht and G. Kresze, *Chem. Ber.*, **98**, 1205 (1965).
2. R. Albrecht, G. Kresze, and B. Mlakar, *Chem. Ber.*, **97**, 483 (1964).
3. D. Klamann, U. Kramer, and P. Weyerstahl, *Chem. Ber.*, **85**, 2694 (1962).
4. G. Kresze and R. Albrecht, *Angew. Chem.*, **74**, 781 (1962); *Angew. Chem. Intern. Ed. Engl.*, **1**, 595 (1962).
5. G. Kresze, D. Somerfeld, and R. Albrecht, *Chem. Ber.*, **98**, 601 (1965).
6. A. J. Kretov and J. A. Abrashanova, *Zh. Obshch. Khim.*, **27**, 1993 (1957); *Chem. Abstr.*, **58**, 5327 (1958).
7. J. Lichtenberger, J. P. Fleury, and B. Barette, *Bull. Soc. Chim. France*, **1955**, 669.
8. A. Schönberg and K.-H. Brosowski, *Chem. Ber.*, **92**, 2606 (1959).
9. G. Schulz and G. Kresze, *Angew. Chem.*, **75**, 1022 (1963); *Angew. Chem. Intern. Ed. Engl.*, **2**, 736 (1963).
10. A. Senning, *Acta Chem. Scand.*, **18**, 1958 (1964).
11. A. Senning, *Rec. Trav. Chim.*, **82**, 790 (1963).
12. G. Tosolini, *Chem. Ber.*, **94**, 2731 (1961).

# AUTHOR INDEX

Numbers in parenthese are reference numbers and indicate that the author's work is referred to although his name is not mentioned in the text. Numbers in *italics* show the pages on which the complete references are listed.

## A

Abendroth, H. J., 88(2,3), 89, 94(2), *101*

Abraham, D. J., 208(52), 210(52), 212(52), 224(52), *240*

Abramovitch, R. A., 1(3,15), *3,* 6(1), 8(1), 14(1), 16(2), 20(1,3), 26(1,4), *38,* 97(4), *101,* 105(1), 106(1), *107*

Abrashanova, J. A., 332(6), *337*

Abshire, C. J., 103(25), *107*

Acheson, R. M., 5(5), *38*

Achmatowicz, O., 114(2), 119(1,2,4), 120(1,5), 128(3), 129(3), *136,* 146, 147(1), 150(1), *166*

Achmatowicz, O., Jr., 119(1), 120(1), *136*

Adolph, H., 208(34), 210(34), 215(34), 227(34), *239*

Ahlström, L., 165(33), *166*

Ahmad, Y., 1(3), *3*

Alazzi-Mancini, M., 260, *274*

Albrecht, R., 287(9), 288(9), 290(9), *290,* 332, 335(4,5), *337*

Alder, K., 12(12), 16(6–11,13), *38*

Alessandri, L., 258, 260, *274*

Allen, P. W., 121(6), *136*

Anastassiou, A. G., 30(14), 31(176), *38, 42*

Anbar, M., 97(5,72), *101, 103,* 105(32), *107*

Anderson, H. M., 78(3), *84*

Anderson, M. M., 121(30), *137*

Anderson, W. A., 147(2), *166*

Andraschek, H. J., 45(26), *49*

Andreads, S., 263, 264(2), 269(4), 270(3), 271(4), *274*

Andrews, L. J., 170(1,6), *173*

Anet, F. A. L., 313(1), *329*

Angeli, A., 260, *274*

Anglin, J. H., Jr., 32(57), *39*

Anselme, J.-P., 97(40), 101(39), *102*

Appel, R., 17(129), *41*

Appel, Z. B. R., 97(6), *101,* 104(2), 106(2), *107*

ApSimon, J. W., 14(15,16), 16, *38*

Archer, S., 276(31), *286*

Arens, J. F., 115(90), *139,* 187, 188(61), 199(61), *200, 201*

Arnold, D. R., 115, 116, 117(7), 120–124(7), 129(7), *136*

Ashley, J. N., 26(17), *38*

Atkins, B., 264(6), *274*

Atkinson, J. G., 121(8), 124(8), *136*

Atwell, W. H., 46(6), 48, 52(17), *53*

Audrieth, L. F., 97(7–10), *101, 102,* 103, 104, *107*

Augestad-Jenson, H., 22(214), *43*

Ault, A., 181(60), *200,* 242(9), *246*

Ayer, D. E., 121(8), 124(8), *136*

## B

Bachman, W. E., 136(9), *137*

Backer, H. J., 80(35,36), *85,* 210(1,24–26), *239*

Badger, G. M., 60(1), *84*

Bäckström, H. L., 115(10), *137*

Baeyer, A., 139(3–5), *166*

Bafford, R. A., 32(70), *40*

Bailey, P. S., 103(25), *107*

Bailey, R. E., 45(25), 49, 51, *53*

Baker, B. R., 33(197), *43*

Balhorn, H., 140(106), *168*

Ballard, S. A., 203(1), *205*

Bangert, K. F., 21(18), *38*

Barakat, M. Z., 74(59), 78(59), *86*

Barette, B., 332(7), *337*

Barker, N. G., 32(57), *39*
Barnett, B., 149(6), 154(6), *166*
Barr, D. A., 260(7), 261, 262(7–9,11a), 263(8,9,11), 264(9), 269(7,9,10), 270(8,11), 271(11), *274*
Barrow, G. M., 121(11), *137*, 146(81), 147(81), *167*
Barsukov, L. I., 307(5), *329*
Bartlett, P. D., 32(19–21), 33(20), *39*, 120, 134(82), *138*, 147(7), 152(69), *166, 167*
Barton, D. H. R., 1(4), *3*, 14(22), *39*
Basselier, J. J., 188(49), *200*
Battiste, M., 50(3), *53*
Bauer, A., 32(32), *39*
Baumgarten, H. E., 33(23), 37, *39*
Bayerlein, F., 17(131), *41*
Beckett, A., 115(12), *137*
Beckmann, E., 303(1), *304*
Bederke, K., 287(9), 288(9), 290(9), *290*
Beecken, H., 287, 288, 290(1), *290*
Beereboom, J. J., 120, 129(13), *137*
Belew, J. S., 103(7), *107*
Bellamy, L. J., 79(2), *84*
Bellasio, E., 188(64), *201*, 288(2,11–13), *290*
Belniak, K., 119(1), 120(1), *136*
Bender, H. S., 32(108), *41*
Berchtold, G. A., 314(2), *329*
Bereza, S., 139(92), 140(92), 142(92), 147(92), 163(92), *168*
Bergelson, L. D., 307(3–8,65), *329, 331*
Bergmann, E. D., 147(8), 148(9), 160(9), 162(9), *166*
Bergmann, M., 32(96), 33(96), *40*
Bergreen, H., 295(1), *300*
Berry, R. S., 17, 19, *39*
Berson, J. A., 175(1), *199*, 216(2), *239*
Bertho, A., 25, 26, *39, 40*
Bertin, H. J., Jr., 264(49), *275*
Bestian, H., 5(29,30), 32(31,32), *39*
Bestmann, H. J., 174(128), 178(128), *202*, 250(30), *257*, 306(9), 307(9), 310(10), 324(10), 325(10), *329*
Biazhetti, G., 28(91), *40*
Bickel, A. F., 6(219), *44*
Binder, O., 246(26), *257*
Birchall, J. M., 263(12), 271(12), *274*

Bird, C. W., 247, 250, 254(1,2), *256*
Bissell, E. R., 119(14), 133(14), *137*
Bissing, D. E., 306(67,68), *331*
Bjork, C. W., 100(11), *102*
Blacet, F. E., 44(8), 48(8), *48*
Bladé-Font, A., 307(12,13), *329*
Blank, R., 174(2), *199*
Blaschke, H., 14(130), 31(130), *41*
Blomstrom, D. C., 297(32–35), *301*
Bloom, A. L., 263(12), 271(12), *274*
Bock, H., 31(32a), *39*
Bockhorn, G. H., 20(149), *42*
Bode, H., 317(14), *330*
Boekelheide, V., 21(18), *38*, 136(60), *138*
Boerema, J. S., 210(25), *239*
Boese, A. K., 142(10), 148(11,12), 155(11), 157(11), 158(11,12), 159(12), 160(12), 163(11,12), *166*, 182(3,4,8), 188(5–7,78,79), *199, 201*
Bohlmann, F., 307(15), *330*
Bonati, A., 171(3,16), *173*
Bonnet, R., 103(8), *107*
Booker, A. C., 32(109), *41*
Bordwell, F. G., 78(3,4,46,47), 81(47), 82, *84, 85*, 210(31), 214(3), *239*, 276(1–7,28), 277, 278(3), 280(1–5), *285*
Borowitz, I., 208(4,46), 210(4,46), 212(4), 214, 224(4), 226(4,46), 228(4), *239, 240*
Bos, H. J. T., 115(90), *139*
Boswell, G. A., *166*
Bothner-By, A. A., 313(16), *330*
Bottei, R. S., 54(11), 55(11), *57*
Bottini, A. T., 31(34), *39*
Bove, J. L., 32(112), *41*
Boyer, J. H., 14(199), 16, *39, 43*
Boyland, E., 32(36), *39*
Bradley, W. E., 33(215), *43*
Brady, L. E., 34(150,157,159), 36(150,157,159), *42*
Brandon, R. L., 116(88), *139*
Brannock, K. C., 311(18), 314(17), *330*
Brattain, R. R., 188(124), *202*
Braunholtz, W., 315(73), *331*
Braye, E. H., 51(1), *53*
Breckpot, R., 188(9), *199*
Breiter, J. J., 208(52), 210(52), 212

(52), 224(52), *240*

Breslow, D. S., 19(179), 20(178,179, 198), *43*

Breslow, R., 49(2,5–9), 50(3), 52(4), *53*

Brewer, L., 264(13), *274*

Breyfogle, P. L., 148(97), *168*

Bridge, N. K., 116(15), *137*

Brindell, G. D., 28(37), *39*

Brizzolara, A., 213(47), *240*

Bro, M. I., 279–281(16), *285*

Brosowski, K.-H., 296(26), 299(26), 300(26), *301,* 316(64), 317(64), *331, 332, 337*

Brown, B. B., 14(200–202), *43*

Brown, D. M., 313(19), 317(19), *330*

Brown, G. W., 310(21,22), 313(20,22), 314(22), 325(22), 326(22), 328(21, 22), *330*

Brown, R. D., 27(38), *39*

Brown, W. G., 113(89), *139*

Brückner, K., 307(39), *330*

Bruegel, W., 184(11), 197(11), *199*

Brune, R., 208, *240*

Brutcher, F. V., Jr., 113(26), *137*

Bryce, W. A. 116(16), *137*

Bryce-Smith, D., 114(17), 118, 126(18), 127(18,19), 128(18), *137*

Buchanan, G. L., 26(17,39), *38, 39*

Buckhard, C. A., 45(1), *48*

Buckley, G. D., 12(40), *39*

Büchi, G., 21(41), *39,* 111, 112(20), 113, 114(21), 117(20), 120(20,21), 121(8,20), 122(20), 124(8), *136, 137*

Büchner, W., 97(6), *101,* 104(2), 106 (2), *107*

Bütow, K., 317(14), *330*

Buhle, E. L., 188(80,85), *201*

Bunyan, P. J., 1(7), *3*

Burg, A. B., 310(23), 312(23), 313 (51), 328(51), *330, 331*

Burgess, E. M., 21(41), *39*

Burgess, H., 208(5), *239*

Burgison, R. M., 78(28), *85*

Burgstahler, A. W., 147(14), *166*

Burkhardt, G. N., 260(14–16), 261(14, 16), *274,* 278(8), *285,* 302(2), *304*

Burlitch, J., 45(19), *48*

Burpitt, R. D., 311(18), 314(17), *330*

Burr, M., 49(16), *53*

Burwell, R. L., Jr., 278(9,10), *285*

Bush, J. J., Jr., 32(223), *44*

Butler, P. E., 33(119), *41*

Buttery, R. G., 264(17), *274*

Bykhovskaya, E. G., 171(7), *173,* 262 (50), 264(50), 269(50), *275*

**C**

Cabaleiro, M. C., 189(74), *201*

Cabat, G. A., 29(238), *44*

Cadogan, J. I. G., 1(7), *3*

Cairns, T. L., 168(8), *173,* 297(12,35), 300(12), *300, 301*

Calderaro, E., 268(57), *275*

Caldwell, J. R., 147(19), 148(17–22), 149(16,23), 153(21,22), 158(15), 161 (16,20,22), 162(21), 164(22,23), *166*

Calvin, M., 103(30), *107,* 147(24), *166*

Campbell, R. W., 208(53), 210(53), *240*

Campbell, T. W., 121(22), *137,* 310(24–26), 318(24–26), 319, 320(24–26), 329(25,26), *330, 331*

Canter, F. C., 16, *39*

Caplier, I., 51(1), *53*

Caramack, M., 79(24–26), *85*

Caronna, G., 16(42), *39*

Carrara, G., 291, *300*

Castellucci, N. T., 9(170), 20(170), 21, *42*

Chabrier, P., 121(40), *137*

Chachatyrov, A. S., 54(7), *57*

Chanley, J., 277(17), *285*

Chapman, N. B., 33(43,44), *39*

Chatt, J., 310(27), 312(27), *330*

Chattaway, F. D., 16(45), *39*

Chatterjee, B. G., 188(5,12), *199*

Chaudhuri, N., 264(17), *274*

Cheburkov, Y. A., 147(66), 160(66), *167*

Chemie Wacker, 148(109), *168*

Chen, S. I., 121(23), *137*

Chernyshev, E. A., 49(20), *53*

Chieffi, G., 111, 121(66), 124(66), 129 (66), *138*

Chinoporos, E., 19(46), *39,* 88(12), *102*

Christie, B. J., 60(1), *84*

Christmann, A., 1(14), *3*, 14(124,125), 16(124), 26(124), *41*, 97(23), *102*, 105, *107*

Christy, M. E., 222(6,7), 223(6), *239*

Cignarella, G., *199*

Clapp, L. B., 31(177), 32(47–49), *39*, 42

Clark, R. D., 33(50,118), 37(24), *39, 41*

Clark, V. M., 103(8), *107*

Clarke, H. T., 175(14,16), 181(14,17), 182(15), 188(14), 194(14), *199*

Clark-Lewis, J. W., 202(14–16), *206*

Clegg, J. M., 14(203), *43*

Coates, C. E., 51(10), *53*

Coffman, D. D., 118, 129–131(51), 132 (24,51), 133(24,51), *137, 138*, 168 (8), *173*

Cohen, B., 32(51), 33(52,53), *39*

Cohen, S., 147(8), 148(9), 160(9), 162 (9), *166*

Collins, C. R., 287(3), 289(3), *290*

Colton, F. B., 276(1), 280(1), *285*

Cook, A. G., 7(54), 12(54), *39*

Cook, A. H., 181(18), *199*, 248, 249 (4), 250(4), 254(4), *256*

Cookson, R. C., 310(21,22), 313(20, 22), 314(22), 325(22), 326(22), 328 (21,22), *330*

Cooper, D. S., 148(54), 161(54), 162 (54), *167*

Cooper, G. D., 78(4), *84*

Coover, H. W., Jr., 147(74), 162(74), *167*

Cope, A. C., 20(55), *39*

Corby, N. S., 310(28), 317(28), *330*

Corey, E. J., 188, *199, 201*

Cornand, P., 121(31), *137*

Cornell, D., 17, 19, 20, *39*

Cornforth, J. W., 148(25,26), 160(25, 26), *166*

Cornforth, R. H., 145, 148(25–27), 150 (27), 160(25–27), *166*

Cottis, S. G., 46(6), *48*, 52(17), *53*

Craig, N. C., 100(11), *102*

Cram, D. J., 32(58), *40*

Cramer, R. D., 242, 245(1), *245*

Crawford, G. H., 263(59), 271(59), *275*

Cristiani, G., 147(102), *168*, 171(3,17–

20), *173*, 188(121–123), *199, 202*, 204(25), *206*

Cristol, S., 28(37,213), *39, 43*, 111(25), *137*

Cromwell, N. H., 32(57–60), *39, 40*

Culvenor, C. C. J., 78(5,6), *84*

Curtius, T., 8(65), 9(65), 16(63), 25, 26, 32(63), 37(64), *39, 40*, 87, *102*, 243(2), *245*

**D**

Dachlauer, K., 78(7,8), *84, 85*

Danish, A. A., 16(66), *40*

Dashkevich, B. N., 163(28), *166*

Dauben, W. G., *166*

Davidson, A. J., 31(34), *39*

Davidson, N., 79(17), *85*

Davies, W., 78(5,6), *84*

Davis, B. A., 1(15), *3*, 6(1), 8(1), 14 (1), 16(2), 20(1,3), 26(1), *38*, 97(4), *101*, 105(1), 106(1), *107*

Davis, F. A., 222(8,9), *239*

Davis, J. W., 32(19), *39*

Davis, S. J., 16(67), *40*

Dearborn, F. E., 77(9–12), 78(9–12), *85*

Deinema, M. H., 80(36), *85*, 210(26), *239*

Delépine, M., 78(13–16), *85*, 291, *300*

Deming, S., 16(188), *43*

De More, W. B., 79(17), *85*

Dermer, O. C., 14(68), 15(68), 26(68), *40*

Deutsch, A. S., 32(69,83), *40*

Dewey, C. S., 32(70), *40*

Deyrup, J. A., 7(71), 14, *40*

Diamond, L. H., 97(8), *101*, 104(4), *107*

Diassi, P. A., 147(29), *166*

Diehr, H. J., 186, 187(36,37), 193(36), 197(36,37), *200*

Diekmann, J., 45(2), *48*, 211, 212(43), *240*

Dietrich, M. W., 10(89), 29, *40*

Dietrich, M. A., 279–282(14), 284(14), 285(14), *285*

Dimroth, K., 17(72,73), *40*

Dittmer, D. C., 78, 79(18), *85*, 222(6–

10), 223(6,10), *239*, 296, *300*
Dixon, R. N., 17(74,75,122), *40, 41*
Dmitriev, M. A., 278–282(11), *285*
Dobyns, V., 98(45), 99(45), *102*
Dodds, E. C., 80(19–21), *85*
Doepper, K., 189(24), *200*
Doering, W. v. E., 6(76), 19(77,78), *40,* 44(3), *48,* 50(11,12), *53,* 97(14), *102,* 264(17), *274*
Dörr, W., 16(63), 32(63), *40*
Domagk, G. F., 307(39), *330*
Donoghue, E., 314(36,37), *330*
Dorfman, L., 314(37), *330*
Dubov, S. S., 242(4), 243(4), 245(4), *245,* 264(20), 272(20), 273(20), *274*
Duffner, P., 309(30), 310(30), *330*
Dulova, V. G., 45(23), *49,* 49–51(25), *53,* 54(5,12,13), 55(12,13,18), 56 (18), *57,* 84(80), *86,* 97(71), *103,* 110 (11), *110*
Durst, T., 83(33), *85,* 208–210, *239*
D'yakonov, I. A., 49(13), *53*
Dylion, C. M., 147(29), *166*

**E**

Eaborn, C., 49(14), 51(15), *53*
Easson, A. P. T., 26(17), *38*
Ebnöther, A., 203, 204(3,9–12), 205(3), *205, 206*
Edmison, M. T., 1(11), *3,* 14(68,105), 15(68,105), 26(68,105), *40, 41*
Edwards, J. O., 6(138), 7(138), 12 (139), *42*
Edwards, O., 14(15,16), 16, *38*
Effenberger, F., 183(20–22), 184(22), 185(20–22), 195(20–22), *199, 200*
Ehlers, G., 32(32), *39*
Eibner, A., 287(5,6), *290*
Einhorn, A., 139(30), 142(30), *166*
Eistert, B., 33(79), *40,* 57(22), *85*
Eiter, K., 307(84), *331*
Elam, E. U., 148(58), 152–157(57), *167*
El-Hewehi, Z., 60(76), 62(76), 63(76), *86*
Eloy, F., 14(80), *40*
Emmons, W. D., 103(9–11), *107,* 276 (12), *285,* 307(85), 308(85), *331*
Endle, R., 139(94), 141(93,94), 142

(94), *168,* 289, *291,* 302, *304*
Engelhard, H., 250, 254(24), *257*
England, D. C., 279(13,14), 280(14), 281(13,14), 282(14), 284(14), 285 (14), *285*
Englehardt, V. A., 168(10), *173*
English, J., Jr., 113(26), *137*
Erdmann, H.-M., 307(39), *330*
Erickson, J. A., 188(23), *200*
Erickson, R. E., 103(25), *107*
Erlenmeyer, E., 139(31), 142(31), *166*
Ermolaev, V., 117, *137*
Ertel, H., 307(34), 308(34), *330*
Etienne, Y., 139(32), 151(32), *166,* 206 (11), *239,* 292(6), *300*
Etter, R. M., 19(195), 24(81), *40, 43*
Ettinger, R., 99(15), *102*
Ettlinger, M. G., 78(23), *85*
Euler, H. v., 163(33), *166*
Evans, P. B., 276(29), 277(29), *286*

**F**

Fahr, E., 189(24), *200*
Fanta, P. E., 5(82), 32(69,83,140–142, 217), 33(84), *40, 42, 43*
Farnum, D. G., 12(235), *44,* 49(16), *53*
Farrow, M. D., 302(3,4), *304*
Fateen, A., 60(60), 64(60), 65(60), 67(60), 68(60), *86*
Fathy, I., 60(41), 63(41), 64(41), 68–71(41), 75(41,42), *85*
Fauran, C., 265(19), *274*
Fava, F., 147(102), *168,* 188(118,122, 123), *202*
Fehnel, E. A., 79(24–26), *85*
Fernandez, J. R., 121(29,43), *137*
Fetter, M. E., 32(110), *41*
Feuer, B. I., 14(210), 15(210), *43*
Ficini, J., 187(25), *200*
Fielding, H. C., 310(27), 312(27), *330*
Fields, D. B., 119(14), 133(14), *137*
Fields, D. L., 57(53), *86*
Fields, E. K., 6(85,86), 7(54,85,86), 12 (54), *39,' 40*
Fierz, H. E., 211(28), *239*
Filatov, A. S., 264(54,55), 272(54,55), 273(54,55), *275*
Finch, G. K., 159(34), *166*

Finzenhagen, H., 16(6), *38*
Fischer, A., 116(48), *137*
Fischer, K., 83(48,49), 84(48), *86,* 208 (35,36), 210, 215(36), 217(36), 227 (36), *239, 240*
Fischer, N., 139(32), 151(32), 153(35), 154(35), *166*
Fischer, P., 251, 252(22), 255(22), *256, 257*
Fitzpatrick, J. T., 149(36,115), 152 (115), *166, 168*
Fleming, G., 121(30), *137*
Fleury, J. P., 332(7), *337*
Foldi, V. S., 310(25), 318(25), 319(25, 56), 320(25), 329(25), *330, 331*
Fontanella, L., 147(102,103), *168,* 171 (17–20), *173,* 188(26,27,118–123), *200, 202,* 204(24,25), *206*
Fonteyne, R., 121(31,32), *137*
Ford, J. A., Jr., 308(86), 321(86), *331*
Ford, W. K., 278(8), *285*
Foss, R. P., 115(64), 116(64), *138*
Francis, W. C., 263(18), *274*
Frank, V. S., 188(83), *201*
Frankenfeld, J. W., 37(190), *43*
Franz, J. E., 9(88), 10(88,89), 27(88), 28(88), 29, 30, *40*
Franzen, V., 46(4), *48*
Franzus, B., 243, 245(13), *246*
Fray, G. I., 114(17), *137*
Frei, K., 121(69), *138*
Frerich, G., 254, *256*
Frese, E., 60(61), 63(61), 64(61), *86,* 296(26), 299(26), 300(26), *301*
Frey, H., 99(17), 101(16,18), *102,* 112 (33), *137*
Freyermuth, H. B., 37(182), *43*
Freyschlag, H., 17(72,73), *40*
Friedländer, P., 174(28), *200*
Friedrichsen, W., 16(7), *38*
Frierholzer, J. F., 37(24), *39*
Frobenius, O., 32, *42*
Frosin, V. N., 262(50), 264(50), 269 (50), *275*
Fruton, J. S., 5(90), 32(96), 33(96), *40*
Fulmer, R. W., 34(153), *42*
Fusco, R., 28(91), *40,* 210, 226(12), *239*
Fuson, R. C., 32(144), 33(92), *40, 42*

**G**

Gabriel, S., 32(93), *40*
Gal, P., 52(4), *53*
Gallegos, E. J., 121(34), *137*
Gallo, G. G., 288(7), *290*
Gambaryan, N. P., 6(148), *42,* 188(54, 55), *200*
Garner, A. Y., 6(196), *43*
Garratt, P. J., 21(143), *42*
Garratt, S., 182(3,4), *199*
Gash, V. W., 34(153), *42*
Gassman, P. G., 181(29), *200,* 242(3), *245*
Gatti, E., 171(16), *173*
Gaule, A., 87(69), 88(69), *103*
Gautier, A., 265(19), *274*
Geissler, G., 305, *331*
Gellert, H. G., 46(29), *49*
Genge, C. A., 19(179), 20(179), *43*
George, M. V., 45(27), *49*
Ghosh-Mazumdar, B. N., 188(5,7), *199*
Gibbs, H. H., 279(16), 280(15,16), 281 (16), 282(15,16), 285(15), *285,* 288 (8), *290*
Gilbert, A., 114(17), 118, 126(18), 127 (18,19), 128(18), *137*
Gilman, A., 32(94), *40*
Gilman, H., 45(7,27), 46, *48, 49,* 52, *53,* 55(3,4), *56,* 188(30), 191(30), *200*
Ginsburg, V. A., 242, 243(4), 245(4), *245,* 264(20,54,55), 272(20,54,55), 273(20,54,55), *276, 275*
Gleiter, R., 183(20–22), 184(22), 185 (20–22), 195(20–22), *199, 200*
Glick, A. H., 115, 116(7), 117(7), 120– 124(7), 129(7), *136*
Göhring, D., 202(21), 204(21), *206*
Gösl, R., 97(19), *102,* 106(12), *107*
Goetz, H., 307(31), 310(31), *330*
Gohlke, R. S., 45(9), *48,* 51, *53,* 55, *56*
Goldberg, A. A., 32(95), *40*
Goldberg, L., 80(19–21), *85*
Goldish, E. J., 121(35), *137*
Goldstein, E. J., 44(20,21), 45(20,21), 47, 48(20,21), *48*
Goldstern, I., 174(31), *200*
Golovaneva, A. F., 264(54,55), 272(54, 55), 273(54,55), *275*

Golovinskii, E., 188(92), *201*
Golumbic, C., 32(96), 33(96), *40*
Gomberg, M., 80(27), *85*
Goodlett, V. W., 314(17), *330*
Goodman, L., 33(197), *43*
Gosselink, E. P., 181(60), *200,* 242(9), *246*
Gott, P. G., 210(13), 213(13), 217–219 (13), 236(13), 238(13), *239*
Gowenlock, B. G., 257(21), 260(21), *274*
Graf, R., 171(4), *173,* 184(32,35), 185 (32–34), 186(32), 196(32,35), 197 (32–34), 198(32), *200,* 203, 204, 205 (19), *205, 206,* 266(22), *274*
Graham, J. D. P., 33(44,97), *39, 40*
Graham, W. H., 99(20), *102*
Gram, H. F., 33(197), *43*
Grant, D. M., 147(37,38), *166*
Grashey, R., 1(1), 2(1), *3,* 303(6), *304*
Greene, F. D., 118(36–38), *137*
Greenwald, R. B., 7(71), 14, *40*
Greiner, R. W., 32(112), *41*
Griffin, C. E., 260( 25,26), 261(25,26), 263(23), 270(23,24), *274*
Griffin, G. W., 122(39), *137*
Grigsby, W. E., 277(17), *285*
Groskopf, W. R., 33(84), *40*
Gross, A., 14(125), 16(126), *41,* 178 (46), 182(46), *200,* 250(14), 251 (14), 254(14), *257*
Grossman, O., 34(163), *42*
Günthard, H. H., 121(69,94,95), *138, 139*
Guenther, D., 171(4), *173*
Guepet, R., 121(40), *137*
Gunberg, P. F., 277(33), *286*
Gunning, H. E., 75(37–39,75,82), *85, 86*
Guth, E., 97(6), *101,* 104(2), 106(2), *107*
Gutowsky, H. S., 121(41), *137,* 147(37, 38), *166*
Gwinn, W. D., 121(23,29,42,43), *137*

**H**

Haag, W., 305(92), *331*
Habisch, D., 89(58), 90(58), 91(58), 92(58), 101(59), *102, 103*

Häuser, H., 181, *200,* 242, 245(5), *246,* 264(39), *275*
Hafner, K., 9(99), 14(100), 17, 20 (180), 22, 24, 25(99), *40, 41, 43*
Hagemeyer, H. J., Jr., 143, 144(39), 145, 147(50), 148(39,40,42–54), 149(23, 46), 152(39), 158(39,49), 159(39, 49), 161(39,40,42,45,54), 162(39, 54), 163(47,52), 164(23,39,42,47), 165(42,50), *166, 167*
Hager, C. P., 78(28), *85*
Haggag, B., 75(42), *85*
Hale, R. L., 29(238), *44*
Hale, W. J., 253, *256*
Hales, J. L., 292(8), *300*
Hall, C., 310(32), 327(32), *330*
Hall, J. H., 1(8), *3,* 14(203,204), *43,* 251, *256*
Ham, C. E., 31(102), *41*
Hamamoto, K., 158(55), *167*
Hamer, J., 2(18), *3,* 260(29), 261, 269 (28), *274,* 303(7), *304*
Hammond, G. S., 115(47,64), 116(44, 45,48,49,64), 122(47), 129(46,72), 136(44), *137, 138*
Hammond, P. R., 313(19), 317(19), *330*
Hanby, W. E., 33(103), *41*
Hanson, R., 16(174), *42*
Harley-Mason, J., 97(21), *102*
Harris, J. 32(51), 33(52,53), *39*
Harris, J. F., 118, 129(51), 130(51), 131 (50,51), 132(24,50,51), 133(24,50, 51), *137, 138*
Harrison, A. J., 121(30), *137*
Harrison, W. F., 21(226), *44*
Hart, F. A., 310(27), 312(27), *330*
Hart, R., 148(56), *167*
Hartenstein, A., 17(164), *42*
Hartley, G. S., 33(103), *41*
Hartmann, W., 122(74), *138*
Hartwig, L., 254, *256*
Hartzler, H. D., 169–172(5), *173*
Hasek, R. H., 148(58), 152–157(57), *167,* 210(13), 213(13), 217(13), 218 (13), 219, 220, 236(13,14), 237(14), 238(13,14), *239*
Hassall, C. H., 268, *274*
Hasselström, T., 208(15), *239*
Hasspacher, K., 147(82), *167*

Haszeldine, R. N., 260(7), 261, 262(7–9,11a,32), 263(8,9,11,12,18,23,33–35), 264(9,32), 269(7,9,10), 270(8, 11,23,24,31), 271(11,12), *274*, 292, *300*
Hauck, F. P., Jr., 34(151), *42*
Hauser, E., 316(74), *331*
Hay, A. S., 33(152), 34(153), *42*
Hay, A. W., 32(104), *41*
Haynie, R., 49(5), *53*
Hays, H. R., 78(66), *86*
Heacock, J. F., 1(11), *3,* 14(105), 15 (105), 26(105), *41*
Heath, N. S., 78(5), *84*
Heckert, R. E., 168(8,11), *173*
Heine, H. W., 32(106–117,223), *41, 44*
Heins, A., 98(22), *102*
Helmkamp, G. K., 33(50,118), *39, 41,* 78(29), *85*
Helmreich, R. F., 111(25), *137*
Henderson, R. B., 120(92), *139*
Henderson, W. A., Jr., 6(76), *40*
Hendrickson, J. B., 310(32,33), 327(32, 33), *330*
Henery-Logan, K. R., 188(84), *201*
Henmo, E., 210(16), *239*
Henne, A. L., 118(52), *138*
Hennion, G. F., 33(119), *41*
Henrich, G., 88(2,3), 89, 94(2), *101*
Henry, J. P., 116(88), *139*
Henya, J., 32(32), *39*
Hepfinger, N. F., 260, 261, *274*
Herbst, P., 307(15), *330*
Herzberg, G., 20(120), 31(121), *41*
Hesse, G., 78(31), 79(31), 81, 82(30, 31), *85,* 210(17,18), *239*
Heyns, K., 98(22), *102*
Hickinbottom, W. J., 260(38), *275*
Hill, H. W., Jr., 188(85), *201*
Hill, R. K., 2(20), *3*
Hind, J., 277(17), *285*
Hinman, R. L., 115, 116(7), 117(7), 120–124(7), 129(7), *136*
Hirsekorn, B., 32(32), *39*
Hirsjärvi, P., 147(61), *167,* 210(19,51), *239, 240*
Hoeksema, H., 32(59), *40*
Höver, H., 49(6), *53*
Hoffman, E., 147(8), 148(9), 160(9), 162(9), *166*
Hoffmann, A. K., 44(3), *48,* 50(11), *53,* 97(14), *102*
Hoffmann, A. W., 109, *110*
Hoffmann, H., 186, 187(36,37), 193 (36), 197(36,37), *200,* 307(34,35), 308(34), *330*
Hoffmann, R., 3, *3*
Hoffmann, R. W., 181, *200,* 242, 245(5), *246,* 264(39), *275*
Hofmann, A. W., 251(10), *256*
Hofmann, R., 251(11), *256*
Holbert, J. M., 276(6), *285*
Holland, R., 17(122), *41*
Holley, A. D., 175(40), 178, 188(41, 42), 189(40), *200*
Holley, R. W., 175(40), 178, 188(41, 42), 189(40), *200*
Holloway, D. F. 292(31), *301*
Holroyd, R. A., 44(8), 48(8), *48*
Hooker, W. M., 181(29), *200,* 242(3), *245*
Hopff, H., 145(62), *167*
Horeau, A., 188(43), *200*
Horner, L., 1(14), *3,* 14(123–125), 16 (124,126), 26(124), *41,* 88(24), 97 (23), *102,* 103(14), 105, *107,* 178, 179(44,53), 182, 190(53), 191(53), *200,* 250, 251(14), 254(13,14), *257,* 307(34,35), 308(34), *330*
Horning, M. G., 148(25,26), 160(25, 26), *166*
Hornung, K. A., 16(8), *38*
Howard, E. G., 73(44), 74(44), *85,* 292 (18,19), 293(19), 298(18,19), *301*
Hsuan, Y-H., 188(43), *200*
Huck, G., 89(43), 94(43), 97(43), *102*
Hübel, W., 51(1), *53*
Huebner, C. F., 314(36,37), *330*
Huisgen, R., 1(1), 2(1), *3,* 14(130), 16, 17(129,131,132), 31(128,130), *41,* 303(6,8), *304,* 310(38), *330*
Hunter, W. T., 16(174), *42*
Hurd, C. D., 143, 147(24), 148(63), *166, 167*

I

Ingold, C. K., 189(47), *200,* 241, 242,

244(7,8), *246,* 247, 248(15), 249,
250, 254(15), *257,* 257–261, *275,* 301,
302, 303(9,10), *304*
Inhoffen, E., 307(15), *330*
Inhoffen, H. H., 307(39), *330*
Inman, C. G., 111–113(20), 117(20),
120–122(20), *137*
Irving, J., 32(223), *44*
Isoshima, T., 158(55), *167*
Iwakura, Y., 32(134,135), *41*
Izzo, P. T., 37(192), 38(191,192), *43,*
180(86,87), 192(86,87), *201*

## J

Jackel, L., 78(7,8), *84, 85*
Jackman, L. M., 121(53), *138*
Jacobs, T., 32(32), *39*
Jacobson, P., 109, *110*
Jacox, M. E., 8(136), 15(136), *41*
Jacques, J., 147(64), *167,* 188(43), *200*
Jäger, A., 179, 182, 190(71), 191(71),
194(71), 195(71), *201*
Jaffeaux, P., 78(15,16), *85*
Jambotkar, D., 78(74), *86,* 307(44),
*330*
James, J. W., 33(43,44), *39*
Jander, J., 1(13), *3,* 97(25–27,31), *102,*
104, *107*
Jankowski, A., 98(28), *102*
Jann, K., 33, 34(156), 35(154–156),
36(156), *42*
Jelagin, S., 174(102), 175(102), 179,
182, 190(103), *201,* 265, 266,
273(69), *275,* 287, *291*
Jensen, H., 171(4), *173*
Jiang, S. H.-K., 278–281(18), 283(18),
*285*
Johnson, A. W., 306(40–42), *330*
Johnson, D. A., 188(48,84), *200*
Johnson, E. M., 32(114), *41*
Johnson, F., 45(9), *48,* 51, *53,* 55, *56*
Johnson, H. W., Jr., 115(67), *138*
Johnson, J. R., 175(14,16), 181(14,17),
182(15), 188(14), 194(14), *199*
Johnston, H. S., 264(49), *275*
Jones, D. G., 248, 249(4), 250(4),
254(4), *256*
Jones, G. D., 33(137), *41*

Jones, J. I., 292(8), *300*
Jones, S. O., 77(32), 78(32), *85*
Jones, W. M., 175(1), *199*
Jorgenson, M. J., 117(93), 118(93),
120–122(93), 124–126(93), *139*
Jucker, E., 203(3), 204(3,8–12),
205(3), *205, 206*
Juergens, E., 103(14), *107*

## K

Kabitzke, K. H., 294(24), *301*
Kadaba, P. K., 6(138), 7(138),
12(139), *42*
Kagan, H. B., 147(64), *167,* 188(43,49),
*200*
Kaiser, W., 9(99), 22, 24(99), 25(99),
*40*
Kaltschmitt, H., 294(28,30), *301*
Kaminski, R. A., 118(38), *137*
Kamlet, M., 103(18), *107*
Kammermeier, A., 17(132), *41*
Kandiah, A., 157(65), *167*
Kaplan, L., 103(18), *107*
Kapur, B. L., 32(111–113), *41*
Karplus, M., 147(38), *166*
Kartsev, G. N., 49(20), *53*
Kasha, M., 116(58), 117(54), 136(58),
*138*
Kashelikar, D. V., 32(140–142), *42*
Katz, T. J., 21(143), *42*
Kauck, E. A., 115(56), 116(56),
118(56), *138*
Keefer, R. M., 170(1,6), *173*
Kelber, C., 295(9,10), *300*
Kelly, W., 32(95), *40*
Kennedy, C. D., 11(236), 27(236), *44*
Kennedy, J., 108(2), *110*
Kenner, G. W., 310(28), 317(28,43),
*330*
Kennyon, W. G., 32(114), *41*
Kerwin, J. F., 32(144), *42*
Ketcham, R., 78(74), *86,* 307(44), *330*
Khan, M. S., 189(74), *201*
Kharasch, M. S., 111(57), 113, *138*
Kidd, J. M., 292, *300*
Kiefer, E. F., 34(157), 36(157), *42*
Kiefer, H., 21(226), *44*
Kiefer, J. M., 276(29), 277(29), *286*

Kimbrough, R. D., Jr., 175(50), *200*
King, F. E., 5(145), *42,* 173(51), *200,* 202, *206*
King, J. F., 80(34), 83(33), *85,* 208–210, *239*
Kirk, P. F., 78(52), *86*
Kirmse, W., 1(2), *3,* 19(146,147), *42,* 174(52), 178, 179(53), 182, 190(53), 191(53), *200*
Kisel, Ya. M., 262(50), 264(50), 269 (50), *275*
Kiser, R. W., 121(34), *137*
Kjelsberg, F., 315(77), *331*
Klabre, G., 307(35), *330*
Klamann, D., 333(3), *337*
Klever, H. W., 174(104), 175(104–106), 188(105), 189(104,105), *202*
Klinger, K. H., 32(112), *41*
Klink, W., 307(34), 308(34), *330*
Kloosterziel, H., 80(35,36), *85,* 210(1,24–26), *239*
Klug, H., 74, 78(54), *86*
Knell, M., 276(1), 280(1), *285*
Knight, A. R., 75(37–39,82), *85, 86*
Knox, L., 19(77,78), *40*
Knudsen, P., 99(29), *102*
Knunyants, I. L., 6(148), *42,* 147(66), 160 (66), *167, 171*(7), *173,* 188(54,55), *200,* 262(50), 264(50), 269(50), *275,* 278–282(11), *285*
Köber, P., 174(57), 175(105,106), 188(105), 189(105), *200, 202*
Köch, J., 182(67), 193(67), 194(67), *201*
König, C., 14(100), 17, *41*
Kofron, J. T., 114(21), 120(21), *137*
Kohen, H., 104, *107*
Kolesnikov, S. P., 54(6–8), 56(8), *57*
Koller, E., 114(21), 120(21), *137*
Komendantov, M. I., 49(13), *53*
Kon, N., 139(95), 142(95), *168*
Koreshkov, Yu. D., 45(23), *49,* 49(25–27), 50(21,25,26), 51(25), *53,* 54(13), 55(13), *57,* 84(80), *86,* 97(71), *103,* 110(11), *110*
Korte, F., 116, 122(73), *138,* 287, 288, 290(1), *290*
Koskinen, J. R., 33(118), *41*
Kostka, 305(45), *330*

Kovacs, E., 78(79), 80(79), *86,* 210(59), *240*
Kovtun, V. Yu., 307(6), *329*
Kramer, K., 45(10,11), *48*
Kramer, U., 333(3), *337*
Kratzer, O., 306(9), 307(9), *329*
Krbechek, L. O., 1(10), *3*
Kreher, R., 20(149), *42*
Krespan, C. G., 168(11), *173,* 297(11,12), 300(11,12), *300*
Kresze, G., 180, 192(58), *200,* 266, 273(51), *275,* 287(9), 288, 290(9), *290,* 332, 334(9), 335(4,5), 337(9), *337*
Kretov, A. J., 332(6), *337*
Kreuzblicher, L., 45(26), *49*
Krimm, H., 103(19), *107*
Krizkalla, H., 203(17), *206*
Kröhnke, F., 103(20), *107*
Krolls, U., 37(25), *39*
Kuderna, B. M., Jr., 111(57), 113(57), *138*
Kuehne, M. E., 215(27), *239,* 310(46), 311(46), *330*
Künig, F. E., 142, 146(67), 148(67), *167*
Kupfer, O., 175(107), *202*
Kursanov, D. N., 45(23,24), *49,* 49(25–27,29), 50(21,25,26), 51(25,28), *53,* 54(12–17), 55(12–14, 17,18), 56(18), 57, 84(40,80), *85, 86,* 97(71), *103,* 110(3,11), *110*
Kuwana, T., 115(67), *138*
Kynaston, W., 292(8), *300*

**L**

Labro, L., 291(4), *300*
Lacey, R. N., 139(68), 142, 143(68), 144(68), *167,* 174(59), *200,* 250(17), *257*
Lacher, J. R., 262(61), 263(59,60), 269 (61), 271(59,60), *275*
La Count, R. B., 306(41,42), *330*
Lahr, T., 16(174), *42*
Landesman, H., 213(47), *240*
Lange, F., 291(4), *300*
Lange, N. A., 253, *256*
Langsjoen, A., Sr., 33(137), *41*

Lapworth, A., 260, 261, *274,* 302, *304*
Laschtuvka, E., 17(131,132), *141*
Latif, N., 60(41), 63(41), 64(41), 68–71(41), 75(41,42), *85*
Lau, A., 99(30), *102*
Laubach, G. D., 188(80,88,89), *201*
Laughlin, R. G., 264(17), *274*
Lawson, W., 80(19–21), *85*
Leader, H., 37(186), *43*
Leavitt, F. C., 51(22), *53*
Lee, C., *42*
Leermakers, P. A., 116(44,49), 136(44), *137*
Le Feure, R. J. W., 248(18), 249(18), *257*
Lehman, D. S., 51(22), *53*
Leickenbach, T. A., 1(12), *3*
Leitermann, H., 303(6), *304*
Leites, L. A., 54(5), *57*
Lemal, D. M., 181(60), *200,* 242(9), *246*
Lengyel, I., 37(193,194), *43*
Leonard, N. J., 33, 34, 35(154–156), 36(150,156–159), *42*
Leplawy, M., 114(2), 119(2), 128(3), 129(3), *136,* 146, 147(1), 150(1), *166*
Leusen, A. M. van, 187, 188(61), 199(61), *200*
Levine, R. M., 26(39), *39*
Levisalles, J., 305(47), *330*
Levy, G. C., 78, 79(18), *85*
Lewis, G. N., 33(44), *39,* 116(58), 136 (58), *138*
Liang, H. T., 152(69), *167*
Libbey, W. J., 16(188), *43*
Lichtenberger, J., 332(7), *337*
Lidov, R. E., 16(66), *40*
Lienau, G., 317(14), *330*
Lindsey, R. V., 279–282(14), 284(14), 285(14), *285*
Lingnau, E., 88(24), *102*
Linnell, R. H., 147(70), *167*
Lipinsky, E. S., 111–113(20), 117(20), 120–122(20), *137*
Lippman, A. E., 268, *274*
Litchenwalter, G. D., 45(7), *48*
Little, E. L., 168(11), *173*
Liu, R. S. H., 116(45), *137*
Locher, A., 211(28), *239*

Lochte, H. L., 243(14), *246*
Logothetis, A. L., 13(161), 14(162), *42*
Loncrini, D. F., 28(229), *44*
Lowenlock, B. G., 301(5), *304*
Lowry, T. M., 208(5), *239,* 258(52), *275*
Lucas, H. J., 277(34), *286*
Luche, J. L., 188(49), *200*
Lüscher, G., 309(48), *330*
Lüttke, W., 257(21), 260(21), *274,* 301(5), *304*
Lüttringhaus, A., 1(13), *3,* 97(31), *102,* 104(21), *107*
Lukes, R., 34(163), *42*
Lumbroso, H., 206(11), *239*
Lutz, E. F., 78(66,67), *86*
Lutz, R. E., 210(42), *240*
Lwowski, W., 1(5), *3,* 8(166), 14(165,166,168), 15(166), 16–18, 19(165–167), 20, *39, 42*

## M

Macaluso, A., 260(29), 261, 269(28), *274, 275,* 289(10), *290,* 303(7), *304*
McClure, D. S., 116(65), 117, *138*
McConnell, R. L., 147(74), 162(74), *167*
McElvain, S. M., 213(29), *239*
McEwen, W., 307(12,13), *329*
McGrew, L. A., 319(56), *331*
McKellin, W. H., 214(3), *239*
McKusick, B. C., 168(8,22), 169(22), *173,* 297(12), 300(12), *300*
McShane, H. F., 310(26), 318(26), 320(26), 329(26), *330*
Madelung, 140(71), *167*
Maercker, A., 305, 306(49), 307(49), *331*
Magel, T. T., 147(24), *166*
Mahler, W., 312, 313, 328(50,51), *331*
Maier, J., 175(108), 189(108), *202*
Maiorano, S., 210, 226(12), *239*
Majer, J. R., 264(56), *275*
Majmudar, S., 78(31), 79(31), 81(30,31), 82(30,31), *85,* 210(17,18), *239*
Mak, T. C. W., 310(21), 313(20), 328(21), *330*

Makarov, S. P., 264(54,55), 272(54,55), 273(54,55), 275
Malachowski, M., 146, 167
Malkemus, J. D., 276(30,31), 286
Malm, S. M., 75(39), 85
Manakov, M. N., 45(12,13,15), 46(14,15), 47(12,13), 48(12,13), 48, 54(9,10), 57
Manhas, M. S., 188(6,7), 199
Manuel, T. A., 51(22), 53
Maone, T., 180(76), 193(76), 201
Marcantonio, A. F., 19(179), 20(178,179), 43
Marckwald, W., 32, 42
Margerum, J. D., 121(59), 138
Margrave, J. L., 264(13), 274
Mariani, L., 147(103), 168, 171(18–20), 173, 204(25), 206
Maricich, T. J., 8(166), 14(165,166), 15(166), 17(166), 18(166), 19(165,166), 42
Marsh, F. D., 30(14), 38
Martin, J. C., 96(70), 99(70), 103, 148(58), 167, 210(13), 213(13), 217–219(13), 220, 236(13,14), 237(14), 238(13,14), 239
Martin, J. G., 2(20), 3
Martin, K., 78, 85, 293, 298(13), 301
Martinelli, L., 307(44), 330
Martinez, A. P., 33(197), 43
Martynova, L. L., 242(4), 243(4), 245(4), 245, 264(20,54,55), 272(20, 54,55), 273(20,54,55), 274, 275
Masamune, S., 9(170), 20(170), 21, 42
Maschke, A., 287(9), 288(9), 290(9), 290
Masson, C. R., 136(60), 138
Mastyukov, U. S., 55(18), 56(18), 57
Matternas, L. U., 51(22), 53
Matterstock, K., 171(4), 173
Matthews, J. S., 147(113), 168
Mattingly, T. W., 1(5), 3, 8(166), 14(166,168), 15(166), 16, 17(166), 18, 19(166,167), 20(167), 42
Mayer, H., 303(13), 304
Mayo, P. de, 80(34), 85, 116(62), 117(61), 138, 208(23), 210(16,23), 239
Meaburn, G. M., 108(2), 110

Medvedev, A. N., 242(4), 243(4), 245(4), 245, 264(20), 272(20), 273(20), 274
Meen, R. H., 210(13), 213(13), 217–219(13), 220, 236(13,14), 237(14), 238(13,14), 239
Meerwein, H., 143(73), 167
Meisert, E., 251(7), 256
Melstrom, D. S., 203(1), 205
Merrifield, R. E., 170(9), 173
Merritt, J. A., 99(32), 102
Meuwsen, A., 97(19), 102, 106(12), 107
Meyer, H., 174(62), 200
Meyer, J., 107, 108, 110, 175(109), 177, 202, 268(70), 275, 309, 315(75,76), 316(75,76), 331
Meyer, R. J., 121(29), 137
Meyer, V., 109(4), 110, 295(14–16), 301
Michael, A., 277(19), 286
Michaelis, H., 307(31), 310(31), 330
Middleton, W. J., 73(44), 74(44,45), 85, 115, 138, 168(10,11), 173, 207, 223(30), 239, 292, 293, 298(17–19), 301
Miescher, K., 260, 267, 268(71), 275, 302, 304
Miller, M., 108(12), 110
Milligan, D. E., 8(136), 15(136), 41
Mina, G., 182(8), 199
Mironov, V. F., 49(20), 53
Mirra, J., 49(5), 53
Misrock, S. L., 118(37), 137
Mitch, C., 32(112,113), 41
Mitsch, R. A., 100, 101(33–36), 102
Mitsunobu, O., 317(54), 318(54), 331
Mizsak, S. A., 182(70), 194(70), 201
Mlakar, B., 332(2), 337
Mole, T., 50(12), 53
Monagle, J. J., 310(24–26), 318(24–26, 55), 319(25), 320(24–26,55), 329(25,26), 330, 331
Moniz, W. B., 32(49), 39
Moore, C. W., 115(64), 116(64), 138
Moore, D., 295, 299(39), 301
Moore, J. A., 168(12), 173, 173(63), 200, 202, 206, 240, 246, 253(19), 257
Moore, P. T., 20(55), 39
Moore, W. R., 20(55), 39

Moosmüller, F., 251(11), *256*
Morgan, C. R. P., 202(16), *206*
Morgan, L. R., 1(4), *3*, 14(22), *39*
Morimoto, G., 147(75), *167*
Moritz, K.-L., 24(101), *41*
Morkved, E., 80(34), *85*, 208(23), 210 (23), *239*
Mortenson, H. E., 121(80), *138*
Mosby, W. L., 5(171), *42*
Mower, H. F., 168(8), *173*
Moza, P. N., 188(12), *199*
Müller, E., 88(37), *102*, 248(20), *257*
Mukaiyama, T., 108(5), *110*, 317(54), 318(54), *331*
Mundlos, E., 146, 150(80), 151(80), *167*, 203, 205(19), *205*, *206*
Murawski, D., 104(27,28), 105(27,28), 106(27,28), *107*
Murov, S., 117(93), 118(93), 120–122(93), 124–126(93), *139*
Murray, R. W., 20(222), *44*
Mustafa, A., 12(172), *42*, 115(75), 136 (76), *138*

**N**

Naar-Colin, C., 313(16), *330*
Nabeya, A., 32(134,135), *41*
Nambu, H., 108(5), *110*
Nations, R. G., 152(60), *167*
Nefedov, O. M., 45(12,13,15), 46(14,15), 47, 48(12,13), *48*, 54(6–10), 56(8), *57*
Neidlein, R., 253(21), 256(21), *257*
Nerdel, F., 307(31), 310(31), *330*
Nery, R., 32(36), *39*
Neuman, M. S., 278(20), *286*
Neumann, M. M. C., 33(137), *41*
Neumann, W., 251, 252(22), 255(22), *257*
Neureiter, N. P., 78(46,47), 81(47), 82, *85*, 210(31), *239*
Newburg, N. R., 20(198), *43*
Newman, D., 1(3), *3*
Nicholaus, B. J. R., 188(64), *201*, 288(11–13), *290*
Nicholson, E. M., 32(110), *41*
Nieuwenhuis, J., 187, *201*
Noll, W., 32(32), *39*

Norell, J. R., 208(32,52–54), 210(52–54), 212(52,54), 213(54–56), 214, 217(54), 222(55,57), 224(52, 54), 225(54), 228(57), *239*, *240*
Noro, K., 147(75), *167*
Nowack, G. P., 16(188), *43*
Noyes, W. A., Jr., 136(60), *138*, 147(70), *167*
Nussim, M., 117(93), 118(93), 120–122(93), 124–126(93), *139*
Nyman, F., 263(33–35), *274*

**O**

Ocamp, S. R., 118(38), *137*
Oehlschlager, A. C., 10(237), 27(237), 29, *42*, *44*
Ohme, R., 89(61,66), 94(62), 95(61,62), 96(62,66), 97(65–67), 98(60–64,66), 99(30,38,62), *102*, *103*, 104(27,28), 105(27–29), 106 (27–29), *107*
Okamoto, M., 108(5), *110*
Oliveri-Mandala, E., 268(57), *275*
Olson, F. W., 32(57), *39*
Opitz, G., 83(48,49), 84(48), *86* 182(66,67), 193(67), 194(67), *201*, 208(34–36,38), 210, 213(37), 215, 217(33,36), 219, 227(34,36,38), 228(38), 236–238(37), *239*, *240*
Osuch, C., 9(88), 10(88,89), 27(88), 28(88), 29, 30, *40*
Ott, E., 142(76), *167*, 203(22), *206*
Ourisson, G., 147(79), *166*, *167*
Overberger, C. G., 97(40), 101(39), *102*
Overend, J., 100(11), *102*
Owen, J. S., 268, *275*

**P**

Paddock, N. L., 313, *331*
Padwa, A., 103(22), *107*
Pagani, G., 171(16), *173*, 188(64), *201*, 288(2), *290*
Palazzo, S., 16(42), *39*
Panaiotova, B., 188(92), *201*
Pandya, L. P., 33(84), *40*
Paquette, L. A., 78(50,51), *86*, 215, 216 (39), 217, 222(41), 223(41), 231

(39), 233(40), *240*
Parham, W. E., 2(16), *3,* 16(174), *42,* 44(16), *48,* 50(23), *53*
Park, J. D., 262(58,61) 263(59,60), 269 (58,61), 271(59,60), *275*
Parkes, G. D., 16(45), *39*
Pasqualucci, C. R., 288(7), *290*
Paterno, E., 111, 121(66), 124(66), 129(66), *138*
Pati, S., 308, *331*
Patrick, C. R., 264(56), *275*
Patzcheke, H. P., 287(9), 288(9), 290(9), *290*
Paukstelis, J. V., 34(156,158,159), 35 (156), 36(156,158,159), *42*
Paulsen, S. R., 88(42), 89, 94(43), 97(43), 98(28,41), *102*
Pausacker, K. H., 78(6), *84*
Pavlovskaya, I. V., 264(54,55), 272(54,55), 273(54,55), *275*
Payne, G. B., 147(111), 163(111), *168*
Pechmann, H. v., 87(44), *102,* 180, *201*
Pelc, B., 305(59), *331*
Pelosi, J. J., 182(4), *199*
Pelter, A., 148(25,26), 160(25,26), *166*
Pepouse, H., 277(21), *286*
Perelman, M. 182(70), 194(70), *201*
Perkins, P. P., 78(83), *86*
Person, J. T., 103(7), *107*
Peterson, D. J., 45(17), *48*
Peterson, E., 294(28), *301*
Peterson, M. L., 276(2–4), 277, 278(3), 280(2–4), *285*
Peterson, R., 47(7), *53*
Petrenko-Kritschenko, P., 295(20), *301*
Petrov, A. D., 45(15), 46(14,15), *48,* 54(7), *57*
Pettit, R., 22(175), *42*
Pettitt, D. J., 78(29), *85*
Pfenninger, F., 58, 59(69), 78(70), 79, 80, *86,* 210, *240,* 276, *286,* 286, 287(16) *291*
Pfleger, R., 179, 182, 190(71), 191(71), 194(71), 195(71), *201*
Phillips, F. S., 32(94), *40*
Phillips, W. D., 170(9), *173*
Pickett, L. W., 121(30), *137*
Pierce, L., 98(45), 99(45), *102*

Pierson, W. G., 314(37), *330*
Piganiol, P., 121(40), *137*
Piggott, H. A., 241, 242, 244(7,8), *246,* 257(43–46), *275*
Pitts, J. N., Jr., 115(67), 121(59), *138*
Pocar, D., 28(91), *40*
Pohoryles, L., 78(55), *86*
Pommer, H., 307(60), 317(94), *331, 332*
Pontrelli, G. J., 31(176), *42*
Popjak, G., 148(25,26), 160(25,26), *166*
Porter, G., 115(12,68), 116(15), *137, 138*
Porter, R. F., 264(13), *274*
Postma, J. C. W., 187(72), *201*
Powell, E. O., 33(103), *41*
Powers, D. H., Jr., 31(177), *42*
Price, C. C., 78(52), *86*
Primas, H., 121(69), *138*
Pritchard, H. O., 79(17), *85*
Proctor, Z., 32(115), *41*
Prosser, T. J., 19(179), 20(178,179, 198), *43*
Putney, R. K., 14(202), *43*
Puttner, R., 9(99), 20(180), 24(99, 181), 25(99), *41, 43*

**Q**

Quadbeck, G., 142, *167, 174(73), 201,* 250(23), *257,* 276(22), *286*
Quane, D., 54(11), 55(11), *57*
Quin, L. D., 108(6), *110*

**R**

Rahman, A., 189(74), *201*
Raiford, L. C., 37(182), *43*
Ramsay D. A., 17(122), *41*
Randall, H. M., 188(124), *202*
Rand-Meir, Z., 147(8), 148(9), 160(9), 162(9), *166*
Rapp, W., 145(62), *167*
Raschig, F., 97(46–48), *102,* 103(23, 24), *107*
Rasmussen, R. S., 188(124), *202*
Rathke, B., 291, 298(21,22), *301*
Rathsam, G., 315(77), *331*

Ratts, K. W., 306(69), 307(69,70), *331*
Rauterberg, F., 37(64), *40*
Ray, W. J., Jr., 312(83), *331*
Re, G. D., 180(76), 193(76), *201*
Rees, R., 310(32,33), 327(32,33), *330*
Regenass, F. A., 303(15), *304*
Regnault, H. V., 277(23–25), *286*
Reiber, H. G., 33(183), *43*
Reichle, A., 251(11), *256*
Reichold E., 78(31), 79(31), 81(31), 82(31), *85*, 210(18), *239*
Reid, E. E., 77(32), 78(32), *85*
Reid, W., 74, 78(54), *86*
Reinisch, R. F., 14(202), *43*
Renault, J., 265(19), *274*
Resemann, W., 1(10), *3*
Reusch, W., *138*
Reynolds, D. D., 57(53), *86*
Rhoads, S. J., 310(29), 311(29), *330*
Rice, F. O., 1(12), *3*
Richman, J. E., 222(57), 228(57), *240*
Rick, E. A., 32(49), *39*
Riebel, A. H., 103(25), *107*
Rieber, M., 305(92a), *331*
Rissi, E., 203(3), 204(3,9–12), 205(3), *205, 206*
Robb, E. W., 121(8), 124(8), 136
Roberts, J. D., 2(21), *3*
Robinson, E. B., 302(2), *304*
Robinson, M. M., 314(37), *330*
Robinson, R., 80(19–21), *85*, 175(14, 16), 181(14,17), 182(15), 188(14), 194(14), *199*
Rodd, E. H., 292(23), *301*
Rokhlin, E. M., 6(148), *42*
Roland, J. R., 297(35), *301*
Romer, F., 32(32), *39*
Rondestvedt, C. S., Jr., 16(67), *40*, 276(4–6), 277(5), 280(4,5), *285*
Rosenthal, D., 114(21), 120(21), *137*
Rosowsky, A., 2(17), *3*, 121(71), *138*, 147(78), 148(78), 157(78), *167*
Ross, S. D., 32(19–21,184), 33(20), *39*, *43*
Rossi, S., 210, 226(12), *239*
Rothe, O., 310(10), 324(10), 325(10), *329*
Rowe, R. A., 97(7,9,10), *101*, 104 (3,5,6), *107*

Roy, J., 26(4), *38*
Roy, S. K., 188(12), *199*
Rüber, C. N., 240(11), *246*
Rührmann, R., 16(9), *38*
Rull, T., 147(79), *166, 167*
Runge, F., 60(76), 62(76), 63(76), *86*
Russell, K. E., 5(185), *43*
Rutgers, J. G., 121(59), *138*
Ruthdge, R. L., 121(41), *137*
Rutschmann, J., 203–205(3), *205*
Ruzicka, L., 175(110), 189(110), *202*
Ryan, J. J., 188(80,90,91), *201*
Rydon, H. N., 33(103), *41*
Rylander, P. N., 147(7), *166*
Rytslin, E. E., 188(55), *200*

**S**

Saltiel, J., 129(46,72), *137, 138*
Sammour, A., 60(60), 64(60), 65(60), 67(60), 68(60), *86*
Samuel, D., 317(61), *331*
Sandri, J. M., 6(85,86), *40*
Sandros, K., 115(10), *137*
Sarel, S., 37(186), *43*, 78(55), *86*
Sasse, L., 108, *110*
Sattar, A. B. M. A., 80(34), *85*, 208 (23), 210(16,23), *239*
Sauer, J., 1(1), 2(1), *3*, 310(38), *330*
Scarpati, R., 180(75,76), 192(75), 193(76), *201*
Schaefer, F. C., 32(187), *43*
Scharf, D., 116, 122(73), *138*
Schatz, V. B., 31(177), 32(49), *39, 42*
Scheckenbach, E., 189(24), *200*
Scheinbaum, M. L., 182, 192(77), *201*
Scheiner, P., 16(188), *43*
Schempp, H., 213(37), 219, 236–238 (37), *240*
Schenck, G. O., 22(189), *43*, 122(74), *138*, 250, 254(24), *257*
Schenk, D., 80(81), *86*, 208, 210(60), *240*, 286(17), *291*
Schimmelschmidt, K., 146, 150(80), 151 (80), *167*
Schinkowski, K., 89(68), 91–93(68), 97(68), *103*
Schlenk, V. W., 60(56), *86*
Schlosser, M., 306(95), *332*

Schmidt, E., 109(8), *110,* 251(11), *256*
Schmidt, F., 8(65), 9(65), 26, *39, 40*
Schmidt, R. D., 89(66), 97(65,66), 98(66), *103*
Schmidt, U., 294(24), *301*
Schmitz, E., 88, 89(49,51,52,55–58,61, 66,68), 90(50,52,55,58), 91(52,58, 68), 92(58,68), 93(68), 94(43,56), 95(56,61,62), 96(62,66), 97(65–68), 98(49,60–64,66), 99(30,38,62), 101(59), *102, 103,* 103(26), 104(27, 28), 105(27–29), 106(27–29), *107*
Schneider, H., 175(111,112), 189(111, 112), *202*
Schneider, R., 1(13), *3,* 97(31), *102,* 104(21), *107*
Schneider, S., 16(10), *38*
Schöller, M., 202(21), 204(21), *206*
Schöllkopf, U., 305(62,93), 307(93), 309(62), 317(62,63,94), *331, 332*
Schönberg, A., 57(58,63–65), 60, 63 (61), 64(60,61), 65(60,64), 66(64,65), 67(60), 68(60), 69(63), 70(63), 71(63,65), 72(63,65), 73(63), 74(59,62), 78(59,62), *86,* 115(75), 136(76), *138,* 291, 294, 296, 298(27), 299(25,26), 300(26), *301,* 316(64), 317(64), *331, 332, 337*
Scholer, F., 32(116), *41*
Schomaker, J. H., 16(188), *43*
Schotz, P., 175(112), 189(112), *202*
Schramm, S., 97(67), *103,* 104(28), 105(28, 29), 106(28,29), *107*
Schreier, E., 203–205(3), *205*
Schütz, O., 74(62), 78(62), *86*
Schulten, H., 294(28), *301*
Schulz, G., 334(9), 337(9), *337*
Schulz, H., *329*
Schumb, W. C., 292(31), *301*
Schupp, O. E., III, 308(86), 321(86), *331*
Schwartz, A., 308, *331*
Schwarz, A., 295(10), *300*
Schwebke, G. L., *48,* 52(24), *53,* 55(3,4), *56*
Schweizer, E. E., 2(16), *3,* 44(16), *48,* 50(23), *53*
Scott, R. B., Jr., 210(42), *240*
Searles, S., 78(66,67), *86,* 111(77),

113(78), 120(79), 121(11,41,59,80), *137, 138,* 146(81), 147(81), *167*
Seemann, G., 98(22), *102*
Seiner, A., 253(25), *257*
Senning, A., 333, 336(10,11), *337*
Senyavina, L. B., 307(6), *329*
Seus, E. J., 308(86), 321(86), *331*
Seyden-Penne, J., 121(40), *137*
Seyferth, D., 45(19), *48*
Shah, V. P., 78(74), *86*
Shapiro, B. L., 260(25,26), 261(25,26), *274*
Sharkey, W. H., 73(44), 74(44,45), *85,* 292(18,19), 293(19), 298(18,19), *301*
Sharts, C. M., 2(21), *3*
Shchekotikhin, A. I., 264(54,55), 272(54,55), 273(54,55), *275*
Sheehan, J. C., 37, 38(191,192), *43,* 147(82), *167,* 180(86,87), 188, 192 (86,87), *201*
Sheichenko, V. I., 54(8), 56(8), *57*
Shemyakin, M. M., 307(3–8,65), *329*
Shepheard, F. G., 253(25), *257*
Sheppard, W. A., 211, 212(43), *240*
Shoshan, R., 78(55), *86*
Shpanskii, V. A., 264(54,55), 272(54,55), 273 (54,55), *275*
Sidky, M. M., 57(63), 60(63), 69–73 (63), *86*
Siegwart, S., 57(71,72), 58(71), 59(71,72), 60, 61(71,72), 62(72), 78(71), *86*
Silver, D. B., 317(61), *331*
Simmons, H. E., 30(14), *38,* 296(5), 297(32–35), *300, 301,* 311(66), *331*
Simons, J. H., 115(56), 116(56), 118(56), *138*
Simons, J. P., 114(81), *138,* 264(62), *275*
Singer, L. A., 120, 134(82), *138*
Singleton, E., 278(8), *285*
Sirrenberg, W., 303(14), *304*
Skell, P. S., 6(196), 19(195), 24(81), *40, 43,* 44(20,21), 45(20,21), 47, 48(20,21), *48*
Skinner, W. A., 33(197), *43*
Skovronek, H. S., 24(81), *40*
Skraup, S., 246(26), *257*

Sloan, M. F., 20(198), *43*
Smalla, H., 287(9), 288(9), 290(9), *290*
Smick, R. I., 17(164), *42*
Smith, C. W., 276(26), *286*
Smith, G. L., 32(233), *44*
Smith, L. E., 268(63), 269(63), *275*
Smith, P. A. S., 1(8,10), *3,* 14(199–204), *43*
Smolinsky, G., 1(6,9), *3,* 14(205–207, 209,210), 15(210–212,231), 20(211, 212,222,231), *43, 44*
Sokol'skii, G. A., 278–282(11), *285*
Soloway, S. B., 28(213), *43,* 78(68), *86*
Somerfeld, D., 332(5), 335(5), *337*
Son, P. N., 217(58), 218, 220(58), 225(58), *240*
Soulas, R., 206(11), *239*
Spasov, A., 188(92), *201*
Speeter, M., 188(30), 191(30), *200*
Speziale, A. J., 306(67–69), 307(69,70), *331*
Spietschka, E., 16(126), *41,* 178 (44–46), 179(44), 182(44–46), *200,* 250(12–14), 251(14), 254(13,14), *257*
Splitter, J. S., 103(30), *107*
Srinivasan, R., 121(84), *138*
Stark, A., 101(59), *103*
Staude, E., 45(26), *49*
Staudinger, H., 57(71,72), 58, 59(69,71, 72), 60, 61(71,72), 62(72), 78 (70,71), 79, 80, *86,* 87, 88(69), *103,* 107–109, *110,* 139–141, 142(83,85, 87–92,94,95), 147(85,86,92), 165 (92), *167, 168,* 170(13,14), *173,* 173–175, 176(93), 177, 179, 182, 188 (98,105), 189(93,96,97,99,100, 104,105,108,110–112), 190(93,103), 191(95,97), 192(97), *201, 202,* 202, 203(20,22), 204(21), *206,* 206, 210, *240,* 241(12), *246,* 246(27,28), 248, 249, 252(27), 254(27), *257,* 260, 265–268, 269(66), 273(69), *275,* 276, *286,* 286, 287, 289, *291,* 302, *304,* 309, 315, 316, *331*
Steadman, T. R., 148(96,97), *168*
Stefani, A. P., 262(58,61) 263(59,60), 269(58,61), 271(59,60), *275*

Stein, G., 12(12), 16(11,13), *38*
Steiner, R., 203(3), 204(3,9–12), 205 (3), *205, 206*
Steinhardt, C. K., 34(156), 35(156), 36(156), *42*
Steinkopf, W., 22(214), *43*
Steinmetz, R., 22(189), *43,* 122(74), *138*
Stelzner, R., 32(93), *40*
Stephenson, A., 291, 294(28), 298(27), *301*
Stevens, I. D. R., 99(17), 101(16,18), *102,* 310(21,22), 313(20,22), 314 (22), 325(22), 326(22), 328(21, 22), *330*
Stevens, T. S., 120(85), *139*
Stewart, J. M., 78(73), *86*
Stewart, T. D., 33(183,215), *43*
Stoessl, A., 80(34), *85,* 208(23), 210 (16,23), *239*
Stolle, R., 251(29), *257*
Stone, H. G., 148(98), 163(99), *168*
Stork, G., 208(46), 210(46), 213(47), 214, 226(46), *240*
Strachan, P., 314(37), *330*
Strait, L. A., 78(74), *86*
Strating, J., 208, 211, *240*
Strausz, O. P., 75(37–39,75,82), *85, 86*
Stringer, C. D., 159(34), *166*
Strong, P. M., 175(112), 189(112), *202*
Strothers, J. B., 116(62), *138*
Struchkov, Yu. T., 55(18), 56(18), *57*
Stüsser, R., 208(61,62), *240*
Style, W. D., 17(122), *41*
Su, H.-J., 33(84), *40*
Süess, R., 203–205(3), *205*
Süs, O., 188(116), *202*
Sullivan, W. J., 147(111), 163(111), *168*
Sunagawa, G., 188(114,115), *202*
Suter, C. M., 276(6,7,28–32), 277(28, 29), *285, 286*
Suter, E., 174(113), 175(113), *202*
Sutton, L. E., 121(6), *136*
Swain, C. G., 32(19–21), 33(20), *39*
Sweeny, W., 319(56), *331*
Swern, D., 29(216), *43*
Synder, L. C., 15(211), 20(211), *43*
Syrkin, Ya. K., 49(20), *53*

Szmuskovicz, J., 213(47), 215(50), *240*

**T**

Taeger, E., 60(76), 62(76), 63(76), *86*
Talukdar, P. B., 32(217), *43*
Tamelen, E. E. van, 78(78), *86*
Tamres, M., 121(41), *137,* 146(81),
147(81), *167*
Tarbell, D. S., 26(218), *43,* 121(71),
*138,* 147(78), 148(78), 157(78),
*167*
Taskashina, N., 222(10), 223(10), *239*
Taylor, T. W. J., 268, *275*
Tempel, E., 208(38), 215(38), 227
(38), 228(38), 236(37), *240*
Templeton, J. F., 310(32,33), 327(32,
33), *330*
Templeton, W., 116(62), *138*
Tennessee Eastman Co., 146(100), *168*
TerBog, A. P., 6(219), *44*
Terenin, A., 117, *137*
Terrell, R., 213(47), *240*
Testa, E., 139(101), 147(102,103),
*168,* 171(3,15–20), *173,* 173(117),
188(26,27,64,118–123), *199–202,* 204
(23–25), *206,* 288(2,11–13), *290*
Tetel'baum, B. I., 242(4), 243(4), 245
(4), *245,* 264(20), 272(20), 273(20),
*274*
Thaler, W., 116(91), *139,* 243, 245(13),
*246*
Thesing, J., 119, *139,* 303(13,14), *304*
Thiele, J., 140(106), 141, *168*
Thijs, L., 211(49), *240*
Thomas, C. L., 143, 148(63), *167*
Thompson, A. L., 32(104), *41*
Thompson, H. W., 188(124), *202*
Thompson, R. D., 37(24), *39*
Thun, J., 243(2), *245*
Thweatt, J. G., 311(18), 314(17), *330*
Ticket, M., 121(31,32), *137*
Tiers, G. V. D., 121(87), *139*
Tilney-Bassett, J. F., 14(220), 26(220),
27(220), *44*
Tisler, M., 32(221), *44*
Todd, A. R., 103(8), *107,* 310(28), 317
(28,43,78), *330, 331*
Tomalia, D. A., 32(117), *41*

Tommila, E., 210(19,51), *239, 240*
Toscano, V., 307(34), 308(34), *330*
Tosolini, G., 332(12), *337*
Travis, D. N., 31(121), *41*
Trecker, D. J., 116(88), *139*
Trede, A., 180, 192(58), *200,* 266, 273
(51), *275,* 287(9), 288(9), 290(9),
*290*
Trevoy, L. W. 113(89), *139*
Trippet, S., 305(79,80), 306(81,82),
*331*
Trotter, J., 310(21), 313(20), 328(21),
*330*
Trozollo, A. M., 20(222), *44*
Truce, W. E., 208(52–54), 210(52–54),
212(52,54), 213(54–56), 214, 217
(54,58), 218, 220(58), 222(55,57),
224(52,54), 225(54,58), 228(57),
*240,* 276(32), 277(33), *286,* 312(83),
*331*
Truscheit, E., 307(84), *331*
Tschitschibabin, A. E., 80(77), *86*
Tuan, G., 288(7), *290*
Turner, A. B., 32(223), *44*
Turro, N. J., 115(47), 116(48,49), 122
(47), *137*

**U**

Uebel, J. J., 96(70), 99(70), *103*
Ugi, I., 17(132), *41*
Uhlig, G. F., 314(2), *329*
Ullyot, G. E., 32(144), *42*
Urry, W. H., 111(57), 113(57), *138*
Utzinger, G. E., 303(15), *304*

**V**

Vaculik, P., 46(22), *48*
Van Artsdalen, E. R., 32(51), 33(52,
53), *39*
Vanderhorst, P. J., 32(57), *39*
VanderWerf, C. A., 307(12,13), *329*
Van Ess, P. R., 147(111), 163(111),
*168*
Van Etten, R. L., 31(34), *39*
Vargha, L. v., 57(64,65), 60(64), 65
(64), 66(64,65), 71(65), 72(65),
78(79), 80(79), *86,* 210(59), *240,*

294(29,30), *301*
Vasil'eva, M. N., 242(4), 243(4), 245 (4), *245,* 264(20), 272(20), 273(20), *274*
Vaver, V. A., 307(5–8,65), *329, 331*
Vest, R. D., 296(5), 297(32–35), *300, 301*
Vieregge, H., 115(90), *139*
Vilkov, L. V., 55(18), 56(18), *57*
Villiger, V., 139(4,5), *166*
Vine, H., 248(18), 249(18), *257*
Vita, C. de, 17(164), *42*
Vogel, A., 203(3), 204(3,9–12), 205 (3), *205, 206*
Vogel, E., 21(224–226), *44*
Volpin, M. E., 45(23,24), *49,* 49(25–27, 29), 50, 51, *53,* 54, 55, 56(18), *57,* 84, *85, 86,* 97(71), *103,* 110, *110*
Vorländer, D., 139, *168*

## W

Wachter, W., 295(36), *301*
Wadsworth, D. H., 308(86), 321(86), *331*
Wadsworth, W. S., 307(85), 308(85), *331*
Wagner, A., 26(227), *44*
Wagner, W. M., 12(228), *44*
Wailes, P. C., 307(87), *331*
Walborsky, H. M., 28(229), *44*
Walkden, J., 260(16), 261(16), *274*
Walker, D. M., 306(81,82), *331*
Walker, J. F., 151(110), *168*
Walker, P., 15, *44*
Walling, C., 116(91), *139*
Walsh, J. P., 222(57), 228(57), *240*
Wankel, R. A., 32(57), *39*
Wannagat, U., 104, *107*
Wasserman, A., 2(19), *3*
Wasserman, E., 15(211,212,231), 20 (211,212,222,231), *43, 44*
Waters, W. A., 15, *44*
Weaver, C., 26(218), *43*
Weaver, S. D., 189(47), *200,* 247, 248 (15), 249, 250, 254(15), *257,* 257(47, 48), 258, 259(47,48), 261, *275*
Webber, A. J., 276(7), *285*
Wedekind, E., 80(81), *86,* 108(12), *110,*

174, *202,* 208, 210(60), *240,* 286 (17), *291*
Wege, H., 295(16), *301*
Weibezahn, W., 32(32), *39*
Weigmann, H.-D., 306(95), *332*
Weiner, N., 277(19), *286*
Weiss, A., 292(37), *301*
Weisswange, W., 174(126,127), *202*
Wells, C. H. J., 116(16), *137*
West, R., 45(25), *49,* 51, *53*
West, W., *44*
Westheimer, F. H., 277(17), *285*
Wetmore, D. E., 147(14), *166*
Weyerstahl, P., 333(3), *337*
Weygand, F., 174(128), 178(128), *202,* 250(30), *257*
Weymouth, F. J., 317(43), *330*
Whippel, H., 307(35), *330*
White, R. W., 292, *301*
Whitlock, H. W., Jr., 32(233), *44*
Whittaker, D., 268, *275*
Wiberg, E., 45(26), *49*
Wiebe, H. A., 75(82), *86*
Wiedemann, W., 21(226), *44*
Wiegräbe, W., 31(32a), *39*
Wieland, H., 247(31), *257*
Wieland, W., 264(13), *274*
Wiley, D. W., 12(235), *44,* 168(22), 169(22), *173*
Wilkinson, T., 115(68), *138*
Williams, J. K., 168(21,22), 169(22), *173*
Williams, P. H., 147(111), 163(111), *168*
Willis, C. J., 226(11a), 263(11,12), 270(11), 271(11,12), *274*
Wilson, C. E., 277(34), *286*
Winberg, H. E., 147(112), *168*
Winkler, C. A., 32(104), *41*
Winstein, S., 120(92), *139*
Winter, R., 49(8), *53*
Witt, I. H., 32(60), *40*
Wittenau, M. S. v., 120, 129(13), *137*
Wittenberg, D., 45(27), *49*
Wittig, G., 305, 306(95), 307(93), 317 (94), *331*
Witzel, D., 119, *139*
Wleügel, S., 174(28), *200*
Wolff, J. R., 118(37), *137*

Wolff, K. L., 12(234), *44*
Woods, W. G., 45(28), *49*
Woodward, R. B., 3, *3*
Wotz, J. H., 147(113), *168*
Wright, A., 45(10,11), *48*
Wrobel, J., 119(1), 120(1), *136*

# Y

Yager, W. A., 15(212,231), 20(212,222, 231), *43, 44*
Yagil, G., 97(5,72), *101, 103,* 105(32), 107
Yakubovich, A. Ya., 242(4), 243(4), 245(4), *245,* 264(20,54,55), 272(20, 54,55), 273(20,54,55), *274, 275*
Yang, N. C., 117, 118(93), 120–122 (93), 124–126(93), *139*
Yanoaskaya, L. A., 305(96), *332*
Yarwood, A. J., 264(62), *275*
Yates, P., 12(235), *44,* 295, 299(39), *301*
Yeh, Y. L., 147(82), *167*
Yoshida, N. 188(114,115), *202*
Yoshioka, M., 158(55), *167*
Young, F. G., 144(114), 145(114), 148

(114), 149(115), 152(115), *168*
Youtz, M. A., 78(83), *86*
Yuan, C., 49(9), *53*

# Z

Zalkow, L. H., 10(237), 11(236), 27 (236,237), 29, *42, 44*
Zamojski, A., 119(4), *136*
Zaugg, H. E., 139(116), 143–145, *168*
Zbiral, E., 309–311, 325(97), 326(97), *332*
Zey, R. L., 37(25), *39*
Ziegler, K., 46(29), *49*
Zimmer, H., 97(7), *101,* 104(3), *107*
Zimmer, M., 104(3), *107*
Zimmerman, B. G., 243(14), *246*
Zincke, T., 208, *240*
Zinn, J., 121(23,43), *137*
Zinser, D., 24(101), *41*
Zirkle, C. L., 32(144), 33(92), *40, 42*
Zollinger, H., 19(239), *44*
Zomlefer, J., 33(137), *41*
Zürcher, R. F., 121(94,95), *139*
Zwanenburg, B., 211(49), *240*
Zwierzak, A., 120(5), *136*

# SUBJECT INDEX

Acetylene dicarboxylic esters, and
   phosphazines, 314
   and phosphinimines, 313, 314
   and phosphoranes, 310, 311
Aldehydes, see carbonyl compounds
Alkenes, and azodicarboxylic esters,
   242–244
   and carbonyl compounds, 111–137
   and carbonyl cyanide, 119, 120, 128,
   129
   and hexafluorothioacetone, 207
   and imines, 187, 188
   and isocyanates, 181
   and nitrenes, 15–32
   and nitrosobenzene, 258–261
   and silenes, 44–49
   and sulfenes, 212
   and sulfines, 210
   and sulfonylisocyanates, 184–187
   and sulfur trioxide, 276–290
Alkynes, and carbonyl compounds,
   114, 115
   and germenes, 54–56
   and nitrobenzene, 182
   and silenes, 49–52
Arynes, and phosphoranes, 309, 310
Azetidinediones, 202–205, physical data,
   204, 205
Azetidines, 168–173, physical data, 172
Azetidinones, 173–199, physical data,
   189–199
Aziridines, 5–32, from carbenes, 5–15
   from nitrenes, 15–32
   physical data, 7–11
Aziridinium salts, 32–37, from carbenes,
   32–37
   physical data, 35, 36
Aziridinones, 37, 38
Azobenzene, and ketenes, 248–252
Azo compounds, and carbenes, 87, 88
   and ketenes, 246–257
Azodicarboxylic esters, and alkenes,
   242–244

and norbornene, 243, 245
Benzynes, and phosphoranes, 309, 310

Carbenes, aziridinium salt formation,
   32–37
   and azo compounds, 87, 99
   and imines, 5–15
   and isocyanates, 37, 38
   and sulfenes, 79–84
   and thiocarbonyl compounds, 57–60
Carbodiimides, 318–321, and
   isocyanates, 252
   from isocyanates, 252, 253
Carbon dioxide, and phosphinimines,
   315
Carbon disulfide, and diazo compounds,
   58, 296
   and phosphinimines, 315
   and triphenylphosphine, 109
Carbonyl compounds, and alkenes,
   111–137
   and alkynes, 114,115
   and carbonyl cyanide, 146, 147
   in diaziridine syntheses, 89
   and ketenes, 139–147
   and nitrenes, 103–106
   and perfluoroalkenes, 118, 119, 133
   and phosphinimines, 317, 318
   and N-sulfinyl amines, 332, 333, 335
   and N-sulfinyl sulfonamides, 334
Carbonyl cyanide, and alkenes, 119,
   120, 128, 129
   and carbonyl compounds, 146, 147
Chloramines, in diaziridine syntheses, 89
   in oxazirane syntheses, 104, 105
Cyanic acid, and imines, 254

Desaurins, 291–301, physical data, 299
Diazete, 243
Diazetidines, 240, 246
1,3-Diazetidines, 241–244, physical data,
   244

Diazetidinones, 246–257, isomerization, 247
  physical data, 254–257
Diaziridines, 87–101, physical data, 90–96
Diazirines, 98–101
Diazo compounds, and carbon disulfide, 58, 296
  and dithiobenzoic acid esters, 58
  and isocyanates, 180,181
  and sulfur, 60
  and sulfur dioxide, 57, 58, 210
  and sulfur dioxide, 79–83
  and thiocarbonyl compounds, 57–60
  and thioisocyanates, 59
  and thiophosgene, 59
Diazoketones, decomposition to ketenes, 178, 179
  and imines, 178, 179
Diphenylketene, see ketenes
Dithiacyclobutanes, 291–301
1,3-Dithietanes, physical data, 298
1,2-Dithietenes, 291–301, physical data, 300

Enamines, and isocyanates, 182
  and sulfenes, 207, 214, 226
  and sulfines, 212

Germenes, and alkynes, 54–56
Germirenes, 54–56

Hexafluorothioacetone, adducts, 223
  and alkenes, 207
  dimerization, 292, 293

Imines, and alkenes, 187,188
  and carbenes, 5–15
  and cyanic acid, 254
  in diaziridine syntheses, 89, 97, 98
  and diazoketones, 178, 179
  dimerization, 241–244
  and isocyanates, 253, 254
  and ketenes, 173–179
  and nitrenes, 97
  and nitrosobenzene, 302–304
  and sulfenes, 286–290
  and $N$-sulfinyl sulfonamides, 333, 336
Isocyanates and alkenes, 181
  and carbenes, 37, 38

  and carbodiimides, 252
  and diazo compounds, 180, 181
  and enamines, 182
  formation of carbodiimides, 252, 253
  and imines, 253, 254
  and ketene acetals, 180, 181
  and ketenes, 37, 38, 202, 203
  and Michler's ketone, 289
  and nitrones, 302, 303
  and nitrosobenzene, 302
  and phosphinimines, 315
  and phosphoranes, 316
  and triphenylphosphine, 109
  and vinyl ethers, 182

Ketenes and azobenzene, 248–252
  and azo compounds, 246–257
  and carbonyl compounds, 139–147
  from diazoketones, 178, 179
  from 1-ethoxy-1-alkynes, 187
  and imines, 173–179
  and isocyanates, 37, 38, 202, 203
  and nitrones, 267, 268
  and nitrosobenzene, 179, 180, 265, 266
  and oxazoles, 175, 176
  and phosphines, 107–109
  and phosphinimines, 315
  and phosphoranes, 309
  and quinones, 139–147
  and $N$-sulfinyl amines, 287, 288
  and $N$-sulfinyl sulfonamides, 287
  and sulfonylisocyanates, 203, 204
  and sulfur dioxide, 276
  and sulfur trioxide, 276–280
  and thiazoles, 175, 176
  and thiazolines, 181, 182
  and thioketones, 206
Ketene derivatives, and isocyanates, 180, 181
  and sulfenes, 219–222
Ketones, see also carbonyl compounds
  and alkenes, 111–137

Lactams, 173–199, catalysts for the formation of, 148, 149
  physical data, 189–199
Lactones, 139–167, physical data, 147–165

Methanesulfonyl chloride, see sulfenes

Nitrenes, and alkenes, 15–32
  and carbonyl compounds, 103–106
  and imines, 97
  Staudinger's definition, 267, 268
Nitrobenzene, and tolane, 192
Nitrones, 258–261, 267–269, and
    ketenes, 262, 268
  and isocyanates, 302, 303
Nitrosobenzene, and alkenes, 258–261
  and imines, 302–304
  and isocyanates, 302
  and ketenes, 179, 180, 265, 266
  and phosphazines, 317
  and phosphoranes, 316, 317
  and thioketones, 332
Nitroso compounds, substituent effect,
    266, 267
Nitrosyl halides, and perfluoroalkenes,
    262–264
Norbornene, and azodicarboxylic esters,
    243, 245
  and benzazide, 16
  and benzenesulfonylazide, 27–31
  and N-sulfinyl aniline, 289

Oxathietane-1,1-dioxide, 276–286
  physical data, 281–284
Oxathietane-1-oxides, 276–286
Oxazetidines, 257–275
1,2-Oxazetidines, physical data, 269–372
1,2-Oxazetidinones, 265, 266, physical
    data, 273
Oxaziranes, 103–106, physical data, 106
Oxaziridines, 103–106, physical data, 106
Oxazoles, and ketenes, 175,176
Oxetanes, 111–137, physical data,
    121–134
Oxetene, 114, 115

Perfluoroalkenes, and carbonyl
    compounds, 118, 119, 133
  and sulfur, 77, 78
  and sulfur trioxide, 278–280
  and trifluoronitrosomethane, 242,
    243, 261, 263
Perfluoroethylene, and nitrosyl halides,
    262–264

Perfluoronitrosomethane, see
    trifluoronitrosomethane
Perfluorothioacetone, see
    hexafluorothioacetone
Phosphazines, and acetylene
    dicarboxylic esters, 314
  and nitrosobenzene, 317
  and sulfur dioxide, 315
Phosphines, and carbon disulfide, 108
  and isocyanatews, 108
  and ketenes, 107–109
  and thioisocyanates, 108
Phosphinimines, and acetylene
    dicarboxylic esters, 313, 314
  and carbon dioxide, 315
  and carbon disulfide, 315
  and carbonyl compounds, 317, 318
  and isocyanates, 315
  and ketenes, 315
  and thioisocyanates, 315
Phosphiranes, 107–109
Phosphoranes, and acetylene
    dicarboxylic esters, 310, 311
  and arynes, 309, 310
  and isocyanates, 316
  and ketenes, 309
  and nitrosobenzene, 316, 317
  and thiobenzophenone, 309

Quinones, and ketenes, 139–147

Schiff bases, see imines
Silacyclopropanes, 44–48
Silenes, 44–48, and alkenes, 44–48
  and alkynes, 49–52
Silirenes, 49–53
Sulfenes, and alkenes, 212
  and bicyclic enamines, 215–219
  and carbenes, 79–84
  and enamines, 207,214,226
  and imines, 286–290
  and ketene acetals, 219–222
  and ketene aminals, 219–222
  preparation, 208–211
Sulfines, aliphatic, 212
  aromatic, 211
  and enamines, 212
  preparation, 211
N-Sulfinyl amines, and carbonyl

compounds, 332–335
and ketenes, 287–288
N-Sulfinyl aniline and norbornene, 289
N-Sulfinyl sulfonamides, and
　benzalazine, 333, 336
　and carbonyl compounds, 334
　and diketones, 335
　and imines, 333,336
　and ketenes, 287
　and sulfoxides, 334, 337
　and thioamides, 334, 336
Sulfonylisocyanates, and alkenes,
　184–187
　and carbonyl compounds, 184
　and ketenes, 203, 204
　and vinyl ethers, 183
Sulfoxides, and N-sulfinyl sulfonamides,
　334,337
Sulfur, and alkenes, 77, 78
　and diazo compounds, 60
　and perfluoroalkenes, 77,78
Sulfur dioxide, and diazo compounds,
　57, 58, 79–83, 210
　and ketenes, 276
　and phosphazines, 315
Sulfur trioxide, and alkenes, 276–280
　and ketenes, 276–280
　and perfluoroalkenes, 278–280
Sultones, 276–280, NMR spectra, 284
　physical data, 281–284
　rearrangements, 285

Tetrafluoroethylene, see
　perfluoroethylene
Thiazetidine-1,1-dioxides, 286–290
Thiazetidine-1-oxides, 286–290
　physical data, 290

Thiazoles, and ketenes, 175, 176
Thiazolines, and ketenes, 181, 182
Thietane-1,1-dioxides, 206–240,
　physical data, 224–228,236
Thietanes, 206–240
Thietanone dioxides, 206–240
Thiete-1,1-dioxides, 206–240,
　1,4-cycloadducts, 239
　physical data, 236
Thiirane-1,1-dioxide, physical data,
　80–83
Thiiranes, 57–60, oxidation of, 78, 79
　physical data, 61–76
Thioamides, and N-sulfinyl
　sulfonamides, 334, 336
Thiobenzophenone, see also thioketones
　and phosphoranes, 309
Thiocarbonyl compounds, and diazo
　compounds, 57–60
　and ketenes, 206
　and nitrosobenzene, 332
　and phosphoranes, 309
Thioisocyanates, and diazo compounds,
　59
　and phosphinimines, 315
　and triphenylphosphine, 109
Thioketones, and diazo compounds,
　57–60
　and ketenes, 206
　and nitrosobenzene, 332
　and phosphoranes, 309
Thiophosgene, and diazo compounds, 59
　dimerization, 291, 292
Trifluoronitrosomethane, and
　perfluoroalkenes, 242, 243, 261, 262

Wittig reaction, 305ff

3,4 dimetho